# READER'S DIGEST PUZZLES ANNUAL 2002

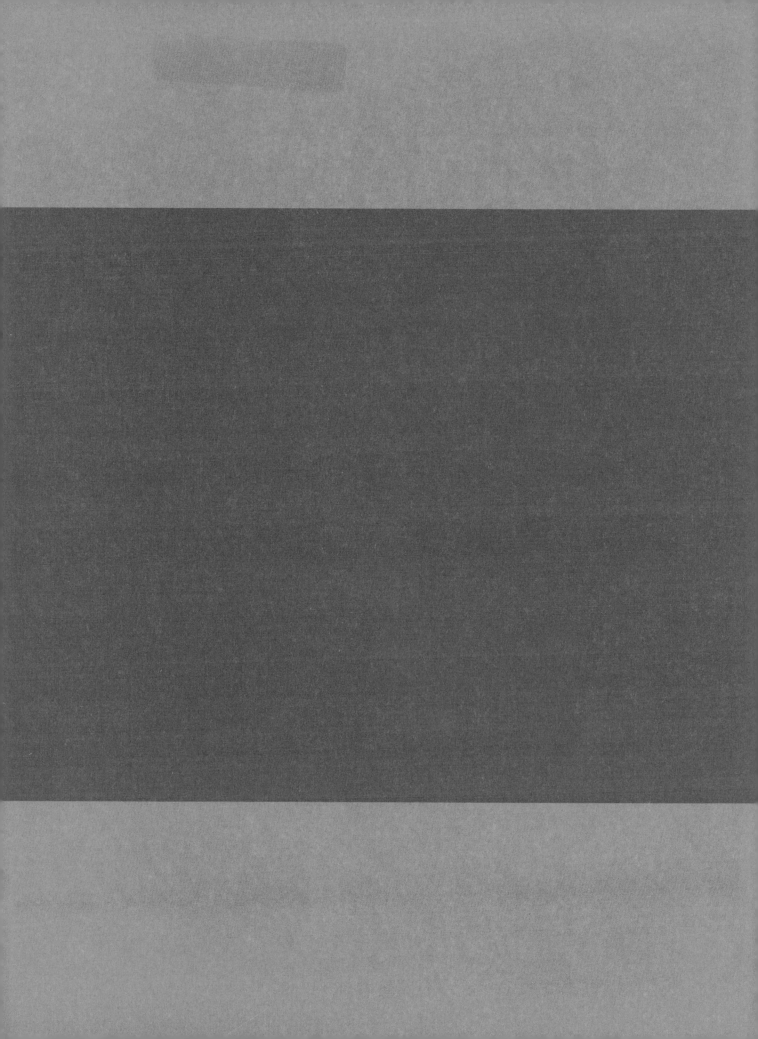

READER'S DIGEST

# PUZZLES ANNUAL 2002

Published by The Reader's Digest Association Limited

LONDON ★ NEW YORK ★ SYDNEY ★ MONTREAL

Puzzles Annual 2002

was commissioned and produced by:

Book Creation Services, 21 Catherine St, London WC2B 5JS

Editor Alison Moore

Assistant Editor Sarah Barlow

Art Editor Keith Miller

Designer Sylvie Rabbe

Contributors David Bodycombe; Brainwarp; Philip Carter; Lloyd King; Sheena Meredith; Moran Campbell da Vinci; Jeffery Pike; Probyn Puzzles; Puzzlemakers; Ken Russell; Justin Scroggie

For The Reader's Digest, London

Project Editor Rachel Warren Chadd

Art Editor Louise Turpin

Proofreader Barry Gage

Reader's Digest, General Books, London

Editorial Director Cortina Butler

Art Director Nick Clark

Executive Editor Julian Browne

Publishing Projects Manager Alastair Holmes

Development Editor Ruth Binney

Picture Resource Manager Martin Smith

Style Editor Ron Pankhurst

Visit our web site at: www.readersdigest.co.uk

# contents

## puzzles



## answers

# Smart thinking

Some say computers will one day prove the ultimate in thinking technology. But as yet the only system that can tackle an almost infinite range of complex problems is the amazing human brain.

Here's a chance to put yours to the test. Many of the puzzles in this new annual would baffle even the most high-tech computer. But they needn't be out of your reach. Apply yourself to the range on offer here and not only will your puzzling skills improve but you'll also find you're quicker off the mark in everyday life. The more you exercise your grey matter, the better it will perform.

★ easy

★★ medium

★★★ hard

Start with the **warm-up** pages in each section to limber up for the challenges in the pages that follow. At the end of each chapter you can test your freshly honed skills on the **against the clock** puzzles.

As you work through, you may want to start gently by trying the one-star puzzles or head confidently for the trickiest three-star teasers or just take what comes... The different levels offer something for all the family.

To keep all parts of your brain in trim, try as many different types of puzzle as possible. If you've never considered yourself a mathematician, imagine the sense of achievement when you solve a demanding

**number know-how** conundrum. Or, if you're not a natural wordsmith, think of the joy of completing a three-star cryptic in **simply crosswords**. There's nothing to stop you having a go.

Why not share your puzzles with family or friends? Host a ready-made quiz by dipping into the **testing trivia** or **hot topics** sections – then you'll discover who really knows what.

Or if it's words, words and more words you're after, check out **take a letter**. As well as traditional word games, you'll find some craftily constructed variations on familiar themes. All test your linguistic ability and provide a rigorous work-out for the brain.

However, if you tend to think visually, take a look at the **eye see** section – a dazzling collection of pictorial puzzles to test your powers of observation. Remember: what you see is not always what you get...

Then, if you're a real glutton for punishment, put on your thinking cap and prepare to do battle with the most difficult puzzles in **the ultimate challenge**. No star ratings apply here – they're all off the scale!

Most of all, enjoy this book! The pencil icon indicates a space in which to write your answer. If anything has you stumped, consult the colour-coded **answers** section at the back with its helpful explanations.

We each have the ability to surprise ourselves. So, pencils to the ready, it's time to test and train your mental faculties...

# hot

Have you been paying close attention to recent news? These totally topical puzzles are designed to test how well you've kept up with all that's newsworthy in the past year.

Take your time, crank up your memory and be prepared to push your puzzling skills to the limit. From straightforward quickfire question-and-answer challenges to pertinent picture quizzes through to taxing topical crosswords, there's something to keep everyone on their toes.

We hope you'll be pleasantly surprised at how much you do know in certain areas – and not too shocked at your ignorance in others. So turn the page to find out.

★ easy ★★ medium ★★★ hard

# topics

# warm-up...

**1★** Complete the names of these sporting heroes and heroines, all of whom excelled in their fields in 2000 and 2001.

__IGE__ __OO__S

__AR__IN__ __ING__S

NASSER HUSSAIN

DAVID BECKHAM

STEVE WAUGH

J__N__H L__M__

ANDRE AGASSI

S__N__A __'S__ __LIV__N

__ON__TH__N E__WAR__S

MICHAEL SCHUMACHER

**2★** Fill in the missing vowels to complete this headline, which refers to a major news story from the period June 2000 to June 2001.

MENDELSON RESIGNS

FROM CABINET

------------------------------

**3★** Can you find the pop superstar in this anagram?

**Best in prayers (7,6)**

------------------------------

**4★** Who is the subject of this riddle?

My first is in penny
and also in pound;
My second's in earth,
but nowhere in ground.
My third's found in grief,
but absent from sorrow;
My fourth's in tonight,
but not in tomorrow.
My fifth is in healthy
and never in sick;
For years I ruled Walford
as Queen of the Vic.

 PEGGY

**5★** Spell out a ten-letter word, moving through each circle once only. Clue: associated with a fictional English detective.

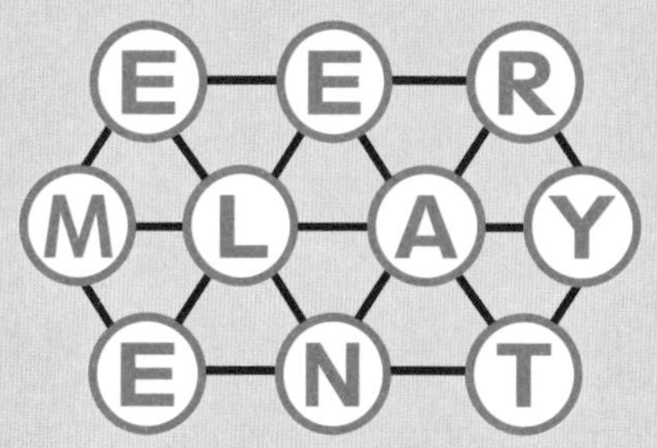


✎ 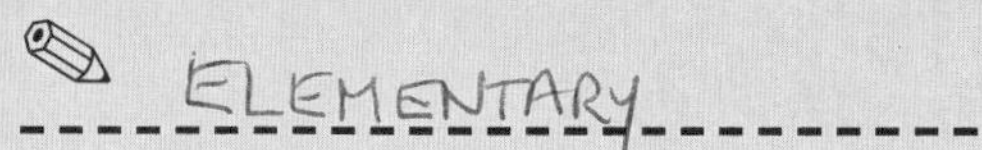

**6★** Can you match up these headlines with the dates from the past 100 years? To make it more difficult, key words need replacing in the headlines.

| 22 January 1901 | 1 May 1931 | 20 July 1969 | 1 June 1957 |
|---|---|---|---|
| 1 August 1976 | 13 April 1980 | 19 September 1985 | 18 November 1991 |

1 In Mexico City .................... kills thousands.

2 Queen .................... dies at Osborne, Isle of Wight.

3 President .................... opens Empire State Building.

4 Spaniard .................... becomes youngest ever winner of the US Masters.

5 Champion driver .................... escapes death in inferno.

6 In Britain, ERNIE draws the first .................... prizes.

7 Shi'ite Muslim faction in Lebanon free ....................

8 .................... is first man to step onto the moon.

**7★** Codes can be complex or quite simple – as in the following example, which, when solved, reveals the headline of a news story relating to a solar flare at the end of March 2001.

14 1 19 1 18 5 22 5 1 12 19 5 1 18 20 8 ' 19 14 5 1 18 13 9 19 19.

✎ ------------------------------

Who's been making the news? Turn over to find out...

## 8★★ How much do you remember about these recent events?

1 Hear'Say's first single went straight to No. 1 in the UK charts. What was it called?

✎ ____________________

2 Queen Elizabeth's real ('unofficial') birthday is 21 April. How old was she in 2001?

____________________

3 When is the Queen's 'official' birthday celebrated?

____________________

4 In March 2001, which film starring John Travolta won the Golden Raspberry for Worst Film of the Year (2000)?

____________________

5 What is the surname of 'Nasty Nick', who was evicted from the Big Brother house in the Channel 4 series?

____________________

6 Which astronomical phenomenon was visible from Britain on 9 January 2001?

____________________

7 The star of *Kind Hearts and Coronets* died in November 2000. Who was he?

____________________

8 Which TV comedy series was filmed mainly in Hadfield, Derbyshire?

____________________

9 What do J.K. Rowling's initials stand for?

____________________

10 What was significant about 3661 seconds past midnight on 1 January 2001?

____________________

11 Which cosmetic company advertises on TV with the slogan: 'Because I'm worth it'?

____________________

12 Complete the film title *Crouching Tiger,* _________ _________.

13 What job did Chris Woodhead leave after six controversial years?

____________________

14 He broke the mould of Scottish politics, delivered a devolved parliament, and died in October 2000. Who was he?

____________________

15 What is the capital of Kosovo?

____________________

**9★★** Can you name these breeds of dog? By unravelling the anagram contained in the boxed letters underneath you'll find a clue that reveals something they all have in common.

**10★★** Can you match these countries with a year in which it won soccer's World Cup?

| | |
|---|---|
| **France** | 1978 |
| **Uruguay** | 1994 |
| **Italy** | 1966 |
| **Brazil** | 1982 |
| **Argentina** | 1950 |
| **England** | 1998 |

**11★** Unravel this to find a sports personality frequently in the news.

**Money kits (4,5)**

## 12★ November 2000 saw one of the most controversial US presidential elections ever. All the words listed are connected with US presidents or the election process. Can you spot them in the grid? They may be found across, down or diagonally in any direction.

| | |
|---|---|
| ADAMS | NOMINATION |
| BALLOT | NIXON |
| BUSH | PRIMARY |
| CARTER | REAGAN |
| CLINTON | RECOUNT |
| CONGRESS | RUNNING MATE |
| ELECTION | SENATE |
| FORD | TRUMAN |
| HOOVER | WASHINGTON |
| KENNEDY | WHITE HOUSE |

| U | C | L | N | P | S | K | E | N | N | E | D | Y | B |
|---|---|---|---|---|---|---|---|---|---|---|---|---|---|
| N | O | I | T | C | E | L | E | D | F | N | R | R | V |
| A | N | W | L | Z | T | T | O | L | L | A | B | U | M |
| M | G | Y | U | C | A | B | H | K | M | E | N | N | J |
| I | R | E | U | R | N | O | X | I | N | A | O | N | E |
| N | E | L | H | V | E | P | R | C | D | K | I | I | S |
| T | S | G | W | Q | S | P | L | A | R | E | T | N | U |
| R | S | P | J | K | Y | I | M | R | N | U | A | G | O |
| R | E | A | G | A | N | S | G | T | E | O | N | M | H |
| L | U | C | Y | T | K | V | D | E | L | H | I | A | E |
| R | E | V | O | O | H | C | E | R | S | P | M | T | T |
| F | U | N | S | U | T | W | I | U | O | G | O | E | I |
| T | R | U | M | A | N | V | B | K | L | F | N | J | H |
| W | O | M | E | N | O | T | G | N | I | H | S | A | W |

## 13★★ Can you match up these headlines with the dates from the past 100 years? To make it more difficult, key words need replacing in the headlines.

| | | | |
|---|---|---|---|
| 23 August 1926 | 14 November 1940 | 17 April 1969 | 2 October 1950 |
| 20 October 1973 | 18 May 1980 | 11 February 1990 | 13 July 1985 |

1 Fantastic .................... in Sydney opened to the public.

2 Movie idol .................... dies at age 31.

3 .................... freed after 26 years in jail.

4 Voting age lowered from 21 to 18 in ....................

5 Live Aid concerts in London and .................... raise millions for famine relief.

6 .................... comic strip makes its debut.

7 Long-dormant Mount .................... erupts.

8 .................... Cathedral destroyed in Blitz.

## 14★ Five friends from different parts of the world met up to attend the Olympic Games in Sydney, but they left their bookings a little late, so ended up in different hotels. What is each friend's nationality, in which hotel did he or she stay and which type of event did he or she most enjoy?

| | NATIONALITY | | | | | HOTEL | | | | | EVENT | | | | |
|---|---|---|---|---|---|---|---|---|---|---|---|---|---|---|---|
| | American | Indian | Japanese | Peruvian | Swedish | Blitz | Charlton | Harriot | Madison | Milton | Gymnastics | High jump | Judo | Swimming | Tennis |
| Chloë | | | | | | | | | | | | | | | |
| Dan | | | | | | | | | | | | | | | |
| Eric | | | | | | | | | | | | | | | |
| Isadora | | | | | | | | | | | | | | | |
| Tom | | | | | | | | | | | | | | | |
| Gymnastics | | | | | | | | | | | | | | | |
| High jump | | | | | | | | | | | | | | | |
| Judo | | | | | | | | | | | | | | | |
| Swimming | | | | | | | | | | | | | | | |
| Tennis | | | | | | | | | | | | | | | |
| Blitz | | | | | | | | | | | | | | | |
| Charlton | | | | | | | | | | | | | | | |
| Harriott | | | | | | | | | | | | | | | |
| Madison | | | | | | | | | | | | | | | |
| Milton | | | | | | | | | | | | | | | |

1 Eric most enjoyed seeing his fellow countryman, the American Tom Malchow, winning the 200-metre butterfly swimming event and thus collecting a gold medal for his country.

2 Ryoko Tamura won a gold medal in the extra lightweight judo event, very much enjoyed by the Japanese woman who stayed at the Harriot Hotel.

3 The Swede, whose fellow countrywoman, Kajsa Bergqvist, won a bronze, very much enjoyed the high jump event in which she competed. Dan (who stayed at the Milton Hotel) isn't Swedish.

4 The Peruvian stayed at the rather imposing Blitz Hotel. Tom didn't stay at the Charlton.

5 Isadora watched the gymnastics, her favourite event.

## 15★★ Each wooden block has a six-letter word written on it, but unfortunately you can see only three sides. When you have solved the clues, the first column will reveal a well-known location.

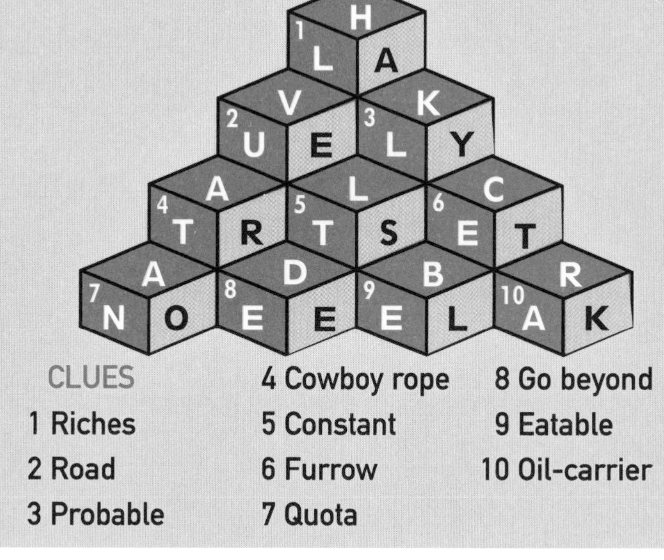


CLUES
1 Riches
2 Road
3 Probable
4 Cowboy rope
5 Constant
6 Furrow
7 Quota
8 Go beyond
9 Eatable
10 Oil-carrier

**16★** Which two answers in this arrow-word grid commemorate a royal anniversary in 2000.

| A century | Of a woman<br>American desert | | Wife of King George V<br>Strike | | Drug abuser | | Meal selection<br>Crow's nest | | Office furniture |
|---|---|---|---|---|---|---|---|---|---|
| | | | | | | | | | |
| Great Lake of America | | | | | Completed<br>End life | | | | |
| Royal tree | | Boring<br>Pottery ovens | | | | | | | |
| | | | Small cut<br>Consumed | | | | | Fish eggs | |
| Width of circle | | | | | | | | | Become smaller |
| Singing voice | | | | | Cowboy's bar | Angler's gear | | | |
| Agree | Webs<br>Vote for | | | | | Evergreen tree<br>Orbits of the sun | | | |
| | | | Dried grass | | | | Operatic song | A ridge of coral | |
| Wager | | Study again<br>Muscular twitch | | | | | | | |
| | | | Made noise like a lion | | | | | | |
| US secret service<br>And so on (abbr.) | | | | Oxford College | | | | | |
| | | | Not secure | | | | | | |

**17★** Spell out a nine-letter place, moving through each circle once only. Clue: It was no more in December 2000.

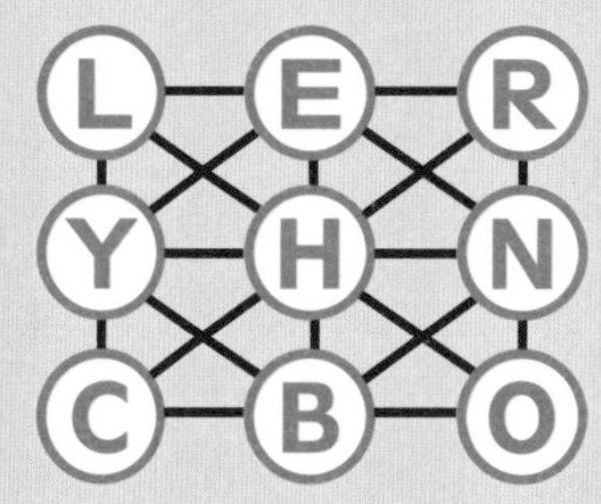


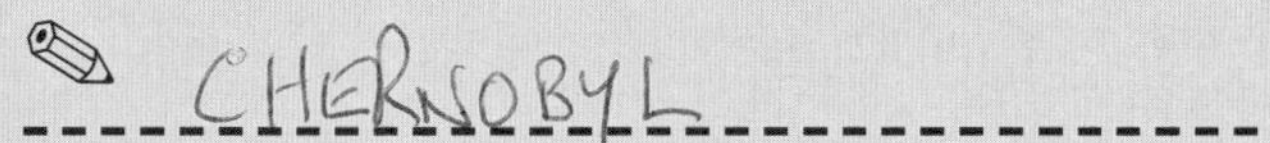


**18★** Which politician's surname can be found in this riddle?

My first is in cable but not in a rope;
My second's in cardinal, not in the Pope.
My third's in a tower but not in a steeple;
My fourth is in crowds and yet not in people.
My fifth is in bangers but not in the mash;
My whole is a Scot who looks after the cash.

BROWN

**19** Test your powers of recall with this memory test. Read the piece through, then turn to page 18 and try to answer as many questions as you can without looking at the original.

★ 1–4 correct answers
★★ 5–8 correct anwers
★★★ 9–10 correct answers

This year's Brooker awards shortlist is as controversial as ever. Last year's finalist Nigel Spexx, author of *Memory*, is back with a new work, *Streams of Consciousness*, at 4932 pages the longest book entered. '*Memory* was everything I could remember since birth,' says Islington-based Spexx, '*Streams* is everything else.'

Bookmakers give *Streams* odds of 2–1. But will it beat the raw appeal of *I Kant Spel* by Jain Dayveez, whose heroine Z writes VCR manuals? Magazine *PC Tipz* said of it: 'Riting has a new voyss', but will the panel agree?

The heaviest book, weighing in at 4.6 kilos, comes from Polish-born Zbgnw Grjnwzc, entitled *The Vowels Have Flown*, which has already won the prestigious 'Doorstop 2001' award.

The popular choice, at odds of 3–2 on, is backpackers' bible *Dog Eared and Dirty* by Nida Barth, an autobiographical account of one woman's 25-year wait for a connecting flight at Orly airport.

This year's outsider, at 33–1, is *Underdog* by first-timer Ian McSpaniel, the fictional diary of a British tennis player who overcomes his fear of spherical objects to become the world No. 5412. The panel is divided. Camilla Goodread broke both arms when her copy of *The Vowels Have Flown* was delivered, while fellow panellist Lord Brain claims Nida Barth's sojourn outside Paris means she is no longer a British citizen.

*Grauniad* sub-editor Grahem Smyth has publicly acclaimed *I Kan't Spel*, a move fellow judge A.S. Dribble called 'contacious'. Watch this space.

## 19 Questions

Now that you've read the story on page 17, can you answer these questions without looking back?

1 Who wrote *Streams of Consciousness*?

------------------------------------------------

2 What is the name of the heroine of *I Kan't Spel*?

------------------------------------------------

3 What did *PC Tipz* say of Jain Dayveez's work?

------------------------------------------------

4 How heavy is the book by Zbgnw Grjnwzc?

------------------------------------------------

5 What did Nida Barth write?

------------------------------------------------

6 At which airport did Nida Barth wait for 25 years?

------------------------------------------------

7 What odds are offered for Ian McSpaniel's book?

------------------------------------------------

8 In *Underdog*, what ranking does the diarist reach by the end?

------------------------------------------------

9 Who broke her arms taking delivery of *The Vowels Have Flown*?

------------------------------------------------

10 How did A.S. Dribble describe a fellow panellist's move?

------------------------------------------------

## 20★★

All these singers or bands had chart hits in 2001. Can you fill in the gaps to complete their names?

_LL S_I_TS

SH_GG_

W_STL_FE

E_INE_

S_E_EO_HO_I_S

_OBB_E _ILL_A_S

_RA_G DA_ID

_AN_C _TRE_T P_EA_H_ _S

_. K_LL_

A_ROS_I_H

## 21★ Use the letters in the shaded squares to find the name of a US politician.

| ACROSS | DOWN |
|---|---|
| 1 Avoid (4) | 1 Creator (5) |
| 3 Sharp taste (4) | 2 Wound mark (4) |
| 5 Capture (5) | 3 God of thunder (4) |
| 6 Always (4) | 4 Avarice (5) |
| 8 Run after (6) | 7 Wear away (5) |
| 10 Banned (9) | 8 Cost (5) |
| 13 Sewing tool (6) | 9 Picture (5) |
| 15 Sea mammal (4) | 11 Wrath (5) |
| 16 Musical speed (5) | 12 Sudden fear (5) |
| 17 Fragrant flower (4) | 14 Day and year (4) |
| 18 Friendly (4) | 15 Display (4) |

## 22★ Can you crack the safe? Your first task is to decide which of the 14 statements below are false. Then shade out the areas on the combination lock that share the same letters as the false statements (so, if you think statement E is false, shade out area E). The remaining 'lit' segments should give the digital numbered combination required.

### True or false – these events happened in 1992?

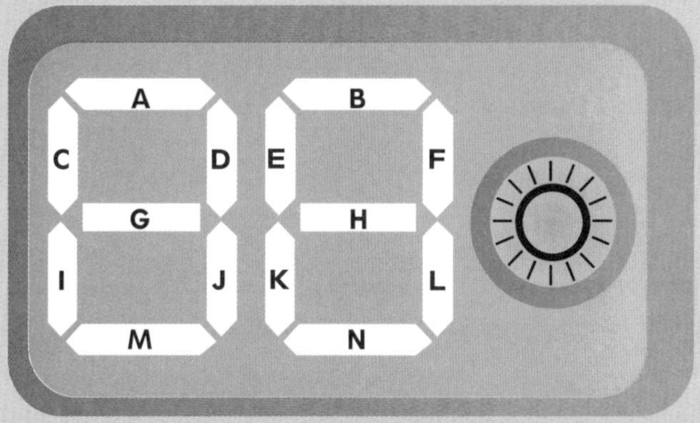


A Chris Patten becomes Hong Kong's last governor

B The *Exxon Valdez* oil tanker runs aground in Alaska

C *Silence of the Lambs* picks up five Oscars

D Bill Clinton becomes 42nd US president

E The Berlin Wall falls

F Butros Butros Ghali takes over as UN Secretary-General

G Los Angeles is ravaged by riots

H Eire appoints its first female president

I Nigel Mansell becomes Formula 1 world champion

J Andrew Morton's biography, *Diana: Her True Story*, published

K Nelson Mandela is freed after 27 years

L The Barcelona Olympic Games take place

M Comedian Benny Hill dies

N Mike Tyson becomes youngest ever heavyweight champion

**23** ★★ Solve the clues to find nine answers. The letters from the answers can then be transferred into the main grid to give you an unflattering comment from a musician who died in December 2000.

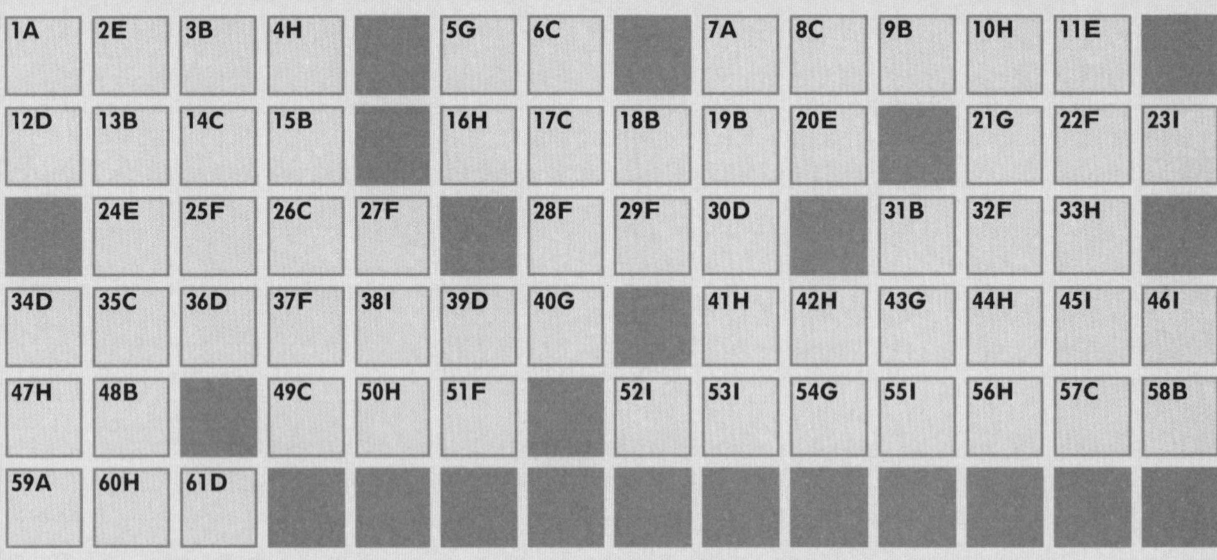


A Came first in a contest — 1 7 59

B Quality that heroes have — 19 15 3 58 13 18 9 31 48

C Small carnivorous freshwater fish (pl.) — 8 17 57 26 6 49 14 35

D Being of service — 34 12 61 30 36 39

E Chopped meat mixed with potatoes — 2 11 20 24

F The part of the face above the eyes — 29 28 51 25 32 22 37 27

G Experiencing pleasure or joy — 21 5 43 54 40

H People hired to fight for another country — 42 33 10 60 50 4 56 44 41 47 16

I Extend over and cover a part of — 45 46 55 23 38 52 53

**24**★★ Again, transfer the letters from the answers to the questions below into the grid to find a quotation by the pilot Neli Vuatalevu in this topical acrostic puzzle.

| | | 1E | 2E | 3D | | 4A | 5B | 6I | 7A | |
|---|---|---|---|---|---|---|---|---|---|---|
| 8A | 9D | 10C | 11I | 12C | 13I | 14D | 15F | 16A | | 17A |
| | 18I | 19B | 20C | 21A | | 22C | 23D | 24C | 25D | |
| 26I | 27A | 28G | 29E | | 30E | | 31G | 32C | | 33F |
| 34H | 35H | | 36D | 37C | 38E | 39H | 40B | | 41F | |
| 42G | 43H | 44I | 45H | | 46B | 47E | 48D | | 49E | 50A |
| 51F | 52I | 53B | 54G | 55H | 56E | | 57E | 58I | 59F | 60D |
| | 61I | 62I | | 63H | 64E | 65H | 66I | 67E | | |

A Perks, in addition to salary
4 21 50 27 8 17 7 16

B Frothy milk drink
S H A K E
46 53 19 40 5

C On the other hand
37 32 12 24 20 22 10

D Get back
25 48 36 14 9 3 23 60

E Florence, the European songbird
N I G H T I N G A L E
29 30 56 2 1 38 67 64 49 57 47

F In small, tight curls – saucy!
15 41 33 59 51

G Broad in scope or content
42 54 31 28

H Relating to the whole country
55 63 35 43 34 39 65 45

I Acts of overt warfare
18 13 26 52 61 44 58 62 66 11 6

**25★★** Can you spot these words, all connected with books and printing, in the grid? They may be found across or down, backwards or forwards. When you have found them all, the remaining letters, when rearranged, give the name of a famous wizard in a series of popular children's books.

| | |
|---|---|
| BOLDFACE | PAPER |
| BOOKSHOP | PAPERBACK |
| CHAPTER | PARAGRAPH |
| COLUMN | PRINT |
| COPY | PRINTRUN |
| COPYRIGHT | PROOFREADER |
| DEADLINE | PUBLISH |
| DICTIONARY | REVISE |
| FLAP | SPINE |
| HARDBACK | STORY |
| IMPRINT | TITLE |
| INDEX | TYPE |
| INK | TYPOGRAPHY |
| ITALIC | VOLUME |
| NOVELIST | WATERMARK |

| | | | | | | | | | | | | | |
|---|---|---|---|---|---|---|---|---|---|---|---|---|---|
| P | A | P | E | R | B | A | C | K | Y | D | K | N | I |
| A | K | R | A | M | R | E | T | A | W | E | C | U | M |
| L | O | B | O | L | D | F | A | C | E | A | A | R | P |
| F | Y | R | A | N | O | I | T | C | I | D | B | T | R |
| Y | B | O | O | K | S | H | O | P | H | L | D | N | I |
| H | P | A | R | T | C | I | L | A | T | I | R | I | N |
| P | A | P | E | R | Y | R | O | T | S | N | A | R | T |
| A | R | T | T | T | I | T | L | E | P | E | H | P | S |
| R | A | Y | P | R | X | E | D | N | I | E | P | U | I |
| G | G | P | A | C | O | P | Y | R | N | S | T | B | L |
| O | R | E | H | V | O | L | U | M | E | I | N | L | E |
| P | A | R | C | O | L | U | M | N | E | V | I | I | V |
| Y | P | R | O | O | F | R | E | A | D | E | R | S | O |
| T | H | G | I | R | Y | P | O | C | T | R | P | H | N |

**26★★** How old are these entertainers? Can you match them with their years of birth?

| 1942 | 1946 | 1947 | 1958 | 1974 | 1981 |
|---|---|---|---|---|---|

1 **Britney Spears**
2 **Barbra Streisand**
3 **Cher**
4 **Robbie Williams**
5 **Michael Jackson**
6 **Elton John**

# 27

1 George W. Bush is which President of the USA?

a 41st b 42nd
c 43rd d 44th

2 Why was the England rugby captain suspended in December 2000?

a taking bribes
b taking drugs
c foul play
d persistent lateness

3 Name the alcoholic robot in the animated TV series *Futurama*

a Hal b Rocky
c Fender d Bender

4 Which of these has not played Mrs Robinson on the London stage?

a Kathleen Turner
b Anne Bancroft
c Jerry Hall
d Amanda Donohoe

5 Abdurrahman Wahid is the president of... where?

a Indonesia b Malaysia
c South Korea d Cambodia

6 Which pair won the Men's Doubles title at the 2001 Australian Open?

a Woodbridge and Woodforde
b Woodforde and Bjorkman
c Woodbridge and Bjorkman
d Bjorkman and Kulti

7 What is Eminem's full name?

a Marshall Billy Mathers II
b Marshall Bruce Mathers III
c Marshall Brent Mathers IV
d Slim Shady

8 Who resigned as chief executive of Railtrack?

a Gerald Corbett
b Ronnie Corbett
c Jeremy Corbyn
d Gerry Corbell

9 How much did Tiger Woods earn on the 2000 PGA Tour?

a $7,382,110
b $9,188,321
c $11,948,012
d $13,398,663

10 Cliff Richard's 'Millennium Prayer' was sung to which tune?

a 'Jerusalem'
b 'Summer Holiday'
c 'Silent Night'
d 'Auld Lang Syne'

11 An invention called RS-01 was launched in March 2001. What was it?

a inflatable umbrella
b clockwork radio
c robot dog
d video telephone

12 Who won the Tour de France in 2001?

a Lance Armstrong
b Joseba Beloki
c Jan Ullrich
d David Millar

13 Which river flooded York in November 2000?

a Aire b Ouse
c Ure d Tees

14 How does Darcy Bussell make her living?

a supermodel
b pop singer
c ballet dancer
d furniture designer

15 Where was England cricket captain Nasser Hussain born?

a Colchester, Essex
b Bradford, Yorkshire
c Madras, India
d Karachi, Pakistan

**28**★★ Identify these birds then guess which one is connected with the 2001 Super Bowl.

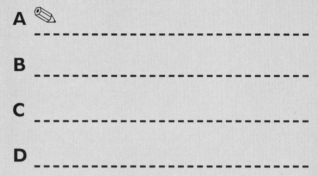

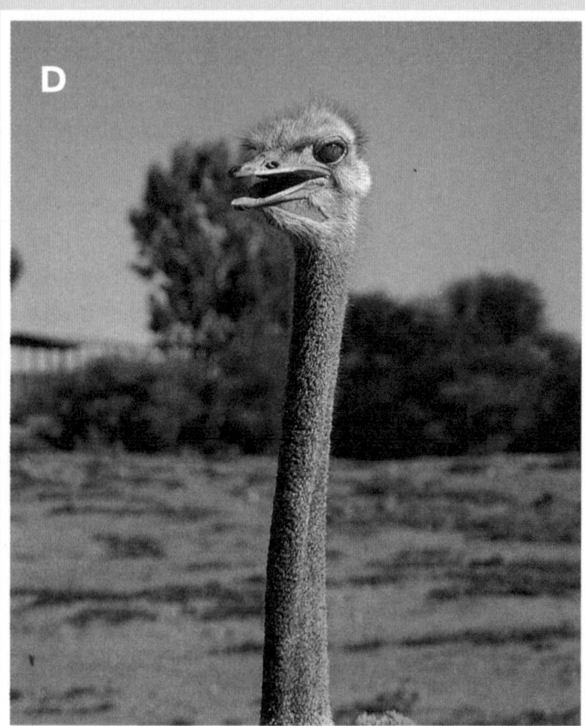


**29**★★ Which star did this celebrity recently marry? Can you name their first child together?

**30** ★★ These foods are associated with countries that all took part in the Sydney Olympics in 2000. Can you name the foods and the countries, then say which country won the most SILVER medals?

**31** ★★ From what star did this celebrity sensationally split in 2001? What was the last film they starred in together and who directed it?

## 32★★ Use the letters in the shaded squares to find the name of a popular singer.

ACROSS
1 Dairy product (5)
3 Croat (anag.) (5)
6 Celebration (5)
7 Shoulder gesture (5)
8 Foe (5)
11 Motionless (5)
13 In the vicinity (5)
14 Latest fashion (5)
15 Jockey (5)
16 Hooked claw (5)

DOWN
1 Packing case (5)
2 Happy (5)
3 Bottomless pit (5)
4 Panic-stricken (9)
5 Firing distance (5)
6 Prophesied (9)
9 Baking ingredient (5)
10 Modify (5)
11 Fragrance (5)
12 Citrus fruit (5)

------------------------------

## 33★★ Can you match up these headlines with the dates from the past 100 years? To make it more difficult, key words need replacing in the headlines.

| 21 June 1919 | 10 February 1942 | 14 November 1963 | 10 March 1969 |
|---|---|---|---|
| 5 July 1980 | 11 May 1981 | 24 January 1986 | 10 November 1989 |

1 Volcanic Island of Surtsey appears off coast of .....................

2 Bulldozers begin to demolish .....................

3 'Chatanooga-Choo-Choo' by ..................... sells a million.

4 Bjorn Borg wins ..................... trophy for 5th time.

5 James Earl Ray sentenced to 99 years for murder of .....................

6 Musical ..................... , based on T.S. Eliot's playful poems, opens.

7 German fleet scuttled off .....................

8 Spacecraft ..................... encounters Uranus.

**34★** Due to an outbreak of foot and mouth disease, the annual Cruft's dog show was cancelled, which was a great disappointment to many who had high hopes for their dogs; among them were the five breeders who appear in this puzzle. What breed of dog had each planned to show, by which name is it known in the kennels at home and what is its Kennel Club registered name?

1 Ms Pooch is the proud owner of Blue Desire II, who is not a bulldog

2 The Skye terrier is affectionately known as Fleece to his owner, who isn't Mr Yapp. Nor does Mr Yapp own the beagle.

3 The Kennel Club registered name of the Rottweiler is Loxwood Rose. Du Barry Lace is given the less pompous-sounding name of Max when at home!

4 Miss Barker's dog, Bo-Bo, isn't the elkhound or bulldog (neither of which belongs to a man).

5 Sweet Loyalty isn't a beagle. Sam isn't a elkhound.

| | BREED | | | | | KNOWN AS | | | | | REGISTERED NAME | | | | |
|---|---|---|---|---|---|---|---|---|---|---|---|---|---|---|---|
| | Beagle | Bulldog | Elkhound | Rottweiler | Skye terrier | Bo-Bo | Fleece | Lucy | Max | Sam | Blue Desire II | Du Barry Lace | Loxwood Rose | Royal Debate | Sweet Loyalty |
| Miss Barker | | | | | | | | | | | | | | | |
| Mr Leash | | | | | | | | | | | | | | | |
| Ms Pooch | | | | | | | | | | | | | | | |
| Mrs Walker | | | | | | | | | | | | | | | |
| Mr Yapp | | | | | | | | | | | | | | | |
| Blue Desire II | | | | | | | | | | | | | | | |
| Du Barry Lace | | | | | | | | | | | | | | | |
| Loxwood Rose | | | | | | | | | | | | | | | |
| Royal Debate | | | | | | | | | | | | | | | |
| Sweet Loyalty | | | | | | | | | | | | | | | |
| Bo-Bo | | | | | | | | | | | | | | | |
| Fleece | | | | | | | | | | | | | | | |
| Lucy | | | | | | | | | | | | | | | |
| Max | | | | | | | | | | | | | | | |
| Sam | | | | | | | | | | | | | | | |

**35★★** Can you work out which anniversaries are being referred to in these statements?

1 The .................... anniversary of the first manned space flight was in 2001.

2 2004 is the .................... anniversary of the sinking of the Titanic.

3 2002 was the .................... anniversary of the assassination of President John F. Kennedy.

4 The .................... anniversary of the first talking film is in 2003.

5 2001 was the .................... anniversary of American Independence.

## 36 ★★ Can you crack the safe? Your first task is to decide which of the 14 statements below are false. Then shade out the areas on the combination lock that share the same letters as the false statements (so if you think statement E is false, shade out area E). The remaining 'lit' segments should give the digital numbered combination required.

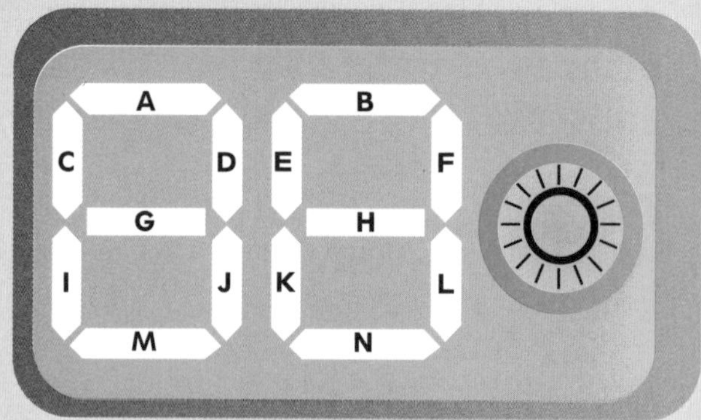


### True or false – these events happened in 1952?

- A Education pioneer Maria Montessori dies
- B Artificial heart used for the first time
- C Eva Peron, first lady of Argentina, dies
- D Jackson Pollock begins 'Action Painting' technique
- E Russian dog Laika launched into space
- F First performance of Agatha Christie's play *The Mousetrap*
- G King George VI dies, Elizabeth is new Queen
- H Anne Frank's diary is published
- I Première of animated film *Snow White and the Seven Dwarfs*
- J Maureen Connolly ('Little Mo') wins Wimbledon singles title
- K Ian Fleming, creator of James Bond, dies
- L 'I Saw Mummy Kissing Santa Claus' is a big chart hit
- M Gene Kelly 'sings in the rain'
- N America tests the first hydrogen bomb

## 37 ★★ The surname of which actor is hidden in this riddle?

My first is in chorus, but not in refrain;
My second's in airport,
but not in a plane.
My third is in road, but never in street;
My fourth is in warmth,
but it's missing from heat.
My fifth's in millennium
and also in dome;
My whole played a warrior,
triumphant in Rome.

## 38 ★★ Spell out a ten-letter word, moving through each circle once only and using every letter. Clue: 2002 is one.

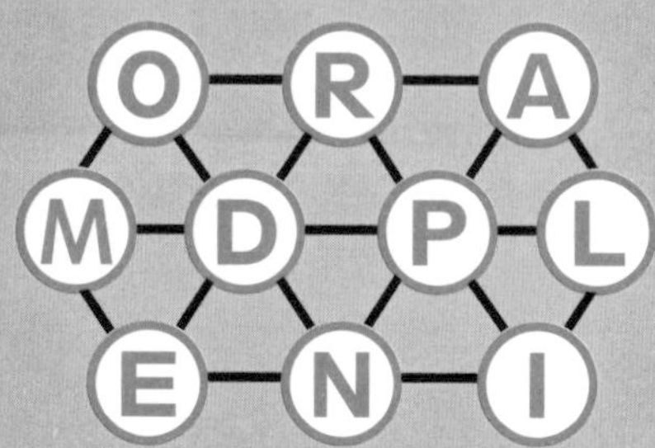

**39** ★★ Can you complete the names of these ten politicians from around the world, each of whom has been in the news in the past year? Clue: they are arranged here in alphabetical order according to their surnames.

| | |
|---|---|
| _ _SS_R _R_F_T | V_C_ _V _AV_L |
| GO_ _O_ _RO_ _ | R_B_R_ _U_ _BE |
| _ _CQ_ _S _H_R_C | _L_D_MI_ _UT_N |
| _L _O_E | A_ _EL S_A_O_ |
| _I_LI_M H_ _U_ | _NN _ _DD_C_ _BE |

**40** ★★ The wooden blocks each have a six-letter word written on them, but unfortunately you can see only three sides. When you have solved the clues, the first column will reveal an annual ceremony.

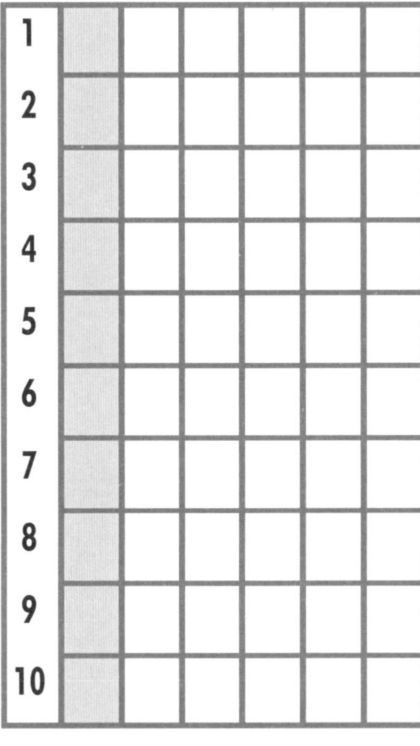


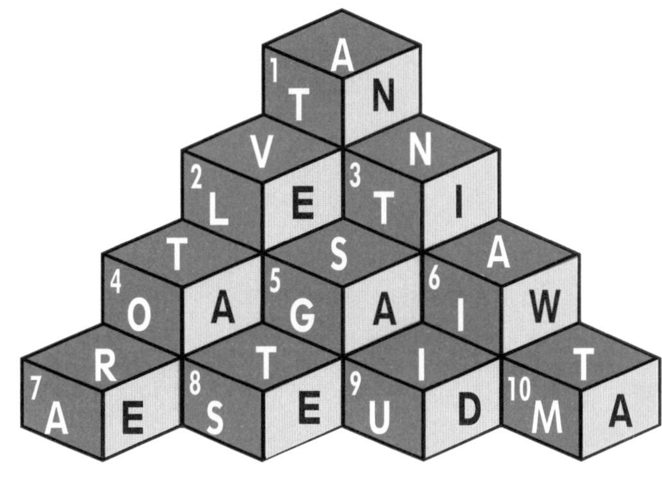


CLUES

1 Outlaw
2 Divulge
3 Catch fire
4 Drum beat
5 Dignified
6 Restaurant worker
7 Blood vessel
8 Outcome
9 Athletics event
10 Rivulet

41★ Can you crack the code and discover a medical headline that appeared in April 2001?

7 13 10 6 20   10 15 20 17 10 19 6   9 6 2 19 10 15 8

2 10 5   21 6 4 9 15 16 13 16 8 26.

✎ ------------------------------------------------------------

42★ Use the letters in the shaded squares to find the name of a sweet film released in 2001.

✎ ------------------------------------------------------------

ACROSS
1 Hurry (4)
3 Prickly plant (6)
6 Cab lane (anag.) (7)
7 Stop (4)
8 Type of wood (4)
9 Sled-dog (5)
10 Neat (4)
12 Bog fuel (4)
15 Bullfighter (7)
16 Amazement (6)
17 Midday (4)

DOWN
1 Get to (5)
2 Fit and well (7)
3 Outer garment (4)
4 Topic (5)
5 Loose-fitting (5)
8 Tropical storm (7)
10 Toss (5)
11 Evil being (5)
13 Giant (5)
14 Couple (4)

43★★ In March 2001, something crashed into the Pacific Ocean. What was it? The answer is in the grid.

| | | | | | | | | | |
|---|---|---|---|---|---|---|---|---|---|
| Soldiers with lances<br>Greenfly | | Wailing alarm<br>Laugh | | A place to live in orbit | Neckwear | | Sign of the Zodiac | Romanian currency | Estab-lished (abbr.) |
| | | | | | Land off the coast<br>Superstar | | | | |
| Hearing aids | | | | | | | | | |
| Forward<br>Spanish dictator | | | | | | Away from home | | | |
| | | | | | | Granny Smith | | Fabric edges | Before |
| Bacteria | | Make less smooth | Pass<br>Married woman | | | | | | |
| | | | | | Sea platform | | | | |
| The Arctic | | | | | | | | | |
| Beer Barrel | United States<br>Italian volcano | | | | Otherwise | | Peaceful | | Writing tools |
| | | | Front of shoe<br>Age | | | | | | |
| Belongs to (group) | | | | | | Long period | | | |
| Roman Emperor<br>Yellow fruit | | | | | Valley | | | | |
| | | | | | | Manuscripts (abbr.) | | | |

## 44★★ How well will you fare with these topical posers?

1 Which date was the 100th day of the year in 2001?

✎ ------------------------------------------------------------

2 Who revealed her Bottom on the London stage?

------------------------------------------------------------

3 Who plays the part of Fred Elliot in *Coronation Street*?

------------------------------------------------------------

4 Which 'accidental MP' wrote a book about it in 2000?

------------------------------------------------------------

5 Reggie Kray died in 2000 after serving 32 years for the murder of … whom?

------------------------------------------------------------

6 What new name has the Post Office adopted?

------------------------------------------------------------

7 Which two Asian countries did England defeat in Test series over the winter of 2000–2001?

------------------------------------------------------------

8 Which pop act consists of Claire, Faye, Lisa, 'H' and Lee?

------------------------------------------------------------

9 Who won the University Boat Race in 2001?

------------------------------------------------------------

10 When did Queen Elizabeth the Queen Mother celebrate her 100th birthday?

------------------------------------------------------------

11 What's the name of the West End musical featuring the songs of Abba?

------------------------------------------------------------

12 Which former Royal Marine published the first volume of his memoirs in 2000?

------------------------------------------------------------

13 Which manager of Chelsea FC was sacked in 2000?

------------------------------------------------------------

14 Supply one of Michael Portillo's other Christian names.

------------------------------------------------------------

15 Which company has a logo officially called 'the Swoosh'?

------------------------------------------------------------

**45** **Test your powers of recall with this memory test. Read the piece through, then turn over the page and try to answer as many questions as you can without looking back at the original.**

★ 1–4 correct answers
★★ 5–8 correct anwers
★★★ 9–10 correct answers

Yesterday's fall on the world stock markets, already known as 'Wobbly Wednesday', has had a mixed reception here in Upper Vordania.

Retail store chain *Chepa* opened 20 points down and then fell a further 35 points by lunchtime. From his yacht on Lake Lucerne, *Chepa* CEO Karl Spanner, aged 76, urged calm: 'The underlying story at *Chepa* is stability,' he rambled.

His main rival *Bondretti's* fared better, opening 12 points down but rallying through the day to finish 3 points back up.

Elsewhere in the markets, new technologies took a beating, with frostware giants *Megahard* slipping 86 to 1479, closely followed by *Hamsta*, who ended the day down 57 at 1467.

A spokesman for *Hamsta*, Adrian Logoff said today: 'We're not only rubbish, we're yesterday's rubbish.'

In the field of medicine, however, pharmaceutical manufacturer *Raybees* held steady at 1356, due mostly to the success of 'Gelapsipan', their new treatment for advanced irrelevancy, and the private hospital chain *Gravestone's* better-than-expected mid-year profits saw their shares fall only 21 points.

Car-makers continue to suffer a winter of discontent. Axle Motors blamed poor sales of their new seven-door hatchback Sluggino, all of which were recalled in October to have steering-wheels fitted. Axle fell 49 points over the course of the day.

The Trixie index closed at 2740, the Bikkie top 100 at 543.2, and of course the markets remain closed tomorrow as Vordania play Belgium in the World Cup.

## 45 Questions

Now that you've read the story on page 33, try to answer these questions without looking back.

1 What is yesterday's stock market fall colloquially known as?

✎ ----------------------------------------

2 By how many points had *Chepa*'s shares fallen in total by lunchtime yesterday?

----------------------------------------

3 How old is *Chepa*'s CEO Karl Spanner?

----------------------------------------

4 Did *Hamsta*'s shares go up or down yesterday?

----------------------------------------

5 What is the name of *Raybees*' new treatment for advanced irrelevancy?

----------------------------------------

6 What is the private hospital chain called?

----------------------------------------

7 What is Axle Motors' hatchback called?

----------------------------------------

8 In what month were these hatchbacks recalled?

----------------------------------------

9 The Trixie index closed at – 4270, 7420 or 2740?

----------------------------------------

10 Who do Vordania play in the World Cup?

----------------------------------------

## 46★★

Can you decipher what Sarah Jessica Parker said on receiving a Golden Globe Award for Best Actress in a TV Series, Musical or Comedy?

'GSRH RH WVORXRLFH! R SRTSOB IVXLNNVMW DRMMRMT.' ✎ ----------------------------------------

## 47★ Identify the people in these photographs and say which is the odd one out and why.

A ______________________________ C ______________________________

B ______________________________ D ______________________________

## 48★★ Can you work out the missing anniversaries from the statements below?

1 2001 was the .................... birthday of Liza Minnelli.

2 The .................... anniversary of Elvis Presley's death is in 2004.

3 2002 is the .................... anniversary of Billie Holiday's death.

4 Stevie Wonder's .................... birthday is in 2003.

5 2002 is the .................... birthday of Woody Allen.

**49★★** Can you find the correct X that marks where the treasure lies? In this puzzle there are two treasures to find. First begin at START 1, which is the shorter route. Decide whether the first statement (a headline from newspapers between June 2000 and June 2001) is TRUE or FALSE, then follow the T or F arrow accordingly. Correct choices take you towards the treasure, wrong answers take you down blind alleys. When you arrive at an X, that is your chosen destination. Then begin the second trek beginning from START 2 at the top of the diagram, which is a longer journey. When you have attempted both paths, turn to the answers section to see if you arrived at the correct X each time.

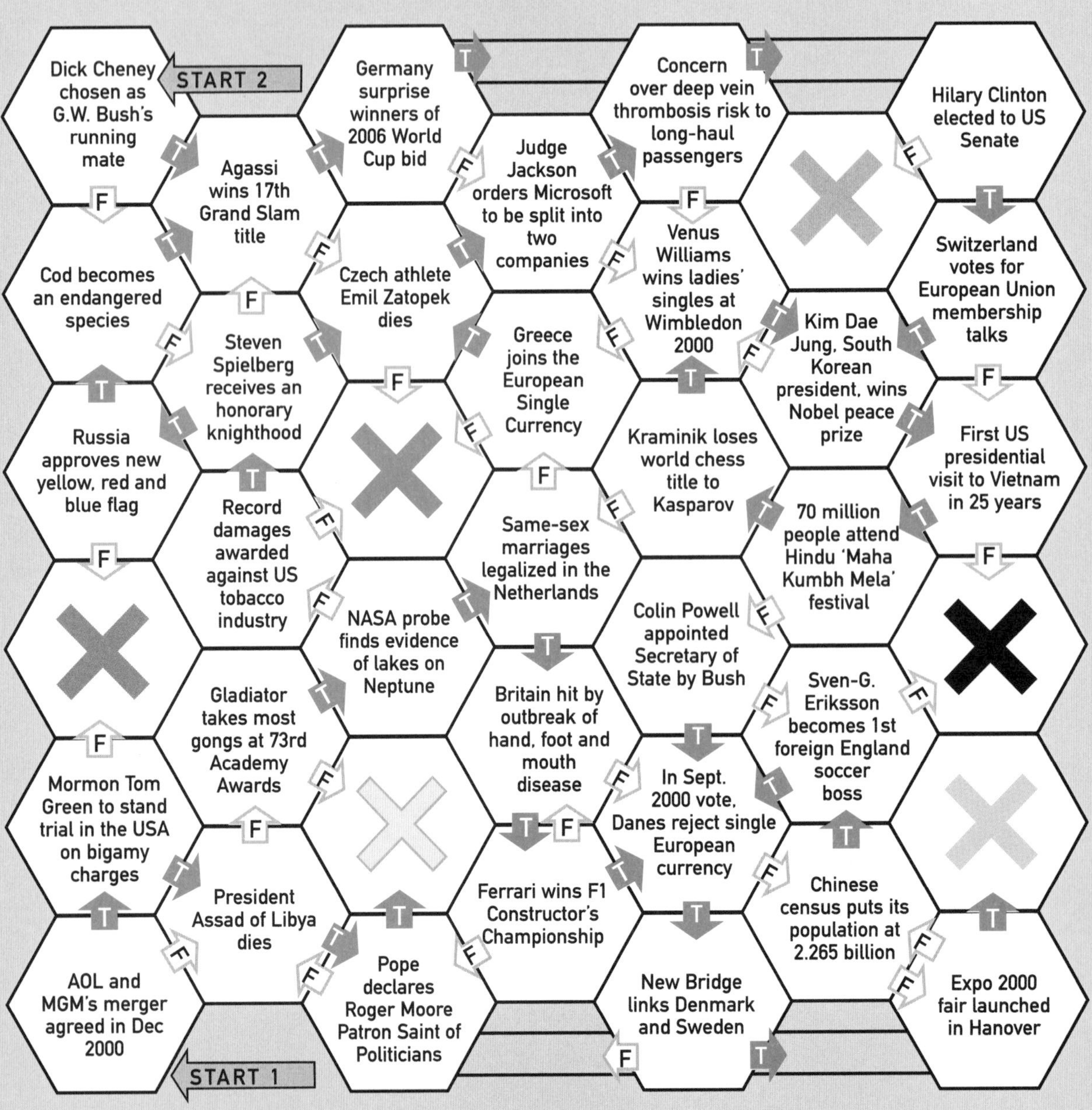

## 50★★ Can you match these tennis players with the years in which they won the singles title at Wimbledon?

| 1987 | 1975 | 1992 |
|---|---|---|
| 1994 | 1998 | 1977 |

Conchita Martinez --------

Jana Novotna --------

Arthur Ashe --------

Virginia Wade --------

Pat Cash --------

Andre Agassi --------

## 51★★ Spell out a person's name, moving through each circle once only. Clue: American epigrammatist born in 1902.

-----------------

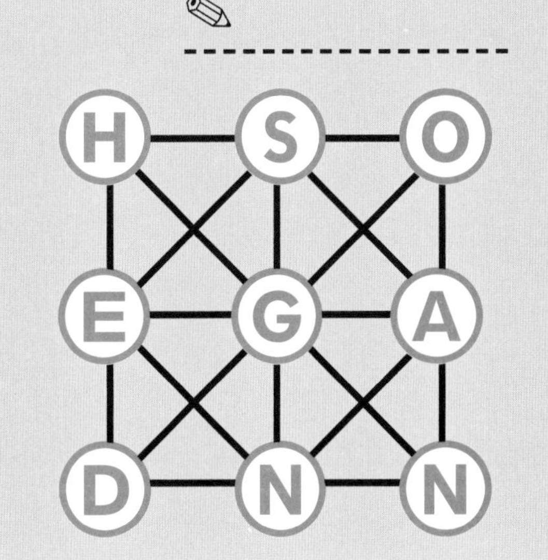


## 52★★ Each wooden block has a six-letter word written on it, but unfortunately you can see only three sides. When you have solved the clues, the first column will reveal the name of a famous daughter.

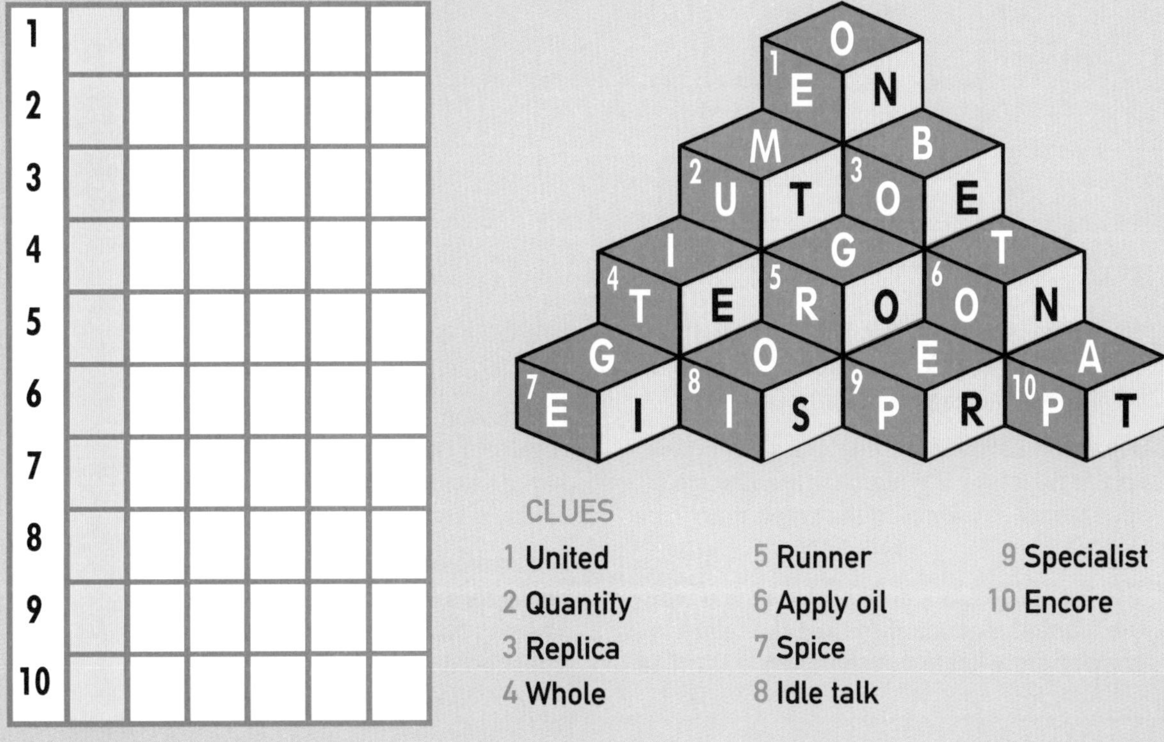


CLUES

1 United
2 Quantity
3 Replica
4 Whole
5 Runner
6 Apply oil
7 Spice
8 Idle talk
9 Specialist
10 Encore

**53**★★ The first six contestants in the nightly gameshow *Who Wants to be a Trillionaire?* didn't win anywhere near that amount – but they're not complaining! On which different night (Monday to Saturday) of last week did each take part, in which subject did each fail to give a correct answer and how much did he or she win in total?

| | NIGHT | | | | | | SUBJECT FAILED | | | | | | AMOUNT WON | | | | | |
|---|---|---|---|---|---|---|---|---|---|---|---|---|---|---|---|---|---|---|
| | Monday | Tuesday | Wednesday | Thursday | Friday | Saturday | Art | Geography | History | Languages | TV | Wildlife | £40,000 | £45,000 | £55,000 | £60,000 | £70,000 | £90,000 |
| Bella | | | | | | | | | | | | | | | | | | |
| Damian | | | | | | | | | | | | | | | | | | |
| Frank | | | | | | | | | | | | | | | | | | |
| Hilary | | | | | | | | | | | | | | | | | | |
| Jack | | | | | | | | | | | | | | | | | | |
| Lavinia | | | | | | | | | | | | | | | | | | |
| £40,000 | | | | | | | | | | | | | | | | | | |
| £45,000 | | | | | | | | | | | | | | | | | | |
| £55,000 | | | | | | | | | | | | | | | | | | |
| £60,000 | | | | | | | | | | | | | | | | | | |
| £70,000 | | | | | | | | | | | | | | | | | | |
| £90,000 | | | | | | | | | | | | | | | | | | |
| Art | | | | | | | | | | | | | | | | | | |
| Geography | | | | | | | | | | | | | | | | | | |
| History | | | | | | | | | | | | | | | | | | |
| Languages | | | | | | | | | | | | | | | | | | |
| TV | | | | | | | | | | | | | | | | | | |
| Wildlife | | | | | | | | | | | | | | | | | | |

1 The contestant who won £60,000 failed in the area of geography, by not being able to remember the capital of Paraguay.

2 Bella won £5000 more than Jack, who took part in the show the night before Lavinia's appearance, but later in the week than Hilary's.

3 The first contestant on the gameshow won the highest amount of money, but failed to answer the wildlife question, while Damian exhibited a total lack of any knowledge in languages, when he took part on Tuesday.

4 Hilary won a lower amount than whoever took part two days later than Bella, but a higher amount than whoever took part in Friday's show.

5 The contestant who won £70,000 failed to correctly answer a TV-related question. The one who correctly answered the art question didn't win £40,000.

**54★★** All of these books featured in the best-sellers list in late 2000 or early 2001. How many titles can you complete?

A_R_AN _O_E: T_ _ C_PP_ _C_N_ Y_A_S

R_TU_ _ _F T_E N_K_D _H_F

_CAR_ET _E_TH_R

T_ _ B_A_LE_ _N_HO_O_Y

_H_ BL_ _D _SS_SS_ _

D_LI_'S _H_CO_ _TE C_ _L_C_IO_

M_R_Y_ _G _ _E _IST_ _ _S

_ _RR_ _ _TT_ _ _N_ T_ _ PR_ _ON_R

O_ A_ _A_AN

H_N_ _B_L

'_IS

**55★★** Can you match up these headlines with the dates from the past 100 years? To make it more difficult, key words need replacing in the headlines.

| 12 July 1998 | 25 January 1924 | 14 August 1945 | 9 January 1972 |
|---|---|---|---|
| 11 July 1975 | 25 July 1978 | 7 June 1982 | 9 November 1988 |

1 The liner *Queen Elizabeth* destroyed by fire in ....................

2 .................... surrenders to the Allies, ending the Pacific War.

3 Brazil lose 3-0 to .................... in soccer World Cup Final.

4 Chinese archaeologists unearth .................... army.

5 Chamonix hosts first Winter ....................

6 .................... beats Karpov to become World Chess Champion.

7 Graceland, home of .................... , opens to the public.

8 Baby .................... is first test-tube baby.

**56**★★ Spell out a person's name, moving through each circle once only and using every letter on the grid.
Clue: she was in the spotlight in September 2000.

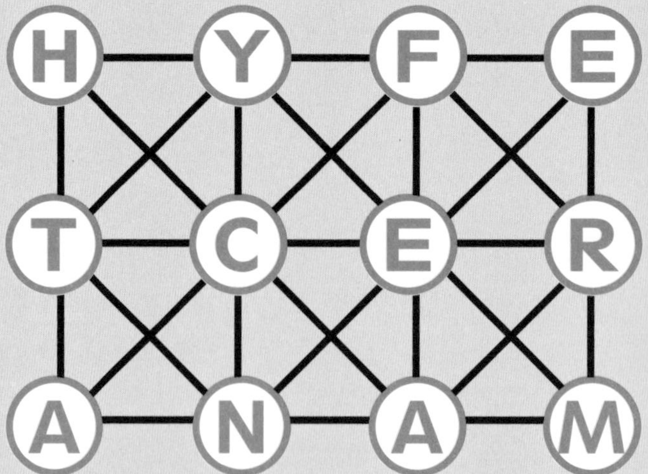

**57**★★ Can you find a world-famous person in the riddle below?

My first is in comfort and not in annoy;
My second's in girl and never in boy.
My third is in hirsute and also in hairy;
See my fourth in a goblin but not in a fairy.
Although it's in chapter, my fifth's not in verse.
My sixth is in doctor but not in a nurse.
My seventh's in morning and also in night;
My whole used to live in a house that is white.

**58**★★★ Which writer is hidden in this anagram?

**Drab mad banal rat-race (4,7,8)**

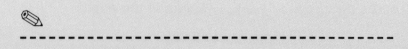

59★ Moving horizontally or vertically from letter to letter, find the name of a posh baby boy.

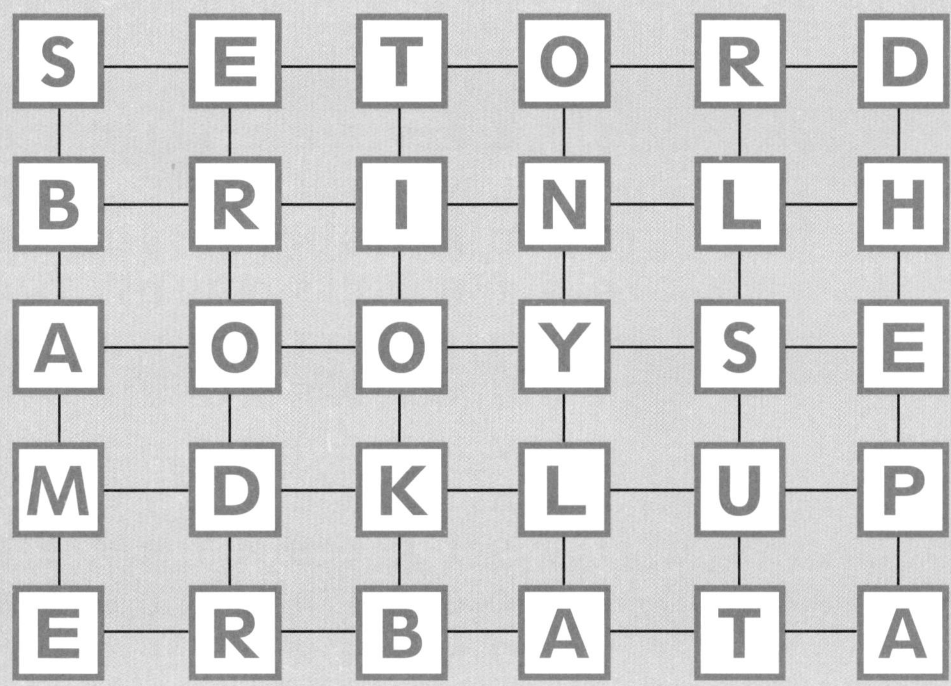


60★★★ Moving horizontally or vertically from letter to letter, find the surname of a Christian who left the Saints behind for a reincarnation in North London.

**61** ★★ Can you spot the following words, all connected with film and the cinema, in the grid? They may be found across, down or diagonally in any direction. The remaining letters, when rearranged give the name of an Oscar-winning actress.

ACTOR
ANIMATION
CASTING
CINEMASCOPE
CINEMATOGRAPHY
COSTUME
CREW
DUB
EPIC
EXTRA
FILM FESTIVAL
FOYER
HERO
INTERVAL
LINE
MATINEE IDOL
MOVIE
OSCAR
POPCORN
PROP
RAVE REVIEW
REEL
SCREENWRITER
SOUNDTRACK
SPECIAL EFFECTS
STUDIO
WIDESCREEN

| S | T | C | E | F | F | E | L | A | I | C | E | P | S |
|---|---|---|---|---|---|---|---|---|---|---|---|---|---|
| C | C | L | M | A | T | I | N | E | E | I | D | O | L |
| R | R | C | A | J | G | N | I | T | S | A | C | S | A |
| E | E | I | N | W | C | S | T | U | D | I | O | O | V |
| E | W | N | I | E | I | T | B | U | D | A | S | U | I |
| N | U | E | M | I | P | F | R | E | E | L | T | N | T |
| W | L | M | A | V | E | O | R | E | H | R | U | D | S |
| R | A | A | T | E | E | Y | E | I | V | O | M | T | E |
| I | V | S | I | R | L | E | X | T | R | A | E | R | F |
| T | R | C | O | E | I | R | O | T | C | A | S | A | M |
| E | E | O | N | V | N | R | O | C | P | O | P | C | L |
| R | T | P | I | A | E | O | R | A | C | S | O | K | I |
| R | N | E | E | R | C | S | E | D | I | W | R | B | F |
| C | I | N | E | M | A | T | O | G | R | A | P | H | Y |

**62** ★★★ Spell out a phrase that's recently become world-famous, moving through each circle only once and using every letter. Clue: goodbye!

**63★★** In this puzzle you have to find the correct X that marks where the treasure lies. Begin at START at the top of the puzzle. Decide whether the first statement (a headline from newspapers between June 2000 and June 2001) is TRUE or FALSE, then follow the T or F arrow accordingly. Correct choices take you towards the treasure, wrong answers take you down blind alleys. When you finally arrive at an X, that is your chosen destination. Now turn to the answers section to see if you arrived at the correct X.

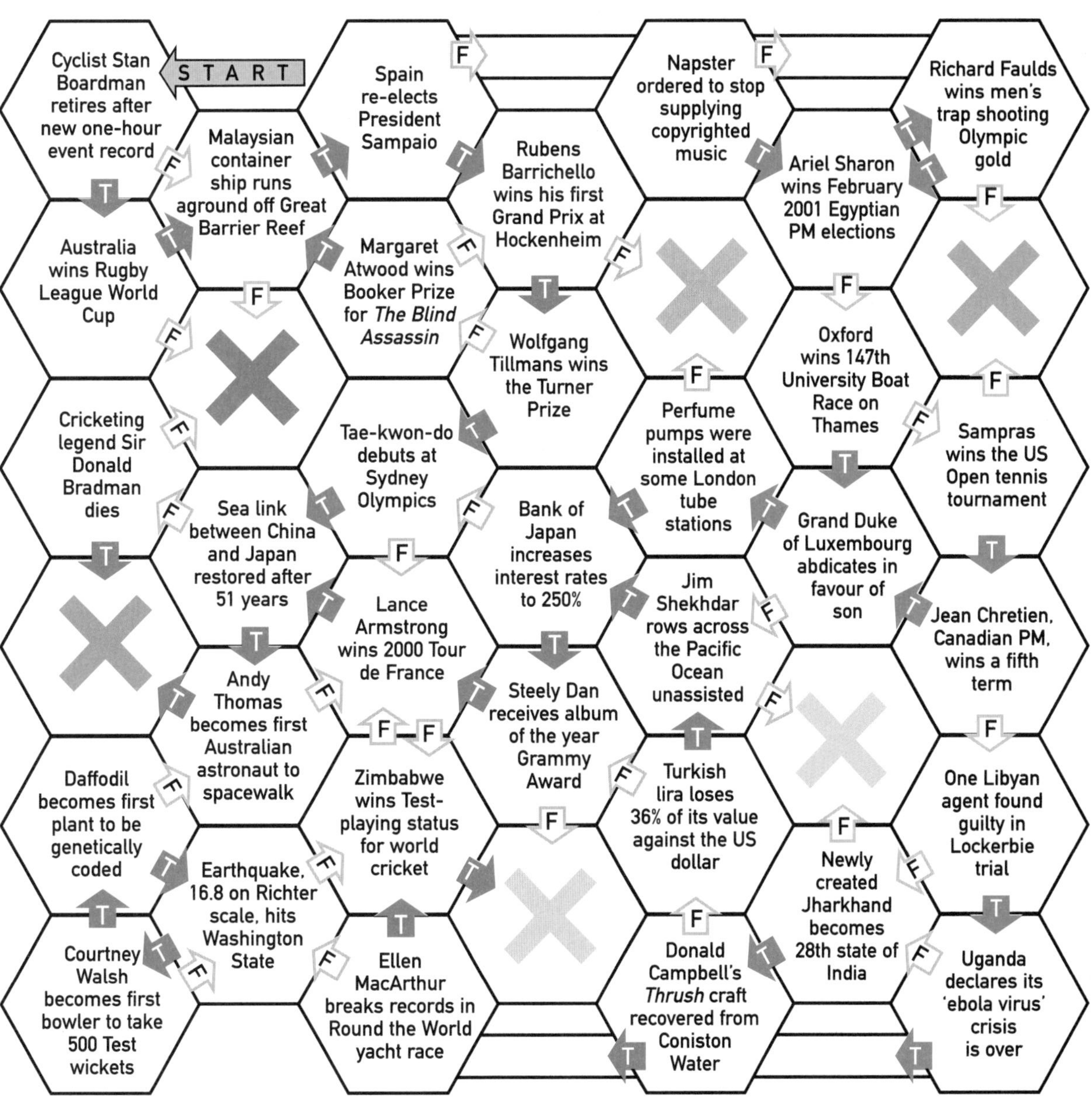

## 64★★ Who's hiding in this riddle?

My first is in table but not in a chair;
My second's in ticket but not in a fare.
My third is in England but nowhere in Spain;
My fourth is in drizzle but never in rain.
My fifth is in bars but is not found in pubs;
My whole is a wild cat, the king of the clubs.

✎ ------------------------------------

## 65★★ Can you match these items with the years in which they were invented?

| 1975 | 1876 | 1955 |
|---|---|---|
| 1892 | 1960 | 1879 |

1 Hovercraft ✎ -----------
4 Telephone -----------
2 Laser -----------
5 Rubik's cube -----------
3 Diesel engine -----------
6 Electric light bulb -----------

## 66★★ Can you decipher this quotation from Russell Crowe, said on his acceptance of Best Actor Oscar for *Gladiator*.

'ELBANIATTANU YLETELPMOC DNA SUORCIDUL YLEUGAV FO DNIK SMEES SIHT EKIL MAERD A, EREHWYNA FO SBRUBUS EHT NI PU WORG UOY FI.'

**67★** Moving horizontally or vertically from letter to letter, find the name of a rap artist with a taste for chainsaws.

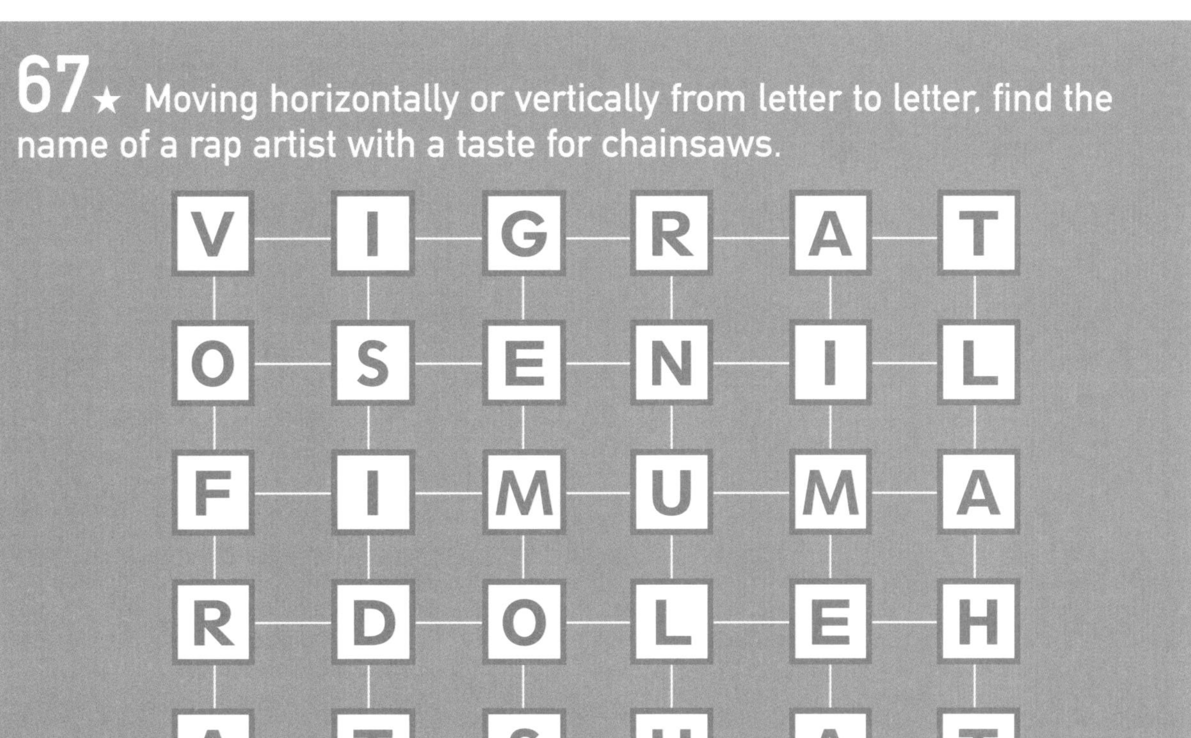


**68★★** Each wooden block has a six-letter word written on it, but unfortunately you can see only three sides. When you have solved the clues, the first column will reveal a sports championship.

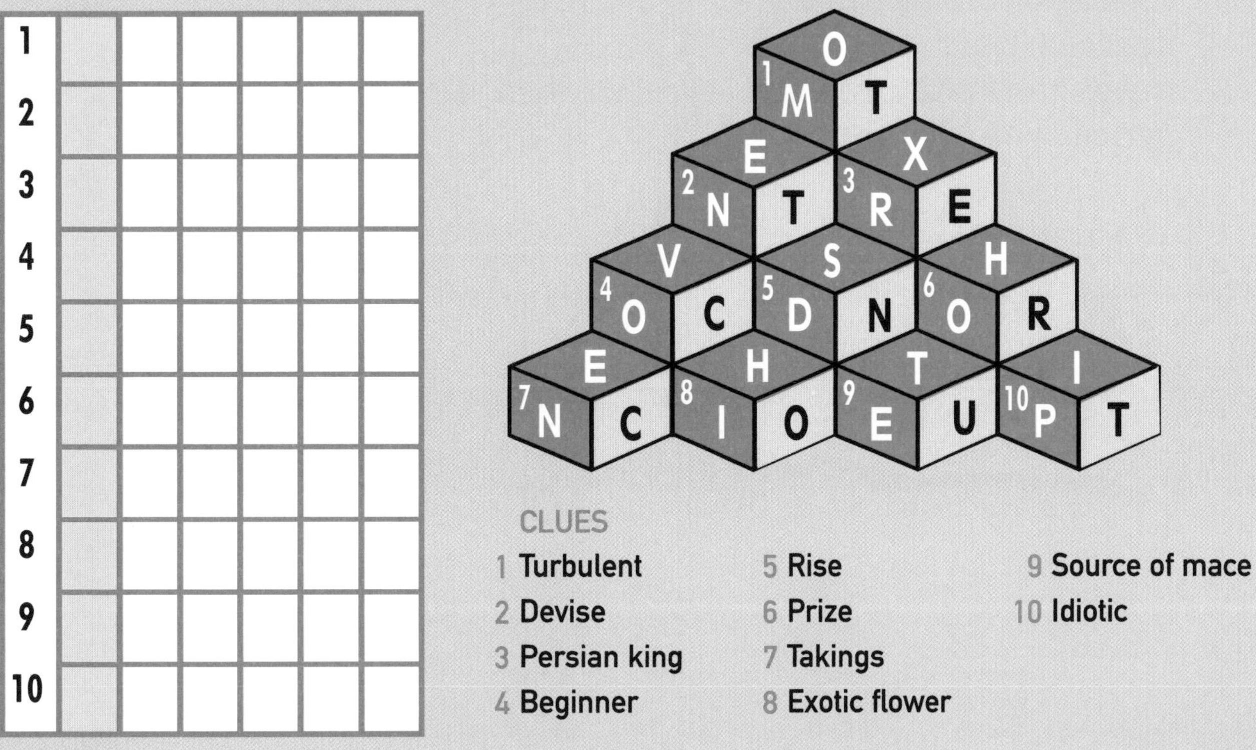


CLUES

1 Turbulent
2 Devise
3 Persian king
4 Beginner
5 Rise
6 Prize
7 Takings
8 Exotic flower
9 Source of mace
10 Idiotic

## 69★ Use the letters in the shaded squares to find the name of a popular author.

| ACROSS | DOWN |
|---|---|
| 1 Holy book (5) | 1 Copper-zinc alloy (5) |
| 3 Cavalry unit (5) | 2 Bird of prey (5) |
| 6 Vision (5) | 3 Sum (5) |
| 7 Ward off (5) | 4 Aim (9) |
| 8 Trap (5) | 5 Ski slope (5) |
| 11 Spin (5) | 6 Type of pasta (9) |
| 13 Absolve (5) | 9 Throw away (5) |
| 14 Similar (5) | 10 Tomb (5) |
| 15 Trophy (5) | 11 Uncanny (5) |
| 16 Male duck (5) | 12 Big (5) |

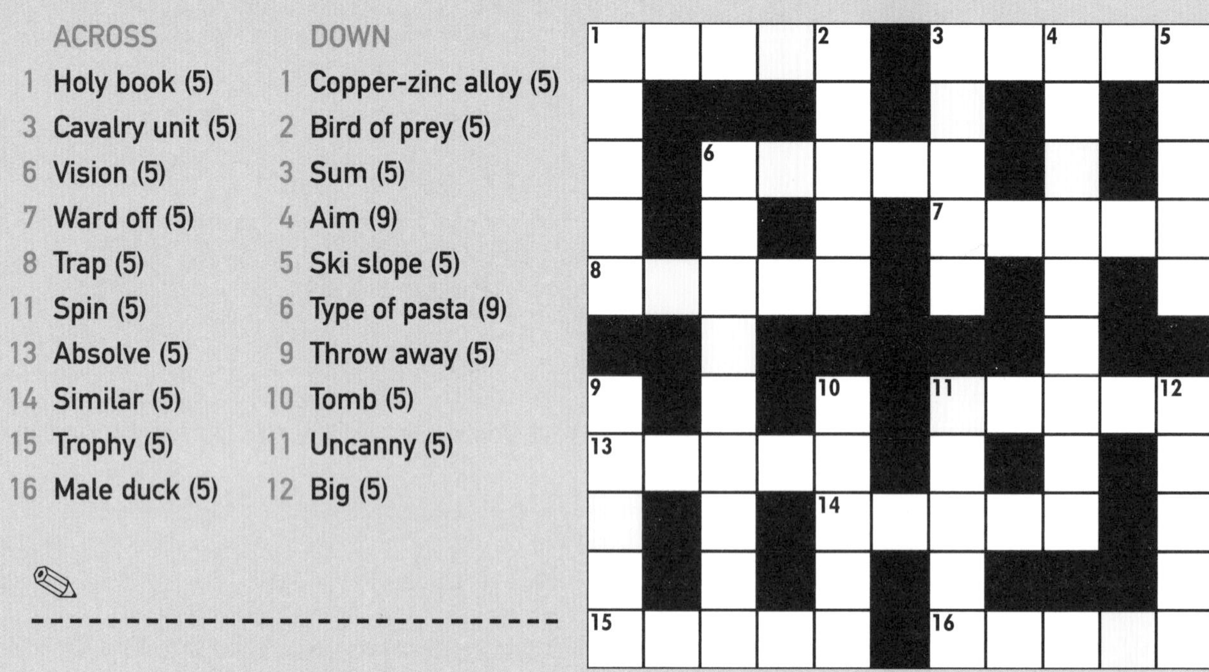

## 70★ Fill in the missing vowels to complete this headline, which refers to a major news story from the period June 2000–June 2001.

M_D_NN_
W_DS G_Y
R_TCH__
_N D_RN_CH

## 71★★ Can you find the name of a politician and world leader in this anagram?

**Mild trivia pun (8,5)**

## 72

Test your powers of recall with these two memory tests. Read each piece through, then turn over the page and try to answer as many questions as you can without looking back at the originals.

★ 1–4 correct answers

★★ 5–8 correct anwers

★★★ 9–10 correct answers

Once again the United States took the lion's share of medals at the 2000 World Championships for the totally unfit, the Limpix.

Martin Snale won three golds in the track events, registering 21 hours, 12 minutes and 57.9 seconds for the 100 metres, the slowest time ever.

Jon Tyre from Teeville, Ohio, competing in his fifth Limpix, also shone on the track, being the first to fall asleep on the starting line in the 200, 400 and 800 metres – officials recorded that unconsciousness kicked in exactly 0.653 seconds after the starting gun.

Tyre said proudly afterwards, 'I'd just opened my copy of *War and Peace*, and next thing I knew I'd got a medal.'

The USA had to settle for silver when Manuela Castilino won Spain a surprise gold in the javelin, which got caught in her shoelaces and flew backwards for 45.28 metres.

In the pool, Valéry Blanc of France and Simone Rockstone of Canada shared gold when their Lilos collided 7.61 centimetres from the edge, whereas the world's laziest diver, Billy 'Flop' Nelson, stunned an audience of over 12,000 by accidentally falling off the board – the first time he has entered the water in a 23-year career.

In gymnastics, there were golds for Pat Carroll and Larry Masters in the Ring Donuts and silver for Sarah Share on the Parallel Barstools. 'It's been a wonderful games,' Ramon Caverara, Limpix chairman, couldn't be bothered to say.

## 73

Isn't the Internet wonderful? Yesterday I wanted to contact an old school friend, Philip Trainset, so I booted up my Quatco GHJ-B401X PC (444 MHz, 128 MB RAM, 25.6 GB hard drive), and logged on.

Using the search engine 'Giggle', I did a general search for 'philip+trainset' and amazingly there were only 127,000 options! I tried two other engines, 'Hurrah!' and 'Toenail', but they advised me to narrow things down to avoid all the railway enthusiasts.

I also remembered that Philip's nickname was 'Earplug', so I typed 'philip+ trainset–railway+earplug'. Incredible! No hits at all.

I had some lunch – I'd been online for four hours – and then decided on a different approach. I typed in my old school's name, 'st+barnabas+woking' and was taken to an amazing site.

Did you know they now have three science labs, or that the Second XV rugby team lost 15-3 to the Barnstormers (as old boys are known)? Fascinating stuff. There was a 'List of the Lost' – and I was on it! So was 'Philip Trainset (1975–8) last heard of working for the BBC'.

I read every page of their (huge) web site, but I don't think he works there now as I found no mention of him. Undeterred I tried 15 other TV and radio channel web sites.

Finally, I visited a new search engine 'Gotlotnot', which lets you ask whole questions, and typed 'where+are+you+philip'. There was a loud knock on my study wall. Of course! Philip has lived next door for 20 years.

## 72 Questions Can you answer these questions without looking back at the first story on page 47?

1 What is the name of the Championship games? ________________

2 How many gold medals did Martin Snale win in the track events? ________________

3 From what US state does Jon Tyre hail? ________________

4 What was he reading on the starting line? ________________

5 How far backwards did Manuela's javelin travel – 45.28 metres, 42.58 metres or 48.25 metres? ________________

6 What is the name of the Canadian competitor? ________________

7 Name the world's laziest diver. ________________

8 How many years has his career lasted? ________________

9 What medal did Sarah Share win on the Parallel Barstools? ________________

10 What is the chairman of the games called? ________________

## 73 Questions Can you answer these without looking at page 47?

1 What is the name of my old school friend? ________________

2 How many GB does my hard drive have – 26.5, 25.6 or 62.5? ________________

3 What was the first search engine I used? ________________

4 Name two of the three other search engines. ________________

5 What is my school friend's nickname? ________________

6 How long had I been online by lunchtime? ________________

7 By what score did St Barnabas lose the rugby match? ________________

8 What are old boys of my school called? ________________

9 During what period was my friend at St Barnabas? ________________

10 For how long has my old friend lived next door? ________________

**74**★★ Six 24-metre yachts took part in this year's ET Round the Globe Challenge Yacht Race, leaving Southampton on 10 September. What were their positions at the end of the first three legs: Southampton to Boston, Boston to Buenos Aires and Buenos Aires to Wellington?

| | FIRST LEG SOUTHAMPTON TO BOSTON | | | | | | SECOND LEG BOSTON TO BUENOS-AIRES | | | | | | THIRD LEG BUENOS-AIRES TO WELLINGTON | | | | | |
|---|---|---|---|---|---|---|---|---|---|---|---|---|---|---|---|---|---|---|
| | First | Second | Third | Fourth | Fifth | Sixth | First | Second | Third | Fourth | Fifth | Sixth | First | Second | Third | Fourth | Fifth | Sixth |
| *Chrysalis* | | | | | | | | | | | | | | | | | | |
| *Hawk Moth* | | | | | | | | | | | | | | | | | | |
| *Imago* | | | | | | | | | | | | | | | | | | |
| *Mayfly IV* | | | | | | | | | | | | | | | | | | |
| *Red Admiral* | | | | | | | | | | | | | | | | | | |
| *Swallowtail* | | | | | | | | | | | | | | | | | | |
| THIRD First | | | | | | | | | | | | | | | | | | |
| THIRD Second | | | | | | | | | | | | | | | | | | |
| THIRD Third | | | | | | | | | | | | | | | | | | |
| THIRD Fourth | | | | | | | | | | | | | | | | | | |
| THIRD Fifth | | | | | | | | | | | | | | | | | | |
| THIRD Sixth | | | | | | | | | | | | | | | | | | |
| SECOND First | | | | | | | | | | | | | | | | | | |
| SECOND Second | | | | | | | | | | | | | | | | | | |
| SECOND Third | | | | | | | | | | | | | | | | | | |
| SECOND Fourth | | | | | | | | | | | | | | | | | | |
| SECOND Fifth | | | | | | | | | | | | | | | | | | |
| SECOND Sixth | | | | | | | | | | | | | | | | | | |

1 No yacht achieved the same position in the second leg as it did in the first, nor the same position in the third leg as it did in either the first or second legs.

2 *Chrysalis* was behind *Hawk Moth* at the end of the first leg of the trip, but entered Wellington harbour one place ahead of *Hawk Moth*. In the second leg, *Chrysalis* wasn't last nor was *Hawk Moth* first.

3 *Imago* was in the same position in the third leg as *Mayfly IV* had been in the second and *Swallowtail* had been in the first leg of the race.

4 *Swallowtail* had reached Boston before both *Hawk Moth* and *Imago*, but reached Buenos-Aires later than *Hawk Moth* and *Imago* in the second leg.

5 The first yacht to enter Boston harbour was the second to arrive in Buenos-Aires. The last yacht to enter Boston harbour was the third to arrive in Wellington.

6 *Red Admiral* didn't finish the third leg in the same position as that in which *Chrysalis* had finished the second leg. *Red Admiral* reached all three ports ahead of *Mayfly IV*.

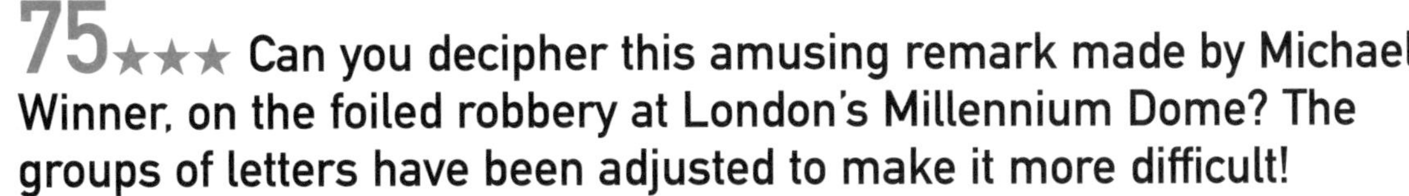

**75**★★★ Can you decipher this amusing remark made by Michael Winner, on the foiled robbery at London's Millennium Dome? The groups of letters have been adjusted to make it more difficult!

'GSVW LNVHS LFOWY VWVOR TSGVW
.RG'H GSVUR IHGGR NVGSV B'EVS
ZWKVL KOVHL PVVMG LTVGR M.'

- - - - - - - - - - - - - - - - - - - - - - - - - - - - - - - - - - -

**76**★★ In which year were each of these famous films made?

| 1970 | 1997 | 1995 |
|---|---|---|
| 1972 | 1976 | 1999 |

1 The Godfather ___________

2 Titanic ___________

3 Toy Story ___________

4 M*A*S*H ___________

5 Bugsy Malone ___________

6 The Blair Witch Project ___________

**77**★★★ Here's a remark made by Jerry Hall following her split from Mick Jagger. Can you decipher it (clue: try the puzzle below first)?

'J8DI 8W Q 29HE34R7O JQH G75 Q 53448GO3 Y7WGQHE.'

___________________________________

**78**★★★ People may have disputed the presidential election results, but there's no arguing with the truth of this remark, made by US President George W. Bush. Can you crack the code to discover what he said?

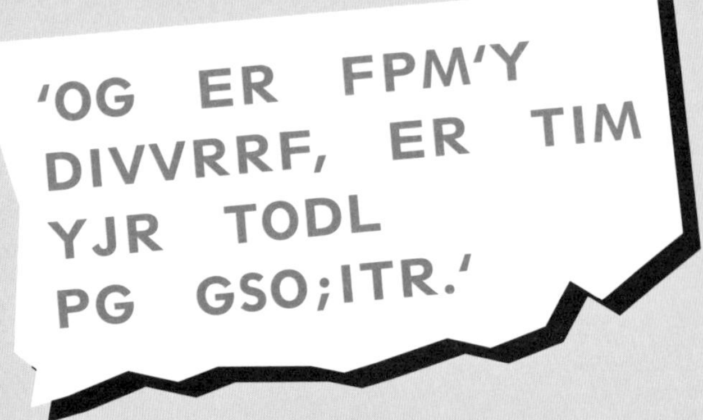

'OG ER FPM'Y
DIVVRRF, ER TIM
YJR TODL
PG GSO;ITR.'

___________________________________

79★ Moving horizontally or vertically from letter to letter, find the name of a former teacher who could make you a millionaire.

✎ ------------------------------------------------------------

80★★ Can you work out the missing anniversaries from the statements below?

1 2001 was the .................... anniversary of Nelson Mandela becoming president of South Africa.

2 The .................... anniversary of Margaret Thatcher becoming British prime minister is in 2002.

3 The .................... anniversary of Boris Yeltsin becoming president of the Russian Federation was in 2001.

4 2003 is the .................... anniversary of Bill Clinton becoming president of the USA.

5 The .................... anniversary of Mrs Indira Gandhi becoming prime minister of India is in 2002.

10 MINUTES

## 81 ★★★ Test your recollection of recent events.

1 Whose illustrations for Dante's *Divine Comedy* were on show in London?

a Leonardo b Botticelli
c Caravaggio d Titian

✎

2 Which of these categories did *Gladiator* not win an Oscar?

a Best Picture
b Best Original Screenplay
c Best Visual Effects
d Best Sound

3 Who succeeded Alex Salmond as leader of the Scottish National Party?

a Alex Neil b Lloyd Quinan
c John Swinney
d Dorothy Grace-Elder

4 2001 was the Chinese Year of the...

a Dragon b Monkey
c Horse d Snake

5 How long did it take yachtswoman Ellen MacArthur to complete the Vendée Globe round-the-world race?

a 74 days b 84 days
c 94 days d 104 days

6 Whose novel won the Booker Prize in 2000?

a Kazuo Ishiguro
b Margaret Atwood
c Michael Collins
d Matthew Kneale

7 Who was the Eurosceptic MP for Ludlow who left the Conservative Party?

a Christopher Gill
b Angus Derwent
c Gerald Dupont d Eric Mayport

8 Which Italian club did Sven Goran Eriksson leave?

a Roma b Inter Milan
c Juventus d Lazio

9 The European City of Culture title is shared by two cities in 2001. Which two?

a Amsterdam and Barcelona
b Florence and Frankfurt
c Rotterdam and Porto
d Athens and Middlesbrough

10 Who won the 2000 World Series?

a New York Yankees
b New York Royals
c New York Dodgers
d New York Mets

**82**★★ Can you crack the safe? Your first task is to decide which of the statements below are false. Then shade out the areas on the combination lock that share the same letters as the false statements (so if you think statement E is false, shade out area E). The remaining 'lit' segments should give the digital numbered combination required.

**True or false – these events happened in 1902?**

A The world's first railway timetable is published

B Aviator-to-be Charles Lindbergh is born

C The British celebrate victory in the Boer War

D *The Tale of Peter Rabbit* is published by Beatrix Potter

E Ulysses Grant becomes 18th US president

F The Berlin Underground system is inaugurated

G Edward VII is crowned king of Great Britain and Ireland

H Painter Gustav Klimt dies

I The first liquid fuel rocket is launched

J Thomas Edison invents the battery

K The first edition of *The Reader's Digest* is published

L Russia abolishes the death penalty

M Joseph Hansom patents a 'safety cab'

N Pope Pius XI denounces the USSR

**83**★★ Can you match each of these men to the year in which he was first elected US President?

| 1960 | 1992 | 1952 |
|---|---|---|
| 1980 | 1932 | 1976 |

1 Ronald Reagan ----------

2 Jimmy Carter ----------

3 F.D. Roosevelt ----------

4 John F. Kennedy ----------

5 Bill Clinton ----------

6 Dwight D. Eisenhower ----------

# simply

There are few things more satisfying than completing a good crossword. And nothing so frustrating as clues that elude you. Well, here's a whole chapter chock-full of empty grids, all hungry for answers.

It's not just your vocabulary that's being tested here – for this chapter you'll need analytical powers, general knowledge, and the talents of a trained wordsmith. Some of the puzzles even rely on your numerical skills. With many variations on the familiar grid, you may have to change the way you approach a standard puzzle – flexible thinking is the name of the game.

★ easy ★★ medium ★★★ hard

# crosswords

# warm-up...

## 1★ Here's a nice, easy crossword to get you started.

ACROSS
1 Level (4)
3 Delete (6)
6 Not a cog (anag.) (7)
7 A sport (4)
8 Direction (4)
9 Combine (5)
10 Fossil fuel (4)
12 Very dry (4)
15 Shyness (7)
16 Give back (6)
17 Shout (4)

DOWN
1 Throw (5)
2 Diplomatic (7)
3 Applaud (4)
4 Small boat (5)
5 Beacon (5)
8 Rich (7)
10 Church singers (5)
11 Confess (5)
13 Reside (5)
14 Enthusiastic (4)

## 2★ Another simple, straightforward puzzle.

ACROSS
1 Beach cover (4)
3 Hairless (4)
5 Scoundrel (5)
6 Jump (4)
8 Time of year (6)
10 Finished doing (9)
13 Pact (6)
15 This is one! (4)
16 Depart (5)
17 Sympathy (4)
18 Desire (4)

DOWN
1 Expertise (5)
2 Reduction (4)
3 Ale (4)
4 Flour paste (5)
7 On high (5)
8 Foolish (5)
9 Just right (5)
11 Postage levy (5)
12 Banquet (5)
14 Friend (4)
15 Ship's company (4)

3★ Can you work your way to the centre of the grid starting from the top left? Words overlap, with the last one or two letters of each answer starting the next word. A few letters have been placed on the grid to keep you on the right track.

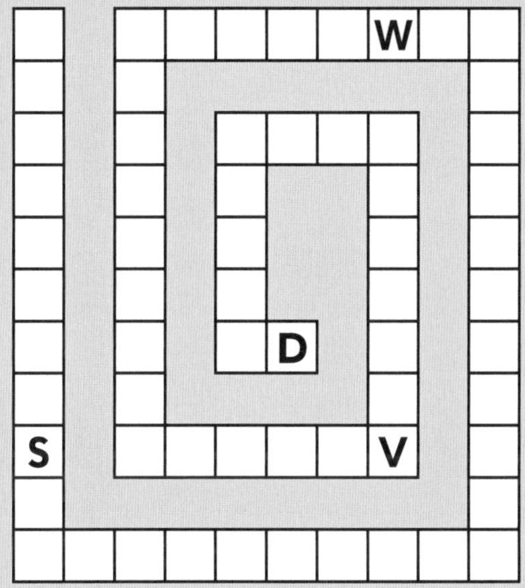


CLUES

1 Holy building (6)
2 Dairy product (6)
3 Not often (6)
4 Final Greek letter (5)
5 Old sailing ship (7)
6 Formerly (4)
7 In the middle (7)
8 Authorize (5)
9 Proprietor (5)
10 Rub out (5)
11 Group of words (8)
12 Sure (7)
13 Hidden (9)
14 Headman (6)
15 Mission (6)

4★ Use the letters in the shaded squares to find the name of a South American country.

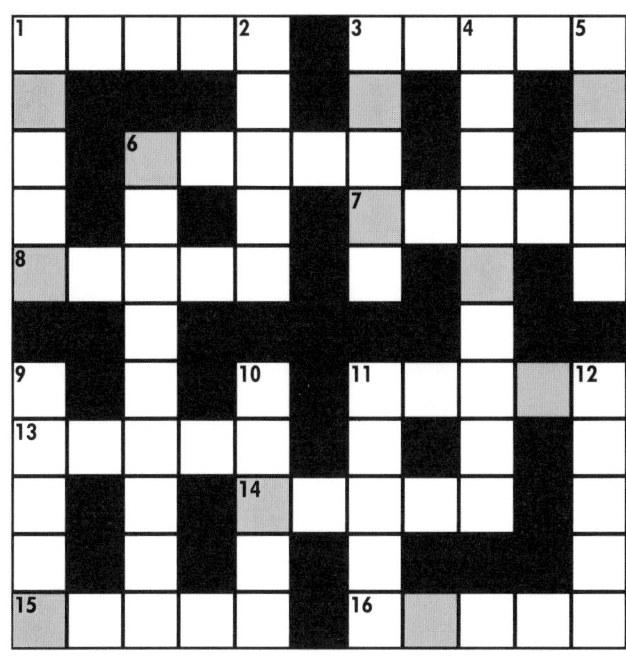


ACROSS

1 Assorted (5)
3 Deadly (5)
6 Short prayer (5)
7 Quota (5)
8 Prepared (5)
11 Pile (5)
13 Eye-cover (5)
14 Surplus (5)
15 Walk (5)
16 Dangerous (5)

DOWN

1 Army rank (5)
2 Journal (5)
3 New (5)
4 Large hairy spider (9)
5 Powerful light (5)
6 Thanks (9)
9 Divide (5)
10 In front (5)
11 Engine (5)
12 Unclean (5)

✎ ----------------------

5★ Can you unravel the anagrams in the clues to fill in the grid and complete this mixed-up crossword?

ACROSS
1 Rice beds (8)
7 Or Len (5)
8 Hated (5)
9 See rum (6)
10 Bare (4)
12 Peat (4)
14 Specie (6)
17 Aides (5)
18 Idles (5)
19 Steep dam (8)

DOWN
1 'D' star (5)
2 Lemons (6)
3 Dire (4)
4 Caber (5)
5 Late throb (9)
6 Shot crier (9)
11 Suites (6)
13 Inapt (5)
15 Raced (5)
16 Meat (4)

6★ Use the letters in the shaded squares to find the name of a famous beach.

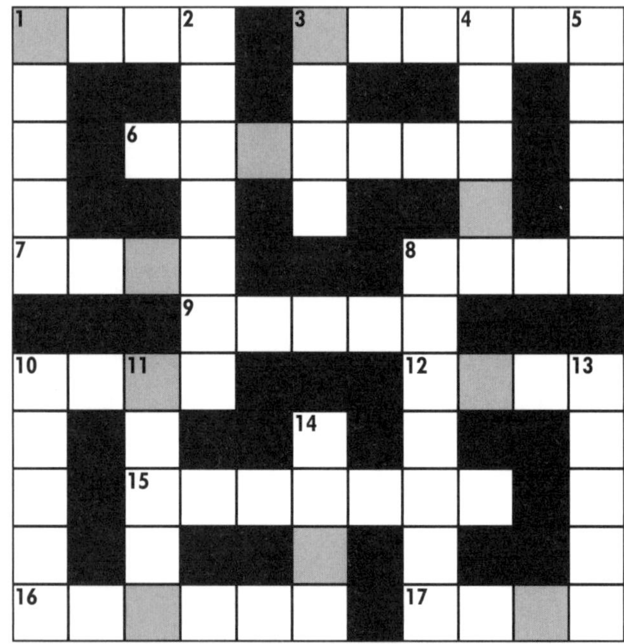

ACROSS
1 Currency unit (4)
3 Allow (6)
6 Floor show (7)
7 Implement (4)
8 Fasten (4)
9 Soil (5)
10 Close (4)
12 Vow (4)
15 Copy (7)
16 Loiter (6)
17 Orderly (4)

DOWN
1 Swindler (5)
2 Film preview (7)
3 Scheme (4)
4 Contest (5)
5 Larceny (5)
8 Reduce (7)
10 Work of fiction (5)
11 Foreign (5)
13 Vital organ (5)
14 Play the lead (4)

-------------------

## 7★ Fill in the blanks in the clues and you'll have the answers for your grid.

ACROSS

5 Theologians hypothesize about whether God _____ or not (6)

7 The sherry was ____ in oak barrels (4)

8 We're going to lift the ___ on his secret (3)

9 I, V, X, L, C, D and M are all _____ numerals (5)

10 I don't watch horror movies – I find they are too ___________ for me (11)

12 She's fed up to the back _____ with work (5)

13 I've been ___ with 'flu the last few days (3)

14 I celebrate each 10 September because I was ____ on that day (4)

15 Be careful not to make a _____ in that puddle (6)

DOWN

1 The adventurers began their _________ of the surrounding area (11)

2 He spent so much of my money I feel that he ____ me (4)

3 There's no sight on a river quite like leaping______ (6)

4 This computer jargon is _________ to me (11)

6 The prisoner was incarcerated for long _______ of time (9)

11 Jimmy, eat your _____ before you start dessert! (6)

13 Eric ____ was one of the Monty Python team (4)

## 8★★ Every row and column contains the same numbers and signs, but they are arranged in a different order each time. Can you find the correct order to arrive at the final totals shown?

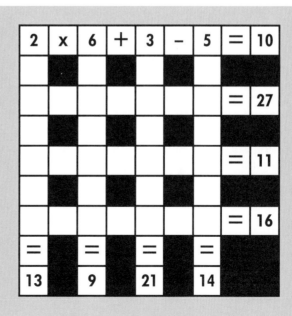

| 2 | x | 6 | + | 3 | - | 5 | = | 10 |
|---|---|---|---|---|---|---|---|---|
| | | | | | | | | |
| | | | | | | | = | 27 |
| | | | | | | | | |
| | | | | | | | = | 11 |
| | | | | | | | | |
| | | | | | | | = | 16 |
| = | | = | | = | | = | | |
| 13 | | 9 | | 21 | | 14 | | |

# 9★ You won't need a compass to find your way round this honeycomb-shaped crossword.

TRAVEL EAST

1 One of the first flowers to appear in spring (8)

3 The first animal Alice saw in *Alice in Wonderland* (6)

5 Twelve o'clock midday (4)

8 The mountainous country where Vienna is to be found (7)

11 The mountain climbed by Edmund Hillary and Tenzing Norgay in 1953 (7)

13 To cut a design into something, often using acid (4)

15 The sweet substance found in flowers by bees (6)

17 Sporting shoes, good for wearing when jogging (8)

TRAVEL SOUTH-EAST

1 Thin rope, used for tying parcels (6)

2 A picture of someone (8)

4 A sea animal with a thick shell that lives for hundreds of years (6)

6 The main part of a Christian church, where the congregation sit (4)

8 The whole set of letters, used for writing (8)

9 A large fish, which lives in the sea but returns to the river to spawn (6)

10 An edible grain, grown in paddy fields (4)

12 A part of a song that's repeated between the verses (6)

TRAVEL NORTH-EAST

7 The inside part of the foot, between the ankle and the toes (6)

8 Financial books containing details of all the income of a company (8)

9 The season that falls between spring and autumn (6)

10 One of a pair of straps used to guide a horse while riding (4)

14 The animal beaten by the tortoise in the famous fable (4)

16 A word puzzle (6)

17 Shiny metallic strips hung in Christmas trees for decoration (6)

18 A quick photograph (8)

## 10★★

All the black squares in this symmetrical grid have been replaced with letters. Can you discover where the black squares should lie and colour them in? Number the squares as you go, then enter the correct numbers against the jumbled list of clues.

| E | R | I | C | L | A | S | S | U | R | E |
|---|---|---|---|---|---|---|---|---|---|---|
| P | U | L | L | E | Y | C | L | O | U | D |
| O | S | S | A | M | P | L | E | I | I | G |
| S | T | A | Y | U | A | N | D | O | N | E |
| T | I | D | E | A | S | T | H | U | S | R |
| O | R | M | A | N | S | I | O | N | C | E |
| R | K | I | S | S | A | P | U | C | E | C |
| M | O | T | H | U | G | E | P | E | L | T |
| O | P | T | A | R | E | N | A | B | O | U |
| F | E | A | R | G | E | T | S | O | O | N |
| F | N | U | D | E | B | U | T | A | K | E |

ACROSS
Remain
Large house
Tug
Phobia
Plenty
School group
Insect
Finished
First appearance
Noisy
Shortly
Animal skin
Stadium

DOWN
Corrosion
Stiff mud
Glance
Beyond
Snow vehicle
Wreck
Difficult
Sea journey
Undo
Small weight
Allow in
Tempest
Build

## 11★★

To get you in the cryptic mood this crossword has standard Down clues but cryptic Across clues.

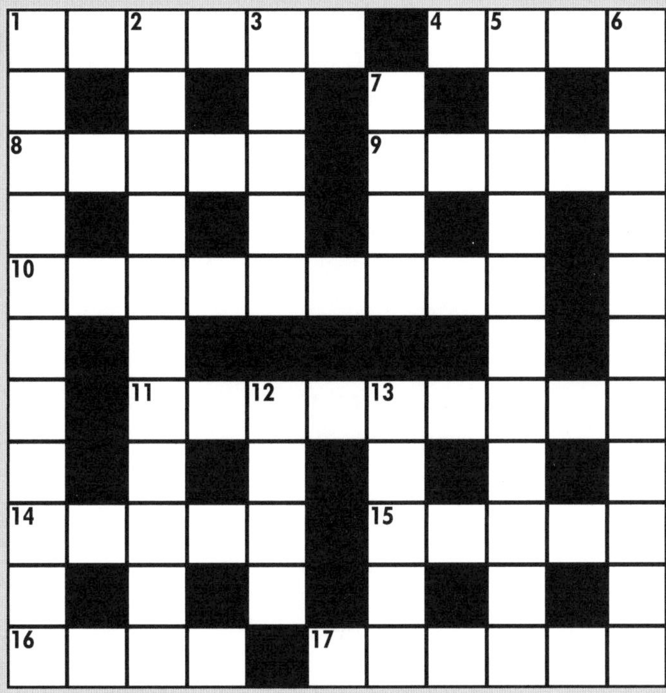

ACROSS
1 Not all those who give birth rest (6)
4 Degas almost looked back and grew older (4)
8 Pen account back to ship's room (5)
9 Lunatic adores no Eastern routes (5)
10 Bought it in crashed-up mess (9)
11 Become friendly with a colleague (9)
14 Circle an electric wire for a Mediterranean fruit (5)
15 Some axe the renal anaesthetic (5)
16 Sing about the indicator (4)
17 Made a lord on close inspection? (6)

DOWN
1 Jobs (11)
2 Sleeping during winter (11)
3 A tract of land for raising cattle (5)
5 The male parent of your parent (11)
6 Became invisible (11)
7 Prepares for a military confrontation (4)
12 Spies (4)
13 Small, thin pancake (5)

## 12★★ Everything's mixed in here! Anagrams *(A)*, cryptics *(C)*, general knowledge *(G)* and standard clues are all included.

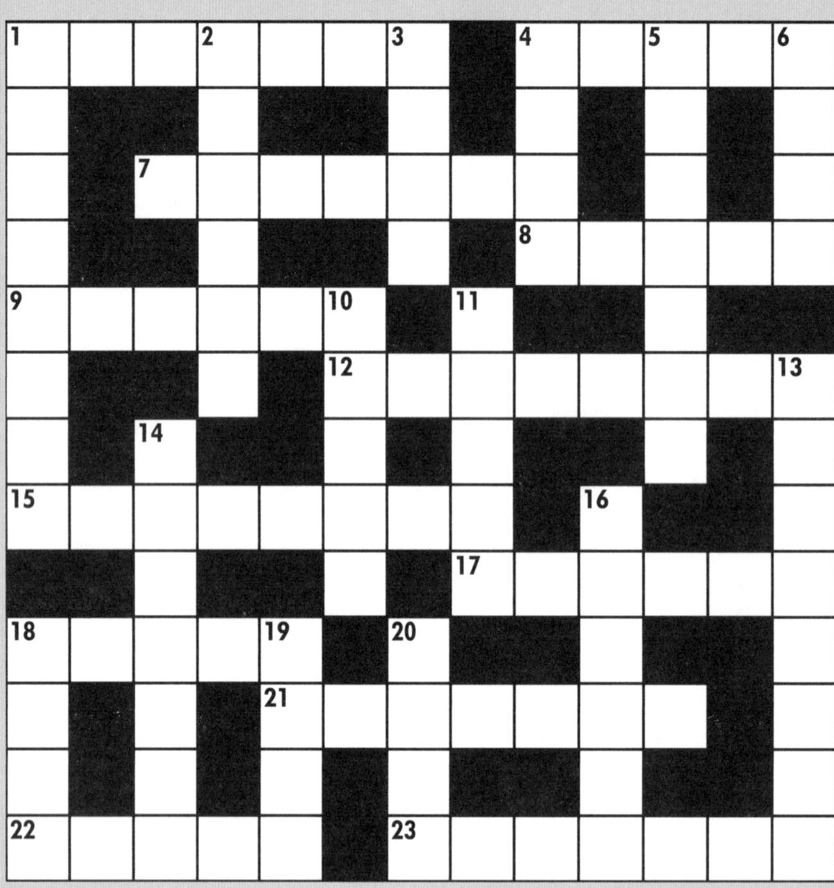

ACROSS

1 *(G)* Solomon Islands' capital (7)
4 Fatality (5)
7 Condone (7)
8 Stealing (5)
9 *West Side Story* gang (6)
12 *(G)* Legendary sunken civilization (8)
15 *(A)* Mole prey (8)
17 Slowly (music) (6)
18 Gambling counters (5)
21 *(C)* For a foreigner, he's nice somehow! (7)
22 Underwater detection device (5)
23 Bill of rights (7)

DOWN

1 *(A)* Demon has (8)
2 Buy from abroad (6)
3 Smallest particle (4)
4 *(A)* Edit (4)
5 *(C)* They put the stops on crime! (7)
6 Sword handle (4)
10 Greek woodland god (5)
11 Plants collectively (5)
13 *(G)* Fore-and-aft rigged ship (8)
14 *(G)* Fifth Greek letter (7)
16 German emperor (6)
18 *(G)* Andrew Lloyd-Webber musical (4)
19 Lesion (4)
20 Metal, symbol Zn (4)

## 13★★ Use the letters in the shaded squares to find the name of a dramatist.

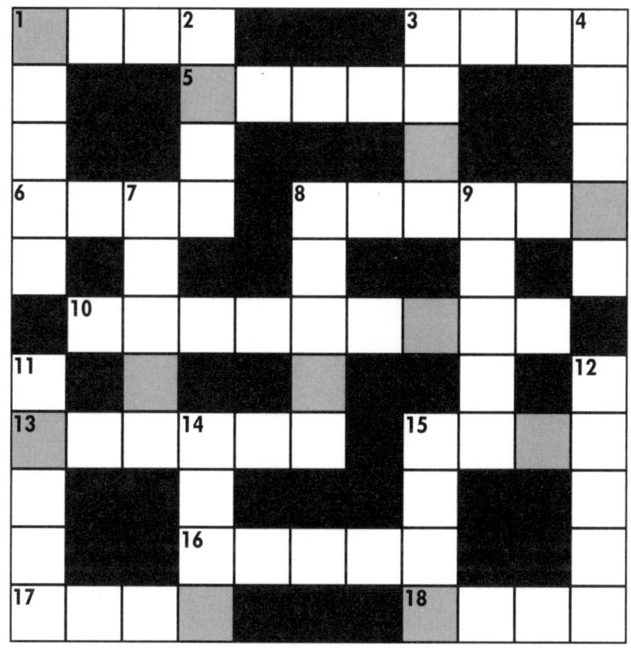

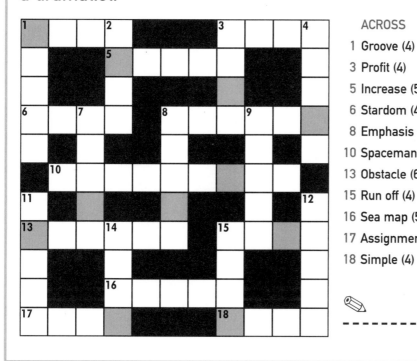

**ACROSS**
1 Groove (4)
3 Profit (4)
5 Increase (5)
6 Stardom (4)
8 Emphasis (6)
10 Spaceman (9)
13 Obstacle (6)
15 Run off (4)
16 Sea map (5)
17 Assignment (4)
18 Simple (4)

**DOWN**
1 Rigid (5)
2 Genuine (4)
3 Equipment (4)
4 Hospital worker (5)
7 Skinflint (5)
8 Incline (5)
9 Identical (5)
11 Flour grain (5)
12 Trivial (5)
14 Ship's floor (4)
15 Destiny (4)

✎ ---------------------------

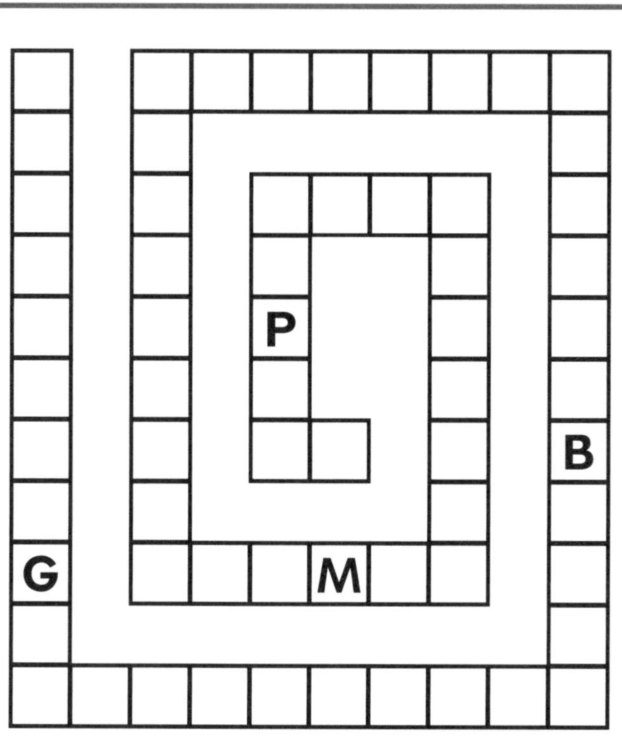


## 14★ Can you work your way to the centre of the grid? Words overlap, with the last one or two letters of each answer starting the next word. A few letters have been inserted on the grid to help you out.

**CLUES**
1 Damaged (6)
2 Sufficient (6)
3 Phantom (5)
4 Possible chess ending (9)
5 Awful (8)
6 Tuition periods (6)
7 Beginning (5)
8 Everlasting (7)
9 Sacrificial table (5)
10 Turn up (6)
11 Snake poison (5)
12 Left out (7)
13 Teach (7)
14 Cooking measure (8)

**15★** The clues are in the grid – just follow the direction of the arrows.

| | | | | | | | | | | |
|---|---|---|---|---|---|---|---|---|---|---|
| | | | | | False | | Present | | Huge | |
| | | | | | | | | | | |
| | | | | | See picture | | Poke | | Chop-ping tool | |
| | | | | | | | | | | |
| | | | | | Do again | Steel rope | | Castle ditch | | Large plant |
| | | | | | Celest-ial body | | | | | |
| | | | | | Fuss | | | | Melt | |
| Contin-ent | Break of day | Groom<br>Injured party | | | | | Dined<br>Tavern | | | |
| | | | | Unwell | Supple | | | | | |
| Declare void | | Warn-ing device | | | | | | Era | | Sedate |
| | | | | | Diplo-macy | Tidings | | | | |
| Tablet | | Vocal range | | | | | Wind instru-ment | | Regret | |
| | | | | Soak up | | | | | | |
| Depend upon | | Fried tortilla | | | | | Signal | | | |
| | | | | Tie up | | | | | | |

16★★ See how you fare with the cryptic clues, but if you get stuck, don't worry – a sneaky peek at the standard clues provided will lead you to the same answer.

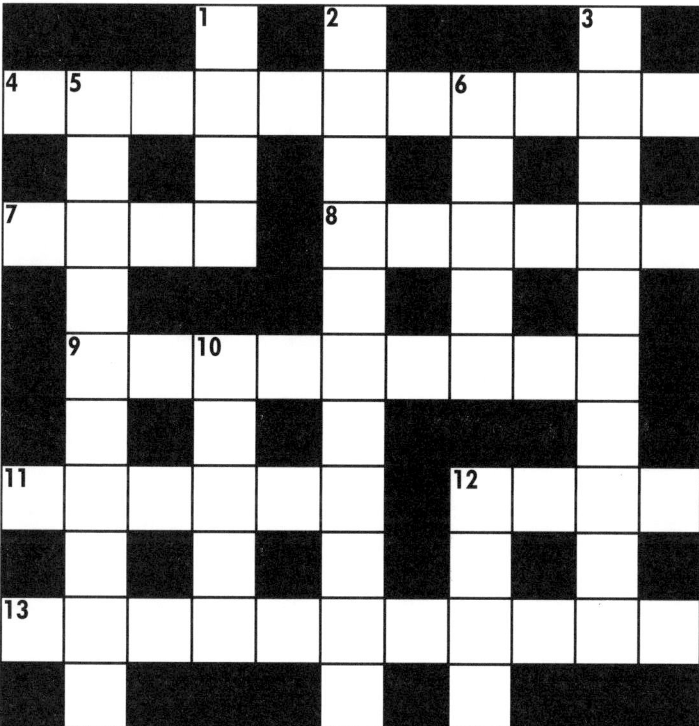

CRYPTIC CLUES

ACROSS

4 Close eyes to the wicked, seething sun (5,6)
7 He's a whirlwind (4)
8 Tread delicately – it upset eccentric poet (6)
9 Adding chicken to head of insect makes no difference (9)
11 Land residue mineral (6)
12 Adjacent and inverted musical instrument (4)
13 Not quite seven strange ratings for Venus (7,4)

DOWN

1 Produced during cow heyday? (4)
2 Goat energy pulses (11)
3 A phonebox I used didn't like strangers (10)
5 Batting critical – it's not firm (10)
6 Brown letter swims in ocean (5)
10 Sing 'No Monster' backwards (5)
12 Throw to the ship (4)

STANDARD CLUES

ACROSS

4 Common clause when buying without opportunity to look at object (5,6)
7 A miniature whirlpool or whirlwind (4)
8 Walk on the balls of the feet (6)
9 Household pest (9)
11 On land (6)
12 The lowest brass wind instrument (4)
13 Planet seen after sunset in the western sky (7,4)

DOWN

1 Watery part of milk produced when it sours and coagulates (4)
2 Small flat pulses (11)
3 A fear of foreigners (10)
5 Hesitating (10)
6 Rich brown pigment prepared from the ink of cuttlefish (5)
10 Sing softly (5)
12 Throw with a light motion (4)

## 17★ Use the context of each sentence to work out the missing word for the grid.

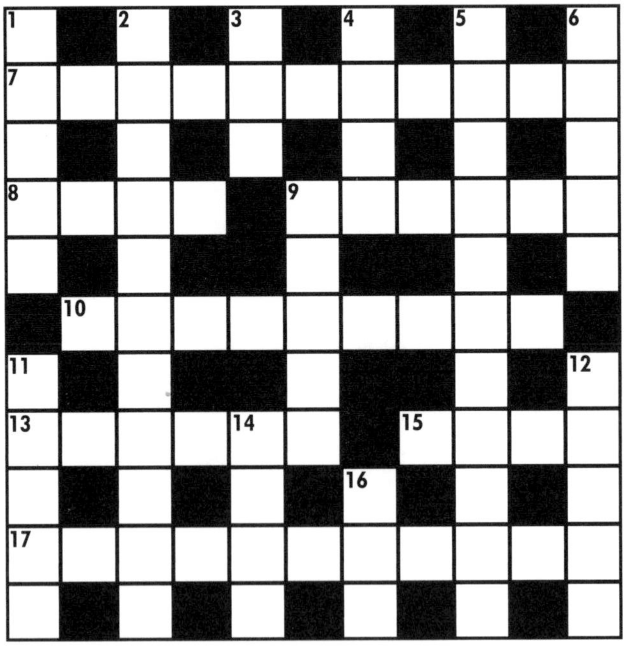

ACROSS

7 Please be more __________ – I need your help (11)

8 The ____ of a church usually contains the altar (4)

9 I go to hear the priest's ______ each Sunday (6)

10 There seems to be a lot of ________ on this telephone line (9)

13 A ______ carries your golf clubs (6)

15 ____ is the largest of the continents (4)

17 My gums hurt because my last _________ is about to come through (6,5)

DOWN

1 The car broke down so often I sold it for _____ (5)

2 I won't eat roast beef without my __________ sauce (11)

3 That rooster courts a new ___ daily (3)

4 I can tell it's a picture of a saint because of the ____ around his head (4)

5 I don't want to __________ you, but real magic doesn't exist (11)

6 Agriculture dominates the economy of _____, particularly the growing of tea and coffee (5)

9 Marry in _____ and repent at leisure (5)

11 Don't _____ or your face will stay like that (5)

12 I like hunky men who are ____ (5)

14 Marilyn Monroe was a 1960s ____ (4)

16 This is the pilot speaking: our ___ is 08:15 hours (1.1.1.)

## 18★★ Can you work your way to the centre of the grid? Words overlap by one or two letters. A few letters have been inserted to keep you on the right track.

CLUES

1 Objection (7)

2 Unusual (7)

3 Sign of the zodiac (6)

4 Catch fire (6)

5 Schoolmaster (7)

6 Decrease (6)

7 Breakfast food (6)

8 Frighten (5)

9 Enigma (7)

10 Racing boat (5)

11 Unrest (7)

12 In front (7)

13 Liquid measure (6)

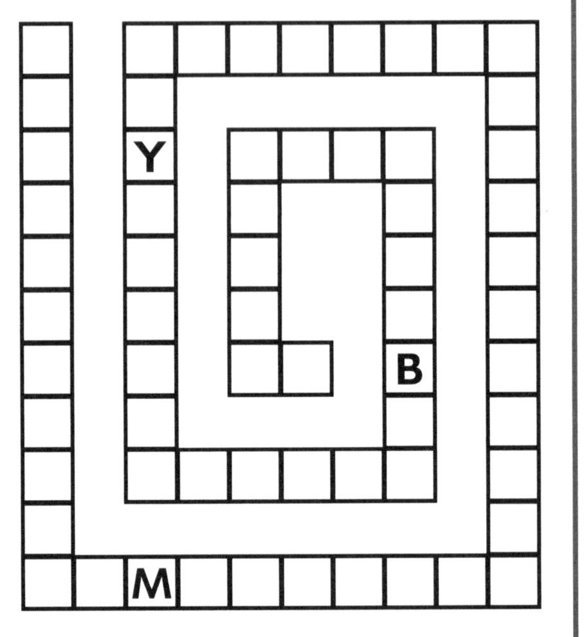

# 19★★ Let's get quizzical with this trivia crossword.

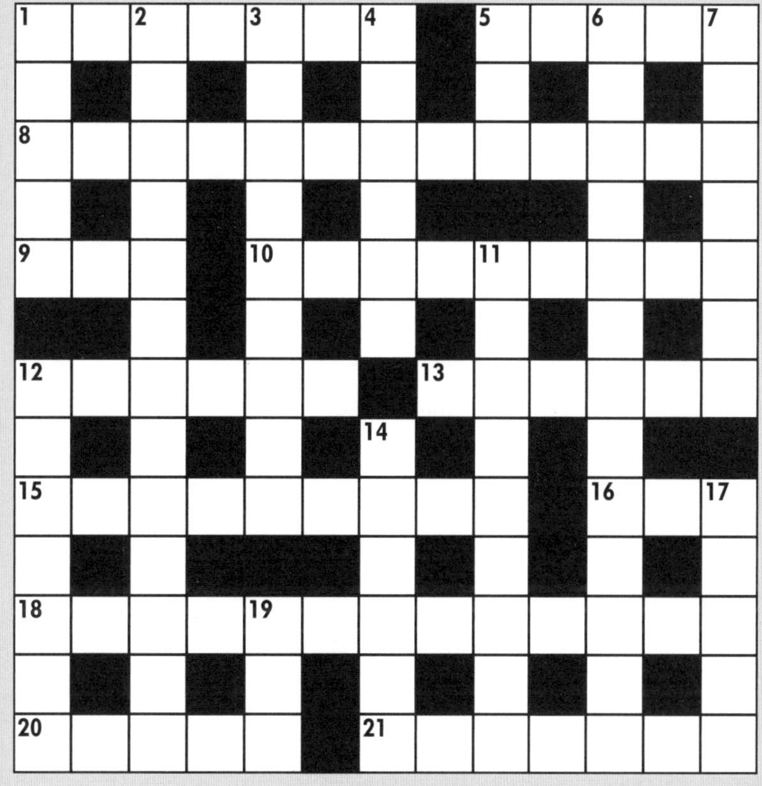

ACROSS

1 Word for the internal organs of poultry (7)

5 What is the capital city of Japan? (5)

8 What term describes an official day of rest when a typical working day would normally occur? (6,7)

9 Which unit of currency is made up of 100 sen? (3)

10 Which alpine perennial plant has leaves covered with whitish down and small flowers held in stars of glistening bracts? (9)

12 Who was goddess of the Moon in *Macbeth*, and goddess of darkness in Greek mythology? (6)

13 Which word means 'disgustingly dirty'? (6)

15 Which large symbolic North American bird has a white head and dark wings and body? (4,5)

16 What name is given to the spike of a cereal plant that bears fruit, especially corn? (3)

18 What is the numeric title of a 1963 Federico Fellini film, winner of an Oscar for Best Foreign Language Film? (5,3,1,4)

20 In law, larceny is the technical term for what? (5)

21 What are skeins of geese called when on the ground? (7)

DOWN

1 What type of person would use the Romany language? (5)

2 Which epidemic was known as the Black Death in the Middle Ages? (7,6)

3 What is the point on the Earth's surface directly above the focus of an earthquake? (9)

4 What is the word, Yiddish in origin, for 'pulling a heavy load'? (6)

5 What is the acronym for 'to take leave'? (3)

6 Which comedy sketch show, broadcast on Channel 4 in the 1990s, featured a troupe of Canadian comics? (4,2,3,4)

7 Which Greek poem, attributed to Homer, describes the journey of its central character after the fall of Troy? (7)

11 Which creature, part-dog, part-wolf, is the title character of a famous Jack London book? (5,4)

12 What is the surname of the ever-chuckling doctor in the cartoon series *The Simpsons?* (7)

14 What drink is made from sweetened milk mixed with eggs and alcoholic liquor? (6)

17 What is both the nickname of William II of England and forename of Mr King, the American anti-slavery campaigner? (5)

19 Which king's tomb was discovered by Howard Carter and Lord Carnarvon in 1922? (abbr.) (3)

## 20★ Take it easy with this simple puzzle.

ACROSS
1 Sprint (4)
3 Horse pace (6)
6 Opposed to (7)
7 Uncommon (4)
8 Costly (4)
9 Din (5)
10 Staple food (4)
12 Final (4)
15 Science of life (7)
16 The son (anag.) (6)
17 Work hard (4)

DOWN
1 Contributor (5)
2 Cleanliness (7)
3 Stylish (4)
4 Heading (5)
5 Leader (5)
8 Pleasure (7)
10 Approximate (5)
11 Timber hut (5)
13 Drying cloth (5)
14 Conspiracy (4)

## 21★★ Another mixed-up crossword to be completed. Can you unravel these anagrams to find the solutions?

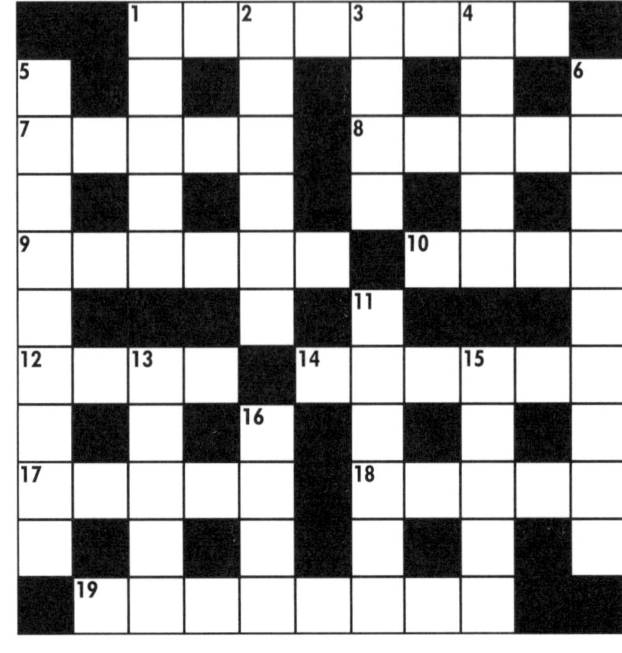

ACROSS
1 Cod traps (8)
7 Sates (5)
8 Sepal (5)
9 Tweeds (6)
10 Side (4)
12 Leap (4)
14 Petard (6)
17 BAFTA (5)
18 Laura (5)
19 Ban a duet (8)

DOWN
1 A step (5)
2 Street (6)
3 Coal (4)
4 A drip (5)
5 As primula (9)
6 Relatives (9)
11 Tapers (6)
13 Renal (5)
15 CIA Dr (5)
16 Bats (4)

## 22★★ Mixed up in this one are a few anagrams *(A)*, cryptics *(C)* and general knowledge *(G)* clues.

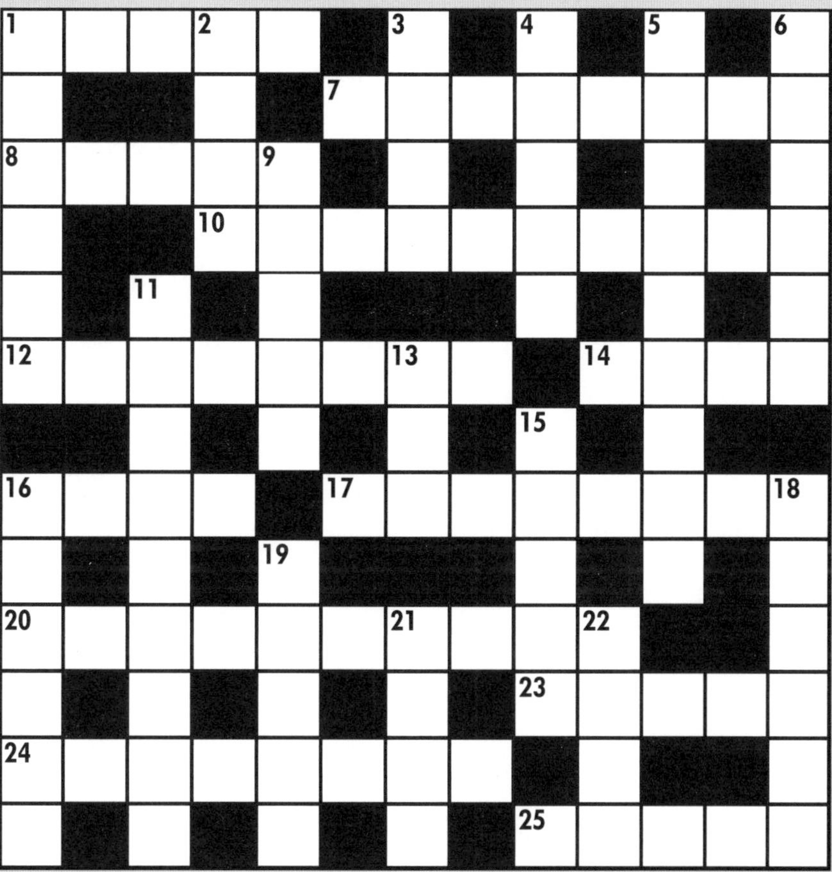

### ACROSS

1 *(A)* Ropes (5)
7 Offspring (8)
8 PC message (5)
10 Reference book (10)
12 Purple gemstone (8)
14 *(A)* Lies (4)
16 *(G)* Third son of Adam and Eve (4)
17 Piston-housing (8)
20 *(C)* Front circle (10)
23 Uncertainty (5)
24 *(C)* Big Laura's kind of country? (8)
25 Citrus fruit (5)

### DOWN

1 *(C)* Father takes girl for a Spanish meal (6)
2 Slide (4)
3 Gossip (4)
4 Metal mixture (5)
5 *(G)* Warship's salvo (9)
6 *(G)* Protein substance (6)
9 Buoyant (5)
11 Four-sided figure (9)
13 Bashful (3)
15 Mended (5)
16 Medieval copyist (6)
18 Climbing tropical palm (6)
19 Sleeveless garment (5)
21 Continent (4)
22 Dramatic part (4)

## 23★★ All the black squares in this symmetrical grid have been replaced with letters. Can you discover where the black squares should lie and colour them in? Number the squares for the Across and Down words, and finally enter the correct numbers against the jumbled list of clues.

| B | E | A | C | H | O | G | R | A | S | P |
|---|---|---|---|---|---|---|---|---|---|---|
| L | O | R | I | A | R | R | I | V | A | L |
| U | N | C | O | N | N | E | C | T | O | E |
| S | O | H | E | D | Y | E | K | A | T | A |
| H | E | A | V | Y | E | T | I | R | E | D |
| S | U | R | F | E | D | A | R | N | N | A |
| C | H | I | L | D | A | H | O | I | S | T |
| A | P | O | E | I | C | O | N | S | E | R |
| R | A | T | H | R | O | U | G | H | L | A |
| O | D | I | N | T | E | N | D | E | L | I |
| L | U | C | K | Y | S | D | O | Z | E | N |

ACROSS
Infant
Between
Fortunate
Seashore
Join
Twelve
Clutch
Winch
Weary
Weighty

DOWN
Roman vehicle
Turn red
Taint
Soiled
Welcome
Christmas song
Hunting dog
Beg
Convenient
Teach

## 24★ Use the letters in the shaded squares to find the name of a popular Christmas ditty.

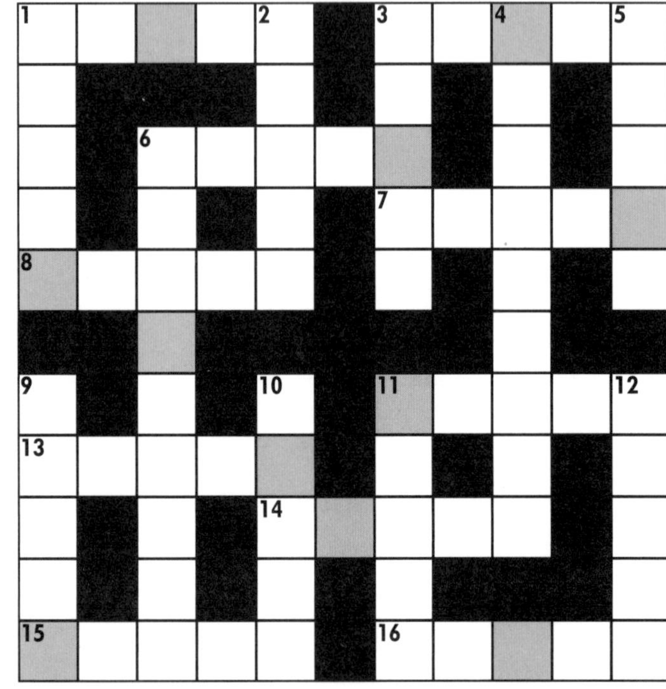

ACROSS
1 Male voice (5)
3 Inferior to (5)
6 Serenity (5)
7 Think alike (5)
8 Phantom (5)
11 Commence (5)
13 Be good at (5)
14 Subside (5)
15 Enticed (5)
16 Religious belief (5)

DOWN
1 Leather strap (5)
2 Oven cook (5)
3 Baker's product (5)
4 Oil (9)
5 Irrigate (5)
6 Film equipment (9)
9 Mutineer (5)
10 Tasteless (5)
11 Workforce (5)
12 Strong (5)

✎ - - - - - - - - - - - - - - - - - -

## 25★★ Another dual crossword – the Across clues are cryptic but the Down clues are standard.

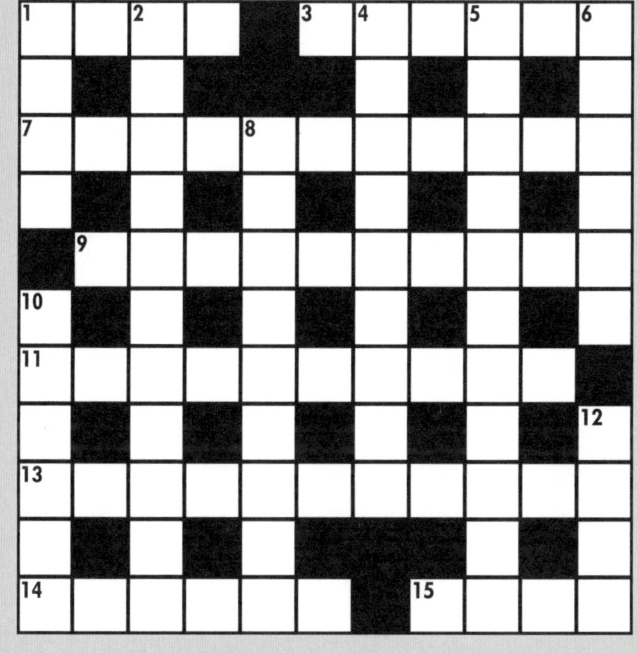

ACROSS

1 Yearn like a Guevara (4)
3 Sounds like I could buy a Mondeo (6)
7 Owing to fatal illness (5,6)
9 Understand course admitted to my size anyhow (10)
11 Resonant? It's ludicrously loud! (10)
13 Tried for undermining the government by being too tall, reportedly (4,7)
14 Give testimony for first April, exam comes after end of August (6)
15 Exclusive tour around Lyon (4)

DOWN

1 Someone who acts as assistant (4)
2 A boxer who weighs more than 81kg (11)
4 Tall plant which gives edible produce (5,4)
5 An evil inherited by all descendants of Adam (8,3)
6 One of Santa's reindeer (6)
8 Viral inflammation of the liver (9)
10 Respiratory disorder (6)
12 Covetousness (4)

## 26★★ A moderately tough fill-in-the-blanks crossword.

ACROSS

4 The seven bright stars of Ursa Major are also known as the ___ ______ (3,6)
7 Make yourself useful and ____ that cream for me (4)
8 I'm going to let my unused gym membership ______ (6)
9 Don't be so _____ – can you do any better?(5)
10 Gordon Sumner changed his name to _____ (5)
12 I can take a joke, but I'm tired of being his ______ (6)
13 My favourite Muppets character was the Swedish ____ (4)
14 The Jolly Green Giant advertises __________ (9)

DOWN

1 The __________ was a stadium for horse races (10)
2 Don't grasp that cow's ____ too tightly! (5)
3 Hey, don't shoot the _________! (9)
5 __________ covers shaping, modelling, carving and sculpture (7,3)
6 Most cities have a __________ area with Asian influences (9)
11 The score is 40 all – _____! (5)

**27★** Another mixed-up crossword! Can you unravel these anagrams to find the solutions?

ACROSS
1 Alien item (9)
6 Was Dr (5)
7 Cruet (5)
9 Tice (4)
10 Cot rod (6)
12 Tin emu (6)
14 Hags (4)
17 Alert (5)
18 Point (5)
19 Ravers day (9)

DOWN
2 Steal (5)
3 Sham (4)
4 On a tin (6)
5 Strut (5)
6 Claimed (7)
8 Hare net (7)
11 Averts (6)
13 To end (5)
15 Sitar (5)
16 Stop (4)

**28★★** Can you work your way to the centre of the grid? Words overlap, with the last one or two letters of each answer starting the next word. Two letters have been placed on the grid to keep you on the right track.

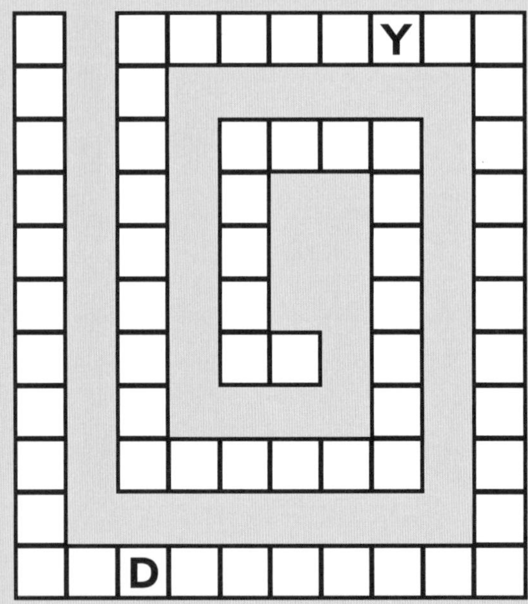


CLUES
1 Gruesome (7)
2 Stay behind (6)
3 Lowest point (5)
4 Sturdy (6)
5 Staying power (7)
6 Lineage (8)
7 Give way (5)
8 Take apart (9)
9 Deadly (6)
10 Height (8)
11 Grow (6)
12 Peril (6)

## 29★★ Travel around this honeycomb and fill up the cells…

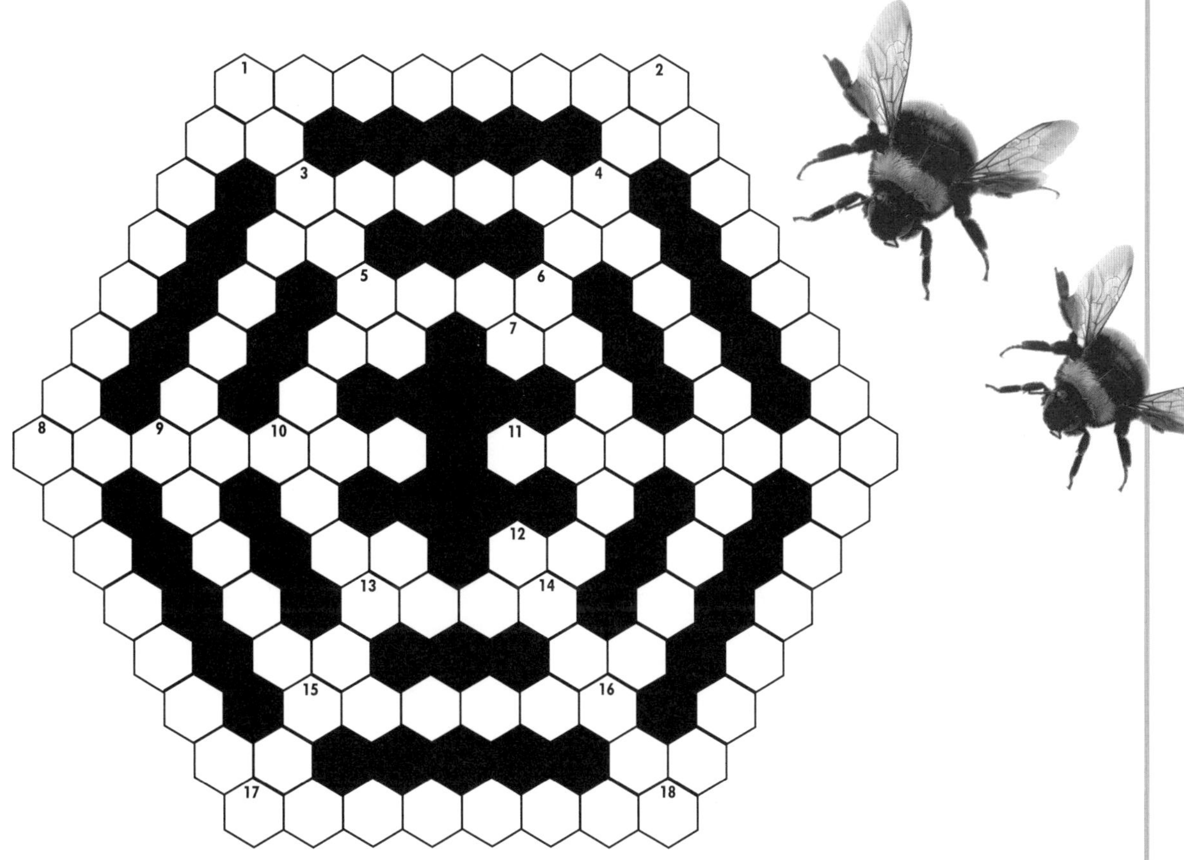

### TRAVEL EAST

1 Soft leather shoe, worn by Native Americans (8)
3 The traditional language of Scotland (6)
5 The cutting side of a blade (4)
8 Popular game played with 22 balls in which a white ball is struck with a cue to pot the other balls (7)
11 Rough fabric, used for making sacks (7)
13 The Irish name for Ireland (4)
15 A person who looks after the health of others (6)
17 The energy source used by plants in photosynthesis (8)

### TRAVEL SOUTH-EAST

1 An attractor of other metals (6)
2 French dictator of the 19th century, who ended his days in exile (8)
4 Spicy fruit, used to make cayenne pepper (6)
6 Statue at the centre of Piccadilly Circus, in London, England (4)
8 Alcoholic drink, very popular in Germany (8)
9 Old university town of England, north-west of London (6)
10 The joint between the thigh and lower leg (4)
12 Small fierce animal, kept as a pet or to catch rats (6)

### TRAVEL NORTH-EAST

7 A clergyman, usually one step down from a priest (6)
8 Angels of the very highest rank (8)
9 A rectangular shape (6)
10 A flying toy (4)
14 The growing points found on the surface of potatoes (4)
16 Latin name for inhabitants of Rome (6)
17 City in Australia, and home of the 2000 Olympics (6)
18 Small turtle with coloured shell, often kept as a pet (8)

## 30★★ This tricky crossword may take two tea breaks to complete.

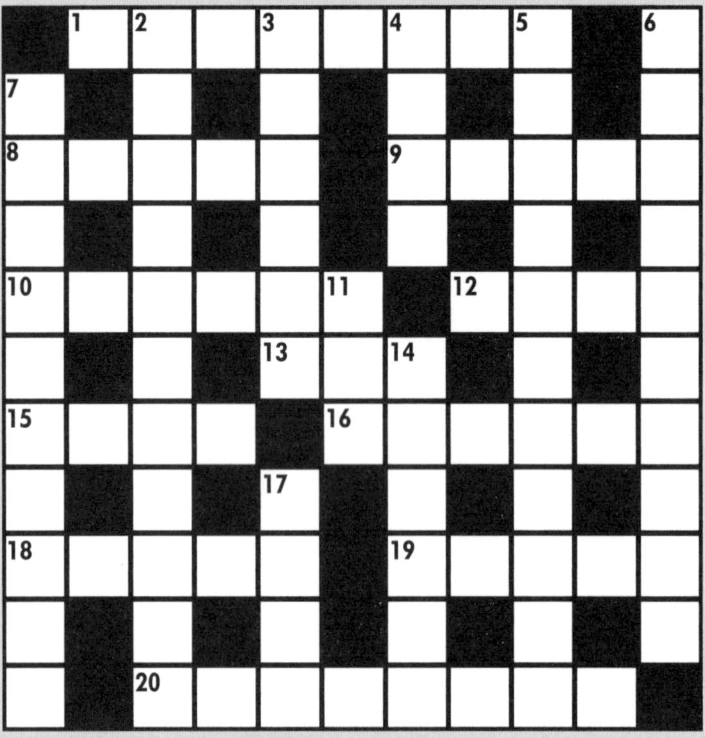

ACROSS

1 Slightly salty (8)
8 A dozen dozen (5)
9 Type of contest where the teams are evenly matched (5)
10 Characteristic of country life (6)
12 To affect deliberately someone's emotions in hope of a reaction (4)
13 Tooth found on a mechanical wheel (3)
15 Certain to occur, inevitable (4)
16 To walk around pompously in an attempt to impress others (6)
18 In sport, the prohibited act of shooting the puck right across the rink (5)
19 The colour of intense heat (5)
20 Pachyderm, symbol of the Republican Party (8)

DOWN

2 One of the perks of staying in a hotel (4,7)
3 Pertaining to the Universe, sometimes used as slang for 'really good' (6)
4 A tiny amount (4)
5 Operating under large voltages (4,7)
6 It is measured by a Plimsoll line (5,5)
7 Hostile behaviour (10)
11 Informally, a policeman (3)
14 A process of becoming larger (6)
17 Look with amorous intentions (4)

## 31★★★ You'll find a real mixed bag of clues in this crossword, testing all facets of your knowledge. *(A)* clues are anagrams. *(C)* are cryptic clues. *(G)* are general knowledge questions. And the rest are straightforward descriptive clues. Can you complete it without consulting a dictionary?

ACROSS

7 *(A)* Avails (6)
8 *(G)* Hard outer covering of a turtle (8)
9 *(G)* Control surface of an aircraft that makes it ascend or descend (8)
10 *(G)* Dried fibrous fruit used as a washing sponge (6)
11 Expression of gratitude (8)
12 *(C)* Point of the compass that some need lending (6)
13 *(C)* Operate as prophetic physician (11)
18 *(C)* Fox and pigs live here beside me, reportedly (6)
20 *(A)* Reveal it (8)
22 *(G)* Light brown colour, often used to describe certain types of horse (6)
23 *(G)* A straw hat with a tall crown and broad brim (8)
24 *(A)* Raw kites (5-3)
25 *(A)* Ace nun (6)

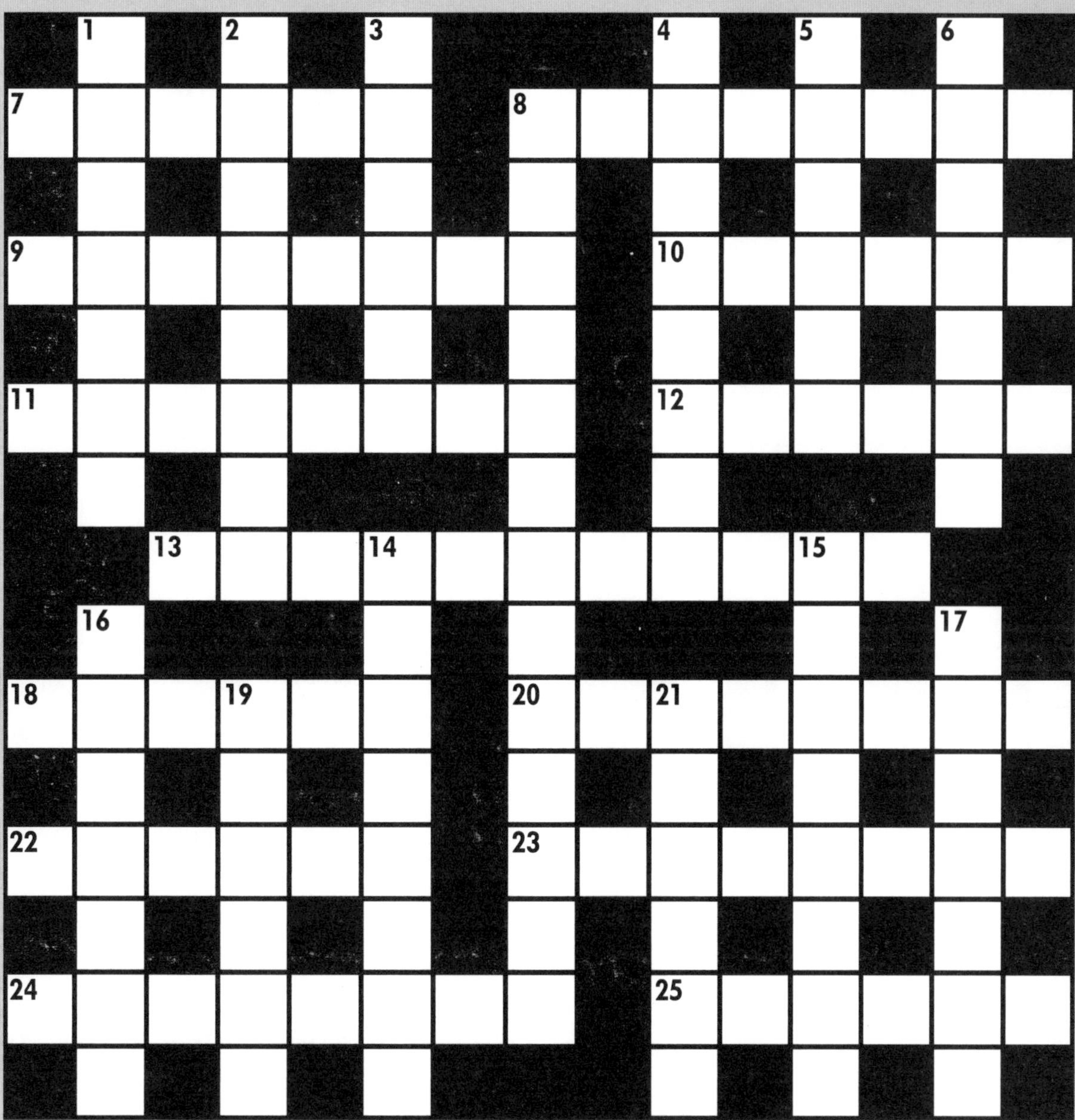

DOWN

1 People in charge of particular tasks (7)

2 *(G)* Casanova's first name (8)

3 Bridge often used to suspend railway signals (6)

4 *(G)* Island republic in the Indian Ocean, formerly called Ceylon (3,5)

5 Contradict, fight back (6)

6 *(A)* Cry laws (7)

8 *(G)* Texas city, and a college found in both Cambridge and Oxford universities (6,7)

14 *(A)* Sleepers (8)

15 *(C)* Former lover, a slender bird with gangster outside (8)

16 Type of footstool (7)

17 Deadly sin (7)

19 *(C)* Trap male sheep returning a weasel (6)

21 *(A)* Animal (6)

## 32★★ Use the letters in the shaded squares to find the name of an American actor.

ACROSS

1 Untamed (4)
3 Enlarge (6)
6 Flightless bird (7)
7 Adhesive (4)
8 Metal barrel (4)
9 Bravery (5)
10 Metal, symbol Au (4)
12 Select (4)
15 See briefly (7)
16 Quiet (6)
17 Discussion (4)

DOWN

1 Mistaken (5)
2 Come down (7)
3 Deserve (4)
4 Detest (5)
5 Jeans fabric (5)
8 Down-payment (7)
10 Estimate (5)
11 Lawful (5)
13 Inuit boat (5)
14 Leave out (4)

## 33★★ Heads down for this jumbo crossword.

ACROSS

1 Deficiency (8)
4 Normal (8)
9 Timepiece (5)
10 Change (5)
11 Eating utensil (5)
12 Readable (7)
13 Old-fashioned (5)
15 Perfect (5)
17 Briskly (music) (7)
20 Method (6)
21 Dissolved (6)
23 Friendly (7)
28 Selection (6)
29 National song (6)
30 Group of lions (5)
31 A river (anag.) (6)
33 Supernatural (6)
35 Gift (7)
38 Decree (anag.) (6)
40 Amount (6)
42 Greatest (7)
45 Secret store (5)
47 Divine messenger (5)
49 Army rank (7)
50 Answer (5)
51 Uninterested (5)
52 Brief (5)
53 Gas, symbol (8)
54 Three-sided polygon (8)

DOWN

1 Holy (6)
2 Get better (10)
3 Elegant (8)
5 Exciting book (8)
6 Reliable (10)
7 Of teeth (6)
8 Tarnish (5)
14 Legion (4)
16 Skilful (4)
17 Astonish (5)
18 Epoch (3)
19 Greek letter (5)
20 Onlooker (9)
22 Playwright (9)
24 Enhance (7)
25 Wound dressing (7)
26 Apologetic (5)
27 Yell (5)
32 Kick out (5)
33 Eight musicians (5)
34 Successful book (4-6)
36 Droop (3)
37 Reinforce (10)
39 Leave (4)
41 Title (4)
43 Congregate (8)
44 Waste (8)
45 Look for (6)
46 Body organ (5)
48 Small (6)

1 2 3 4 5 6 7 8 9 10 11 12 13 14 15 16 17 18 19 20 21 22 23 24 25 26 27 28 29 30 31 32 33 34 35 36 37 38 39 40 41 42 43 44 45 46 47 48 49 50 51 52 53 54

**34★** The clues are in the grid – just follow the direction of the arrows.

Heal | Stalk | Worry

See picture | Statute | Sheep

Hard hat | Got up | Over-due | Hoofed animal

Yelled | Copied | 50%

Excited / Pointed | Provide water | Abhor / Cougar

Simple weapon

Two crotch-ets | India's curre-ncy | Incid-ent | Give in

Lazy | Inform

Arm bone | Stride | Dare | Fasten

Cross out

Border | Charge | No score

Over-joyed

35★★ This crossword is ideal to help you to learn the code of cryptic clues. Each question has an additional hint that reveals the style of the clue being used. For example, 'pieces' means that the word has been chopped up into individual sections, while 'charade' means that the position of the letters is important.

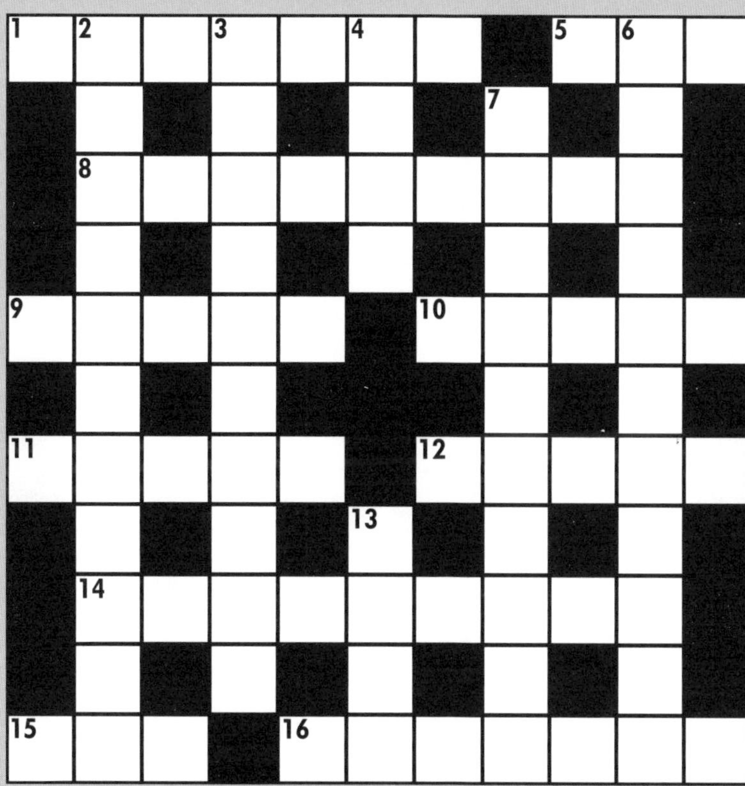

ACROSS

1 Frugality is problematic, coy omen (anag.) (7)
5 Flightless creature: lemur without head or tail (subtraction) (3)
8 Exposes woman's garment within suburbia (insert) (9)
9 Like peach or toast, Mad Mabel? (anag.) (5)
10 Abhorrence means I do return with little hesitation (reversal) (5)
11 Old tales from end to beginning (charade) (5)
12 Lack of perceptiveness in eastern point (pieces) (5)
14 On the subject of shelter, I have tended to hold on (pieces) (9)
15 Take top off scalp's summit (subtraction) (3)
16 Responded with 'The salesman was dishonest' (pieces) (7)

DOWN

2 High HLL creosote can lead to health problems (anag.) (11)
3 Fame isn't skill (pieces) (10)
4 Man picks up sound (two meanings) (4)
6 A fine specimen, but not fit for use (two meanings) (6-5)
7 Fabrication interlaced document attesting facts (anag.) (10)
13 Some work needed for joint (hidden) (4)

## 36★★ Not too tough, but not too easy either. Thinking caps on for this trivia crossword.

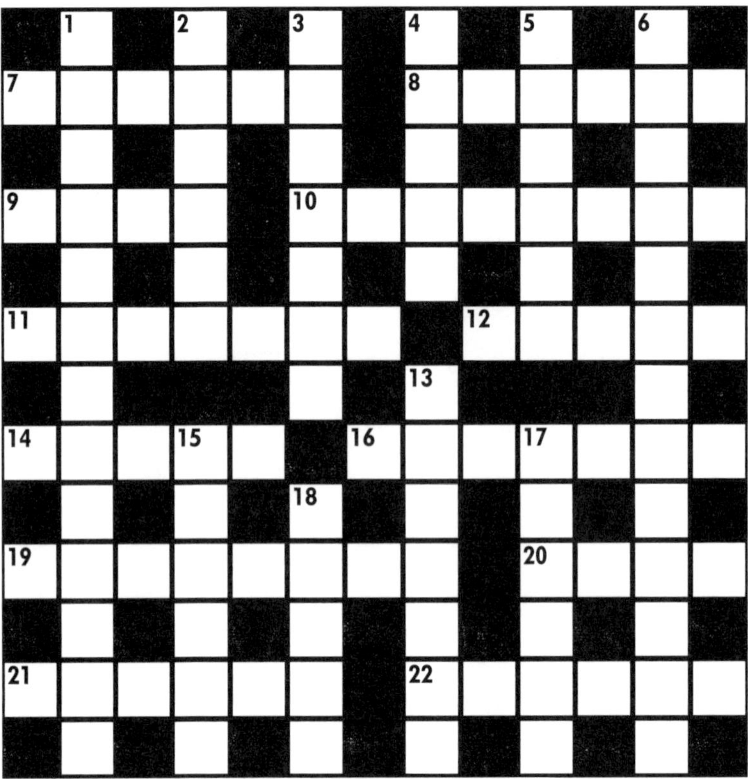

ACROSS

7 What is the native religion of Japan? (6)

8 Name a blanket-like cloak with a hole in the centre (6)

9 In computing, what is a sequence of eight binary digits processed as a single unit of information? (4)

10 Which Australian state does not border any of the others? (8)

11 Forename of Mr Mackintosh, successful musical producer? (7)

12 What is the nautical term for the rear part of a ship? (5)

14 In ancient mythology, which Titan was punished by Zeus? (5)

16 Which small oval fruit has a thin rind and acidic pulp? (7)

19 ______ *Ho!* is the title of which famous book, written by Charles Kingsley? (8)

20 In poker, what is the term for the initial bet that each player makes to the pot? (4)

21 What was the famous exclamation of Archimedes upon discovering an important principle of liquid displacement? (6)

22 What word does a film director use as a cue for the actors? (6)

DOWN

1 Which word describes numerous perennial plants having showy brightly coloured flower heads? (13)

2 Sternutation is the technical term for which involuntary human action? (6)

3 What word represents F in the NATO (phonetic) alphabet? (7)

4 What is the name for a painful and involuntary muscular contraction? (5)

5 What is the French word for a child? (6)

6 Which 1996 film starred Keanu Reeves as a researcher on an alternative energy project who is framed for murder? (5,8)

13 Which type of time-measuring instrument has the fewest possible moving parts? (7)

15 What is the horn of a deer called? (6)

17 Which hard mineral consists of silicon dioxide crystals that vibrate very regularly? (6)

18 In the Bible, who was Abraham's half-sister and subsequent wife? (5)

## 37★★ Can you unravel the anagrams in the clues then fill in the grid to complete this mixed-up crossword?

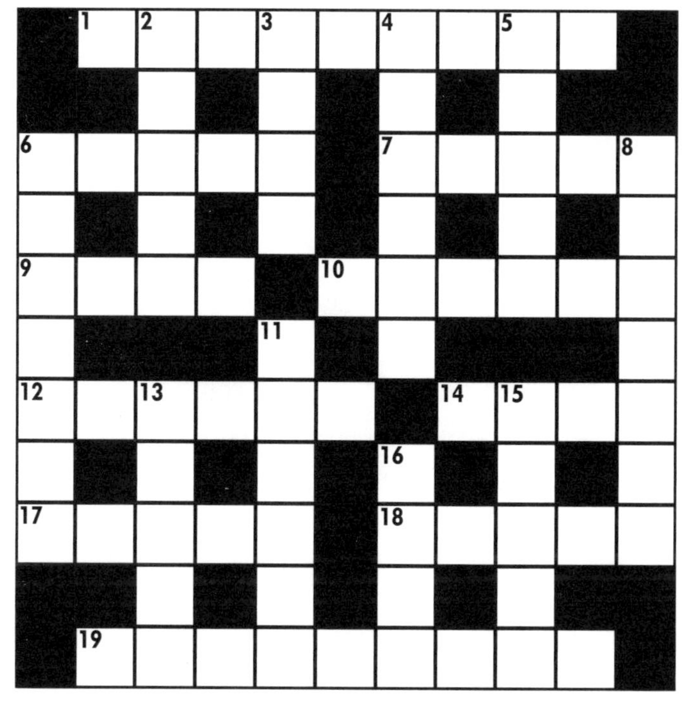

**ACROSS**

1 De-ice bone (9)
6 Siren (5)
7 LA Ram (5)
9 Posh (4)
10 Near St (6)
12 No rage (6)
14 A rip (4)
17 On red (5)
18 Charm (5)
19 Do no trade (9)

**DOWN**

2 No jab (5)
3 Tied (4)
4 Please (6)
5 Trace (5)
6 Ponders (7)
8 Corn ham (7)
11 Geared (6)
13 No tea (5)
15 No rap! (5)
16 Mire (4)

| 5 | + | 6 | x | 3 | – | 9 | = | 24 |
|---|---|---|---|---|---|---|---|---|
| | | | | | | | | |
| | | | | | | | = | 28 |
| | | | | | | | | |
| | | | | | | | = | 36 |
| | | | | | | | | |
| | | | | | | | = | 30 |
| = | | = | | = | | = | | |
| 18 | | 40 | | 22 | | 27 | | |

## 38★★★ Every row and column contains the same numbers and signs, but they are arranged in a different order each time. Find the correct order to arrive at the final totals shown.

## 39★★★ Allow half an hour for this giant crossword.

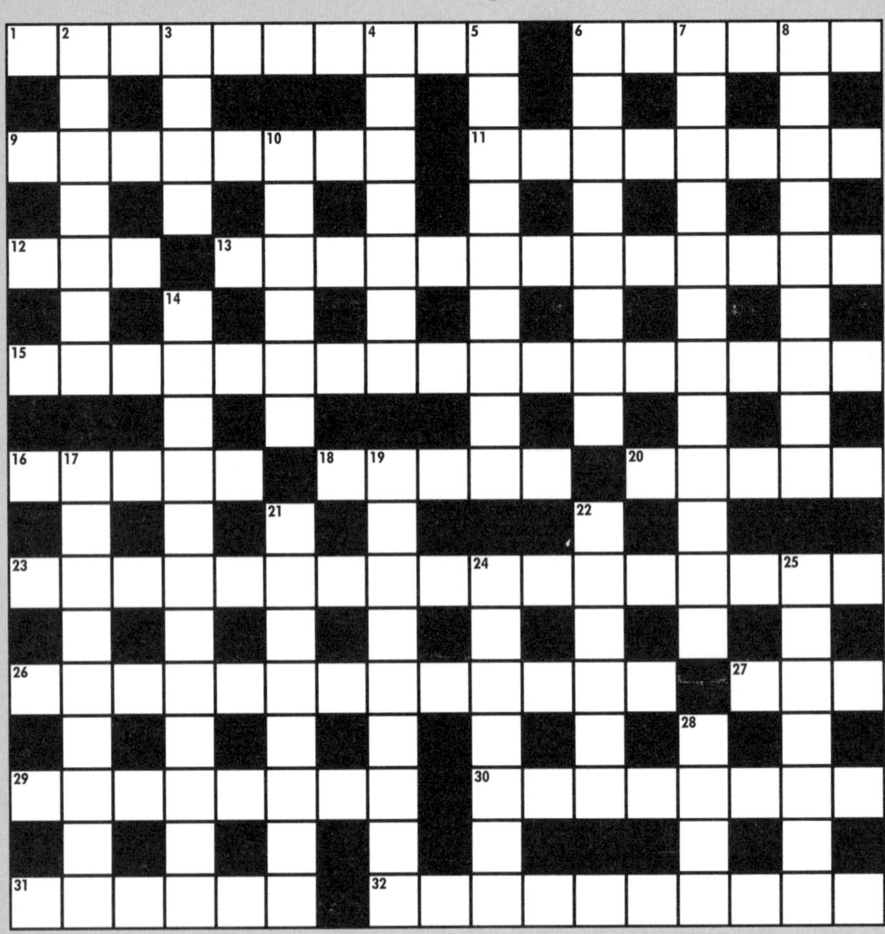

ACROSS

1 A fear of heights (10)
6 Cause to be alert (6)
9 Small European flatfish (8)
11 Made of cloth woven locally (8)
12 Hired secret agent (3)
13 Revised opinion about a previous decision (6,7)
15 Usually required before two fractions can be added together easily (6,11)
16 An involuntary muscular contraction (5)
18 Informal word for 'elegant' or 'fashionable' (5)
20 Once believed to be the substance composing all heavenly bodies, 'the fifth element' (5)
23 Compound used in effervescent drinks and baking powder (11,2,4)
26 Vessel with a rubber teat that holds milk (7,6)
27 Take or consume regularly (3)
29 A valid target of ridicule (4,4)
30 Type of chemical element such as carbon, helium, bromine (3-5)
31 Author of *The Railway Children* (6)
32 Desperate act of resuscitation (4,2,4)

DOWN

2 Improvised Caribbean folk song (7)
3 A musical work (4)
4 Vertical stripes seen on product packaging (3,4)
5 Without water (9)
6 Comfortable padded seat with supports on either side (8)
7 A policy of opposition to the spread of new knowledge (12)
8 The point of the Earth's axis that's found in Antarctica (5,4)
10 The use of pigments to change the colour of cloth permanently (6)
14 Robbery from a window display (5-3-4)
17 A bank's best possible loan charges, usually offered to large institutions (5,4)
19 Fence designed to reduce coastal erosion (9)
21 Present in large quantities (8)
22 Type of revolving ball applicator (4-2)
24 Lockjaw (7)
25 The female side of the family (7)
28 Recurrent ringing of bells (4)

## 40 ★★★ No mercy shown here – this is a tough cryptic.

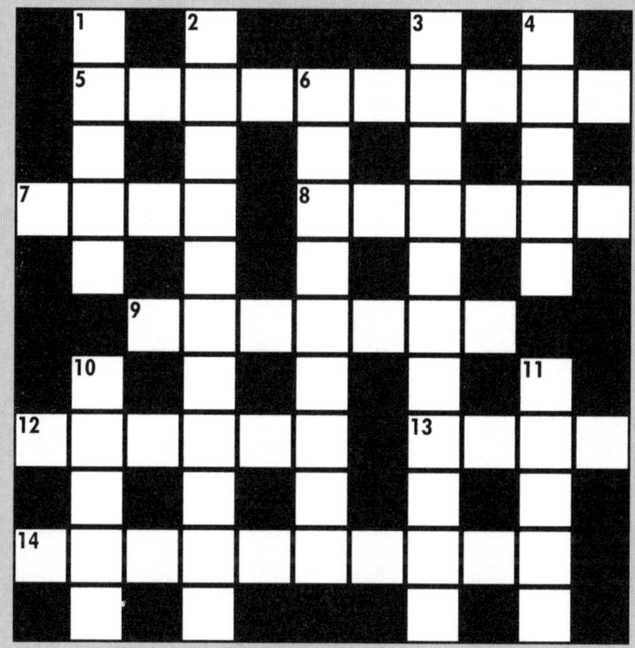

ACROSS

5 A father, hot with the genetically modified adage (10)
7 Buzzer key complaint (4)
8 Reverse wearing French green (6)
9 Two drugs provide a sturdy woman (7)
12 Hardy accompaniment for wreath? (6)
13 Enjoyment: bad end to store (4)
14 Purple SW German territory (10)

DOWN

1 Knead (literally) au naturel (5)
2 Rest of deep brown fracture in earth's crust (6,5)
3 Skinhead owning froth used to remove whiskers (7,4)
4 In the past, Egyptian god in the Greek marketplace (5)
6 People poll, Ohio – one upset (3,6)
10 A canoe, whichever way you look at it (5)
11 Go in green terminal (5)

## 41 ★★★ Here's a thought – why doesn't the word ANAGRAM have any anagrams? While you're thinking about that, unscramble the letters to reveal the answers in this crossword.

ACROSS

5 Vary sou (7)
6 Dan (3)
8 Vain diction (11)
9 My pig (5)
11 Terne (5)
13 Lowlier chat (5,6)
15 Mel (3)
16 Up glade (7)

DOWN

1 A bin (4)
2 Mild ghost (9)
3 Citer (5)
4 So zone (6)
7 Gently ooh (9)
10 Ha! Nile (6)
12 Culls (5)
14 Name (4)

# number

Some people find numbers a little scary ...

but there's nothing too terrifying here. From simple one-star puzzles to testing three-star taxers, this section is full of fun. Have you ever tried a number crossword? Or a number maze? How about a nonogram? Now's your chance!

With a bit of practice on puzzles like these even the most number-phobic could end up being a whizz with figures. And once you get a taste for things numerical, there'll be no stopping you...

★ easy ★★ medium ★★★ hard

# know-how

# warm-up...

1★ At the start of the Grand National, I correctly counted the numbers of horses' legs plus the number of jockeys' legs and the total came to 168. How many runners were there in the race altogether?

2★ Place a number in the middle box by which all the other numbers can be divided without leaving a remainder. The number is greater than 1.

| 56 | | 84 |
|---|---|---|
| 35 | ✎ -------- | 28 |
| 21 | | 63 |

3★ Which three of the four pieces below can be fitted together to form a perfect square?

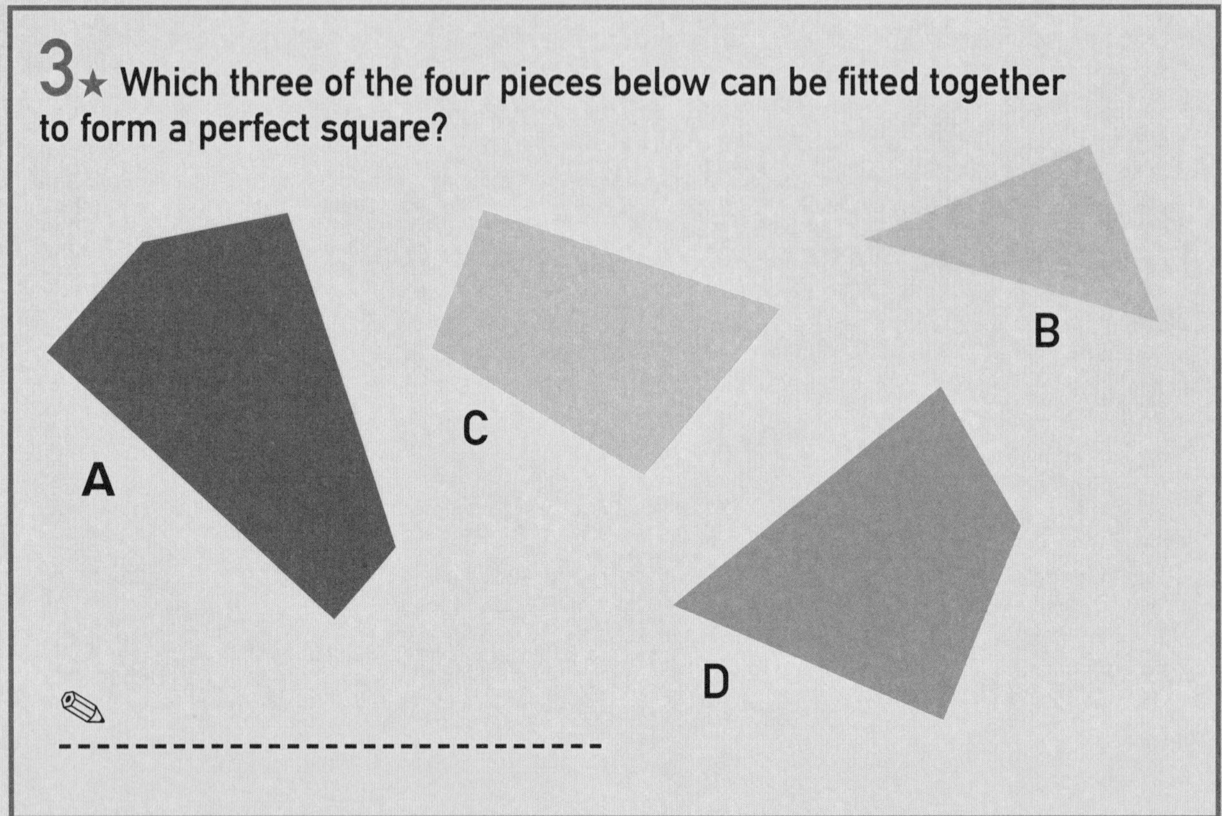

**4★** The number 13579 appears just once in this wordsearch-style grid and occurs in a straight line, running either backwards or forwards in either a horizontal, vertical or diagonal direction. Can you locate it?

| 1 | 3 | 5 | 9 | 7 | 9 | 3 | 1 | 7 | 5 | 3 | 1 |
|---|---|---|---|---|---|---|---|---|---|---|---|
| 3 | 9 | 5 | 3 | 1 | 5 | 7 | 9 | 3 | 1 | 5 | 9 |
| 5 | 1 | 7 | 1 | 1 | 1 | 3 | 5 | 9 | 7 | 1 | 7 |
| 3 | 5 | 1 | 3 | 5 | 9 | 7 | 1 | 5 | 9 | 3 | 5 |
| 9 | 7 | 5 | 3 | 9 | 7 | 1 | 3 | 9 | 3 | 5 | 1 |
| 1 | 9 | 3 | 5 | 7 | 9 | 1 | 5 | 3 | 7 | 9 | 3 |
| 9 | 3 | 7 | 9 | 5 | 1 | 3 | 9 | 1 | 3 | 7 | 5 |
| 5 | 5 | 9 | 5 | 3 | 7 | 5 | 1 | 9 | 1 | 5 | 9 |
| 7 | 9 | 5 | 7 | 1 | 3 | 9 | 7 | 5 | 9 | 1 | 7 |
| 9 | 7 | 3 | 1 | 7 | 9 | 5 | 3 | 1 | 5 | 7 | 9 |
| 9 | 7 | 1 | 1 | 3 | 5 | 1 | 1 | 3 | 7 | 9 | 1 |
| 9 | 7 | 5 | 9 | 7 | 9 | 5 | 3 | 1 | 9 | 5 | 9 |

**5★** Which is the odd number out? 

**3469, 2578, 4579, 1489, 3547, 3679, 1248**

**6★** Complete the sum below using one each of all the numbers and signs in the circle.

**7★★** Place a number in the central box by which all the other numbers can be divided without leaving a remainder. The number is greater than 1.

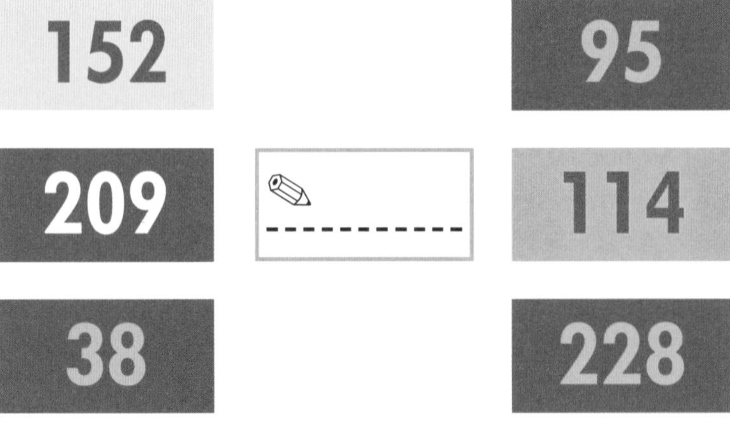


**8★** Replace the question marks with three different mathematical symbols (+, –, ÷ or x) to get the right answer.

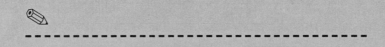

9★★ How many stars are needed to balance scale C? ✎ -------------

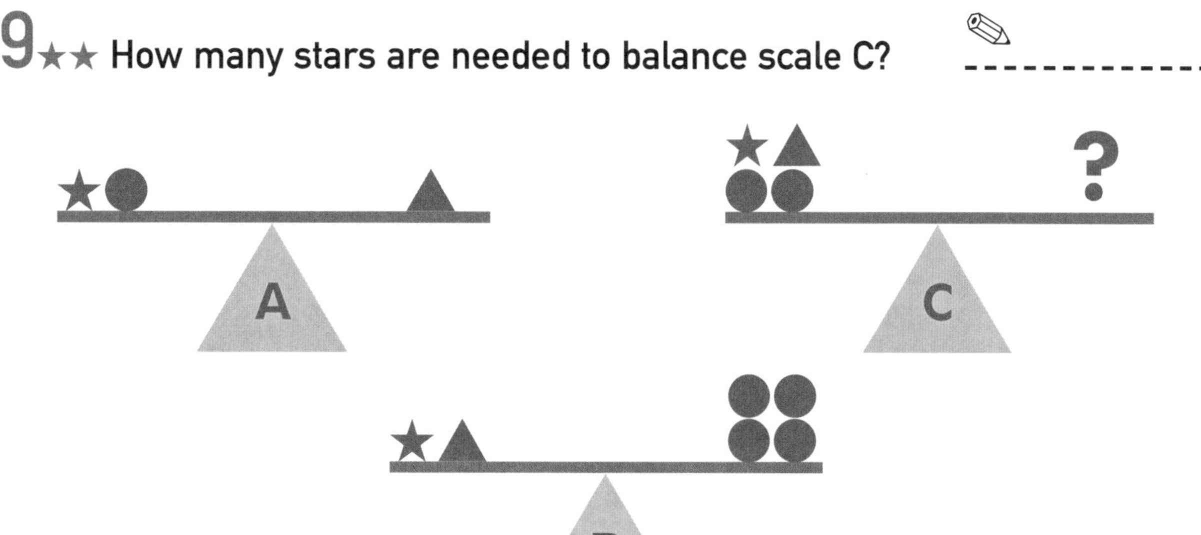


...And in this teaser, how many circles are needed to balance C? ✎ --------

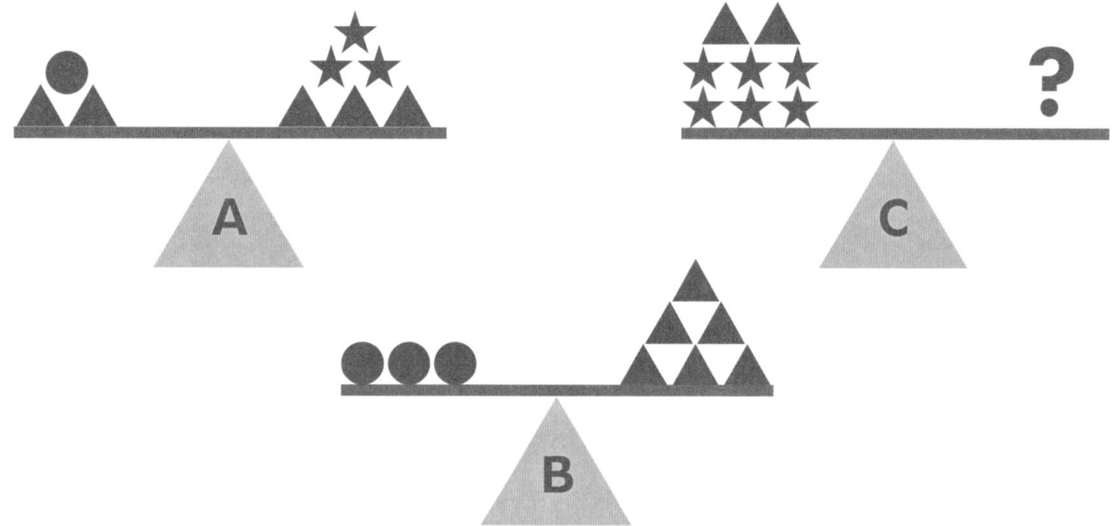


10★★ How many minutes is it before 12 noon if 40 minutes ago it was three times as many minutes past 9am?

✎ ----------------------------------------

**11** ★★ Can you fit these numbers into the grid? One number has been inserted to help you get started.

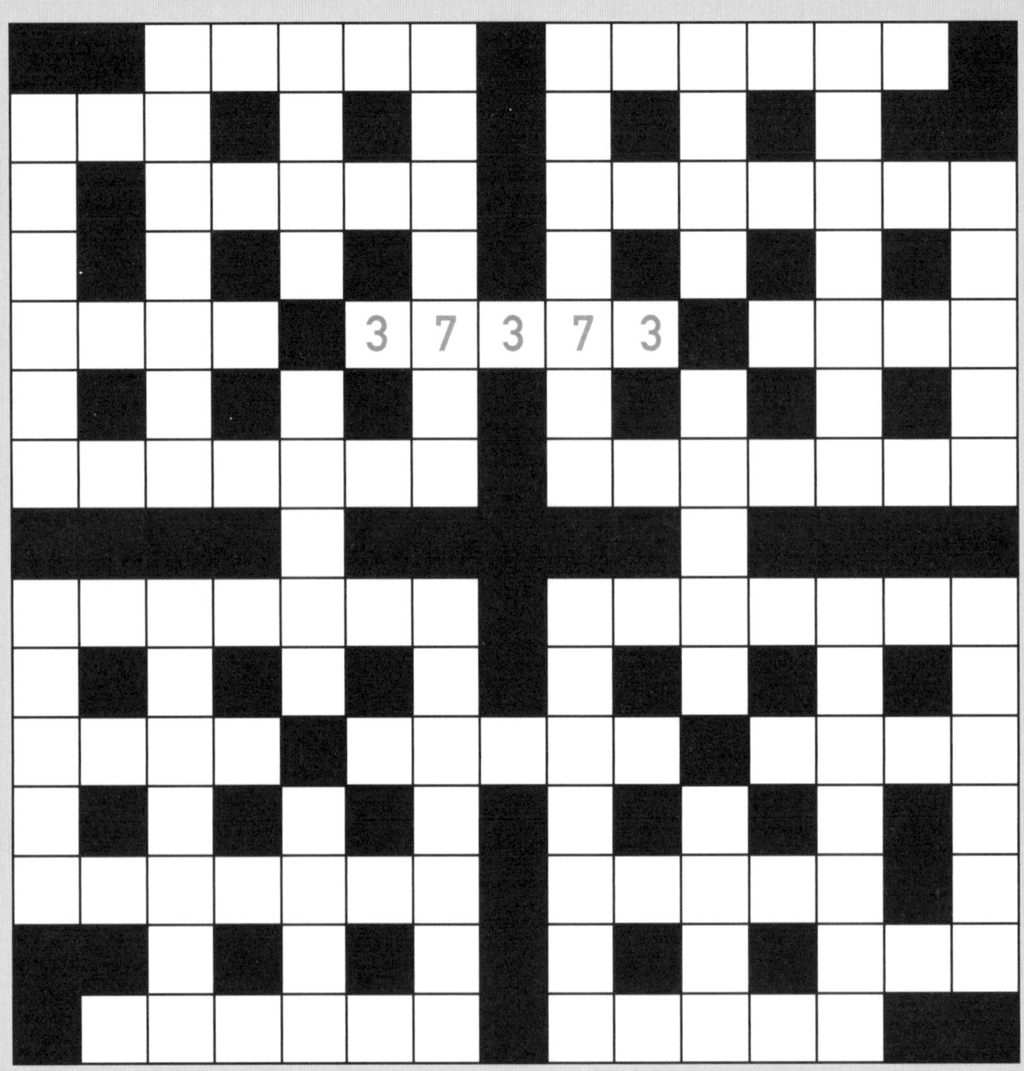


3-FIGURE NUMBERS
493
539

4-FIGURE NUMBERS
1491
2904
5863
5941
6474
7821
8727
9217

5-FIGURE NUMBERS
16741
20829
24393
27997
~~37373~~
40758
46227
47608
75354
90243

6-FIGURE NUMBERS
191053
590775
611252
837701

7-FIGURE NUMBERS
1809043
3804214
4365471
4792944
4917285
5164728
5753765
6284787
7024267
7342818
7892421
8098604
8319745
9215944

12★★ A magic square has the special property that the sum of all the numbers in each row, column and both main diagonals equals the same number. With this in mind, complete this magic square so that it contains nine consecutive numbers.

|   |   | 4 |
|---|---|---|
| 7 | 3 |   |
|   | 1 | 6 |

13★★ The hour hand on the fourth clock is missing. Follow the sequence to discover the number to which it should point.

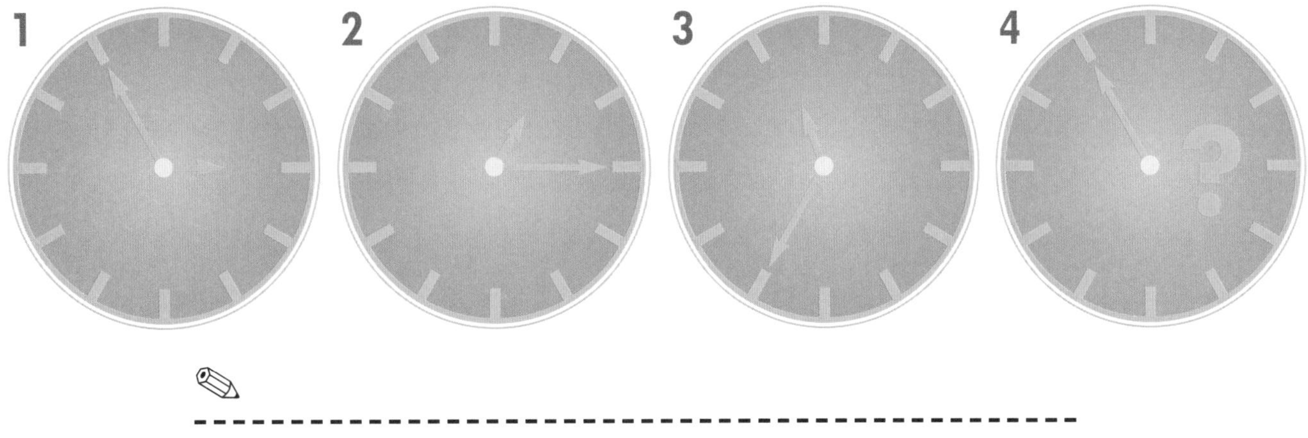

14★★ Which is the odd number out?

481, 296, 384, 479, 387, 794, 926, 148, 843

**15★★** Each row and column contains the same numbers and symbols, but they are arranged in a different order each time. Find the correct order to arrive at the final totals shown.

| 2 | + | 4 | – | 1 | x | 3 | = | 15 |
|---|---|---|---|---|---|---|---|---|
| | | | | | | | | |
| | | | | | | | = | 1 |
| | | | | | | | | |
| | | | | | | | = | 10 |
| | | | | | | | | |
| | | | | | | | = | 6 |
| = | | = | | = | | = | | |
| 5 | | 12 | | 9 | | 13 | | |

**16★★** How many units long is line BC?

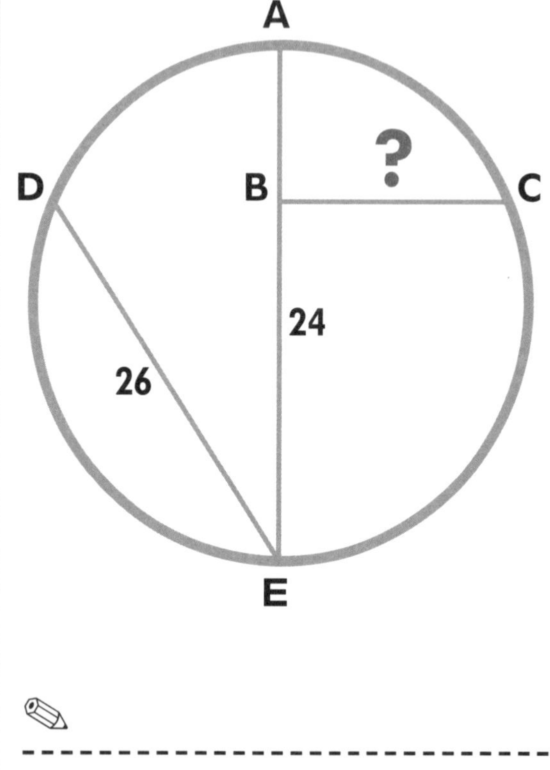


**17★★★** If the yellow inner circle of this disc were removed, what percentage of the whole disc would remain?

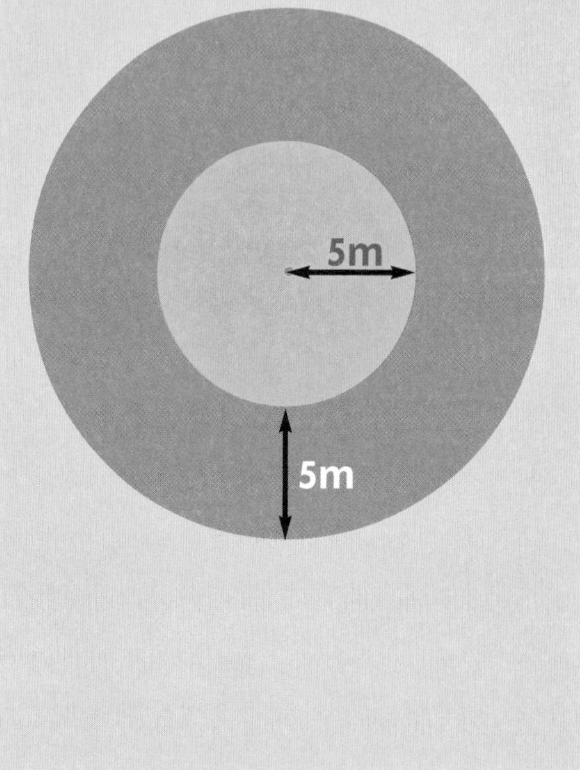

**18**★★ Enter the maze at the top and visit all the letters from A to F in order. On reaching each number the sum of your passed numbers (subtracting is not allowed) must be exactly 10. Make exactly 10 again to leave the maze after visiting the letter F.

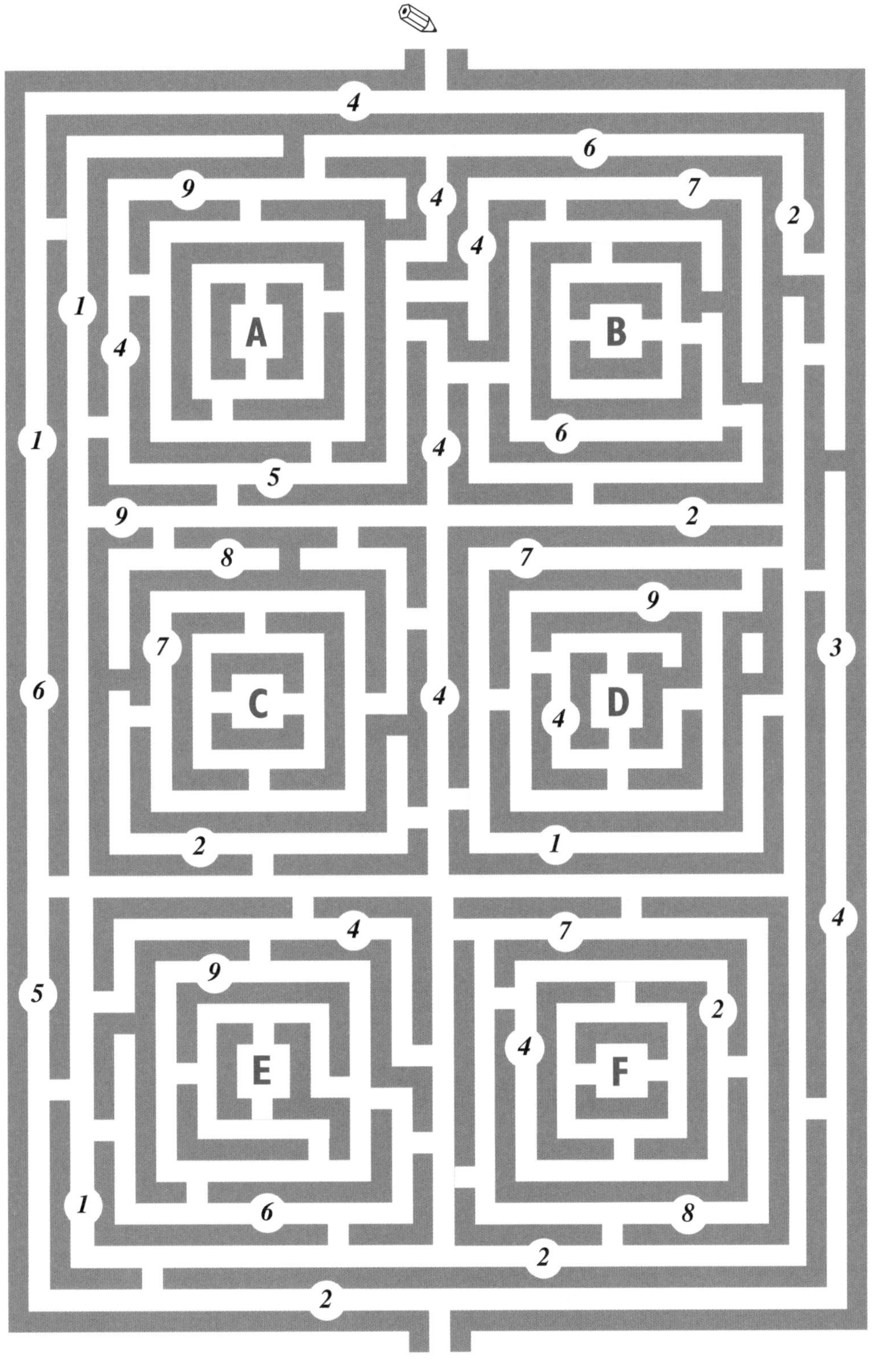

**19**★ Each block in this pyramid is the total of the two blocks below it. Can you find all the missing numbers?

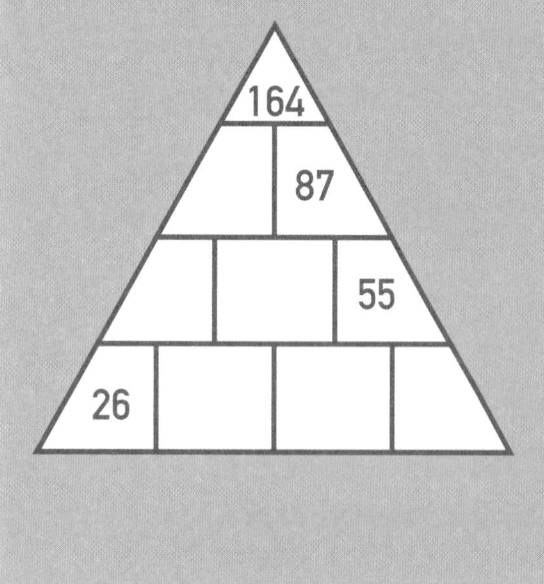


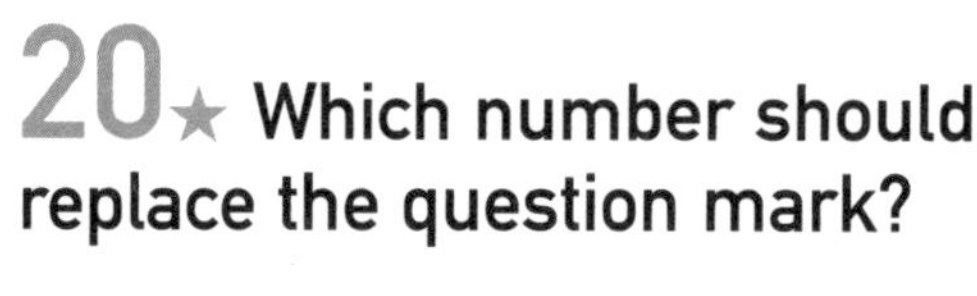

**20**★ Which number should replace the question mark?

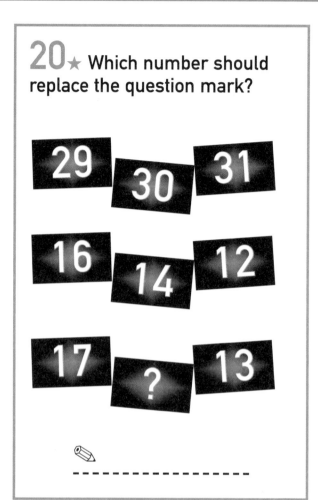

---

**21**★★ Think laterally to find the missing number.

PORTUGAL = 51
EGYPT = 31
CANADA = 39
ETHIOPIA = 53
AMERICA = 46
ENGLAND = ?

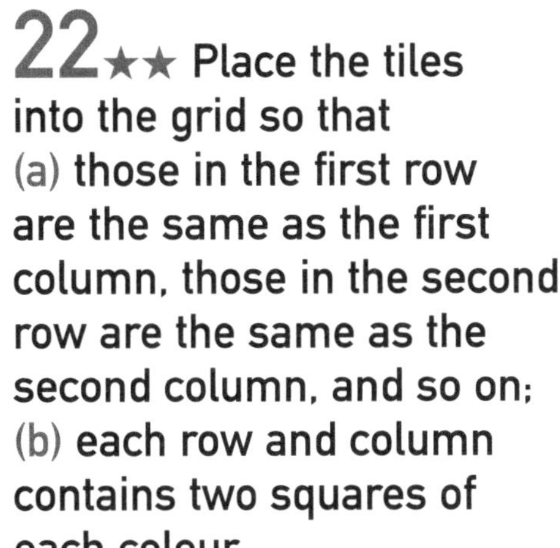

**22★★** Place the tiles into the grid so that (a) those in the first row are the same as the first column, those in the second row are the same as the second column, and so on; (b) each row and column contains two squares of each colour.

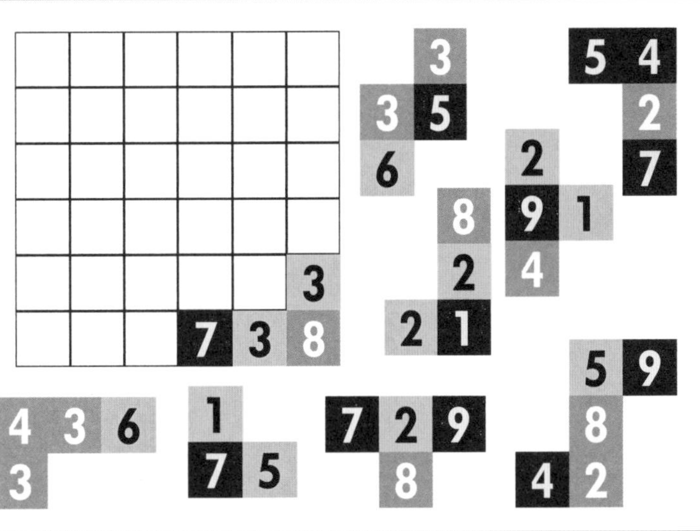

**23★** Watch this space fill before your very eyes – you'll be used to seeing what's hidden in this nonogram!

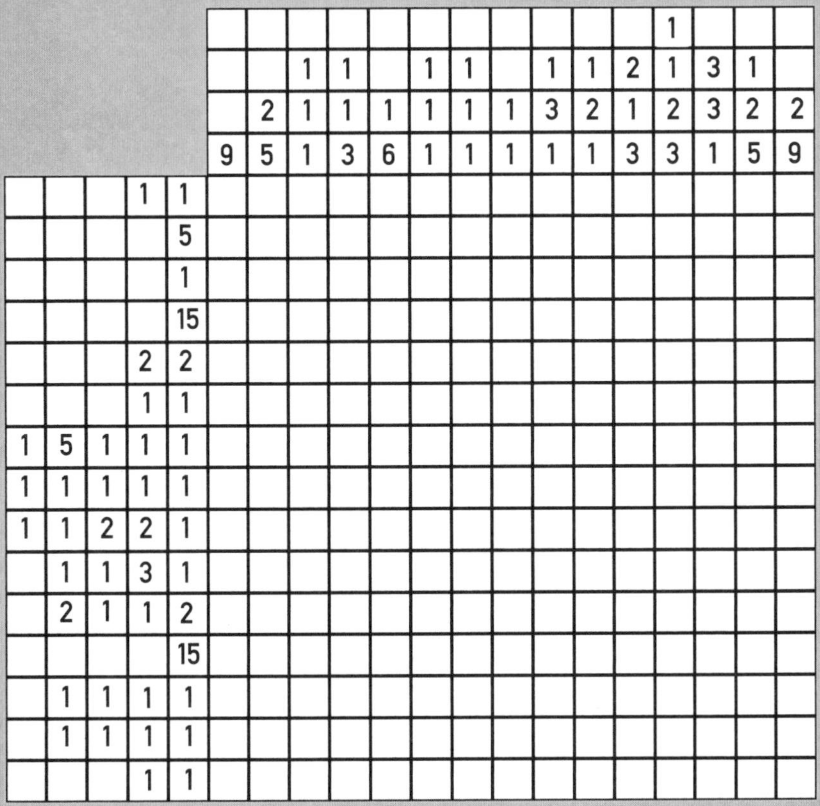

| Col | 1 | 2 | 3 | 4 | 5 | 6 | 7 | 8 | 9 | 10 | 11 | 12 | 13 | 14 | 15 |
|---|---|---|---|---|---|---|---|---|---|---|---|---|---|---|---|
|  |  |  |  |  |  |  |  |  |  |  |  | 1 |  |  |  |
|  |  |  | 1 | 1 |  | 1 | 1 |  | 1 | 1 | 2 | 1 | 3 | 1 |  |
|  |  | 2 | 1 | 1 | 1 | 1 | 1 | 1 | 3 | 2 | 1 | 2 | 3 | 2 | 2 |
|  | 9 | 5 | 1 | 3 | 6 | 1 | 1 | 1 | 1 | 1 | 3 | 3 | 1 | 5 | 9 |

Row clues (top to bottom):

| Row | Clues |
|---|---|
| 1 | 1 1 |
| 2 | 5 |
| 3 | 1 |
| 4 | 15 |
| 5 | 2 2 |
| 6 | 1 1 |
| 7 | 1 5 1 1 1 |
| 8 | 1 1 1 1 1 |
| 9 | 1 1 2 2 1 |
| 10 | 1 1 3 1 |
| 11 | 2 1 1 2 |
| 12 | 15 |
| 13 | 1 1 1 1 |
| 14 | 1 1 1 1 |
| 15 | 1 1 |

## How to complete a nonogram

The numbers alongside each row or column tell you how many blocks of black squares are in a line.

So, for example, 2, 3, 5 tells you that from left to right (or top to bottom) there is a group of two black squares, then a group of three black squares and finally a group of five black squares.

Any of the blocks may (or may not) have a number of white squares before or after them, but each block of black squares on the same line has at least one white square between it and the next block of black squares.

Sometimes you will be able to tell which squares are going to be black without reference to other lines or columns: for instance, in the first example shown here we can deduce that any block of six black squares must incorporate the two central ones.

It will also help to put a small dot in squares where you know them to be empty.

| 6 | | | | | | ■ | ■ | | | | |
|---|---|---|---|---|---|---|---|---|---|---|---|

Here is a simple example filled in:

| 1 | 3 | 2 | • | ■ | • | ■ | ■ | ■ | • | ■ | ■ |
|---|---|---|---|---|---|---|---|---|---|---|---|

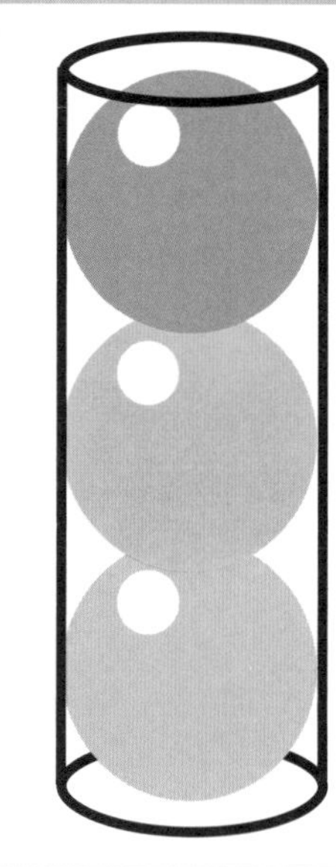

**24**★★★ Three identical solid spheres are packed tightly inside an empty cylinder so all the spheres are touching. Expressed as a fraction, how much of the tube's total volume is left unfilled?

**25**★★★ What is the total value of the angles in an octagon?

**26**★ Replace the question marks with mathematical symbols to produce the correct answer. Only two of the four mathematical signs, +, –, ÷ and x, are used.

**35 ? 7 ? 14 ? 4 = 7**

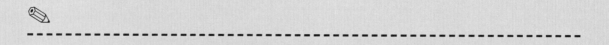

27★★ Rockets A and B are orbiting different suns. Rocket A takes six months to perform one orbit, while Rocket B takes 28 months. At the moment, the middle of both rockets is precisely aligned on the line between the suns. How long will it be before this situation arises once again?

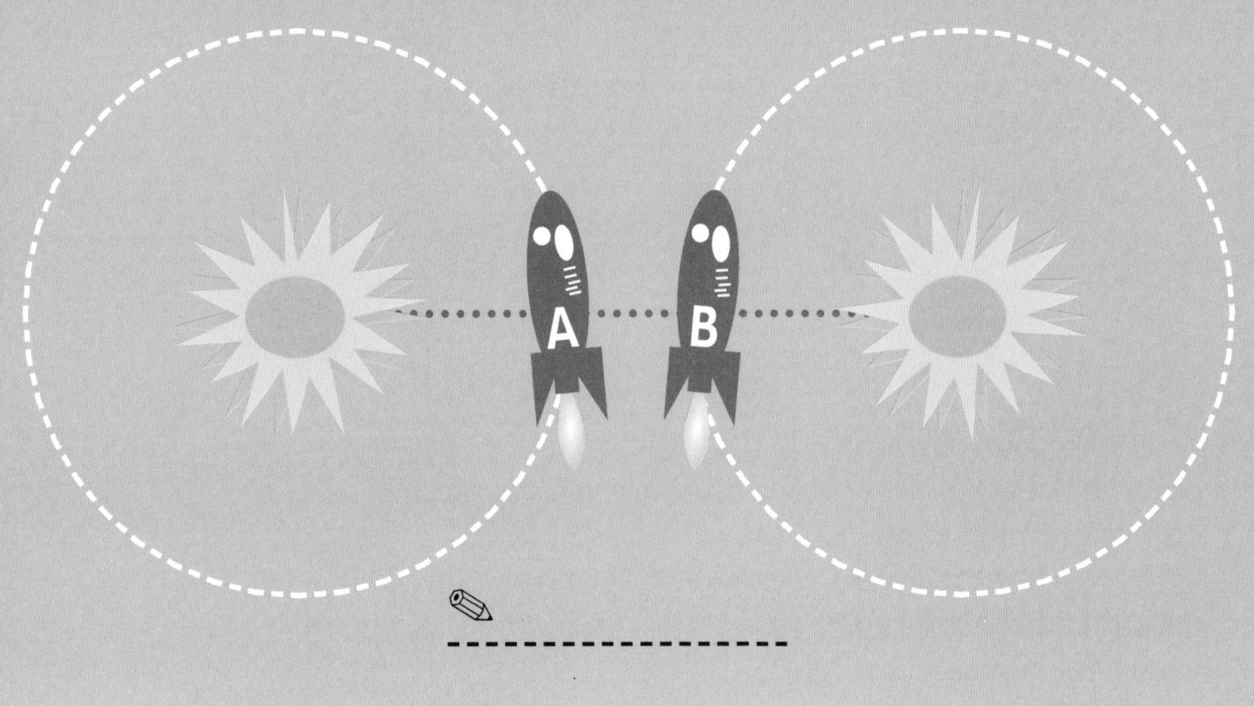


✎ ------------------

28★★ The hour hand on the fourth clock is missing. To which number should it be pointing?

✎ ------------------

**29★** Complete the sum below using every one of the numbers and signs in the circle.

**30★★** Each row and column contains the same numbers and symbols, but they are arranged in a different order each time. Can you find the correct order to arrive at the final totals shown?

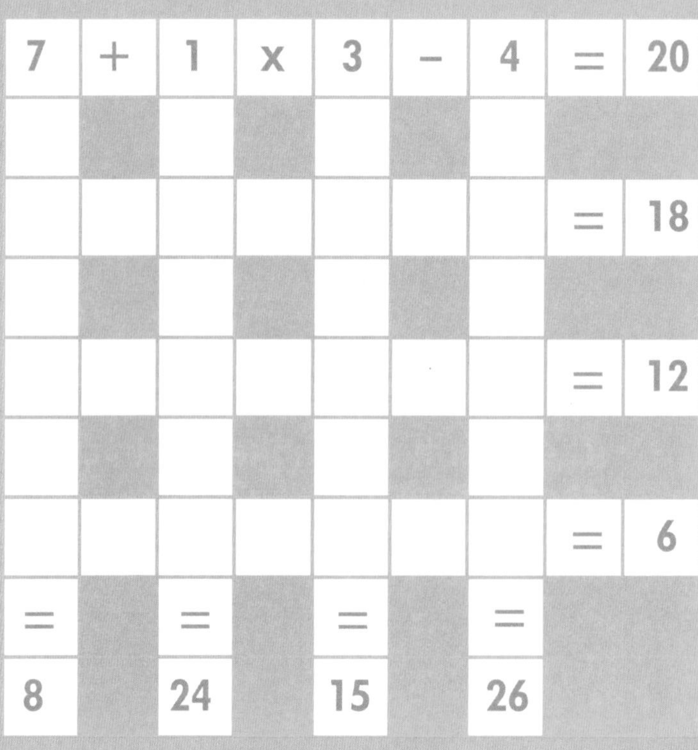

| 7 | + | 1 | x | 3 | – | 4 | = | 20 |
|---|---|---|---|---|---|---|---|---|
| | | | | | | | | |
| | | | | | | | = | 18 |
| | | | | | | | | |
| | | | | | | | = | 12 |
| | | | | | | | | |
| | | | | | | | = | 6 |
| = | | = | | = | | = | | |
| 8 | | 24 | | 15 | | 26 | | |

**31★** Which number comes next?  ______________________

**10, 1, 8, 3, 6, 5, ?**

## 32★★ The totals of the following equations can all be found in our wordsearch-style grid reading up, down, backwards, forwards or diagonally... The bravest won't resort to a calculator!

1. 33 x 33
2. 999 + 999
3. 5 x 5 x 5 x 5 x 5
4. 382 ÷ 2
5. (1000 ÷ 50) x 99
6. 321 x 123
7. 77 x 77
8. 22222 x 4
9. 199 x 5
10. (8 x 8) + (7 x 7)
11. (44 + 44) x (33 + 33)
12. 3240 ÷ 18
13. 143 x 7

| | | | | | |
|---|---|---|---|---|---|
| 0 | 1 | 9 | 8 | 0 | 3 |
| 8 | 0 | 8 | 2 | 9 | 1 |
| 1 | 0 | 8 | 4 | 9 | 2 |
| 3 | 1 | 8 | 9 | 1 | 5 |
| 1 | 3 | 8 | 5 | 9 | 9 |
| 1 | 0 | 8 | 9 | 1 | 1 |

## 33★★ The answers to the general knowledge questions below can be found somewhere – in the correct sequence – in the column of digits on the right. The answers are 2, 3 or 4 digits in length.

| | | |
|---|---|---|
| 1 | Degrees in three right angles | 18052700 |
| 2 | Years of marriage for a diamond anniversary | 40505560 |
| 3 | Isotope of uranium used in an atomic bomb | 12356789 |
| 4 | Minutes in a day | 36214402 |
| 5 | Cost of the utility spaces in Monopoly | 12001500 |
| 6 | Number of the White House on Pennsylvania Avenue | 61600919 |
| 7 | Age to which Methuselah lived | 74519690 |
| 8 | Number for a hurricane on the Beaufort Scale | 12351022 |
| 9 | Minutes of sound held on a standard CD | 41037457 |
| 10 | Number of human chromosomes | 23482460 |

## 34★ In the domino sequence below, which of the options, A, B, C or D, should replace the question mark?

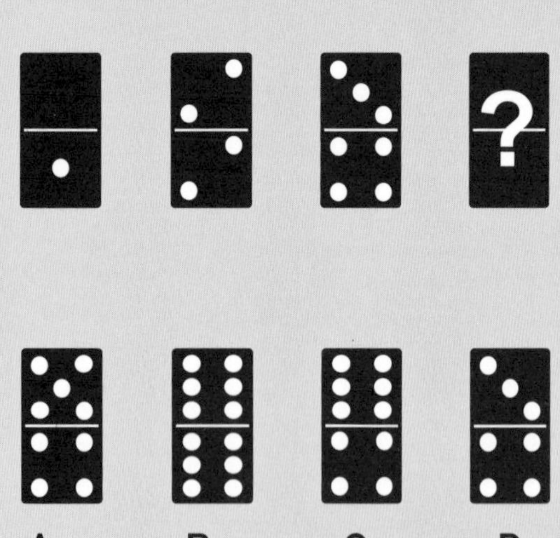


## 35★★ Imagine giant dominoes in place of standing stones in the celebrated sacred circle of Stonehenge, southern England.

If the numerical value of each horizontal domino is equal to the total value of the two dominoes supporting it, can you arrange the nine dominoes (below) in the correct configuration?

## 36★★ Place the tiles into the grid so that (a) the tiles in the first row are the same as the first column, the tiles in the second row are the same as the second column, and so on; (b) each row and column contains two squares of each colour; (c) each row and column contains two of each number.

|  |  |  |  |  |  |
|---|---|---|---|---|---|
|  |  |  |  |  |  |
|  |  | 1 |  |  |  |
|  |  | 1 | 3 |  |  |
|  |  | 3 |  |  |  |
|  |  |  |  |  |  |
|  |  |  |  |  |  |

2 1 / 1 / 3

1 / 3 2 1

1 / 3 / 2

1 2 3 2 / 2

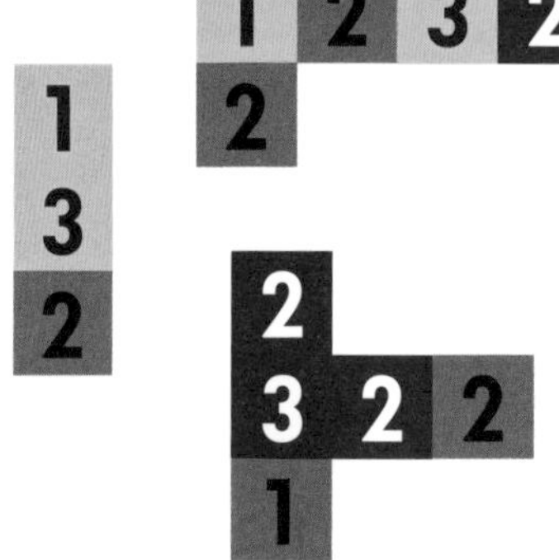


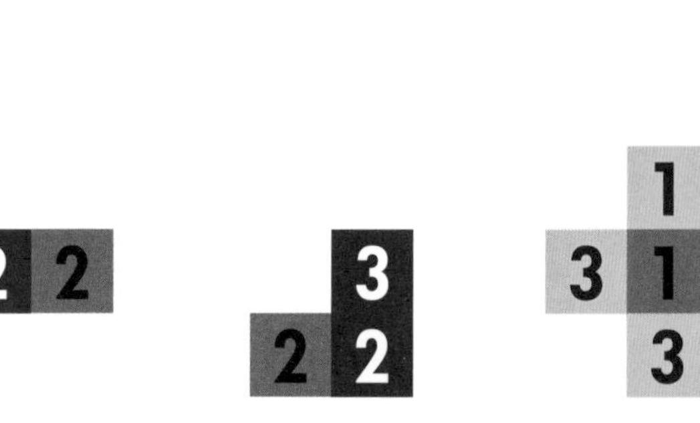

**37**★★★ What is wrong with this magic square, and how can you fix it in just two operations?

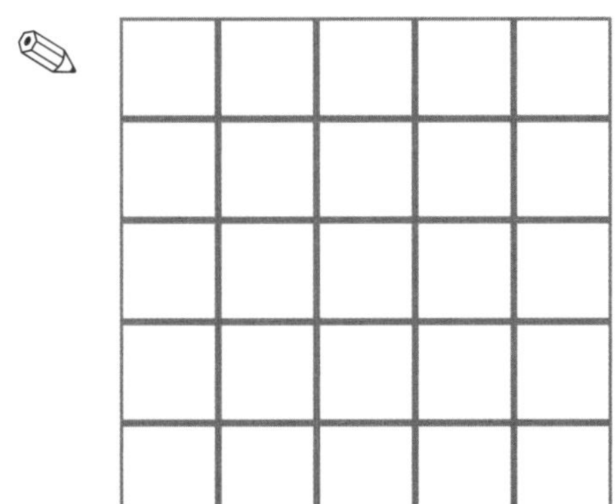

| | | | | |
|---|---|---|---|---|
| 22 | 4 | 6 | 13 | 20 |
| 3 | 10 | 12 | 19 | 21 |
| 9 | 11 | 18 | 25 | 2 |
| 15 | 17 | 24 | 1 | 8 |
| 16 | 23 | 5 | 7 | 14 |

**38**★★★ Each of the four symbols (heart, club, diamond and spade) represents a certain number in all the rows across – and the total at the end of each row refers to the sum of the symbols.

Each symbol also refers to a number (it may or may not be the same number as that in the rows across!) when used in the sums downwards, with the total at the bottom of each column again referring to the sum of the symbols.

Can you work out the value of the symbols shown, both horizontally and vertically?

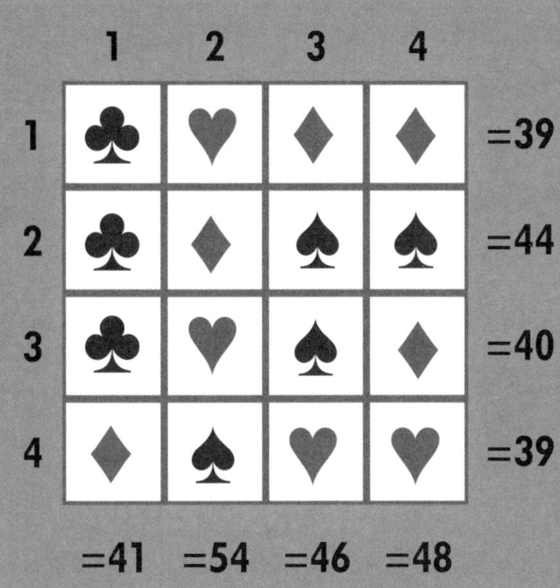


ACROSS

DOWN

**39** ★★ Place a number in the middle box by which all the other numbers can be divided without leaving a remainder. The answer is greater than 1.

**40** ★★ Which number should replace the question mark in the bottom box?

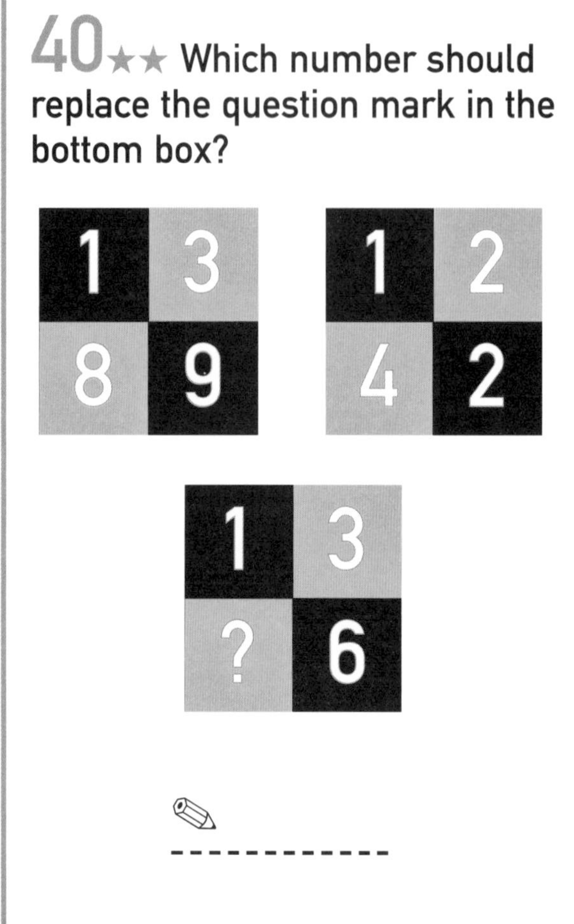


**41** ★ Each block in this pyramid is the total of the two blocks below it. Can you find all the missing numbers?

1523
764
403
147

**42★** The minute hand on the fourth clock is missing. To which number should it be pointing?

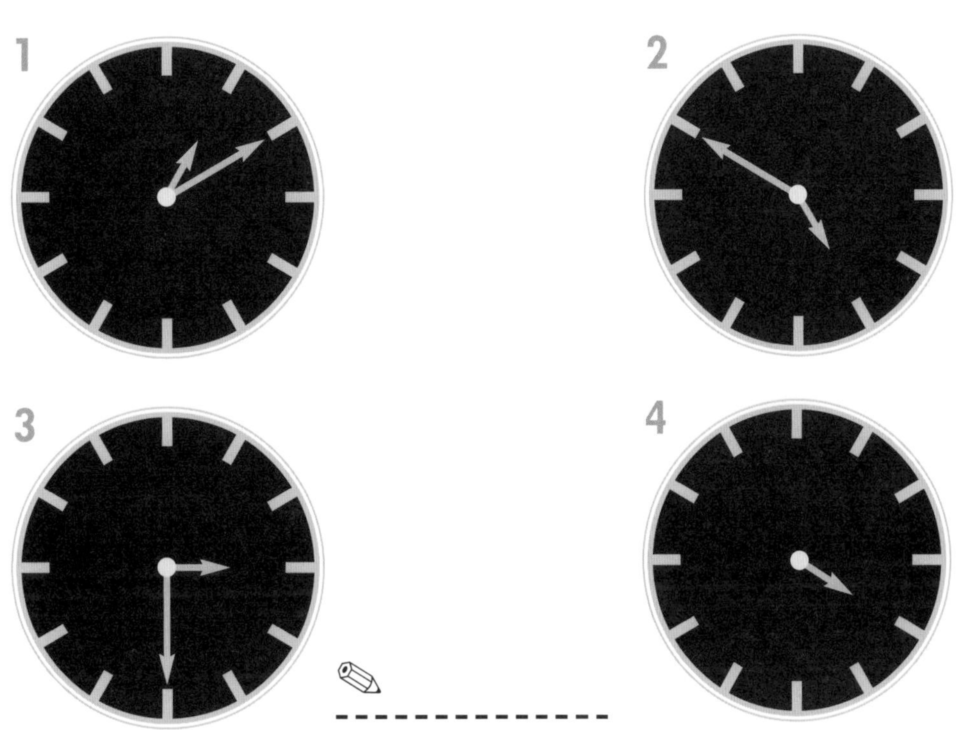


**43★★★** Which number is the odd one out?

**34102, 76304, 46138, 85255, 59177**

**44★★** Place the six numbers in the list on the triangle to make each of the three sides add up to the same total.

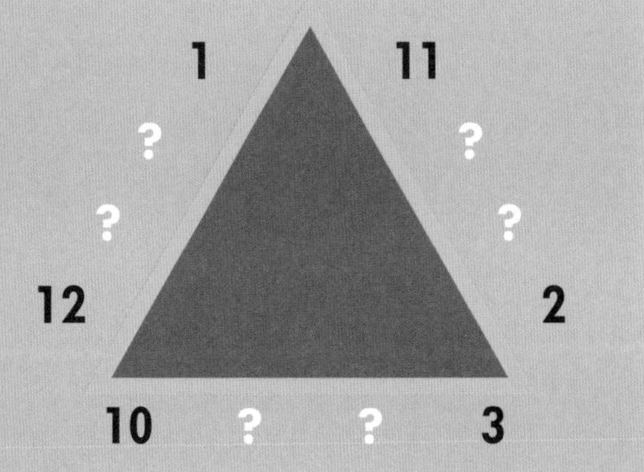

**45★★** Can you fit these numbers into the grid? One number has already been positioned to help you.

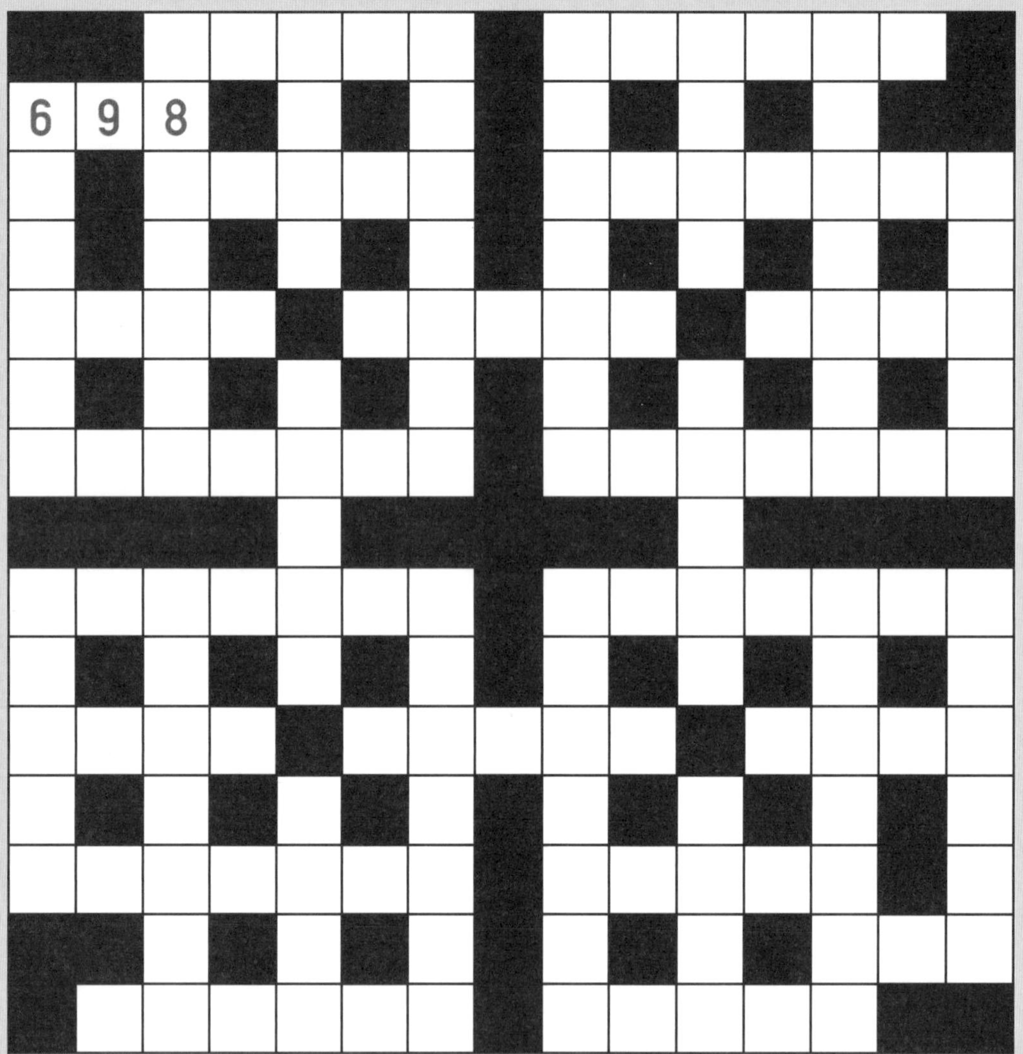


**3-FIGURE NUMBERS**

~~698~~
744

**4-FIGURE NUMBERS**

1217
2046
2268
2586
3168
3735
4584
8603

**5-FIGURE NUMBERS**

10131
18887
21858
59421
61525
72263
84207
84471
84747
89455

**6-FIGURE NUMBERS**

183643
597094
697835
948861

**7-FIGURE NUMBERS**

1433231
1528177
1575181
1648564
1758105
1790241
3059236
3930585
4657542
5968417
7110418
7887137
8141601
8822056

**46** ★★ The answers to the general knowledge questions below can be found somewhere – in the correct sequence – in the column of digits on the right. The answers are 2, 3 or 4 digits long.

| | | |
|---|---|---|
| 1 | Points required to win in a game of cribbage | 12131415 |
| 2 | Whole degrees C below zero of 'absolute zero' | 23927380 |
| 3 | Square yards in an acre | 12484097 |
| 4 | Psalms in the Bible | 12150373 |
| 5 | Days of gestation for an average human baby | 92662309 |
| 6 | Beads in a rosary | 16536566 |
| 7 | The number in a great gross | 21441728 |
| 8 | Spaces on a Go board | 14436105 |
| 9 | The year Theodore Roosevelt won the Nobel Peace Prize | 18191906 |
| 10 | The year (AD) the prophet Muhammad died | 10632049 |

**47** ★★ What number comes next in this sequence?

**3.75, 4.75, 6.25, 8.25, ?**

**48** ★★★ A friend of yours is tossing a coin and you are betting on the outcome. You bet on heads every time. Your unit stake is £1 per toss. You start by betting £1 on the first toss. If you win, you again place £1 on the second toss, but if you lose you double the stake to £2, then £4 and continue to double after every loss. After every win you revert to the £1 stake. After 100 tosses of the coin, heads has come face-up 53 times. How much profit, or loss, are you making, assuming that the 100th toss was heads?

**49★★** The totals of the following equations can all be found in our wordsearch-style grid reading up, down, backwards, forwards or diagonally... The bravest won't resort to a calculator!

1 1111 x 9
2 20 x 20 x 20
3 88 x 88
4 22 x 222
5 1776 ÷ 4
6 3 x 3030
7 1010 ÷ 5
8 (3 x 3 x 3) x (4 x 4 x 4)
9 (5 x 5) x (5 x 5 x 5)
10 7 x 200
11 4994 x 2
12 66000 ÷ 3
13 23624 x 5

| | | | | | |
|---|---|---|---|---|---|
| 5 | 2 | 1 | 3 | 2 | 0 |
| 4 | 4 | 7 | 7 | 0 | 2 |
| 8 | 8 | 9 | 9 | 2 | 1 |
| 8 | 0 | 9 | 0 | 4 | 8 |
| 4 | 9 | 0 | 0 | 4 | 1 |
| 9 | 0 | 9 | 0 | 4 | 1 |

**50★** Replace the question marks with mathematical symbols to produce the correct answer. Only the mathematical signs +, –, ÷ and x may be used. Can you find two possible solutions?

**8 ? 3 ? 2 ? 5 = 17**

51 ★★ Each block in this pyramid is the total of the two blocks below it. Which number should replace the question mark in the bottom row?

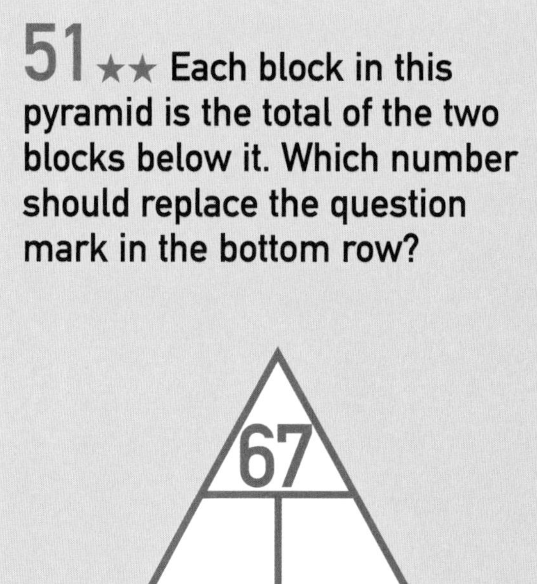

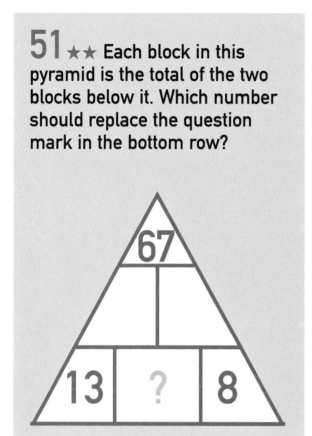


52 ★★ If the yellow and white areas of this flag are of equal areas, how wide is the yellow stripe at point x?

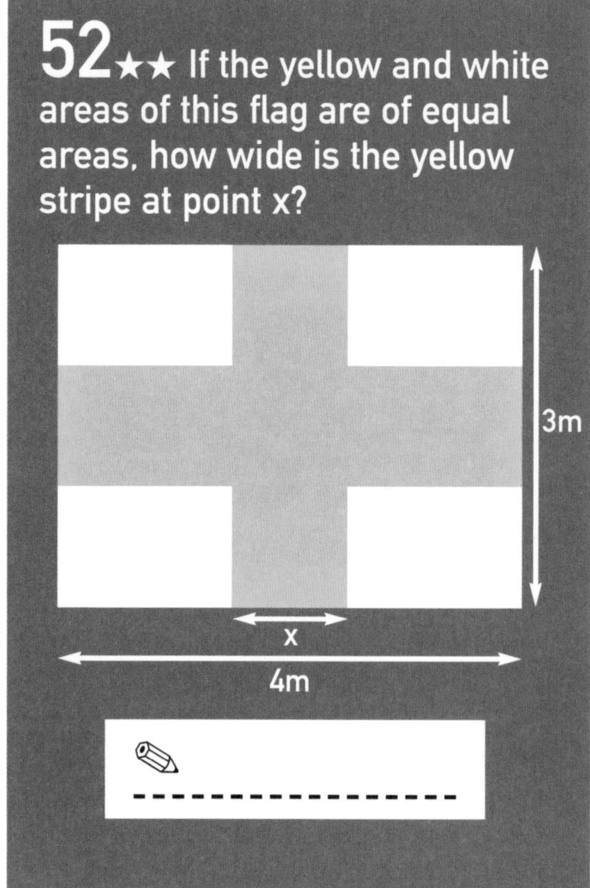


53 ★★ The minute hand on the fourth clock is missing. To which number should it be pointing?

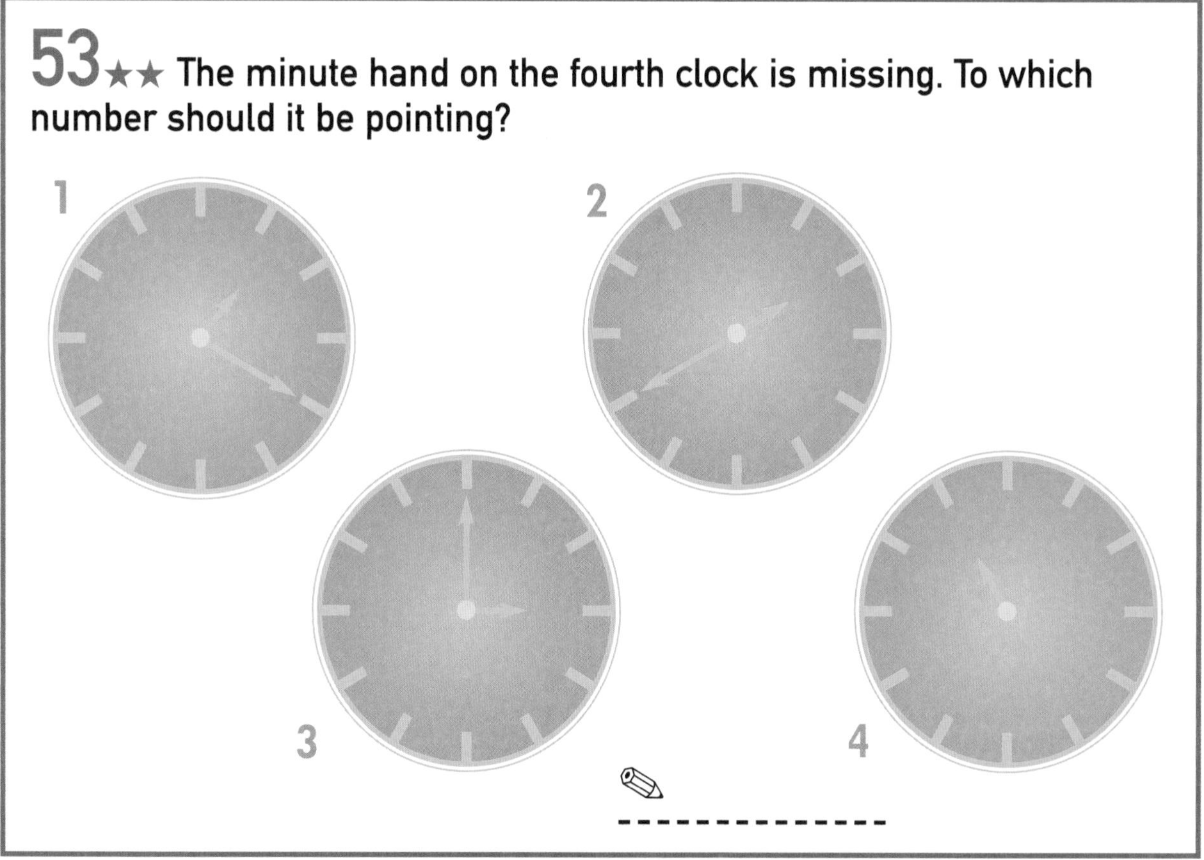

**54**★★ Make a sum totalling 359 using the numbers in the circle and any of the four standard mathematical operations (+, −, x, ÷).

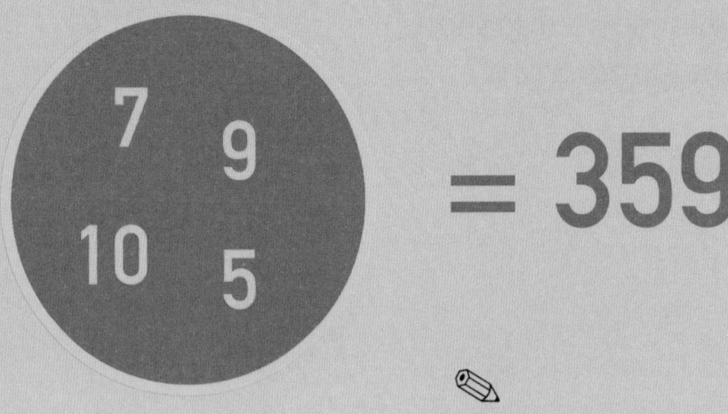


✎ --------------------

**55**★★★ Each row and column contains the same numbers and symbols, but they are arranged in a different order each time. Find the correct order to arrive at the final totals shown.

| 8 | + | 3 | − | 7 | x | 5 | = | 20 |
|---|---|---|---|---|---|---|---|---|
| | | | | | | | | |
| | | | | | | | = | 36 |
| | | | | | | | | |
| | | | | | | | = | 30 |
| | | | | | | | | |
| | | | | | | | = | 42 |
| = | | = | | = | | = | | |
| 44 | | 48 | | 24 | | 40 | | |

**56★** The number 8283531 appears just once in this wordsearch-style grid and occurs in a straight line, running either backwards or forwards in either a horizontal, vertical or diagonal direction. Can you locate it?

| 8 | 1 | 1 | 3 | 5 | 3 | 2 | 8 | 8 | 1 | 3 | 1 |
|---|---|---|---|---|---|---|---|---|---|---|---|
| 8 | 2 | 3 | 5 | 3 | 1 | 8 | 2 | 2 | 8 | 5 | 3 |
| 2 | 8 | 5 | 2 | 8 | 5 | 2 | 8 | 3 | 8 | 2 | 5 |
| 8 | 3 | 2 | 3 | 8 | 2 | 8 | 3 | 2 | 2 | 2 | 3 |
| 3 | 5 | 8 | 8 | 5 | 2 | 3 | 8 | 8 | 1 | 8 | 5 |
| 5 | 3 | 3 | 2 | 3 | 5 | 3 | 1 | 5 | 5 | 2 | 2 |
| 1 | 1 | 5 | 8 | 8 | 5 | 1 | 8 | 8 | 3 | 5 | 8 |
| 1 | 3 | 3 | 5 | 3 | 8 | 2 | 2 | 8 | 5 | 3 | 8 |
| 2 | 5 | 1 | 1 | 2 | 8 | 3 | 1 | 5 | 3 | 1 | 3 |
| 8 | 2 | 8 | 3 | 5 | 2 | 1 | 2 | 3 | 1 | 2 | 5 |
| 8 | 3 | 2 | 8 | 1 | 2 | 5 | 3 | 8 | 2 | 8 | 3 |
| 1 | 8 | 1 | 3 | 8 | 3 | 5 | 2 | 8 | 8 | 5 | 1 |

**57★★★** What number comes next?

**3692, 738, 584, 232, ?**

**58**★★★ Which numbers should replace the question marks?

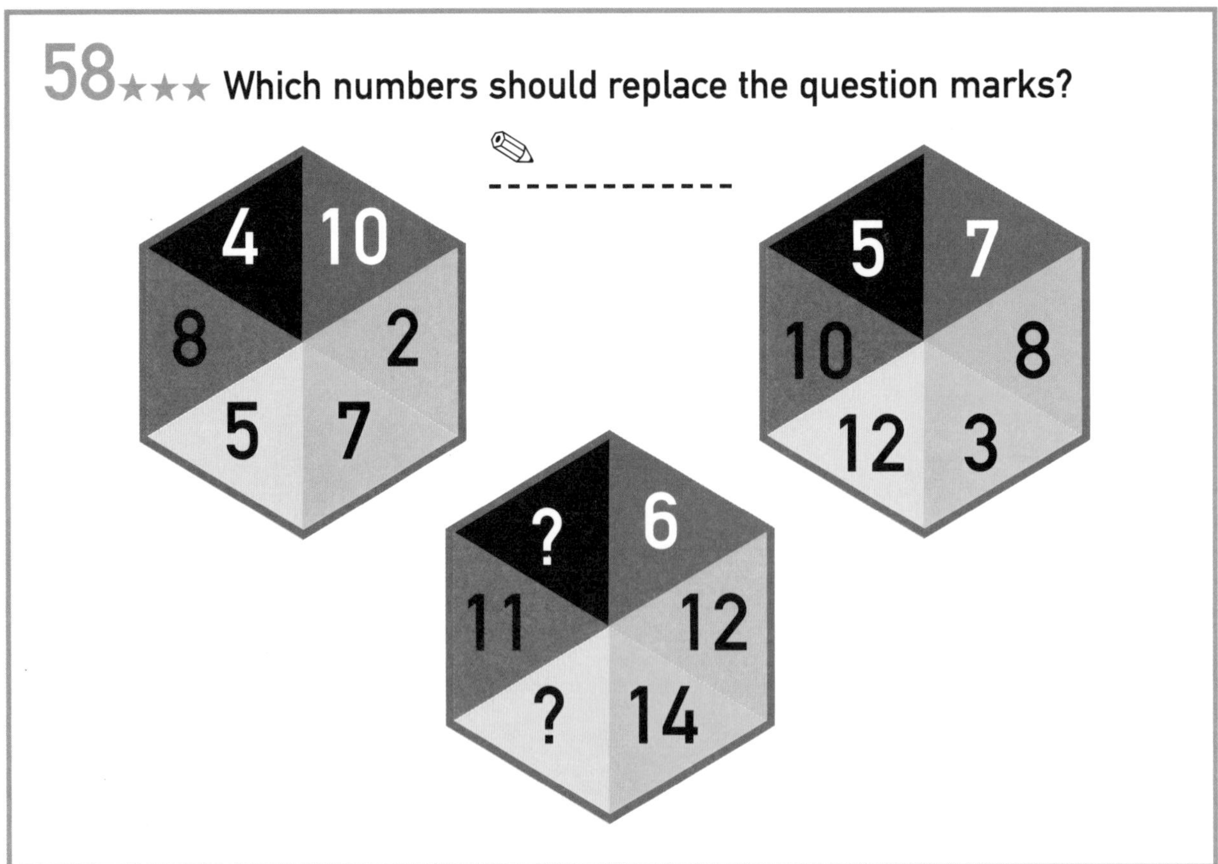


**59**★★★ The answers to the questions below can be found somewhere – in the correct sequence – in the column of digits on the right.

| | | |
|---|---|---|
| 1 | The year (AD) when Roman emperor Claudius was poisoned | 10205419 |
| 2 | Warriors in Valhalla | 80077772 |
| 3 | Temperature at which paper catches fire, in degrees F | 36245178 |
| 4 | Length of the Nile, in miles | 92041458 |
| 5 | Nick Leeson's a/c no., which caused Barings Bank to collapse | 99988888 |
| 6 | Possible positions in a chess game, after Black's second move | 80271852 |
| 7 | The year (AD) in which H.G. Wells's Time Machine arrives | 80270193 |
| 8 | Length of Noah's Ark in cubits | 53001395 |
| 9 | Speed of light, in miles per second | 91862728 |
| 10 | Elvis Presley's army serial number | 53310761 |

**60**★★ Give yourself 15 minutes for this mental arithmetic challenge and see how you get on!

1 Which is greater, millimetres in a mile or seconds in November?

✎ ------------------

2 If 1 gallon = 4.5 litres, how many millilitres are there in 5 gallons?

✎ ------------------

3 What is 10% of 20% of 30% of 40% of 5,000?

✎ ------------------

4 What is a score plus a gross plus a baker's dozen?

✎ ------------------

5 In the sum below, the same number appears in both boxes. If it is not 2, what is it?

□ x □ = 4

✎ ------------------

6 Paul is 40 and his daughter Jane is 13. How many years ago was Paul four times as old as Jane?

✎ ------------------

7 Which three numbers total the same when they are added as when they are multiplied together?

✎ ------------------

8 If 2 rabbits eat 4 carrots, how many carrots do 1½ rabbits eat?

✎ ------------------

**61** ★★ Can you fit these numbers into the grid? One number has already been positioned to help you.

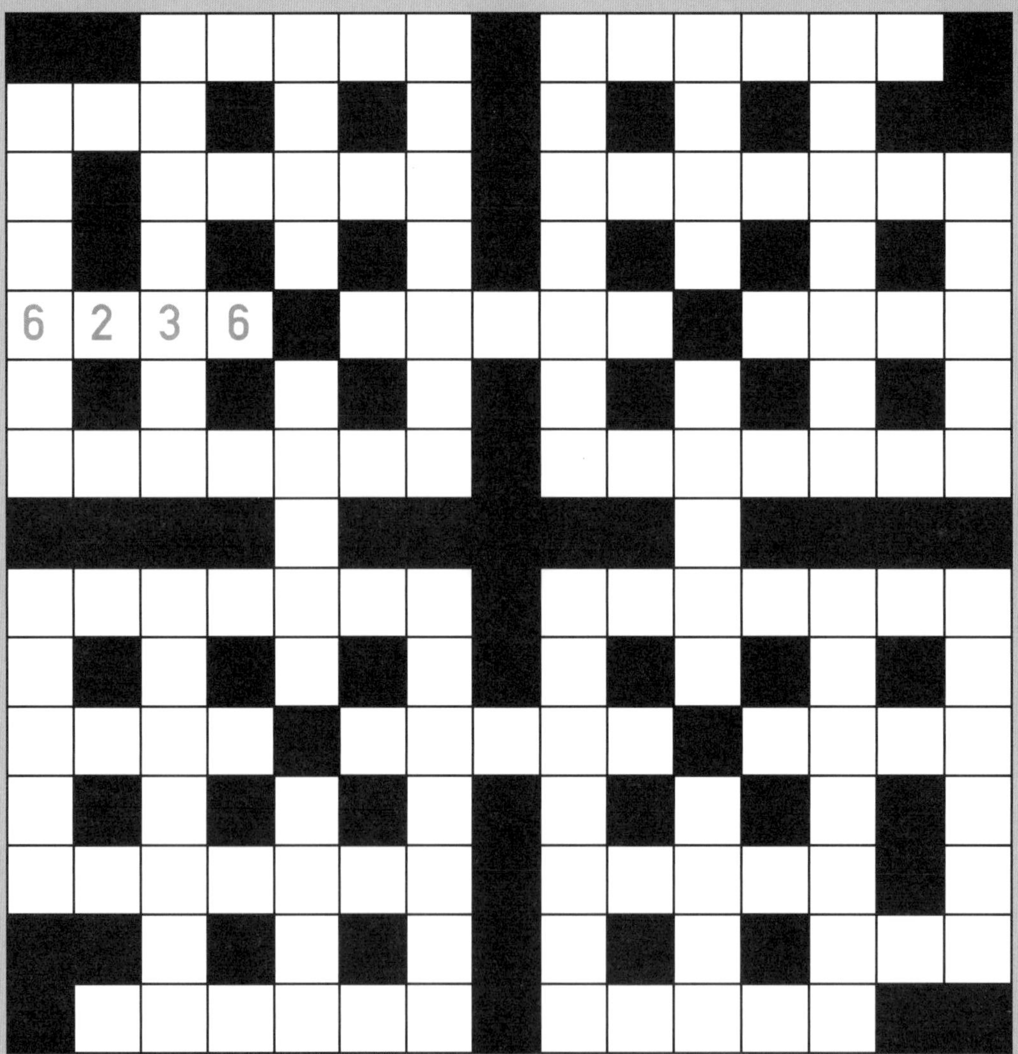


3-FIGURE NUMBERS
789
966

4-FIGURE NUMBERS
1464
1772
3039
4398
4960
~~6236~~
8287
9832

5-FIGURE NUMBERS
12089
13246
36975
37270
38943
44198
44925
53720
74084
91131

6-FIGURE NUMBERS
165889
398713
780664
834046

7-FIGURE NUMBERS
1704417
1984916
2839056
3420719
3909375
3967984
4075787
4739679
5444495
6580871
6843548
6920783
9041529
9953337

**62**★★ A magic square has the special property that all the numbers in each row, column and both main diagonals add up to the same number. With this in mind, complete this magic square.

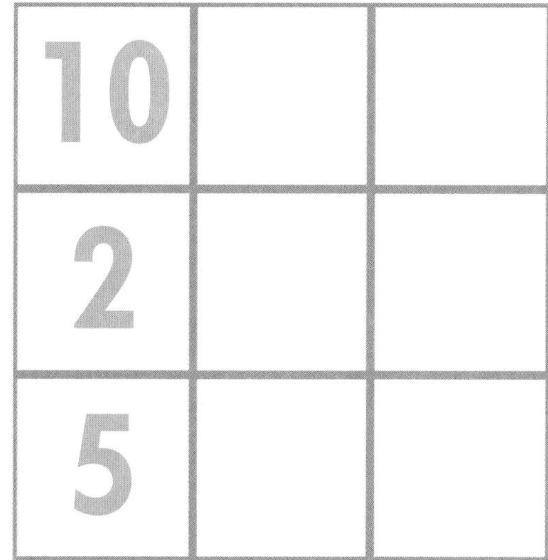


**63**★★ If a quarter of a square is taken from a corner, can you dissect the remaining area into four parts, each of the same shape and size?

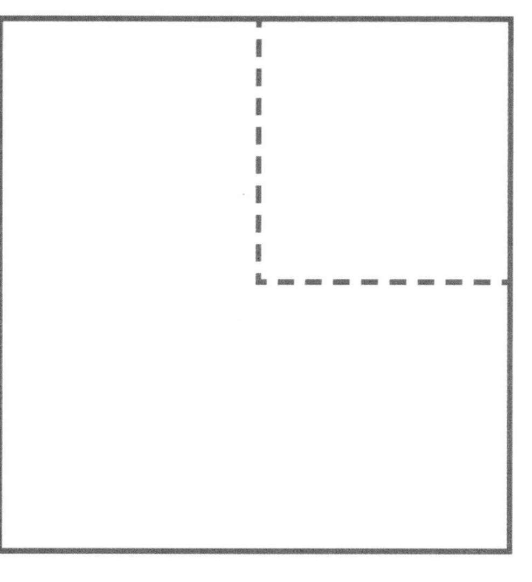

**64**★ What comes next in this number sequence?

6, 17, 50, 149, 446, ?

65★★ Place a number in the middle box by which all the other numbers can be divided without leaving a remainder. The answer is greater than 1.

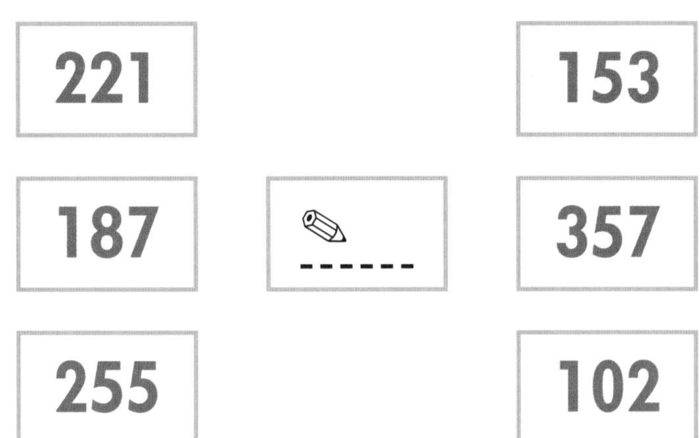


66★★ Rockets A and B are orbiting different suns. Rocket A takes 6 months to complete one orbit, while rocket B takes 15 months. How long will it be before the middle of both rockets is precisely aligned on the line that joins both suns.

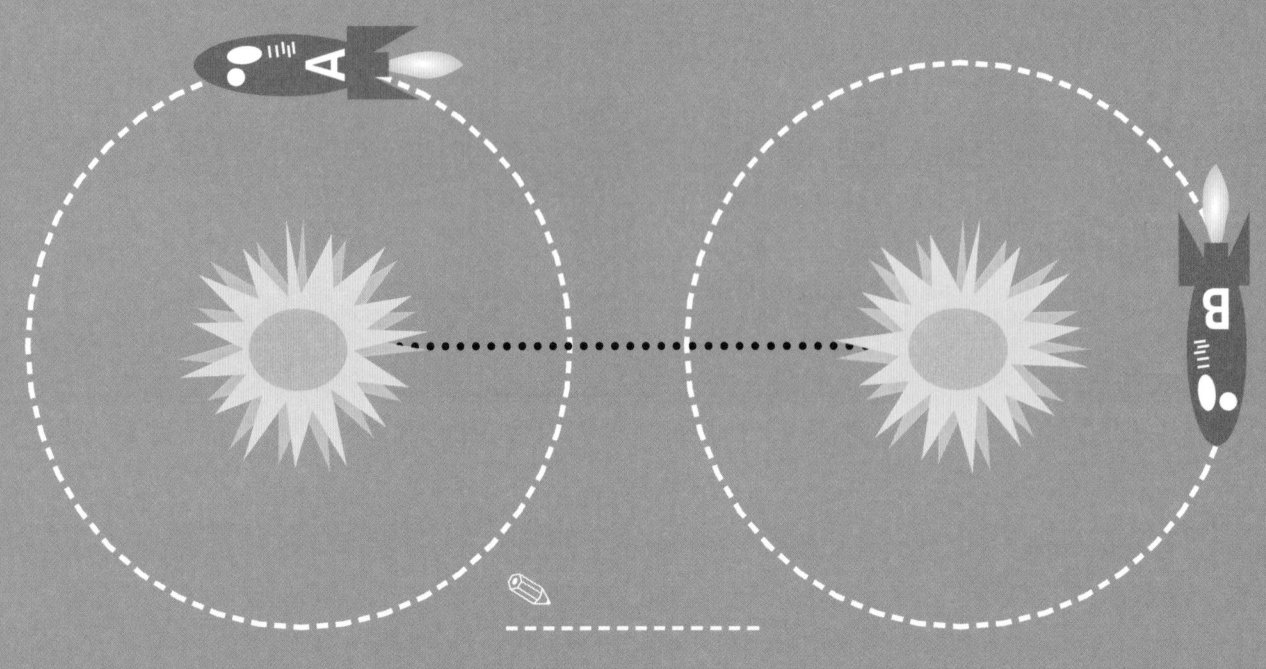


67★★ Which number should replace the question mark? ----------

81, 82, 80, 240, 60, 61, 59, ?

**68** ★★ What two things do all of these, except one, have in common?

**54, 36, 90, 64, 72, 18**

**69** ★★★ How many triangles are there in the figure to the right – and if each triangle you found became a new separate figure, what would the total area of all the triangles be in square metres?

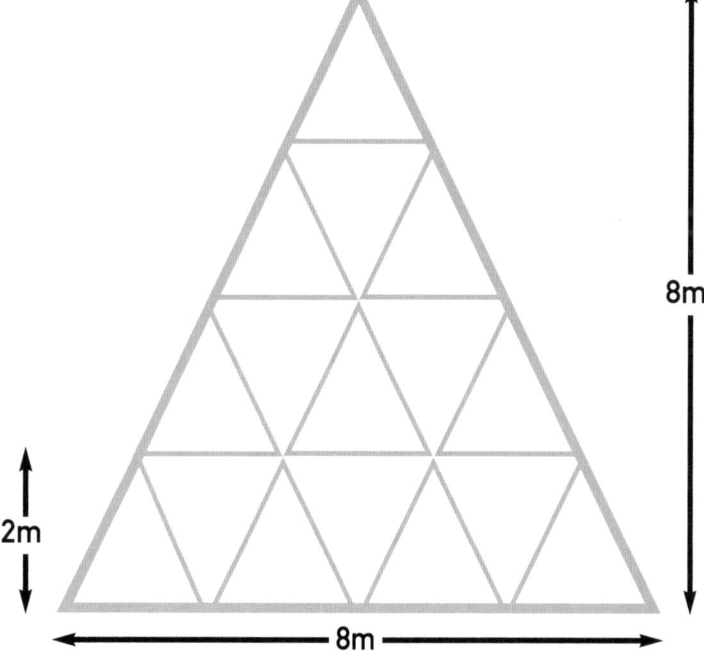


**70** ★★★ All the mathematical symbols in this equation have been omitted. Can you replace them?

**67 ? 18 ? 6 ? 17 ? 18 = 200**

**71** ★★★ Make two different sums, both totalling 891, each using all the numbers in the circle and any of the four standard mathematical operations (+, –, x, ÷).

✎ ----------------------------

**72** ★★★ Magic squares have the special property that all the numbers in each row, column and both main diagonals add up to the same number. In this magic square, several of the numbers have been removed from the grid. However, they are still in their correct row or column. Can you reassemble the square?

| | | 11 | | | | | 19 |
|---|---|---|---|---|---|---|---|
| | | 29 | | 17 | 9 | 25 | 26 |
| 3 | 30 | 4 | | 8 | 31 | | 35 |
| 1 | 5 | 36 | | 28 | | 32 | |
| 7 | 33 | | 34 | | 2 | | 6 |
| 13 | 21 | | 12 | | 22 | | |
| 14 | 27 | 18 | | 10 | | 23 | |
| 15 | 16 | | | | 20 | | 24 |

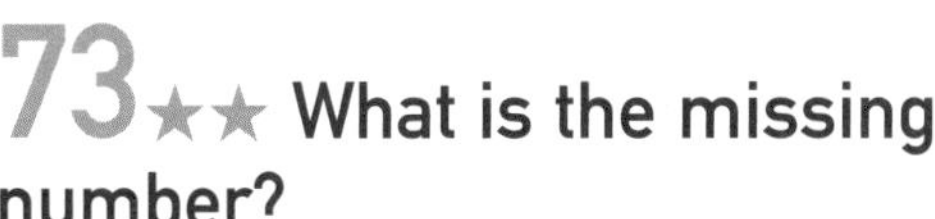

**73★★** What is the missing number?

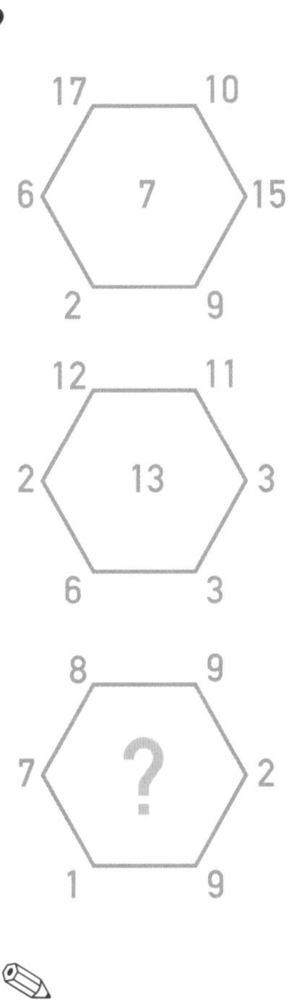


**74★★** Each block in this pyramid is the total of the two blocks below it. Can you find all the missing numbers (fractions are included)?

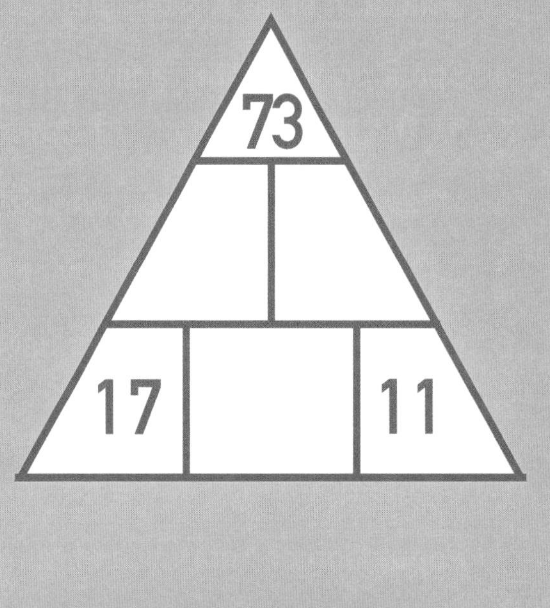


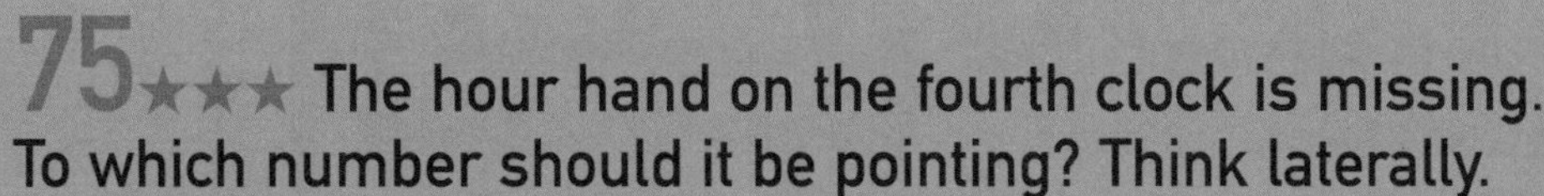

**75★★★** The hour hand on the fourth clock is missing. To which number should it be pointing? Think laterally.

**76★★★** We don't expect you to know the answers to these, but have a guess. The solutions can be found somewhere – in the correct sequence – in the column of digits on the right. Most are 3, 4 or 5 digits long – but look out for surprises!

| | | |
|---|---|---|
| 1 | Patents filed by Thomas Edison | 61093025 |
| 2 | Gestation of an African elephant, in days | 13098660 |
| 3 | Spots drawn by the animators for the Disney film of *101 Dalmatians* | 64699520 |
| 4 | Miles from Chicago to Hong Kong | 25182809 |
| 5 | Sesame seeds on the average Big Mac bun | 17842750 |
| 6 | Number of different words used by Shakespeare | 54176772 |
| 7 | Airports in the USA | 90213387 |
| 8 | Diameter (in feet) of the Pantheon, Rome | 14300000 |
| 9 | Population of Antarctica in summer | 13114115 |
| 10 | Words in the King James edition of the Bible | 20773696 |

**77★★** If the temperature rises 15% to 92°F, what was the temperature before?

---------------------------

**78★★★** Place a figure in the middle box by which all the other figures can be divided without leaving a remainder. The answer is greater than 1.

| 30 | | 37½ |
|---|---|---|
| 41¼ | ✎ ---------- | 22½ |
| 217½ | | 75 |

**79★★★** Each row and column contains the same numbers and symbols, but they are arranged in a different order each time. Find the correct order to arrive at the final totals shown.

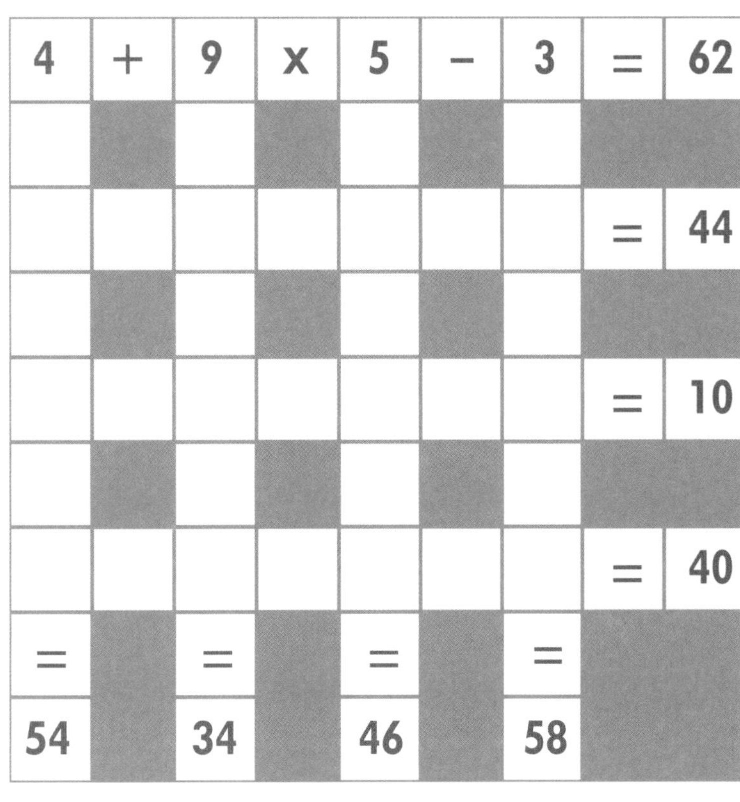

80★★ Here's a mental arithmetic time challenge to keep you on your toes. Can you complete it in 15 minutes?

1 The Black Sea is 508,000 km$^2$. The Red Sea is 175,000 square miles. Which sea is larger?

✎ ----------------

2 Express the number 9 using four 4s.

✎ ----------------

3 In craps, a player 'shoots' a pair of dice. If the spots on every possible combination of the two dice are added together, what is the total number?

✎ ----------------

4 Express the number 0.183 (recurring) as a fraction.

✎ ----------------

5 Make the smallest possible whole number using 1, 2, 3, 4 and 5 only once to make two new numbers, and then adding the new numbers together.

✎ ----------------

6 Which number below is divisible by 11?
401805    39030915    282648

✎ ----------------

7 Six is a 'perfect' number: it is the sum of all the numbers by which it is divisible (1 + 2 + 3 = 6). What is the next largest perfect number?

✎ ----------------

8 If a suit costing £117 now costs 17% more, how much does it cost (to the nearest whole pound)?

✎ ----------------

81 ★★ What number should replace the question mark?

61, 68, 82, 92, 103, 107, ?

82 ★★ Each block in this pyramid is the total of the two blocks below it. Can you find all the missing numbers?

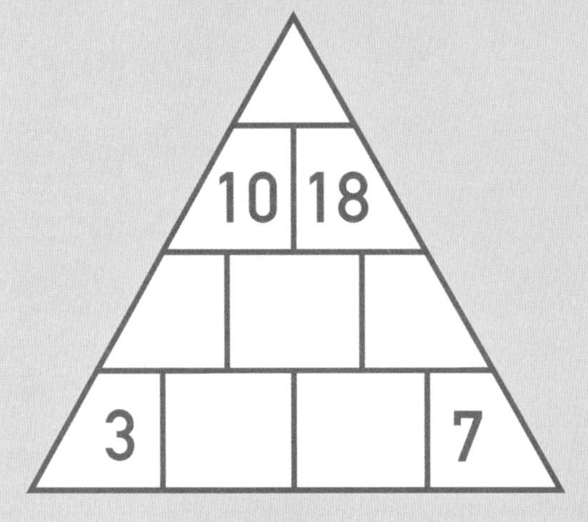


83 ★★ Can you cut this trapezoid into four smaller trapezoids of the same shape?

84 ★★ Place a number (greater than 1) in the middle box by which all the other numbers can be divided without leaving a remainder.

91 52

897 ✎ ---------- 611

351 169

10 MINUTES

**85**★★ Place the tiles into the grid so that (a) the tiles in the first row are the same as the first column, the tiles in the second row are the same as the second column, and so on; (b) each row and column contains three squares of either colour; (c) each row and column contains the numbers 1 to 6 inclusive.

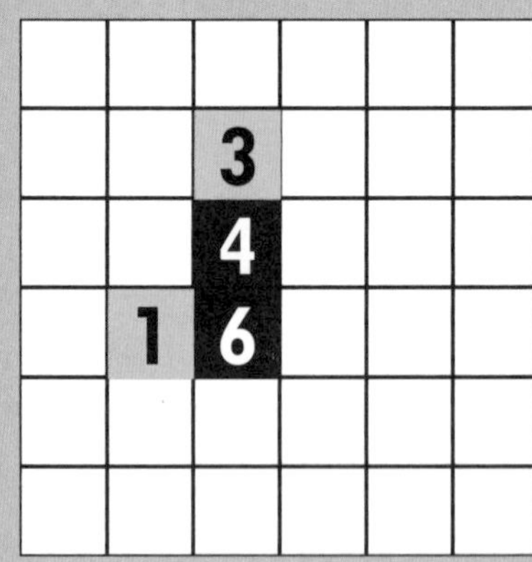

**86**★★★ What number should replace the question mark?

16, 21, 15¼, 18¾, 14½, 16½, 13¾, ?

**87**★★ All of these numbers have something in common except one. Which is it?

25, 36, 41, 49, 64, 81

1 HOUR

## 88★ Don't let this puzzle drive you hopping mad…

(See page 95 for tips on how to do these puzzles.)

Column clues:

| | | | | | | | | | | | | | | |
|---|---|---|---|---|---|---|---|---|---|---|---|---|---|---|
| | | | 2 | 2 | 2 | | | | | | | | | |
| 2 | 1 | 1 | 1 | 1 | 1 | 3 | | | | | 9 | | | |
| 12 | 13 | 8 | 5 | 3 | 4 | 1 | 5 | 6 | 7 | 8 | 1 | 10 | 14 | 7 |

Row clues:

| | | |
|---|---|---|
| | 4 | 8 |
| 1 | 1 | 10 |
| | 1 | 10 |
| | 2 | 9 |
| | 2 | 8 |
| 2 | 1 | 7 |
| | 5 | 6 |
| | 3 | 4 |
| 3 | 2 | 3 |
| | 4 | 2 |
| 4 | 2 | 1 |
| | 6 | 1 |
| | 6 | 1 |
| | 6 | 1 |
| | 2 | 1 |

## 89★★ Don't get taken for a ride with this puzzle!

Column clues:

| | | | | | | | | | | | | | | |
|---|---|---|---|---|---|---|---|---|---|---|---|---|---|---|
| | | | | | | 2 | | | | | | 3 | | |
| | 6 | 9 | 10 | 5 | | 4 | 5 | 5 | 2 | | | 8 | | 2 |
| 4 | 2 | 1 | 1 | 2 | 7 | 2 | 1 | 1 | 2 | 2 | 2 | 1 | 15 | 9 |

Row clues:

| | | | | |
|---|---|---|---|---|
| | | | | 3 |
| | | | | 3 |
| | | | 1 | 2 |
| | | | 2 | 2 |
| | | 3 | 2 | 3 |
| | | 4 | 2 | 4 |
| | | | 6 | 5 |
| | | | 11 | 3 |
| | | | 10 | 3 |
| | | | 8 | 3 |
| | | | 7 | 3 |
| | | 2 | 2 | 3 |
| 1 | 1 | 1 | 1 | 1 |
| 1 | 1 | 1 | 1 | 1 |
| | | 2 | 2 | 2 |

# testing

Get set for the ultimate question-and-answer session. Are you ready to be quizzed on a whole range of subjects? Or can you uncover gaps in someone else's knowledge? To make sure everyone has an equal chance the questions touch on all kinds of topics and vary in difficulty, so the usual star ratings do not apply. Some sections are multiple choice – giving you a 1 in 4 chance of getting it right, even if you haven't got a clue. Other puzzles even offer hidden treasure at the end...

trivia

# warm-up...

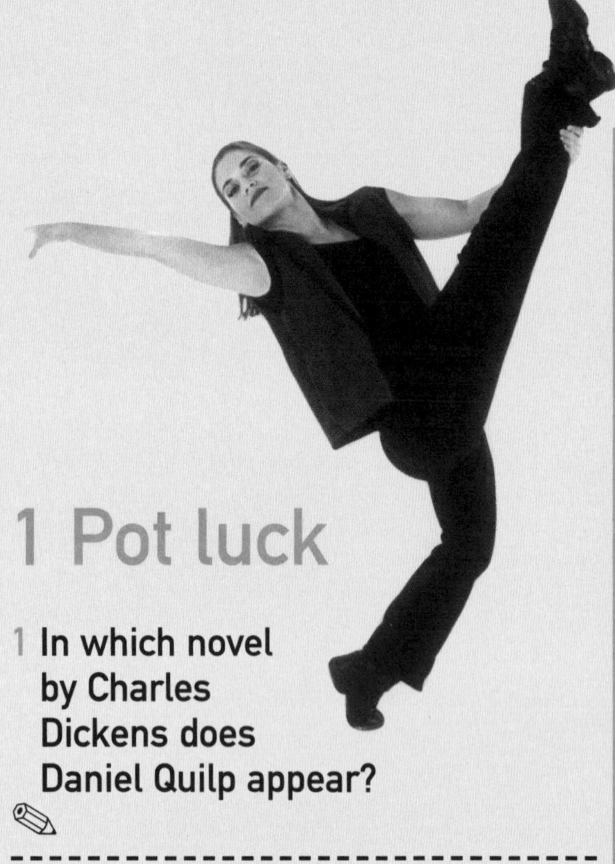

## 1 Pot luck

1 In which novel by Charles Dickens does Daniel Quilp appear?

✎

2 Which singer's surname is Gudmundsdottir?

3 Of which American state is Austin the capital?

4 List the seven colours of the rainbow in alphabetical order.

5 Name the actress who plays Ally McBeal in the eponymous TV show.

6 Who was the second man to set foot on the moon?

7 Which French Impressionist painted the water lilies in his garden at Giverny?

8 What do the initials ABS stand for when applied to cars?

9 Which sport is played by the London Monarchs?

10 Whose mandolin did Louis de Bernières famously write about?

11 In which field are Thierry Mugler and Stella McCartney both well-known?

12 In which year was the Wall Street Crash?

13 Which actor plays the character Brother Cadfael on television?

14 Whose famous last words were: 'I am just going outside, and may be some time'?

15 Who wrote the book *Bridget Jones's Diary*?

16 Which duo comprises Annie Lennox and Dave Stewart?

--------------------------------

17 What was the name of Roy Rogers' horse?

--------------------------------

18 Who on TV played Jeeves to Hugh Laurie's Bertie Wooster?

--------------------------------

19 What is the unit of currency in Greece?

--------------------------------

20 Which flag consists of 12 gold stars on an azure blue background?

--------------------------------

21 What is the second book of the Old Testament?

--------------------------------

22 Who directed the film *Titanic*?

--------------------------------

23 In modern technology, what do the letters DVD stand for?

--------------------------------

24 When Oscar Wilde referred to 'the unspeakable in full pursuit of the uneatable', what was the uneatable?

--------------------------------

25 Where in London would you find the American Embassy?

--------------------------------

26 What is the name of the character played by Helen Worth in the popular soap opera *Coronation Street*?

--------------------------------

27 By what name is Irishman Declan Patrick McManus better known?

--------------------------------

28 In which Shakespeare play do three witches appear?

--------------------------------

29 In Imperial measurement, how many pounds are there in one hundredweight?

----------------

30 Who directed the film *Bread and Roses*?

----------------

Try some more and you'll soon be hooked...

# 2 Topical

1 What is the full name of Madonna's second child?

✎

2 In which county would you find The Belfry, the venue for the 2001 Ryder Cup?

3 Name the former CIA agent who became Transport Commissioner for London.

4 Which fast food chain have Chris Waddle, Stuart Pearce and Gareth Southgate promoted in TV adverts?

5 Whose most recent book is *The White House Connection*?

6 What is Ali G's real name?

7 Who succeeded Peter Mandelson as Secretary of State for Northern Ireland?

8 Whose husband was mauled by a 10-foot Komodo dragon?

9 Who won Best British Group at the 2001 Brit Awards?

10 Which side knocked Manchester United out of the FA cup in January 2001?

11 What was stolen from Bletchley Park and returned to Jeremy Paxman at *Newsnight*?

12 How is the contagious disease *aftosa* better known?

13 How is Thomas Maphother IV better known?

14 Which famous television cook is a director of Norwich City Football Club?

15 Paris elected its first left-wing mayor in March 2001. Can you name him?

# 3 Topical – multiple choice

1 Whom did Pete Sampras beat in the final to become Wimbledon men's champion in 2000?

a Andre Agassi
b Pat Rafter
c Tim Henman
d Vladimir Voltchkov

✎

2 What is George W. Bush's middle name?

a William b Watson
c Washington d Walker

3 Who was the first person in the UK to win £1 million on *Who Wants to Be a Millionaire*?

a Judith Kemp b Judith Kettle
c Judith Keltner d Judith Keppel

4 Who famously announced his intention to resign on 8 June 2001?

a John Prescott b William Hague
c Peter Mandelson d Charles Kennedy

5 When was *2001: A Space Odyssey* first released?

a 1966 b 1967 c 1968 d 1969

6 Robert Ludlum, who died in March 2001, was …

a a novelist b an architect
c a painter d a conductor

7 What was the name of the PR company the Countess of Wessex left in 2001?

a H-RT b R-JH c JH-R d HJ-T

8 Where will the 2002 football World Cup finals be held?

a Korea and Japan
b Japan and Singapore
c Singapore and Malaysia
d Malaysia and Korea

9 Who played Billy Elliot?

a Jamie Draven b Jamie Bell
c Jamie Parker d Jamie Brown

10 Who was the skipper of the ill-fated catamaran *Team Philips*?

a Luke Foss b Dave Boss
c Pete Goss d Nick Ross

11 In March 2001 Puff Daddy was acquitted on charges of possessing guns and bribery. What is the gangsta rapper's real name?

a Sean Combs b Calvin Broadus
c Russell Jones d Earl Simmons

12 Who won the Perrier Award at the 2000 Edinburgh Fringe?

a Dave Gorman b Lee Mack
c Rich Hall d Sean Lock

# 4 Topical

1 Craig David's debut album went straight to No. 1 in the UK charts in August 2000. What was its title?

✎

2 What is advertised on TV as 'a break from the Norm'?

3 Whose latest book is titled *How to Be Good*?

4 Where will the 2004 Olympic Games be held?

5 Which Pacific islands were threatened by an oil spill when the tanker *Jessica* went aground?

6 Which Harriers joined the Football League in 2000?

7 The star is James Gandolfini, the theme song is by Alabama 3 – what's the TV series?

8 Who replaced deposed Slobodan Milosevic as president of Yugoslavia?

9 Who co-wrote the musical *The Beautiful Game* with Andrew Lloyd-Webber?

10 How did market-trader Steven Thoburn's bananas break European Union law?

11 Assassinated Laurent Kabila was president of which country?

12 Who played Professor Higgins to Martine McCutcheon's Eliza Doolittle?

13 Which Second Division team reached the semi-finals of the FA Cup?

14 Who won a landslide victory to become prime minister of Israel in February 2001?

15 Name the internet music trading site founded by Shawn Fanning.

## 5 Topical – multiple choice

1 Who won the women's singles final at the 2001 Australian Open?
a Martina Hingis b Jennifer Capriati
c Lindsay Davenport
d Venus Williams

✎

2 Who shot Phil Mitchell?
a Lisa b Mark c Steve d Dan

3 Alberto Fujimori resigned as president of which country?
a Chile b Japan c Fiji d Peru

4 What was Britain's Tate Modern building used for originally?
a armaments factory
b shopping centre c power station
d music hall

5 In which Indian state was the huge Kumbh Mela festival held?
a Punjab b Kerala c Uttar Pradesh
d Gujarat

6 Who sang the UK's Christmas Number One single in 2000?
a Cliff Richard b Eminem
c Spice Girls d Bob the Builder

7 Who stood down as US Secretary of Labor amid controversy?
a Linda Chavez b Elaine Chao
c Karen Gould d Gail Norton

8 Who wrote *English Passengers*?
a Lorna Sage b Matthew Kneale
c Zadie Smith d Will Self

9 Who succeeded his father as president of Syria in 2000?
a Aziz al Saud b Martin Bashir
c Bashar Assad
d Mohammad Khatami

10 Who is chairman of the US Federal Reserve?
a Jeff Greenblum b Richard Greenbaum c Alan Greenspan
d Harvey Greenberg

11 Which Spice had a solo hit with 'What Took You So Long'?
a Sporty b Scary c Posh d Baby

12 A High Court judge ruled that the 'internet twins' should be returned to which state?
a Missouri b Minnesota
c Mississippi d Montana

**6** In this puzzle you have to find the correct X that marks where the treasure lies. Begin at the START at the top of the puzzle. Decide whether the first statement is TRUE or FALSE, then follow the T or F arrow accordingly. Correct choices take you towards the treasure, wrong answers take you down blind alleys. When you finally arrive at an X, that is your chosen destination. Now turn to the answers section to see if you arrived at the correct X.

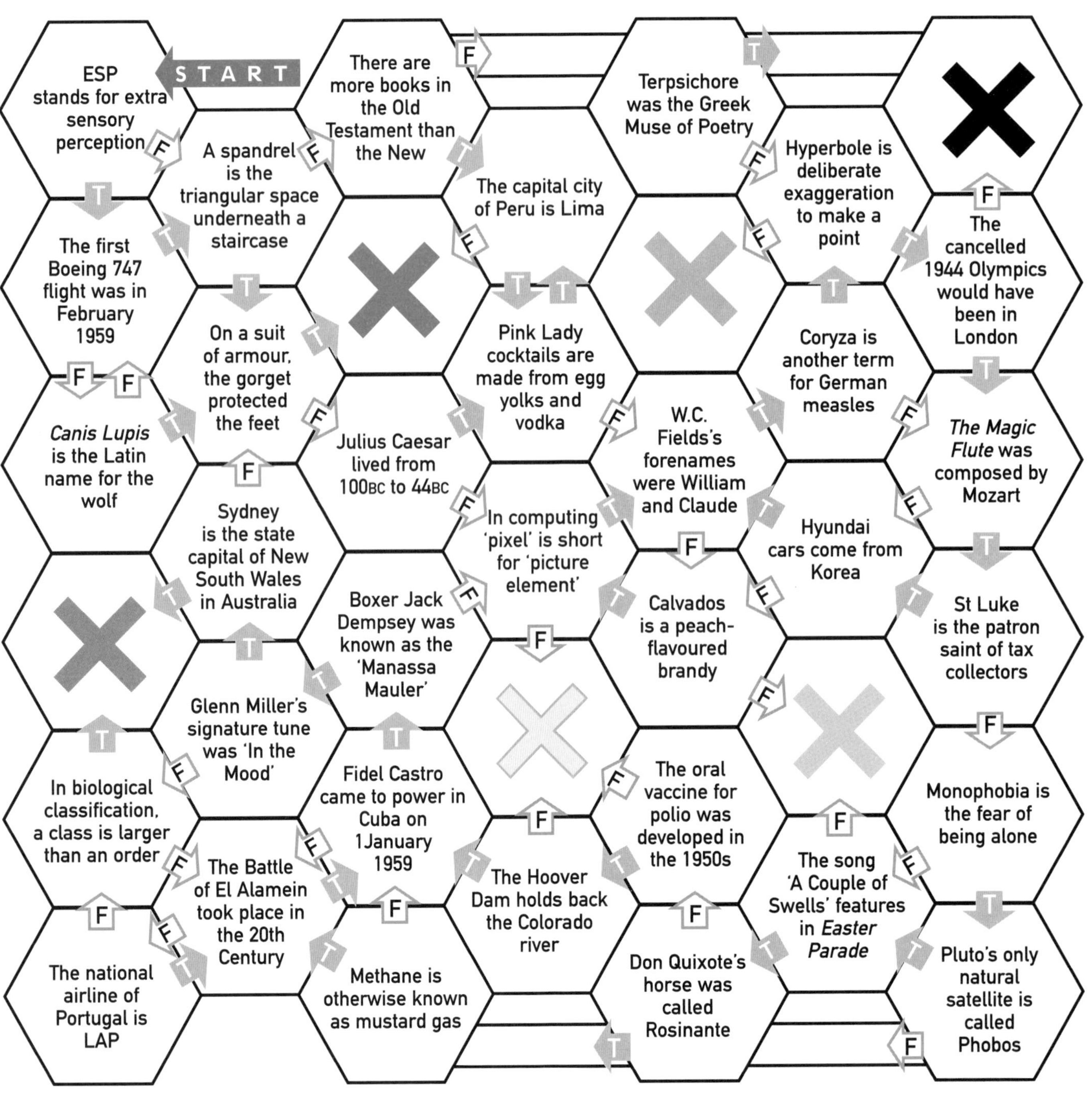

## 7 Can you tell true from false? Circle the correct answers...

1 The average adult body contains about 8 litres of blood.
TRUE FALSE

2 Toenails grow half as fast as fingernails.
TRUE FALSE

3 Colour blindness does not occur in women.
TRUE FALSE

4 The trachea is a bone in the leg.
TRUE FALSE

5 The tibia is a bone in the arm.
TRUE FALSE

6 Eating too many carrots can cause yellow skin.
TRUE FALSE

7 Women have more ribs than men.
TRUE FALSE

8 The spine consists of 33 vertebrae.
TRUE FALSE

9 Human perspiration has no smell.
TRUE FALSE

10 The tooth is the only part of the body that cannot repair itself.
TRUE FALSE

## 8 Another set of true/false questions. Circle the correct answers...

1 Cara, Desirée and Pentland Javelin are varieties of apple.
TRUE FALSE

2 Margarine was invented in the 19th century.
TRUE FALSE

3 The so-called Jerusalem artichoke is in fact the tuber of a sunflower.
TRUE FALSE

4 You cannot make white wine from black grapes.
TRUE FALSE

5 When you buy fresh oysters, they should still be alive.
TRUE FALSE

6 A dish that is called Florentine is made with cheese.
TRUE FALSE

7 Nasturtium flowers are edible.
TRUE FALSE

8 Beaujolais is made mainly from the Cabernet Sauvignon grape.
TRUE FALSE

9 The kiwi fruit was originally called the New Zealand gooseberry.
TRUE FALSE

10 Grappa is produced in Mexico.
TRUE FALSE

## 9 True or false? Circle your answer to each of these regal posers.

1 King George I of England barely spoke English.
TRUE FALSE

2 Henry VIII had three of his six wives beheaded.
TRUE FALSE

3 Elizabeth II was the first British monarch born in the 20th century.
TRUE FALSE

4 The dictator Franco named Prince Juan Carlos king of Spain.
TRUE FALSE

5 Queen Victoria was christened Alexandra Victoria.
TRUE FALSE

6 Louis XIV reigned in France for 72 years.
TRUE FALSE

7 Anne Boleyn, Queen Elizabeth I's mother, had six fingers on each hand.
TRUE FALSE

8 Haile Selassie claimed to be a direct descendant of King Solomon and the Queen of Sheba.
TRUE FALSE

## 10 How good are you on English literature? Here are some quotes and questions to test your knowledge. Circle your answers.

1 'Reader, I married him' is the last line of *Sense and Sensibility.*
TRUE FALSE

2 'Earth has not anything to show more fair' is the first line of Wordsworth's 'Sonnet Composed on Westminster Bridge'.
TRUE FALSE

3 Lewis Carroll's *Through the Looking Glass* was published before *Alice's Adventures in Wonderland.*
TRUE FALSE

4 Charles Dickens originally wrote *The Pickwick Papers* as 'Boz'.
TRUE FALSE

5 Tennyson wrote the couplet: 'Tis better to have loved and lost, Than never to have lost at all.
TRUE FALSE

6 'If music be the food of love, play on' is the first line of Shakespeare's *A Midsummer Night's Dream.*
TRUE FALSE

7 Rudyard Kipling wrote a poem called 'How the Camel got his hump'.
TRUE FALSE

8 Sherlock Holmes never said 'Elementary, my dear Watson' in any Conan Doyle story.
TRUE FALSE

Can you crack the safe? In each case, your first task is to decide which of the 14 statements below are false. Then shade out the areas on the combination lock that share the same letters as the false statements (so if you think statement E is false, shade out area E). The remaining segments will give you the digital numbered combination required.

## 11

A The lowest-pitched brass instrument is the tuba

B Polygraph is another name for a lie detector

C The New York Yankees have won the most baseball World Series titles

D Eddy Merckx was a famous cyclist

E The White and Blue Niles meet at Alexandria

F *The Minute Waltz* and *Cat's Waltz* were composed by Chopin

G A male rabbit is called a buck

H Chives, garlic and onions all belong to the rose family

I The word 'biscuit' is a literal translation for 'baked twice'

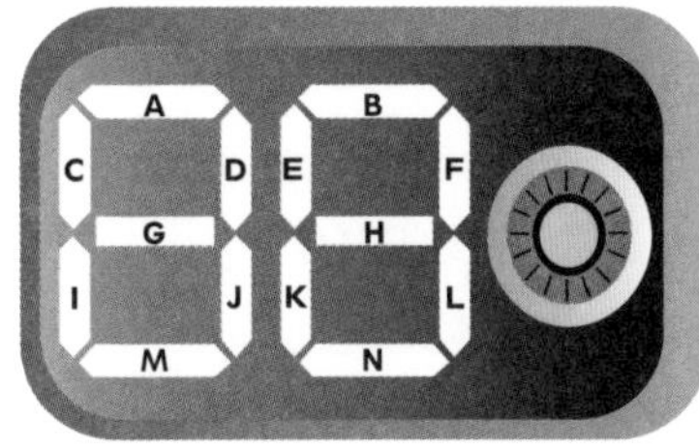


J Libra is the only sign of the zodiac represented by an inanimate object

K It takes 23 minutes for the blood of a human being to circulate once round the body

L The month of March is named after the Roman god of war

M Franklin D. Roosevelt was the only US President elected for four terms

N Moscow stands on the Volga river

## 12

A The lowest region of the atmosphere is the ionosphere

B The musical *Sweet Charity* was composed by Cy Coleman

C The Olympic event that lasts the longest time is the 50km walk

D Electrical capacitance is measured in farads

E The national symbol of Australia is the wattle

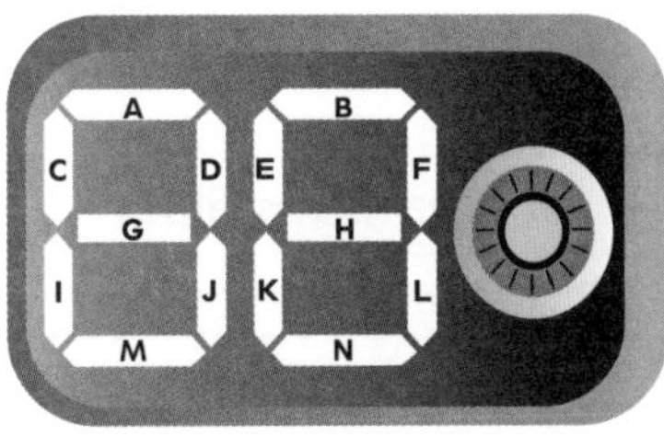


F The *X Files* TV series was created by Chris Bellinger

G 'Derv' stands for 'diesel-engined road vehicle'

H Granth is the Holy book of Sikhism

I The highest vertebra in the human body is the coccyx

J The flag of Nepal is not rectangular

K On TV, Harvey Freeman played the role of newspaperman Lou Grant

L An *entrechat* is a ballet jump where the heels are struck together

M Narita Airport is found in Sydney

N 2002 is the Chinese Year of the Horse

# 13 The Bible – multiple choice

1 How many books are there in the Old Testament?
a 28 b 35 c 39 d 43

2 According to Genesis, what did God create on the fourth day?
a the land and the seas
b the sun, moon and stars
c fish and fowl
d beasts of the earth

3 On which road did the good Samaritan do his good deed?
a Galilee to Nazareth b Tyre to Sidon
c Egypt to Canaan
d Jerusalem to Jericho

4 Which Psalm begins: 'The Lord is my shepherd; I shall not want'?
a 21st b 23rd c 25th d 27th

5 When was David anointed King of Israel?
a when he was a shepherd boy
b when he killed Goliath
c when he played his harp for Saul
d when Samuel died

6 How many sons did Noah have?
a two b three c four d six

7 To which brothers did Jesus say: 'I will make you fishers of men'?
a Peter and Andrew
b Thomas and Matthew
c James and John
d Paul and Barnabas

8 Who fed on locusts and wild honey in the wilderness?
a Moses b Joseph
c John the Baptist d Jesus

9 Who had Shadrach, Meshach and Abed-nego cast into the furnace?
a Nathan b Naboth
c Nehemiah d Nebuchadnezzar

10 How many days had Lazarus been dead before Jesus brought him back to life?
a one b two c three d four

11 Which creatures first plagued the Egyptians?
a locusts b frogs c fleas d snakes

12 What fed the five thousand?
a five loaves and five fishes
b two loaves and five fishes
c five loaves and two fishes
d four loaves and two fishes

# 14 Specialists – multiple choice

1 What, traditionally, would a cordwainer make?

a candles b shoes c furniture d beer

2 What does an oenologist study?

a insects b rings on trees c wine d comets

3 What does a lexicographer make?

a water-colours b crossword puzzles c parchments d dictionaries

4 What does a pediatrician specialize in?

a feet b children c teeth d old people

5 Which of these is another name for a clockmaker?

a horologist b topologist c sidewinder d chironomer

6 What did a costermonger originally sell from his barrow?

a leather b fish c apples d nails

7 In what does a pisciculturalist specialize?

a cutting hair b painting murals c growing potatoes d rearing fish

8 Where does a stevedore work?

a docks b farm c factory d mine

9 Which of these would interest a potamologist?

a molluscs b rivers c horses d root vegetables

10 What does a cartographer make?

a playing cards b cabinets c cartoons d maps

11 Which of these is another name for a dentist?

a odontologist b deontologist c otologist d dendrologist

12 What would a wainwright have made?

a harnesses b armour c wagons d pottery

# 15 Olympic heroes – multiple choice

1 Which of these athletes collected five medals at the Sydney Olympics?
a Marion Jones b Denise Lewis
c Lorraine Graham
d Pauline Davis-Thompson

2 In which event did Steve Redgrave win his first Olympic gold medal?
a coxless four b coxed four
c coxless pair d coxed pair

3 Only one British woman has competed in five Olympics. Can you name her?
a Dorothy Tyler b Liz McColgan
c Tessa Sanderson d Mary Rand

4 What nationality is the 2000 Olympics marathon winner Gezahgne Abera?
a Ethiopian b Kenyan
c Moroccan d Tunisian

5 In which event did Sebastian Coe win gold in two successive Olympics?
a 800 metres b 1500 metres
c 1 mile d 5000 metres

6 Which nation won their first ever Olympic gold medal in the 2000 soccer final?
a Cameroon b Honduras
c Korea d Senegal

7 In which year did Cassius Clay become Olympic Heavyweight Champion?
a 1956 b 1960 c 1964 d 1968

8 Who was the first athlete to win gold medals in the same event in four consecutive Olympics?
a Carl Lewis b Daley Thompson
c Sergei Bubka d Al Oerter

9 Who was the oldest man ever (at 32) to win the Olympic gold for the 100 metres?
a Donovan Bailey b Linford Christie
c Jim Hines d Frankie Fredericks

10 How old was the Romanian gymnast Nadia Comaneci when she made Olympic history by scoring seven 'perfect 10s'?
a 14 b 15 c 16 d 17

# 16 Classical music – multiple choice

1 How many symphonies did Beethoven write?

a six b eight c nine d eleven

✎

2 Which Verdi opera includes the 'Chorus of the Hebrew Slaves'?

a *Tosca* b *Nabucco* c *Aida* d *La Traviata*

3 Who wrote *The Sorcerer's Apprentice*?

a Dukas b Stravinsky c Mendelssohn d Saint-Saëns

4 What nationality was Holst?

a British b Polish c Austrian d Norwegian

5 Which orchestra was founded by Sir Thomas Beecham?

a Hallé Orchestra
b Royal Philharmonic Orchestra
c London Symphony Orchestra
d BBC Symphony Orchestra

6 What does the word '*fine*' mean on a musical score?

a play finely b play quietly c repeat d the end

7 Which Mozart opera has Tamino as its hero?

a *Cosí fan Tutte* b *The Magic Flute* c *Don Giovanni* d *The Marriage of Figaro*

8 In which city was Handel's *Messiah* first performed?

a Edinburgh b Cardiff c London d Dublin

9 With which instrument was Pablo Casals associated?

a guitar b violin c cello d clarinet

10 Who wrote the *Brandenburg Concertos*?

a Handel b Bach c Mozart d Haydn

11 What is a galliard?

a a dance b a choral work c a wind instrument d a music stand

12 Who wrote the *Minute Waltz*?

a Chopin b Schubert c Brahms d Liszt

# 17 Wildlife – multiple choice

1 What is a young seal called?
a cub b pup c kid d wallet

✎

2 Which island is home to lemurs?
a Fiji b Mauritius c Madagascar d Sri Lanka

3 Macaroni, rockhopper, jackass and gentoo are all species of what?
a crab b frog c goat d penguin

4 Which of these is not a bird?
a jerboa b shrike c bulbul d kite

5 Which creature lives in a sett?
a hare b stoat c badger d otter

6 Which is the largest?
a grizzly bear b polar bear c brown bear d black bear

7 How many limbs has a lobster?
a six b eight c ten d twelve

8 A leveret is a young…
a hare b salmon c donkey d monkey

9 Which species has the longest tongue of any mammal?
a African elephant b grey kangaroo c raccoon d giraffe

10 Which of these big cats is not found in the wild in Asia?
a lion b leopard c jaguar d tiger

11 What sort of creature is a bongo?
a Caribbean bird b African antelope c Pacific fish d North American snake

12 Name the largest fish in the sea.
a great white shark b killer whale c whale shark d manta ray

13 What does 'rhinoceros' mean?
a leather skin b large feet c river horse d nose horn

14 What is a termite?
a beetle b ant c caterpillar d worm

15 Where did the dodo live before it became extinct?
a Mauritius b Madagascar c Sri Lanka d Fiji

**18** Answer the clues to find 13 answers. These letters can then be transferred into the main grid to give you a showbusiness quotation.

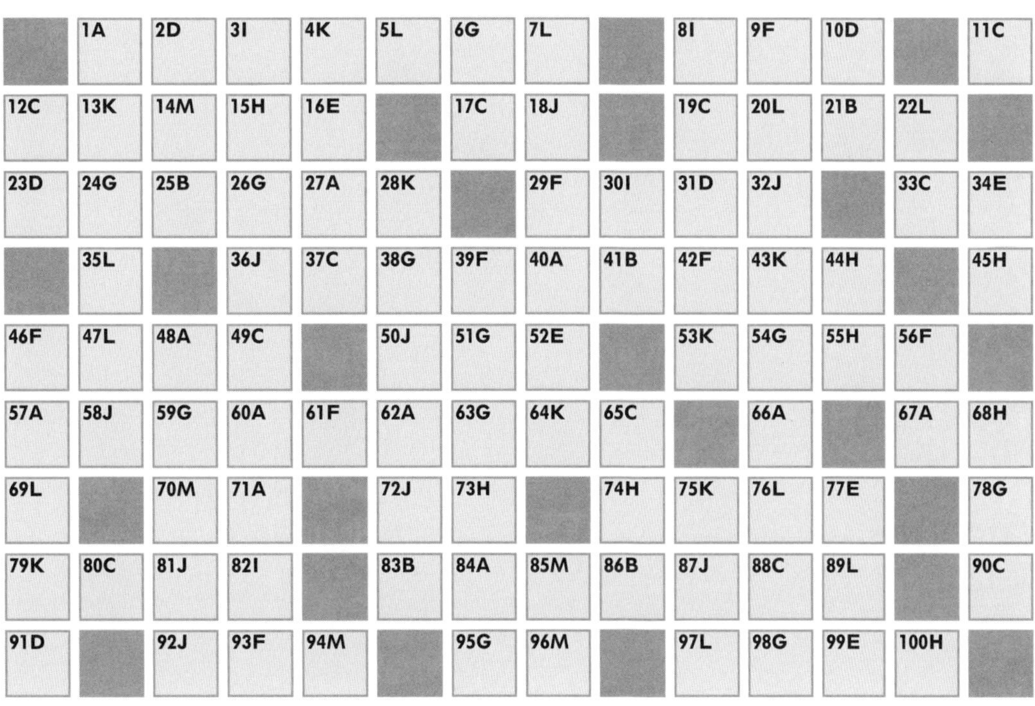

| | 1A | 2D | 3I | 4K | 5L | 6G | 7L | | 8I | 9F | 10D | | 11C |
|---|---|---|---|---|---|---|---|---|---|---|---|---|---|
| 12C | 13K | 14M | 15H | 16E | | 17C | 18J | | 19C | 20L | 21B | 22L | |
| 23D | 24G | 25B | 26G | 27A | 28K | | 29F | 30I | 31D | 32J | | 33C | 34E |
| | 35L | | 36J | 37C | 38G | 39F | 40A | 41B | 42F | 43K | 44H | | 45H |
| 46F | 47L | 48A | 49C | | 50J | 51G | 52E | | 53K | 54G | 55H | 56F | |
| 57A | 58J | 59G | 60A | 61F | 62A | 63G | 64K | 65C | | 66A | | 67A | 68H |
| 69L | | 70M | 71A | | 72J | 73H | | 74H | 75K | 76L | 77E | | 78G |
| 79K | 80C | 81J | 82I | | 83B | 84A | 85M | 86B | 87J | 88C | 89L | | 90C |
| 91D | | 92J | 93F | 94M | | 95G | 96M | | 97L | 98G | 99E | 100H | |

A Undermine the government — 1 66 67 62   40 84 60 48 57 71 27

B What a footballer does for a living — 21 41 83 25 86

C An enacted law — 80 37 65 17 12 19 88 33 90 11 49

D Changing positions on a chessboard — 23 2 31 10 91

E It usually does this in winter — 52 77 34 99 16

F Vigorous and fresh — 56 46 93 61 9 42 39 29

G A detested object — 24 78 95 59 26 6 38 51 63 98 54

H Showing signs of much use — 74 68 55 44 - 45 73 15 100

I Small dogs used by children! — 8 30 82 3

J The most gruesome — 36 81 58 92 72 50 32 18 87

K Having an effect upon — 4 53 43 13 75 79 64 28

L Authorized, in accordance with law — 89 76 7 20 69 5 47 35 97 22

M High in calories — 96 14 70 94 85

# 19 The British Isles

1 Which is the largest lake in Great Britain?

✎

2 What is the County Town of Cumbria?

3 Place these four British rivers in order of length (longest first): Thames, Severn, Avon, Clyde.

4 In which county is the most northerly point in Ireland?

5 Edinburgh and Aberdeen have three each, Dundee and Oban have two each, Inverness and Stirling both have one each. What are they?

6 Which is the second largest city in the UK after London?

7 In which county is Stansted Airport?

8 What is the name of Bristol's main railway station?

9 Which is larger in area, Scotland or the Republic of Ireland?

10 Which of these is not a National Park: Exmoor, Grampians, Brecon Beacons, New Forest?

11 In which county will you find Stonehenge?

12 What body of water lies between Wales and Anglesey?

13 Which of these English towns does *not* lie on the River Thames: Henley, Oxford, Reading, Swindon?

14 On which lake does the town of Keswick stand?

15 Which canal runs through Wigan?

# 20 The wide, wide world

1 Can you list the seven continents in order of size (largest first)?

✎

2 In which ocean are the Seychelles?

3 The city of Firenze is better known in English as … what?

4 Which of these is not one of the Leeward Islands: Antigua, Guadeloupe, St Kitts, St Lucia?

5 Which river flows through the capital of the USA?

6 Which European country name translates as 'Eastern kingdom'?

7 In which country is the Ngorongoro Crater?

8 Arrange these three city-to-city flights in order of distance, longest first: London–Moscow, New York City–Seattle, Sydney–Perth (Australia).

9 Name the six states in the north-east USA that make up New England.

10 The Nepalese call it Sagarmatha, Tibetans call it Chomolongma. How do we know it?

11 In which country is Arnhem Land found?

12 How many time zones are there in China?

13 If you were in Molokai, in which country would you be?

14 Which Caribbean country is made up of 700 islands, the largest of which is New Providence?

15 Which country's capital city means 'Red Hero' in English?

# 21 Sport

1 Which is the quicker swimming stroke – butterfly or backstroke?

2 Anchorage to Nome, 1,049 miles. What is the sport?

3 Who lost his first race in ten years, to Danny Harris in 1987?

4 Name the three competition swords used in fencing.

5 Who was the first tennis player to win the Grand Slam twice?

6 In which sport might a fletcher be useful?

7 In which sport is Juha Kankkunen a four-times world champion?

8 Cross country, swimming, shooting. The other two Modern Pentathlon events?

9 What nationality is the world's most capped international rugby union player?

10 Can you name the three types of Grand Slam tennis court surfaces?

11 Which is faster over a distance of 500 metres, running or speed skating?

12 What are the NFL teams of New Orleans, Cincinnati and Cleveland?

13 Which country produces the most top polo players?

14 Which racket sport is the fastest – squash, tennis or badminton?

15 Which sport is named after the home of the Duke of Beaufort?

# 22 Sport

1 How many players contest a polo match?

✎

2 How old was Tracy Austin when she won the US Open tennis championships in 1979?

3 How many miles long is the Grand National horse race?

4 How many times did Red Rum win the Grand National?

5 How wide in inches is an ice hockey puck?

6 What is the highest 'shot out' in darts?

7 What is the least number of darts required to score 501?

8 What red number was favoured by Grand Prix star Nigel Mansell?

9 How many reds are on the table at the start of a snooker frame?

10 How many times did golfer Jack Nicklaus win the US Masters?

11 What is par on the world's longest golf hole?

12 Within 10 metres, what was the longest ever hole-in-one?

13 How many seconds must a cowboy stay on a bull to score at a rodeo?

14 What is the highest number of goals scored by one team in an NHL hockey game?

15 How tall in feet and inches is NBA giant Magic Johnson?

# 23 Classical music

1 What does the opera style *bel canto* translate as?

✎

2 Who wrote the operas *Peter Grimes* and *Billy Budd*?

3 Hungarian-born conductor Georg Solti has won 31 of which music awards?

4 Which opera supplied the theme tune to TV's *Lone Ranger*?

5 At which sporting event did the Three Tenors record *In Concert*?

6 What is the literal translation of the ballet instruction *fouetté*?

7 Which opera house, opened in 1966, is the world's largest?

8 Which celebrated dancer was strangled by her scarf in 1927?

9 The Japanese Kimigayo is the oldest surviving example of what?

10 Da Ponte wrote the words for *Così Fan Tutte*. Who wrote the music?

11 Under what name did Helen Porter Mitchell achieve worldwide success?

12 Who received an 80-minute ovation for his Otello in Vienna in 1991?

13 Beethoven's *Eroica* was dedicated to which military hero?

14 What instrument does the orchestra leader play?

15 What nationality was Dame Margot Fonteyn?

Can you crack open the safe? In each case, your first task is to decide which of the 14 statements below are false. Then shade out the areas on the combination lock that share the same letters as the false statements (so if you think statement E is false, shade out area E). The remaining segments will give you the digital numbered combination required.

## 24

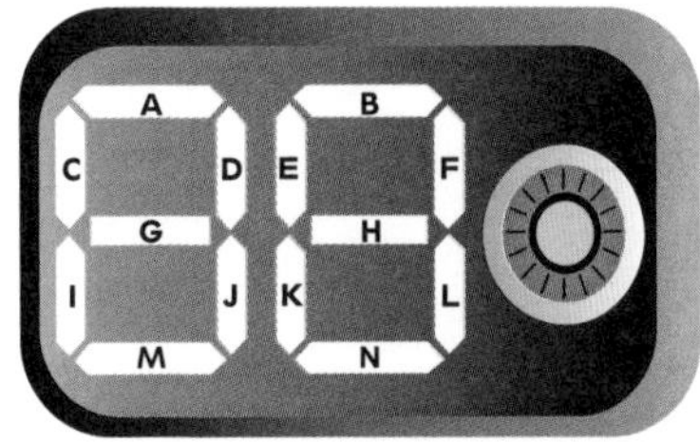


A Bo Diddley was named after an African musical instrument

B Phil Collins played in both the London and Philadelphia Live Aid concerts

C The Beatles' first US record label was Parlophone

D The members of Pet Shop Boys are Neil Tennant and Chris Lowe

E Celine Dion won the Eurovision Song Contest for Switzerland

F Lauryn Hill is the lead singer of the Fugees

G The Carly Simon song 'You're So Vain' is allegedly about Warren Beatty

H *Achtung Baby* and *The Joshua Tree* are albums by U2

I 'American Pie' is a song about the death of Billie Holiday

J Max Yasgur owned the land for the Woodstock pop festival

K The term 'heavy metal' comes from the William Burroughs novel *Neuromancer*

L 'Side Saddle', 'Snow Coach' and 'Roulette' were all hits for pianist Russ Conway

M Cher's 'Shoop Shoop Song' featured in the film *Mermaids*

N The subject of the song 'Hey Jude' is Julian Lennon

## 25

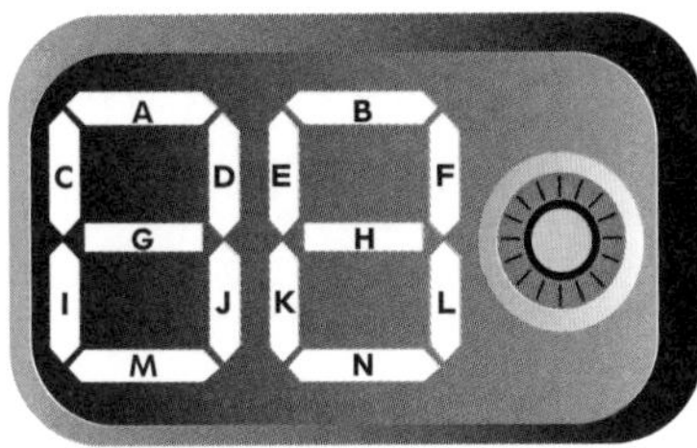


A There are two main patterns of jazz music, called 12-bar and 32-bar

B In typical jazz, musicians improvise new melodies around fixed chord progressions

C Boogie-woogie was a style of piano-playing developed in the 1920s

D Duke Ellington led a band at New York's Cotton Club during the 1900s

E Pianist Dave Courtney composed the jazz standard 'Take Five'

F Count Basie's band originally assembled in Kansas City

G Lionel Hampton was a trend-setting player of the vibraphone in the late 1930s

H Ivie Anderson and Mildred Bailey were famous jazz singers

I Charlie Parker became the leader of a 1940s style known as bebop

J Trumpeter Miles Davis was a protégé of Charlie Parker

K Zoot Sims and Stan Getz played the xylophone

L Pianist Chick Corea's group was called *Return to Forever*

M Joni Mitchell's 1979 album *Mingus* was a tribute to bassist Charlie Mingus

N Nat 'King' Cole was born in 1919 in Montgomery, the state capital of Alabama

# 26 Musical instruments

1 What do you call a piano that plays itself?

2 What was the first name of violin-maker Stradivari?

3 What word connects a chicken with a percussionist?

4 Which keyboard instrument plucks its strings?

5 Which piano-maker was founded in New York in 1853?

6 Which rustic wind instrument is also known as a syrinx?

7 Which tiny flute shares its name with a bean?

8 From what metal are cymbals usually made?

9 Which instrument has varieties called Celtic, Welsh triple and Bardic?

10 The largest musical instrument in the world is in Atlantic City, New Jersey. What is it?

11 What do you call a xylophone that has steel bars instead of wooden ones?

12 What instrument is associated with 'The Boogie Woogie Boy of Company B'?

13 Which bell cast in the 1850s weighs 13.8 tonnes and rings in E natural?

14 Which rock guitarist habitually played his Fender upside down?

15 Which bass brass instrument started life as a bombardon in 1820?

# 27 World music

1 Which musical instrument is the symbol of Ireland?

2 What is the Australian Aboriginal name for a bamboo trumpet that requires circular breathing?

3 The Original Dixieland Jazz Band hailed from which US city?

4 Who wrote the French torch song 'La Vie en Rose'?

5 What South American instrument comprises a gourd full of seeds on a stick?

6 In which country would you be most likely to hear a Mariachi band?

7 Which Indian musician founded the School of Indian Music in Los Angeles?

8 ...and what do you call the 19-stringed Indian lute he famously plays?

9 Which folk instrument comprises bellows, keys and a carrying strap?

10 How many strings has a Russian balalaika?

11 Which traditional Moorish dance music has *jondo* and *chico* styles?

12 Which scandalous variety theatre opened in Paris in 1869?

13 Which Celtic reed instrument has a chanter and a bag?

14 Where did Calypso and Steel Band originate?

15 In Fiji, what shell popularly makes the best trumpet?

# 28 Pop music

1 Who was the first Australian solo artist to top the UK charts?

✎

2 Which brothers wrote 'Chain Reaction' for Diana Ross?

3 Which Abba song was their only US Number 1?

4 Who is Nat 'King' Cole's singer daughter?

5 Which movie featured the Whitney Houston tune 'I Will Always Love You'?

6 Which country produced both Ace of Base and Roxette?

7 Which Beatle had solo hits with 'You're Sixteen' and 'It Don't Come Easy'?

8 In which year did The Beatles fill the top five positions on the US billboard chart?

9 The film *Breakfast at Tiffany's* gave us which Oscar-winning tune?

10 Who was 'The King of Swing' and what was his instrument?

11 Which album entered the US album chart in 1973 and didn't leave it again until 1988?

12 A James Bond theme tune was sung by Scottish singer Sheena Easton. Which one?

13 Can you name the 1986 Prince tune covered by Tom Jones in 1988?

14 If you don't step on his shoes, what could you do to Elvis Presley's face?

15 What was Spice Girl Mel B, briefly, before she became Mel B again?

## 29 In the pipeline

**Decide which instrument (from the seven listed below) each musician was best known for playing. Then draw the corresponding symbol in the appropriate numbered square. For example, question 5 has already been done for you (John Williams usually played the guitar). Correctly repeating this for the other 19 squares will show you how the pipe ends connect together in pairs. The three pipes never join but may cross over other pipes.**

1 Ronnie Scott
2 Pablo Casals
3 Louis Armstrong
4 Paganini
5 John Williams
6 Thelonius Monk
7 Yehudi Menuhin
8 Julian Bream
9 Charlie Parker
10 Johnny Dankworth
11 Jacqueline du Pré
12 Stephane Grappelli
13 Nigel Kennedy
14 Glenn Miller
15 Count Basie
16 Vanessa Mae
17 Tommy Dorsey
18 Duke Ellington
19 Miles Davis
20 Wynton Marsalis

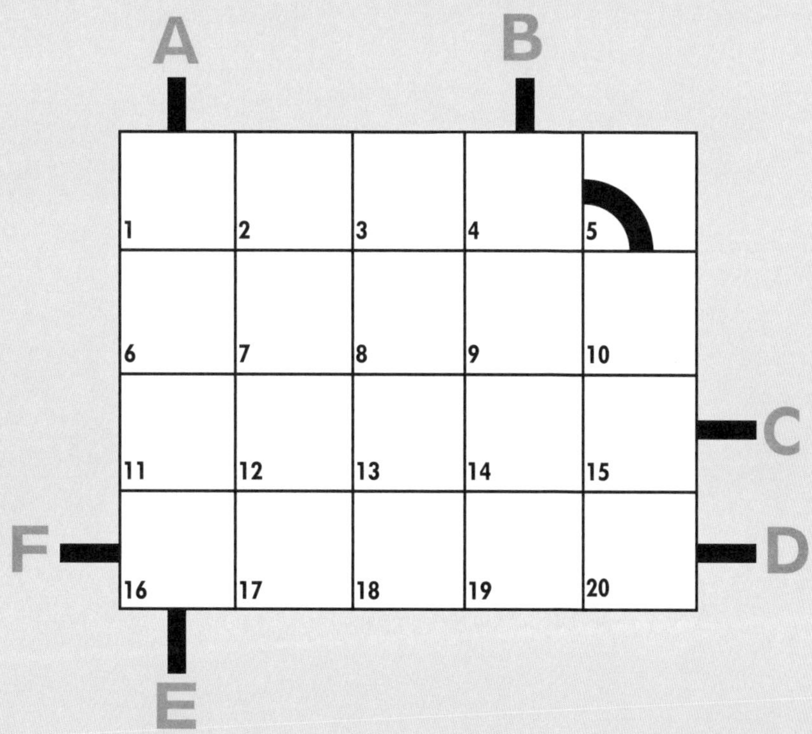

# 30 Science

1 Which chemical element forms both coal and diamonds?

✎

2 Why did a sheep born in 1997 in Scotland and named 'Dolly' become famous?

3 Who was the first scientist to split the atom?

4 Where in the human body would you find the ulna?

5 Why is it easier to stay afloat in the sea than in a swimming pool?

6 Which surgeon performed the first human heart transplant?

7 What is the name of the laboratory module on the International Space Station?

8 Why do sounds echo in an empty room?

9 What is a theodolite used for?

10 What is the difference between incandescence and phosphorescence?

11 What are the two main elements forming the sun?

12 Who invented the rubber pneumatic (air-filled) tyre?

13 An inert gas that does not burn when it gets hot is used instead of air inside light bulbs, to prevent the filament from burning up. What is it called?

14 What was the name of the first space shuttle, and what was it named after?

15 What do delta waves on an electroencephalogram suggest?

# 31 Nature

1 What do zebra stripes and human fingerprints have in common?

✎

2 What proportion of the human body is made up of water?

3 Why are flamingoes pink?

4 What type of animal is the Australian koala?

5 What is the term used for an animal born without any of the pigment melanin that gives colour to skin, fur and feathers?

6 What is the group name for a gang of killer whales hunting in a pack?

7 Which fish can climb trees?

8 An extract of which plant was first used to treat malaria?

9 What use are silvery scales to a fish?

10 Which part of their body do snakes and lizards use to detect smell?

11 The skin of which marine creature is so rough that at one time it was used as sandpaper?

12 What is a wapiti?

13 Unlike bony fish, cartilaginous fish do not possess a swim-bladder. What effect does this have on them?

14 What is the name of the pungent liquid secreted by ants and now synthesized as a preservative?

15 Which bird can fly backwards and hover like a helicopter?

# 32 Books

1 What is Gustave Flaubert's most famous work, featuring a character named Emma?

2 What is the name of the younger boy who hero-worships Harry Potter in the J.K. Rowling series?

3 Which Jane Austen novel featured sisters of opposing temperament called Elinor and Marianne Dashwood?

4 In the F. Scott Fitzgerald novel *The Great Gatsby*, who does Gatsby attempt to woo?

5 Which Roald Dahl book has a father and son who go and poach pheasants?

6 Robert James Waller wrote *The Bridges of Madison County*. What was the title of his second novel?

7 In which novel does Shermann McCoy meet his downfall?

8 Who wrote *All Quiet on the Western Front*?

9 Which dreadful experience shaped Primo Levi's work?

10 Who created the character of Chief Inspector Wexford?

11 The protagonist of which acclaimed 1965 novel was called Nicholas Urfe?

12 J.M. Coetzee's 1986 novel *Foe* is a re-working of what?

13 Who wrote the novel *A House for Mr Biswas*?

14 Which writer lost his job at the Prague Film School and had his books removed from libraries when the Russians invaded?

15 Count Leo Tolstoy experienced what penalty as a result of his religious beliefs?

# 33 The arts

1 Which Shakespeare character speaks the immortal line: 'To be or not to be, that is the question'?

2 Which Edward Lear nonsense poem features characters who 'went to sea in a sieve'?

3 Which Greek poet wrote the epic poems *The Iliad* and *The Odyssey*?

4 The Italian poet Dante Alighieri devoted his major works to which woman who was the early love of his life?

5 Which English playwright wrote *The Birthday Party*, *The Dumb Waiter* and *The Lover*?

6 On which set of German epic poems was the story of Wagner's *Ring* cycle operas based?

7 Which American wrote a poem about suicide that begins 'Razors pain you' and ends 'You might as well live'?

8 Which famous Russian ballet dancer was renowned for the role of Petrushka?

9 Who directed the film of Boris Pasternak's novel *Doctor Zhivago*?

10 Which poem by Alfred, Lord Tennyson, begins: 'On either side the river lie long fields of barley and of rye...'?

11 Which 20th-century dramatist pioneered the 'alienation effect' in Western theatre?

12 On what set of poems is the Hindu religion based?

13 Rabindranath Tagore was the first Asian winner of which prize?

14 Why was Brendan Behan imprisoned in 1939?

15 What do Anton Chekhov and British music director Jonathan Miller have in common?

# 34 Art

1 Who illustrated both *The Wind in the Willows* and *Winnie the Pooh*?

✎

2 What is a fresco?

3 What was the first name of the sculptor Rodin?

4 With which artistic movement are the painters Monet, Manet, Renoir and Cézanne associated?

5 Who painted *The Birth of Venus*?

6 Who painted *Guernica* for the Spanish Pavilion at the Exposition Universelle, Paris, in 1937?

7 Which 20th-century American artist was most famous for his *Saturday Evening Post* covers?

8 The German artist Hans Holbein was court painter to which English monarch?

9 Which Dutch artist was famed for his symmetrical drawings with patterns of regular, similar-shaped figures such as fish.

10 Which Florentine family encouraged a succession of Renaissance artists including Uccello and Michelangelo?

11 Whose works include a lobster telephone?

12 Which Michelangelo statue was carved from a block of marble called 'The Giant'?

13 Who painted the same scene twice at different times, to show the effect of cataracts on his colour perception?

14 Who was visiting Van Gogh just before he cut off his ear?

15 Which Italian painter produced paintings in which animals, flowers and fruit form human likenesses?

**Can you crack the safe? In each case, your first task is to decide which of the 14 statements below are false. Then shade out the areas on the combination lock that share the same letters as the false statements (so if you think statement E is false, shade out area E). The remaining segments will give you the digital numbered combination required.**

## 35

A In *East of Eden*, Caleb's brother is called Aron

B A bound volume of literary work can be termed a 'codeine'

C In Australia, a 'jumbuck' is slang for a rucksack

D Aristotle is quoted as saying 'One swallow does not make a summer'

E The phrase *Ultra vires* means 'Beyond one's powers'

F H. Rider Haggard wrote *King Solomon's Mines*

G The title of C.S. Forester's *The African Queen* refers to Cleopatra

H The clown in Shakespeare's *As You Like It* is called Touchstone

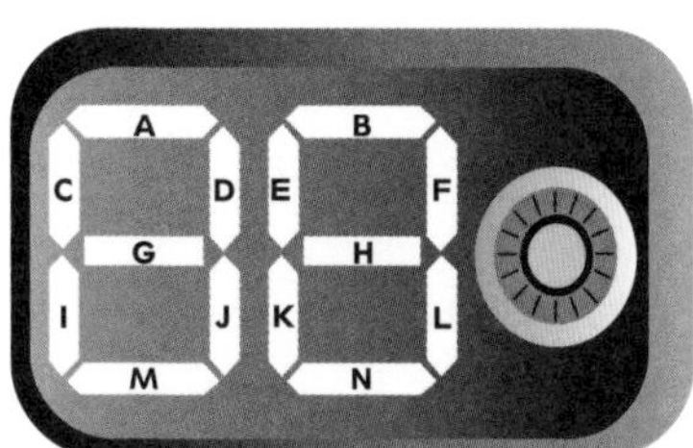


I In 'The Owl and the Pussy Cat', the wedding ring costs one new penny

J Rudyard Kipling was named after a reservoir where his parents were engaged

K *La Stampa* is the name of a Spanish newspaper

L The *Encyclopaedia Britannica* was first published in Edinburgh

M A Japanese haiku poem contains 13 syllables

N Sherlock Holmes's brother is called Watson

## 36

A Poet ee cummings was well known for ignoring punctuation

B When Lucy Locket lost her pocket, it was found by Kitty Fisher

C The St James Bible is the world's most valuable book

D *Where's the Rest of Me?* was the title of Ronald Reagan's autobiography

E The second most frequently used letter in English is T

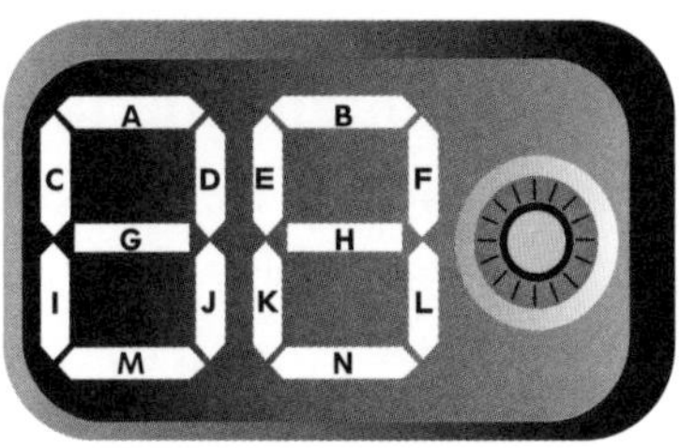


F The slave girl in *Ali Baba and the Forty Thieves* is called Morgana

G Roald Dahl's Matilda overcame the odious headmistress Miss Trunchbull with her remarkable powers

H A palindrome is a manuscript written on re-used vellum

I Incunabula are books printed before AD 1501

J According to the nursery rhyme, Thursday's child is full of woe

K Shakespeare's play *Hamlet* is set within Ellsinore Castle, Denmark

L Shaw's *Pygmalion* caused a scandal because it used the word 'bloody'

M *Reader's Digest* was founded by De Witt Wallace

N *The Cat in the Hat* is a famous children's work by Dr Seuss

# 37 Ancient history

1 Which famous military leader was the son of Philip of Macedonia?

2 By what name is Gautama Siddhartha better known?

3 Which warrior caste from 11th-century Japan practised hara-kiri?

4 Name the 1st-century Queen of the British Iceni tribe who led a revolt against the Romans.

5 What befell those who failed to answer the riddle of the Sphinx?

6 What type of clothing was worn by athletes at the ancient Olympics?

7 The first Russian state was named after the Rus tribe of which trading and warrior people?

8 Name the containers in which the ancient Egyptians stored internal organs during mummification?

9 Which famous leaders were defeated at the Battle of Actium?

10 In which country was the warrior Temujin, aka Ghengis Khan, born?

11 Which legendary ancient Sumerian king wrote an epic work describing his search for immortality and including a description of a flood?

12 What was a *pugio*?

13 Which ancient civilization developed a form of writing, called 'linear A', around 1650 BC?

14 Which ancient people, who founded the cities of Beirut and Tyre, developed an early alphabet from which the Greek and Latin alphabets grew?

15 The city of Tenochtitlan was the centre of which highly developed civilization discovered by the Spanish in the 16th century?

## 38 General history

1 Under what name did William of Normandy rule in England after winning the Battle of Hastings?

✎

2 During the French Revolution, which prison was destroyed by a rioting mob on 14 July, 1789?

3 The Mogul emperor Shah Jahan built which famous monument as a tomb for his favourite wife?

4 Who is reputed to have said 'Dr Livingstone, I presume?'

5 What attracted large numbers of settlers to California in the mid-19th century?

6 Who founded Singapore?

7 Which 1863 American Civil War battle halted the invasion of the north by the Confederates?

8 The Spanish Armada was sent by Philip II in 1588 to attack whom?

9 Who won the battle of Austerlitz?

10 What was the new name given to the former colonies whose independence was recognized under the Treaty of Paris of 1783?

11 What was the nickname of the atomic bomb dropped on Nagasaki in 1945?

12 Name the last Native American uprising in the USA, by the Sioux, in 1890?

13 The Tolpuddle Martyrs were sent from England to Australia as a penalty for what?

14 Name the Argentinian doctor who helped to overthrow President Batista of Cuba in 1959.

15 Which politician in which country made a Unilateral Declaration of Independence from Britain in 1965?

# 39 Film and television

1 In which year did Hitchcock, McQueen and Lennon die?

✎

---

2 In which decade did Al Pacino receive the most Oscar nominations?

---

3 When did Katharine Hepburn win her last Oscar?

---

4 Was the spoof disaster movie *Airplane* released in 1980, 1983 or 1986?

---

5 Which decade saw the release of *Alien*?

---

6 In which decade was 1990 Best Actress Oscar-winner Jessica Tandy born?

---

7 Which year saw the launch of BBC television?

---

8 In which year did 25,210,000 people in the UK watch England play Germany at football?

---

9 When was Channel 4 launched in the UK?

---

10 In which decade did Richard Baker stop reading the BBC news?

---

11 When did the television show *Happy Days* first hit the US screens?

---

12 In which year did Sean Connery first face his adversary Dr No?

---

13 Which year saw the releases of *Casablanca* and *Bambi*?

---

14 In which decade were the first Oscars awarded?

---

15 In which decade was famous film director and actor Charlie Chaplin born?

---

# 40 Film

1 Which *Star Wars* movie is called episode 1?

2 What was the name of the horse Liz Taylor rode in *National Velvet*?

3 What was the name of the villainess in the popular *101 Dalmatians*?

4 In *Every Which Way But Loose*, what was Clyde?

5 *Rebel Without a Cause*, *Giant*. What was the only other movie James Dean starred in?

6 In the film of the same name, what was 'Rainman' a mispronunciation of?

7 What was the title of the long-awaited sequel to *The Hustler*?

8 *Bull Durham* and *Eight Men Out*. What was the common sport?

9 What was Bond villain Oddjob's weapon of choice?

10 Ben Affleck and Matt Damon co-wrote which Oscar-winning movie?

11 What was Tom Cruise's profession in *Jerry Maguire*?

12 Who played the ghost in *Ghost*?

13 In Orson Welles's classic *Citizen Kane*, what was Rosebud?

14 *Primary Colors* was based on the career of which US president?

15 What is the final word spoken in *Casablanca*?

# 41 Film actors and actresses

1 According to a Steve Martin film, who don't wear plaid?

✎

2 Which actor's brain was on the menu in *Hannibal*?

3 Which was Sean Connery's last outing as James Bond?

4 Who was Isabella Rossellini's famous mother?

5 Name the film actress who changed her original initials from N.J.B. to M.M.

6 Which actress links *Charlie's Angels* and *Being John Malkovich*?

7 In the Mel Brooks film *Silent Movie*, who was the only person with a speaking part?

8 Who played Chaplin in *Chaplin*?

9 Which actor shot John Travolta in *Pulp Fiction*?

10 Who provided the funeral to go with the four weddings?

11 In which film did Dame Judi Dench play Queen Elizabeth?

12 John Cleese played Archie Leach in *A Fish Called Wanda*, but whose real name was Archie Leach?

13 Michael Keaton, George Clooney, Val Kilmer: which movie role links them all?

14 At which sport is Geena Davis a world-class competitor?

15 Kevin Costner played golfer Roy McAvoy in *Tin Cup*. What was his nickname?

# 42 Television – general challenge

1 Which TV family lives in Cobblestone County?

✎

2 Who was the dead girl in *Twin Peaks*?

3 Which television detective has a glass eye?

4 In *Cheers*, which character is married to Vera?

5 *Mork and Mindy* was a spin-off of which other sitcom?

6 In *Ally McBeal*, what is John Cage's nickname?

7 Which *Blue Peter* presenter looked after Goldie?

8 Which character in TV's *Red Dwarf* is a hologram?

9 'Suicide is Painless' was the theme tune to which sitcom?

10 In which US state was *Northern Exposure* set?

11 'Here's a story, of a man named' ... what?

12 Who drove a car called the *General Lee*?

13 Who was the drummer in the Muppet band?

14 In which road was Mr Benn a resident?

15 What was the title of the theme song to *Minder*?

# 43 Pot luck

1 What was Lady Chatterley's first name?

2 Which actor/director was responsible for the rebuilding of the Globe Theatre in London?

3 Who invented the clockwork radio?

4 Who is the wife of Othello in Shakespeare's play?

5 How did Emily Davison kill herself in 1913?

6 In the TV series *The Prisoner*, what was Patrick McGoohan's number?

7 How was Iosif Vissarionovich Dzhugashvili better known?

8 Which programme is broadcast on BBC Radio 4 at 10.45pm Monday to Friday?

9 Which stately home in Derbyshire is the family seat of the Duke of Devonshire?

10 Whose *Finnegans Wake* was published in 1939?

11 Tallinn is the capital of which Baltic republic?

12 Which actress co-starred with Marilyn Monroe in *Gentlemen Prefer Blondes*?

13 Czech-born magnate Jan Ludvik Hoch died in mysterious circumstances in 1991. How was he better known?

14 Mrs Thomas Smith of Ryde, NSW, Australia, produced a new variety of fruit in 1868. What is it called?

15 Who created the fictional detective Cordelia Gray?

# 44 Pot luck

1 The Hard Rock Cafe is named after a song by which band?

✎

2 Whom did Michael Portillo succeed as MP for Kensington and Chelsea?

3 Which of these is not a judo belt: yellow, orange, purple, brown?

4 Which English architect redesigned the Brighton Pavilion for George IV?

5 In which country would you find the wine-growing area of Stellenbosch?

6 What useful service was founded in Australia in 1928 by Rev. John Flynn?

7 Which English poet wrote 'Tyger! Tyger! burning bright in the forests of the night'?

8 Which opera features the bullfighter Escamillo?

9 Once a rocket has left the launch site at Cape Canaveral, Johnson Space Center takes over. Where is it found?

10 What number on the Beaufort Scale represents a gale force wind?

11 Who is the Director General of the BBC?

12 At which major sea battle did England defeat the French in 1798?

13 To which country do the Galapagos Islands belong?

14 From which creature is lanolin obtained?

15 Who was the Greek Goddess of Victory?

10 MINUTES

## 45 Pot luck

1 What type of food are sloke, dulse and carageen?

2 Chuck Berry wrote the first song that the Rolling Stones recorded. Which was it?

3 What is special about this large number: 854,917,632?

4 Who married American actress Nancy Davis?

5 How long, exactly, did the Hundred Years' War last?

6 In which country is Amharic the main language?

7 Which poet sold his home, Newstead Abbey, to pay his debts?

8 Where, according to the film title, did Marty McFly go?

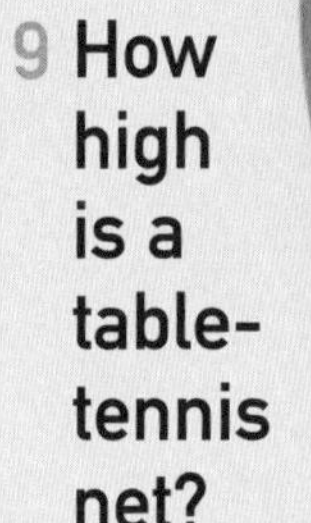

9 How high is a table-tennis net?

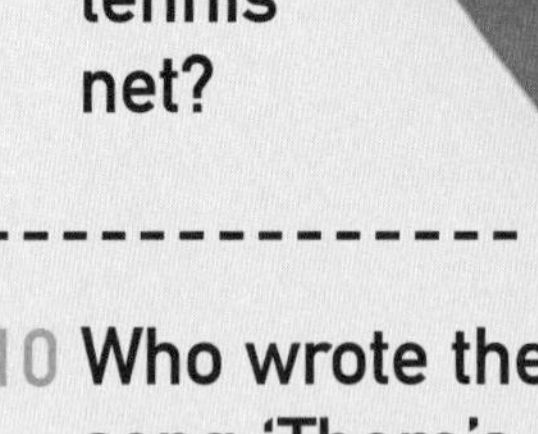

10 Who wrote the song 'There's No Business Like Show Business'?

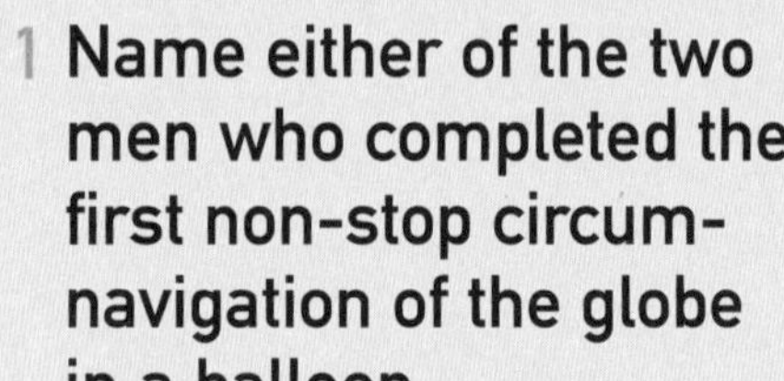

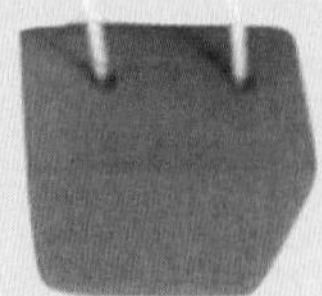

11 Name either of the two men who completed the first non-stop circum-navigation of the globe in a balloon.

12 What was King George VI's first name?

13 Which order of monks are known as the 'White Friars'?

14 Who was Poet Laureate from 1843 to 1850, during which period he wrote no poetry at all?

15 Which village in Norfolk gives its name to a type of cloth?

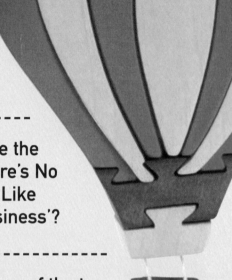

30 MINUTES

## 46 Trivia trail

Your objective is to find the correct route through this quizzical maze. Each intersection contains a question, the answer to which contains either UP, DOWN, LEFT or RIGHT. This tells you which exit you must take to move to the next question. If you go off the left or right side of the grid, you emerge at the box on the opposite side of the same row. In the correct route, all but seven boxes are used.

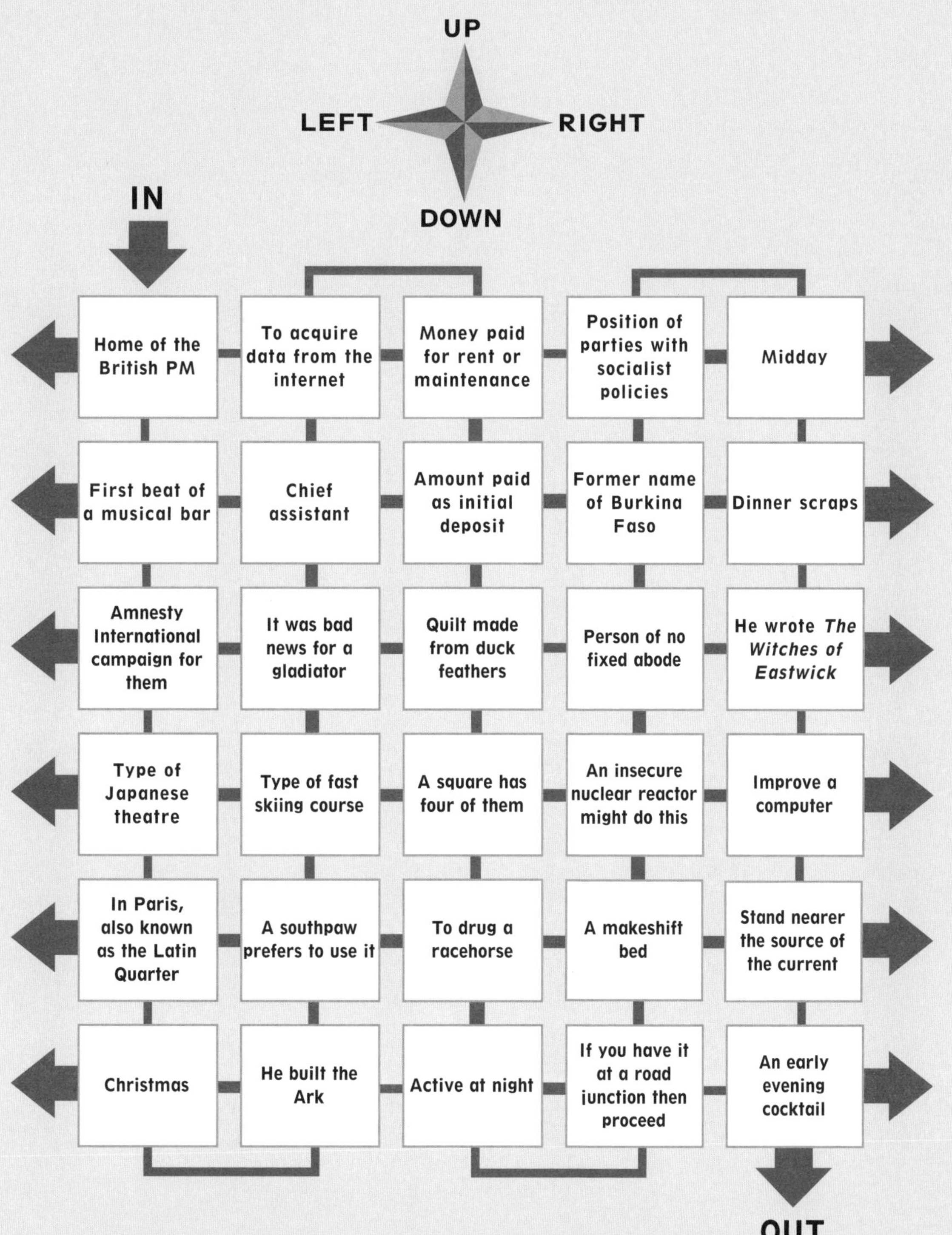
UP
LEFT
RIGHT
DOWN
IN
Home of the British PM
To acquire data from the internet
Money paid for rent or maintenance
Position of parties with socialist policies
Midday
First beat of a musical bar
Chief assistant
Amount paid as initial deposit
Former name of Burkina Faso
Dinner scraps
Amnesty International campaign for them
It was bad news for a gladiator
Quilt made from duck feathers
Person of no fixed abode
He wrote The Witches of Eastwick
Type of Japanese theatre
Type of fast skiing course
A square has four of them
An insecure nuclear reactor might do this
Improve a computer
In Paris, also known as the Latin Quarter
A southpaw prefers to use it
To drug a racehorse
A makeshift bed
Stand nearer the source of the current
Christmas
He built the Ark
Active at night
If you have it at a road junction then proceed
An early evening cocktail
OUT

# eye

Do you think in pictures or words? If you feel more at home with images, you'll take to these visual puzzles like a duck to water. They come in many forms – from familiar spot-the-differences and domino challenges to the more unusual Japanese sokoban puzzles – and if you've never done one, now's the time to try. There is a pictorial element in all of them, so having an eye for detail will certainly help.

In this section appearances most definitely matter. What's important is how you look ... eyes down, observe.

★ easy ★★ medium ★★★ hard

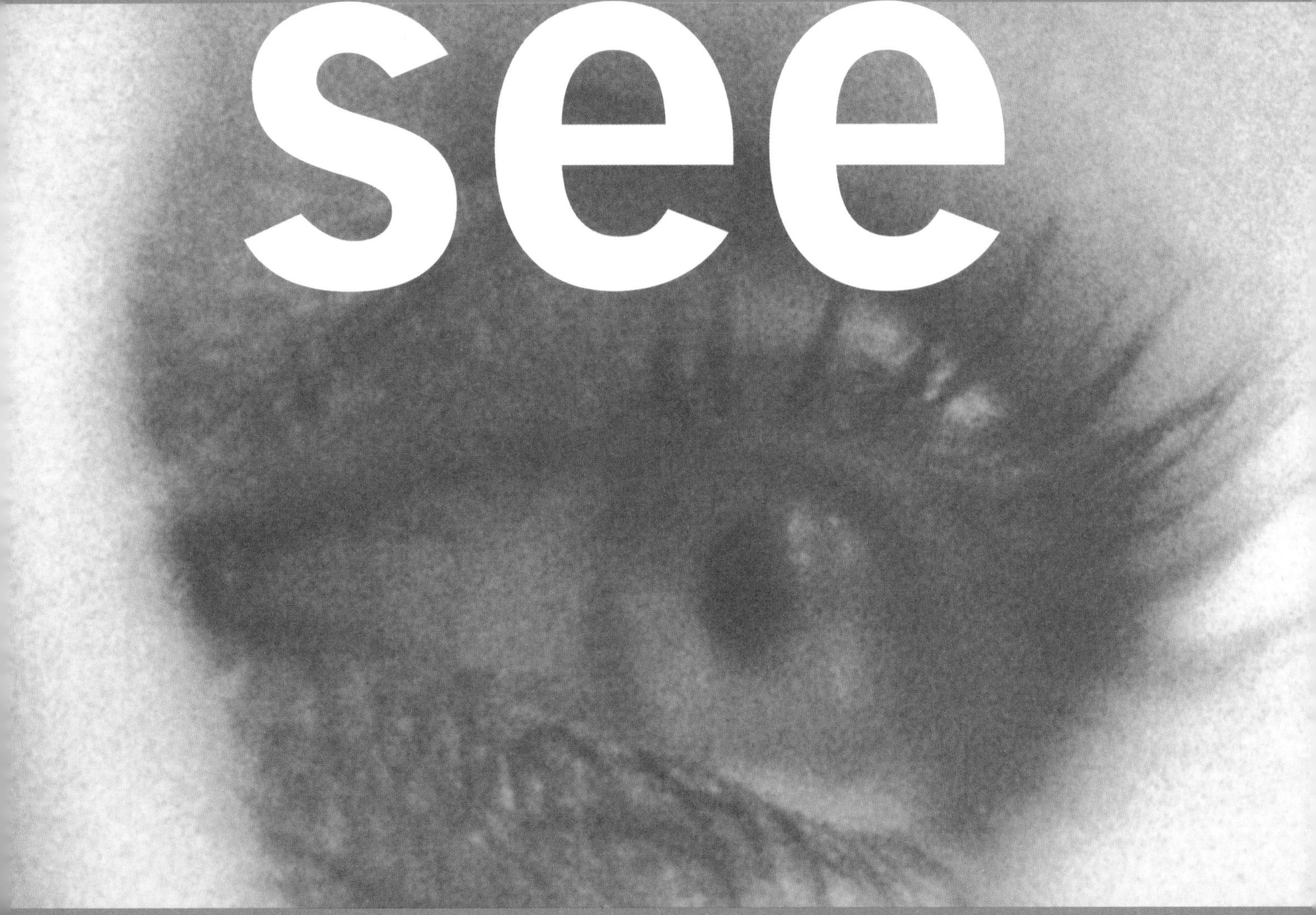

# see

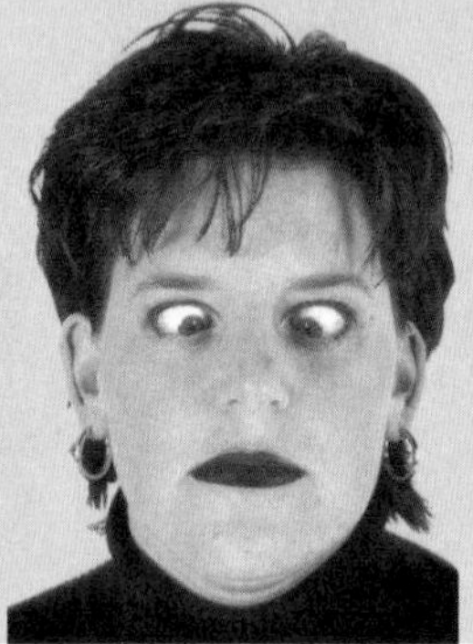

# warm-up...

1★ Can you spot the eight differences between these two pictures? Circle them in the drawing on the right below.

2★ Which of the boxed symbols completes the set?

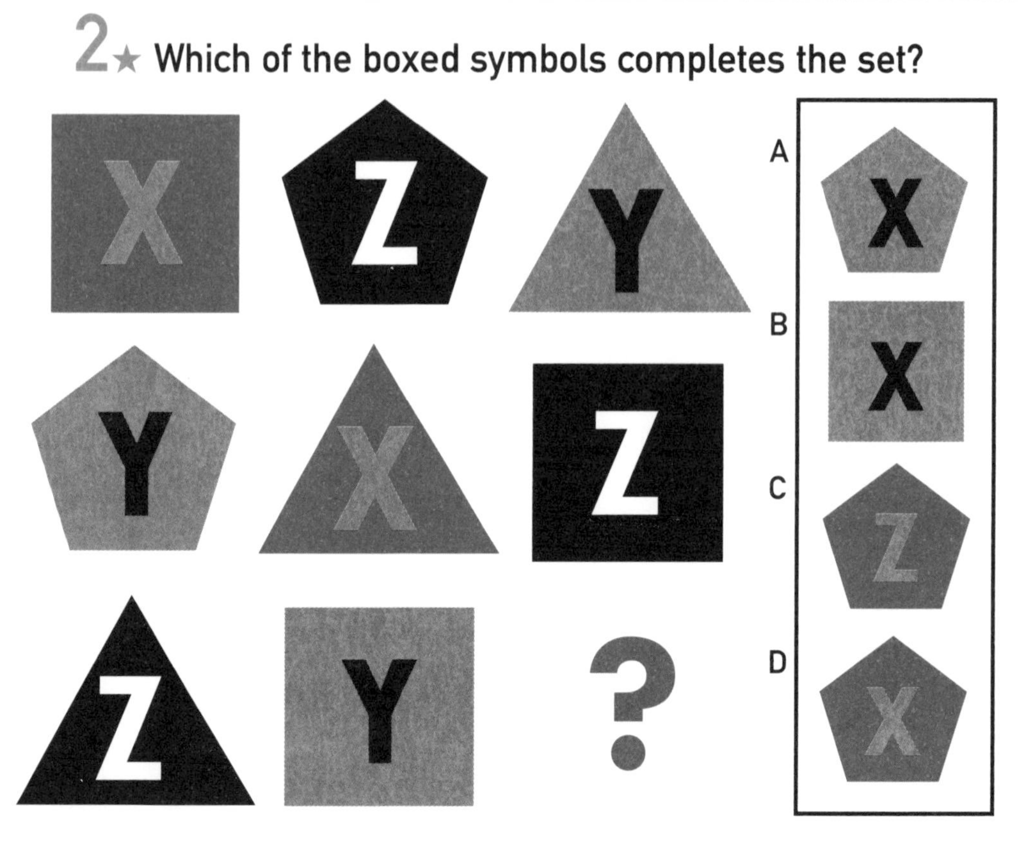

**3★★** What percentage of this grid is yellow and what percentage is white?

**4★** Which arrow comes next in the sequence?

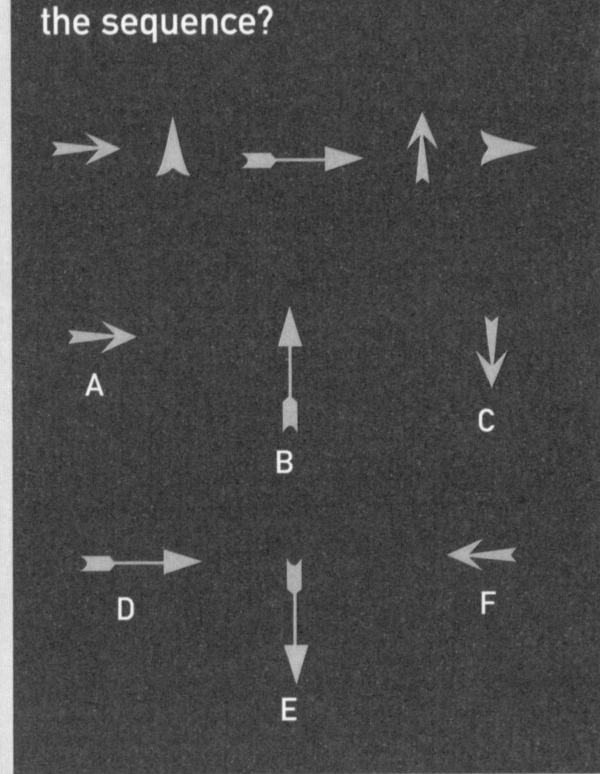


**5★**

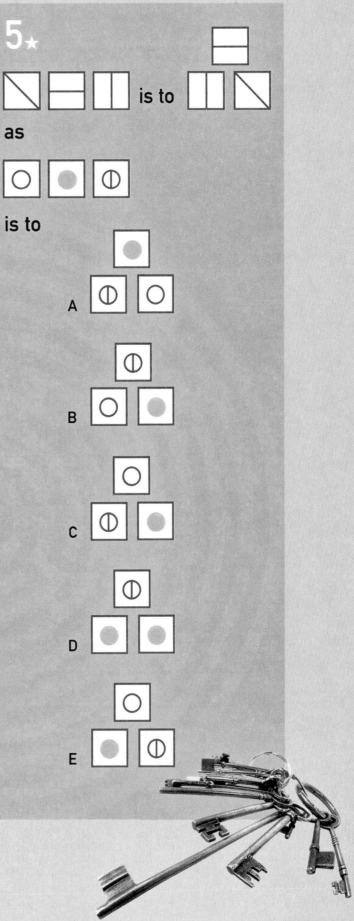

is to

as

is to

A

B

C

D

E

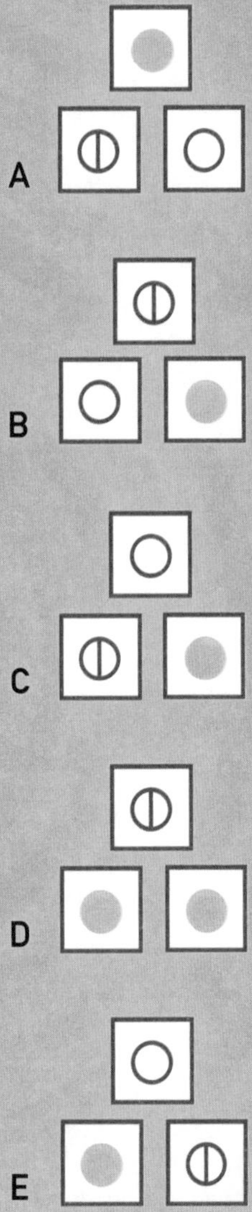

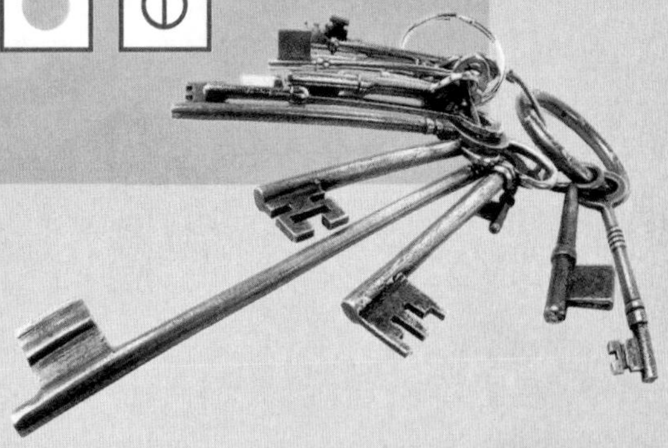

Can you find the key to unlock the teasers that follow?

**6★** Can you find your way to the middle of this circular maze without going goggle-eyed?

**7**★ Don't think too hard about these questions. Trust your initial instincts and see how many you answer correctly. Tick your answers.

1 Are these shapes in alphabetical order?
YES
NO

Palest Staple
Pleats Pastel

2 Are all these words anagrams of PETALS?
YES
NO

Bogart Bergman
Lorre Greenstreet

3 Were these actors all in *Casablanca?*
YES
NO

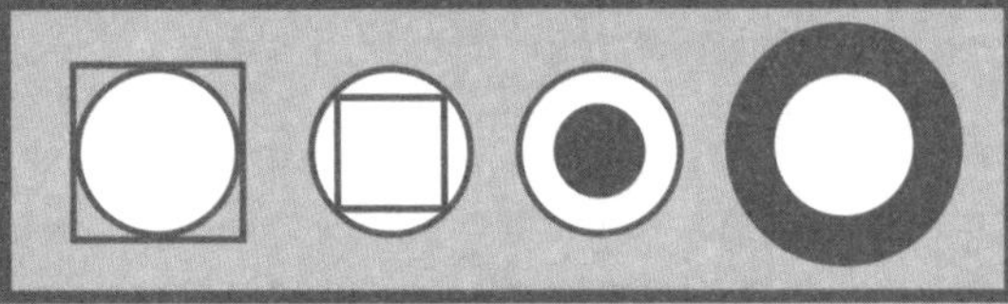

4 Are these white circles all the same size?
YES
NO

Mullet Tench
Piranha Merlin

5 Are these all types of fish?
YES
NO

Blue Red
Green Yellow

6 Are these all the colours of croquet balls?
YES
NO

JAMJAMSFOND

7 Are these the initials of the months of the year?
YES
NO

September April
November June

8 Do these months all have 30 days?
YES
NO

**8★ Can you complete this nonogram puzzle? (See the instructions below.) Clue: we'll drink to that!**

Column clues (top to bottom, columns left to right):

| | | | | | | | | | | | | | | |
|---|---|---|---|---|---|---|---|---|---|---|---|---|---|---|
| | 1 | | 1 | | | 1 | | 1 | | | | | | |
| | 1 | 1 | 1 | | | 1 | 1 | 1 | 6 | 5 | 9 | 9 | 5 | |
| 4 | 1 | 5 | 1 | 4 | 3 | 1 | 4 | 1 | 3 | 3 | 3 | 3 | 3 | 10 |

Row clues (left to right, rows top to bottom):

| | | | |
|---|---|---|---|
| | | | 2 |
| | | | 2 |
| | | | 2 |
| | | | 2 |
| | | | 4 |
| | | | 6 |
| | | 5 | 6 |
| | 1 | 1 | 6 |
| | | 1 | 11 |
| 1 | 2 | 1 | 1 |
| 3 | 1 | 1 | 1 |
| | 1 | 3 | 1 |
| | 1 | 1 | 6 |
| | 1 | 1 | 6 |
| | | 3 | 9 |

## How to complete a nonogram

The numbers alongside each row or column tell you how many blocks of black squares are in a line. So, for example, 2, 3, 5 tells you that from left to right (or top to bottom) there is a group of two black squares, then a group of three black squares and finally a group of five black squares.

Any block may (or may not) have a number of white squares before or after it, but each block of black squares on the same line must have at least one white square between it and the next block of black squares.

Sometimes you will be able to tell which squares are going to be black without reference to other lines or columns: for instance, in the first example below we can deduce that any block of six black squares must incorporate the two central ones.

It will also help to put a small dot in squares you know to be empty.

| 6 | | | | | ■ | ■ | | | | |
|---|---|---|---|---|---|---|---|---|---|---|

Here is a simple example already filled in:

| 1 | 3 | 2 | • | ■ | • | ■ | ■ | ■ | • | ■ | ■ |
|---|---|---|---|---|---|---|---|---|---|---|---|

9★ Can you figure out how to solve this Japanese sokoban (warehouse worker) puzzle and push the 'crates' (the circles) out through the exit? Place coins on each of the crates and a pawn on the X to get started. See below for the rules.

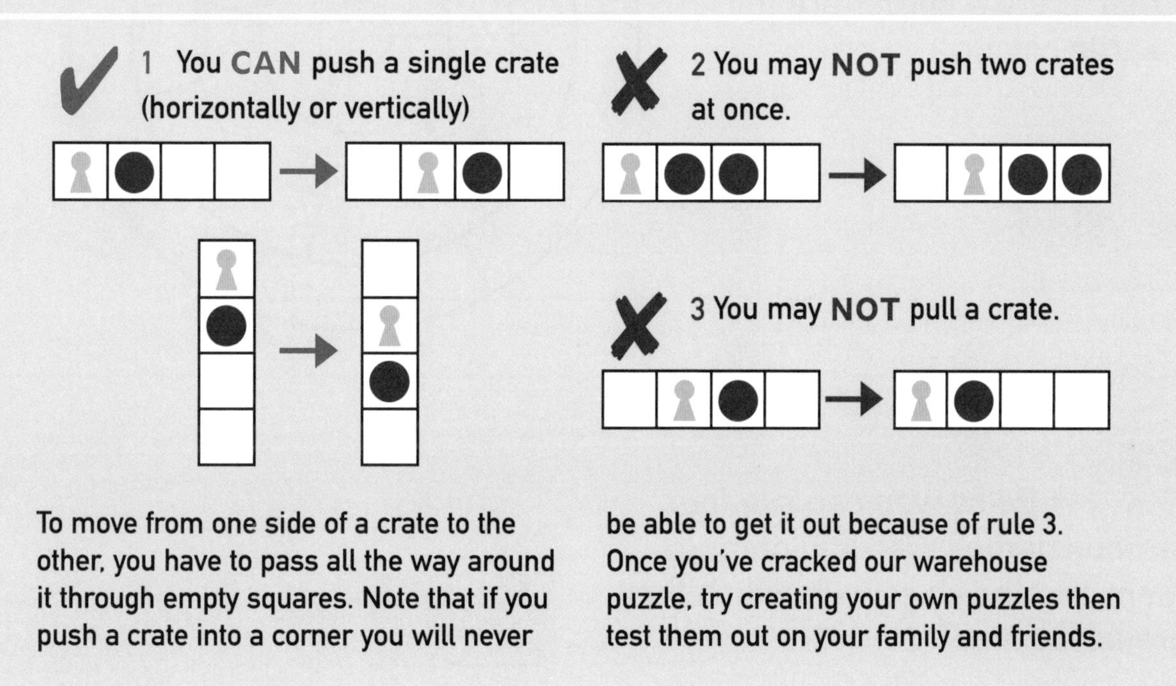

1 You CAN push a single crate (horizontally or vertically)
2 You may NOT push two crates at once.
3 You may NOT pull a crate.


To move from one side of a crate to the other, you have to pass all the way around it through empty squares. Note that if you push a crate into a corner you will never be able to get it out because of rule 3. Once you've cracked our warehouse puzzle, try creating your own puzzles then test them out on your family and friends.

**10★** Using four different colours (or labelling the areas using four different symbols), shade in this diagram so no two areas that share a border are the same colour.

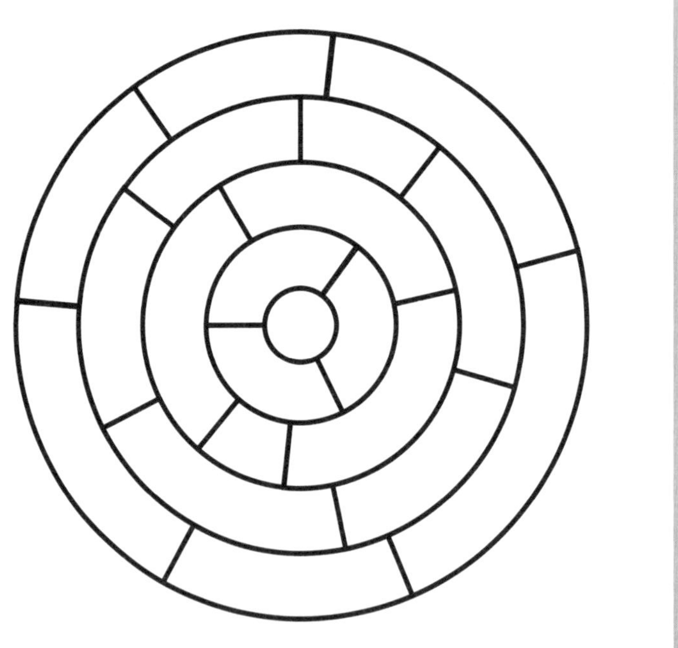

**11★★** Below you can see four famous domes. Can you name them and the cities with which they are associated?

A ------------------------------

B ------------------------------

C ------------------------------

D ------------------------------

12★★ Shipshape and Bristol fashion, that's how Ada runs her shop. Without even looking, she could answer the questions below. See if you can answer them in under 5 minutes…

1 How many elephants does Ada have?

2 What is to the immediate left of the timepiece showing 8 o'clock?

3 Where can you find a bow tie?

4 The smallest lockable box can be found between which other two items?

5 What is to be found lying against the tasselled cushion?

6 Which of the five candles would be most useful outdoors?

7 Whereabouts is the only bird with an open mouth?

8 What proportion of the vases in Ada's shop have handles?

9 How many human masks are there?

10 Where is the clock showing 7 minutes to 2?

13★ Place nine coins on this board as shown. Take any coin and make it jump (via any horizontal, vertical or diagonal move) to land on an empty square on the other side. When a coin is jumped, remove it from the board. The aim is to remove eight coins from the board, similar to a game of solitaire.

Extra kudos if you can get the final piece to land back in the central square!

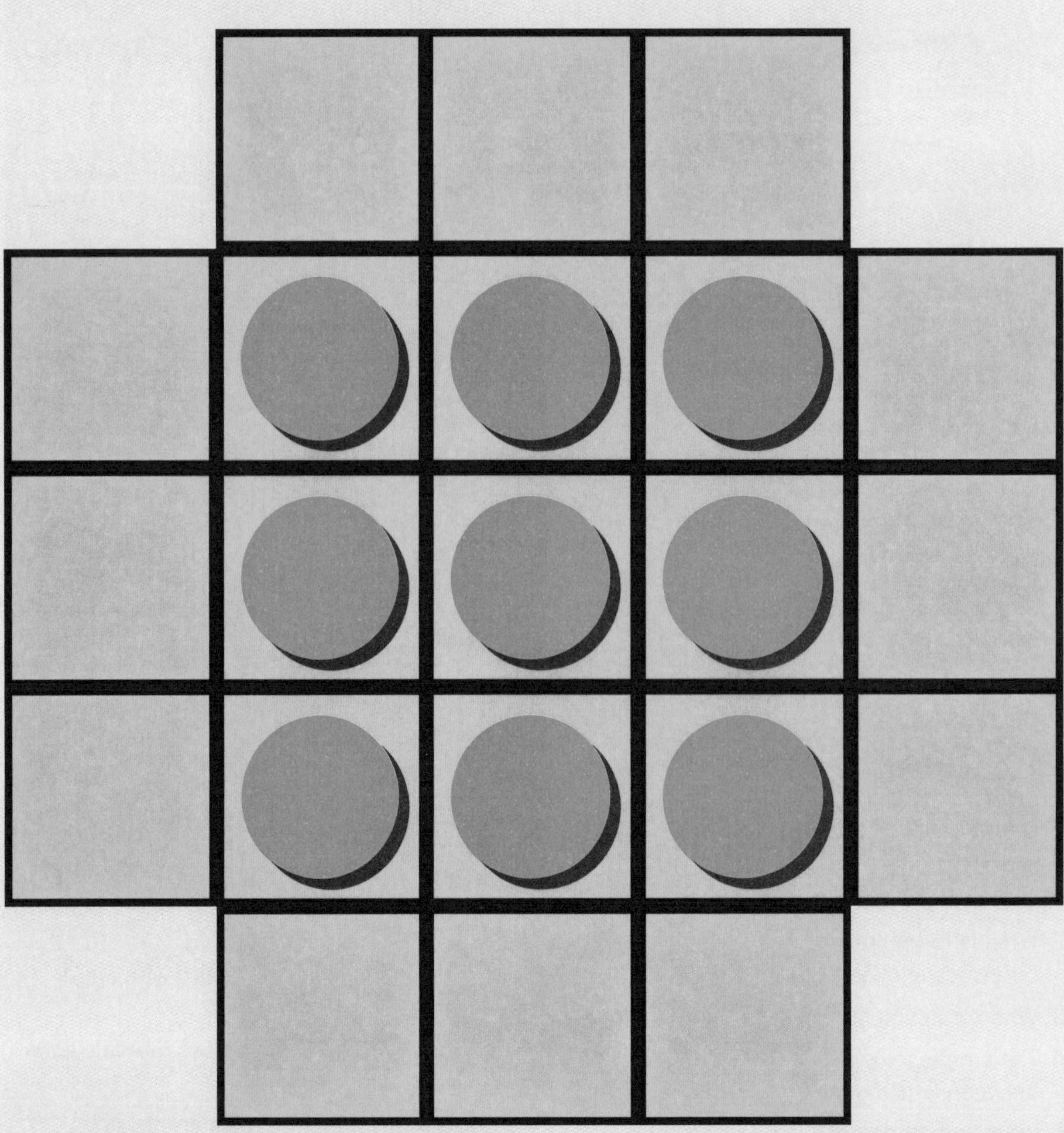

**14★** In the following sequence which domino is missing?

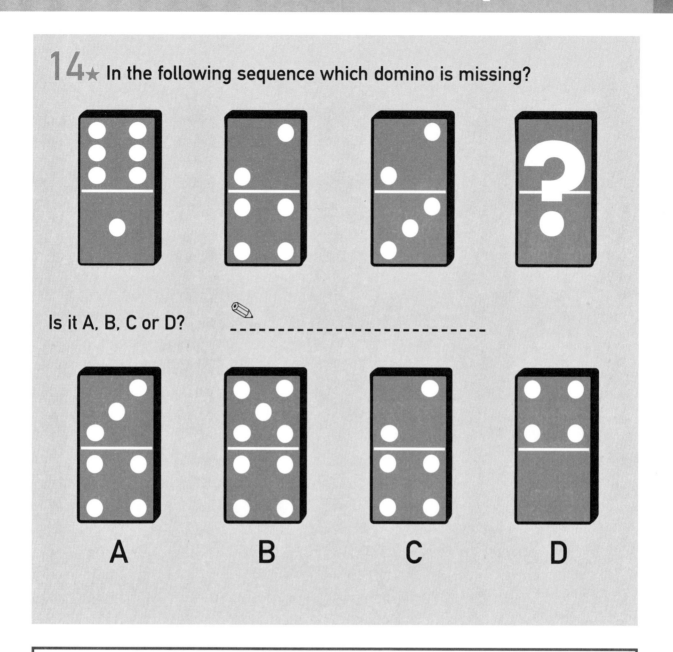

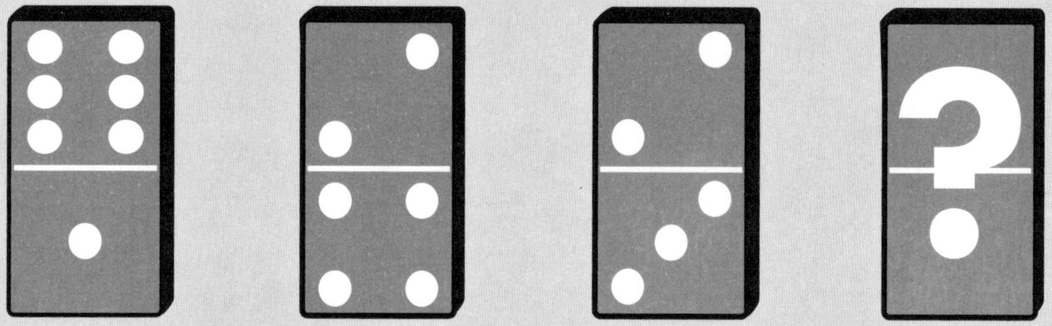

Is it A, B, C or D?

✎ ----------------------------

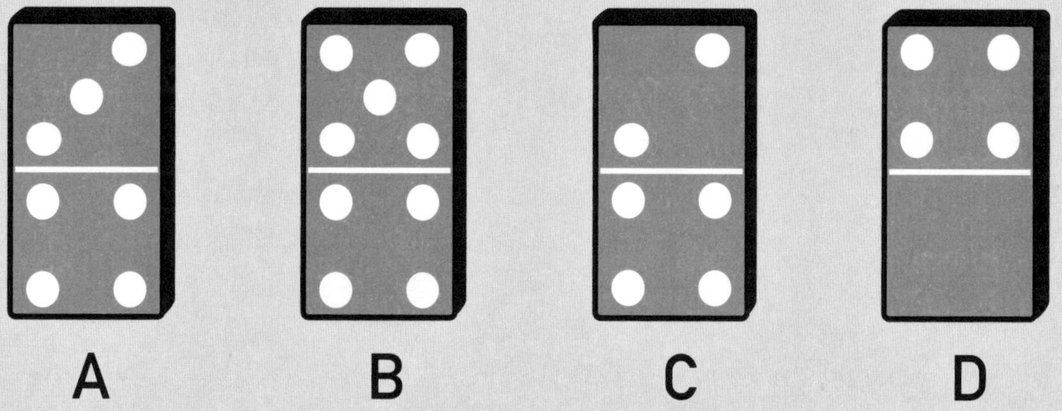

A B C D

**15★★** How many revolutions must the large cog make to return all the cogs to their starting positions?

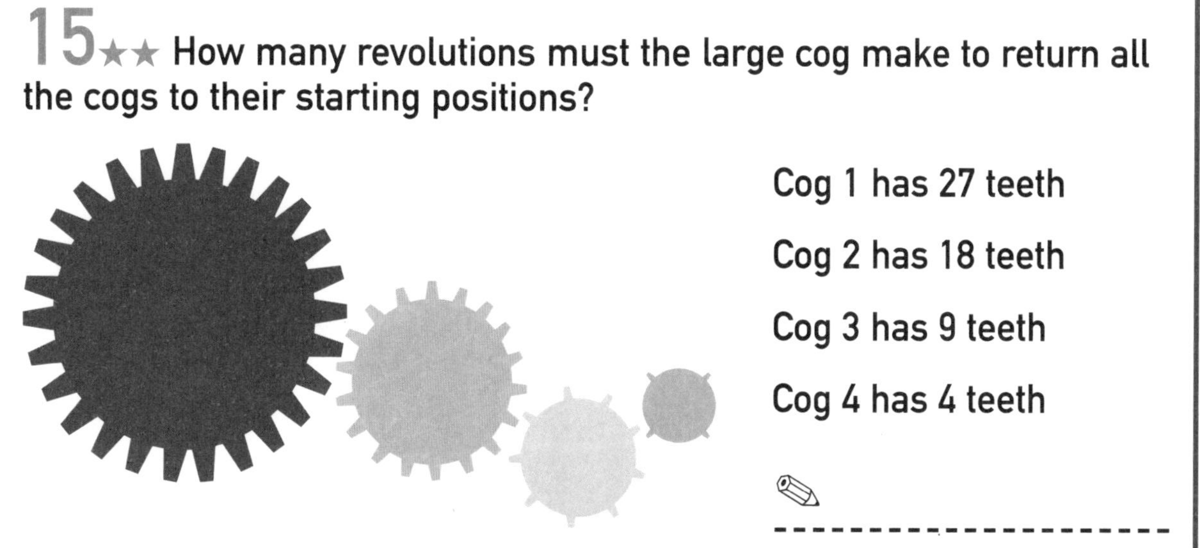
Cog 1 has 27 teeth
Cog 2 has 18 teeth
Cog 3 has 9 teeth
Cog 4 has 4 teeth

✎ ----------------------------

**16**★ Can you divide the picture on the right by drawing three straight lines to produce five sections, each containing one spiral shell, two stars and three squares?

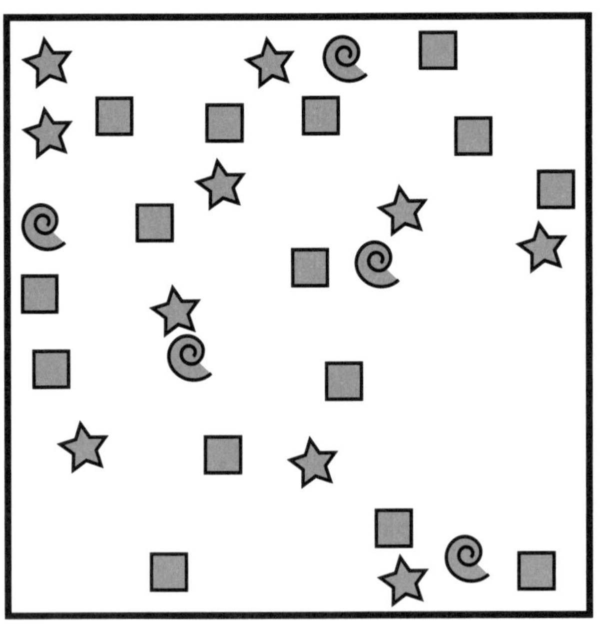

**17**★★ When the shape on the right is folded to form a cube, which is the only one of the following that cannot be produced?

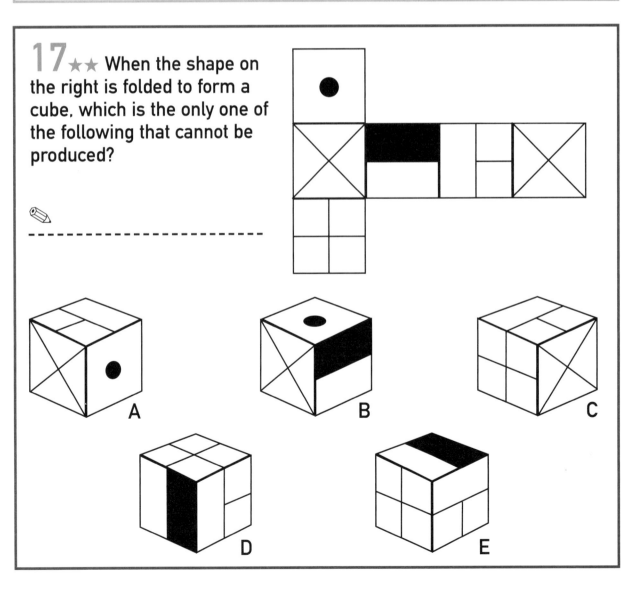

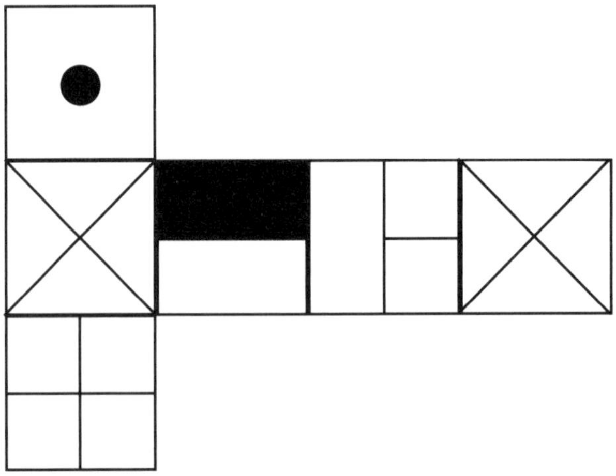

✎ ------------------------------

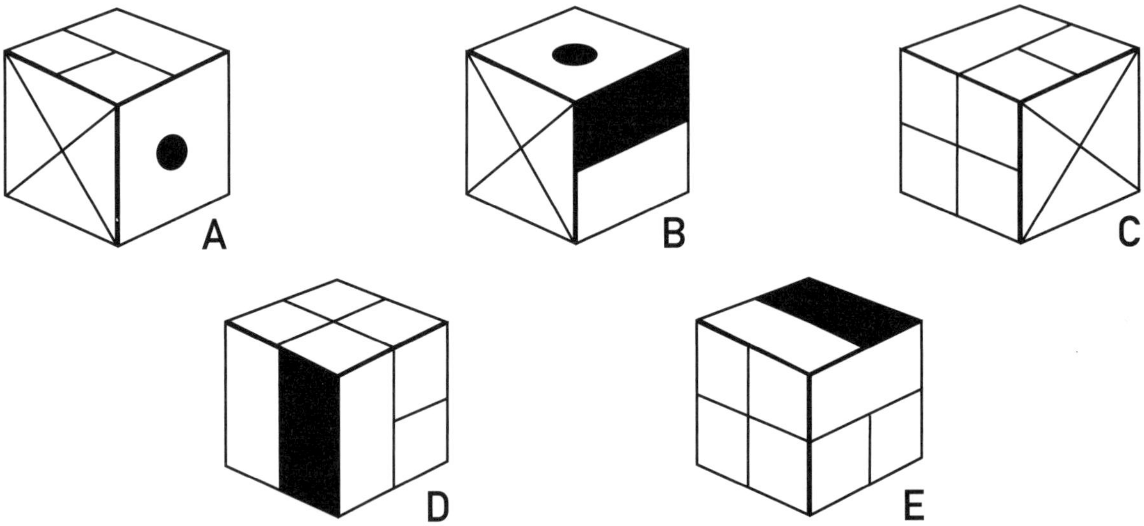

A

B

C

D

E

**18★** How stable is your concentration? Find two rocking horses precisely the same.

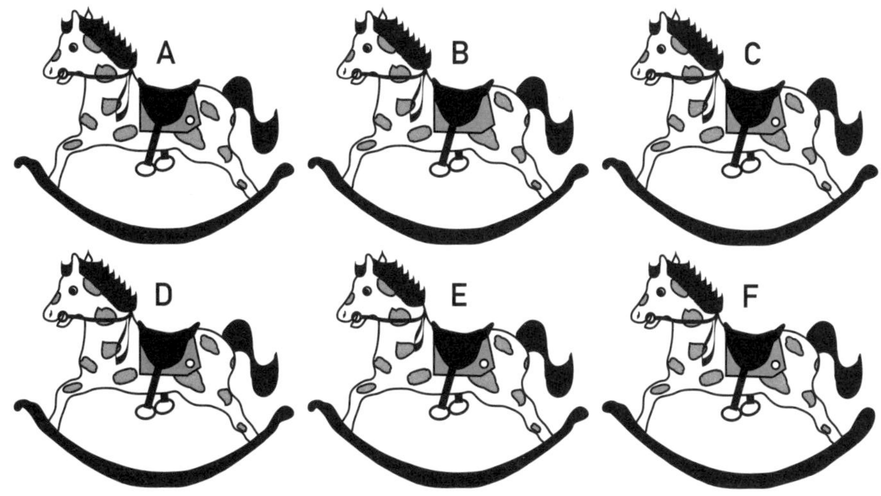


**19★★** Don't think about these questions too hard. Trust your initial instincts and see how many you answer correctly. Tick the correct answers.

YES
NO

1 Do these shapes have 23 sides altogether?

Egypt Denmark
Wales Australia

YES
NO

2 Do all these countries' capitals begin with 'C'?

CV RSVP
RIP PM

YES
NO

3 Are these all Latin abbreviations?

Fulham Everton
Charlton Ipswich

YES
NO

4 Are any of these football teams United?

Adder Bells
Chimp Dirty

YES
NO

5 Are the letters of each of these words in alphabetical order?

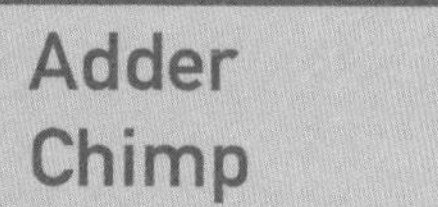

YES
NO

6 Does this spell SOS in Morse code?

YES
NO

7 Do these cars all come from Europe?

11 12
20 40

YES
NO

8 Do these numbers, spelt out, contain the same number of letters?

**20★★★** Add the boxes on the right to the arrangement of boxes on the left to make the letter H. Think laterally (clue: signals).

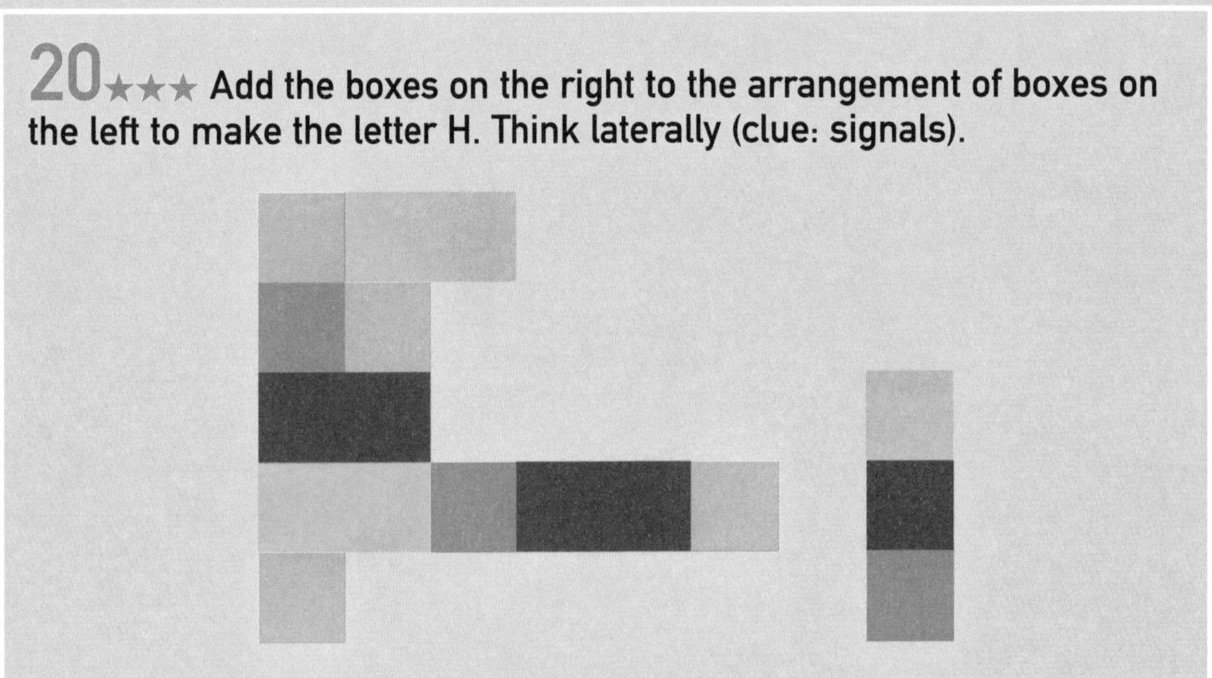

**21★** You might have to be a rocket scientist to work this one out! Carefully study the pictures below. Which is different from the rest?

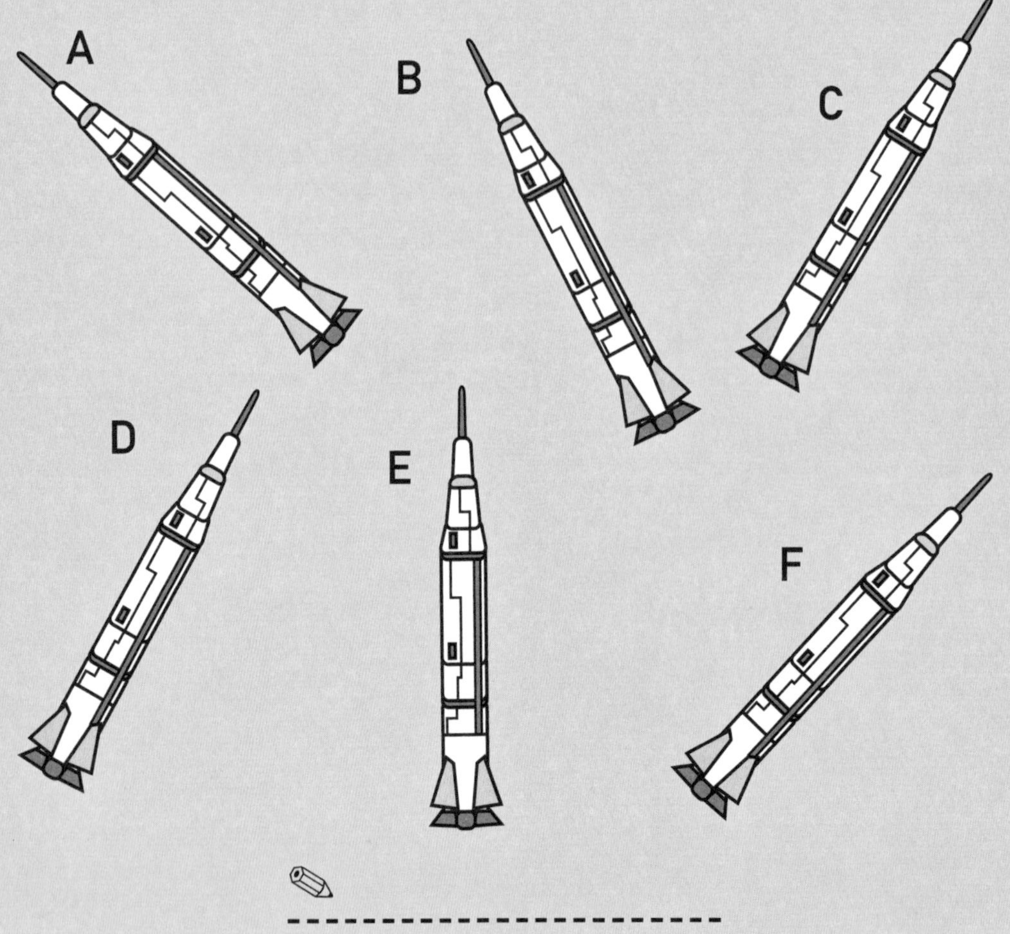


✎ ------------------------

**22★★** Which are the only two pieces that will fit together perfectly, to form a complete circle?

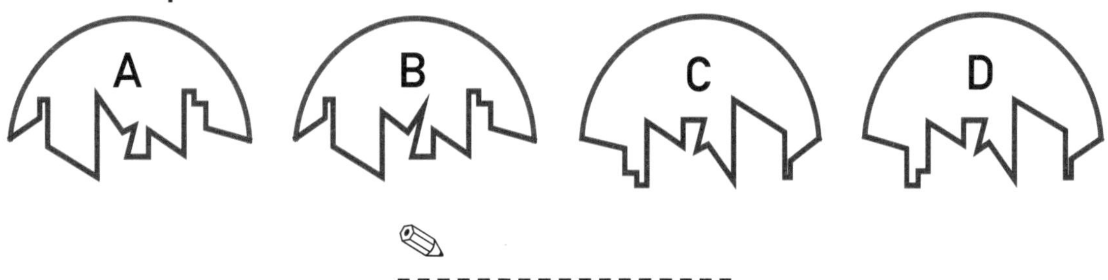


✎ ------------------

**23★★** This nonogram puzzle will leave you burning with curiosity.

(See page 174 for tips on how to do these puzzles.)

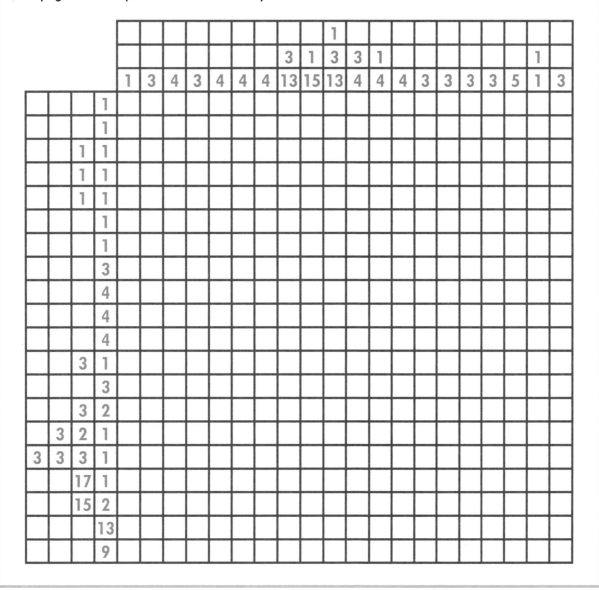

| | | | | | | | | | | | | | 1 | | | | | | | | | | |
|---|---|---|---|---|---|---|---|---|---|---|---|---|---|---|---|---|---|---|---|---|---|---|---|
| | | | | | | | | | | | 3 | 1 | 3 | 3 | 1 | | | | | | | 1 | |
| | | | | 1 | 3 | 4 | 3 | 4 | 4 | 4 | 13 | 15 | 13 | 4 | 4 | 4 | 3 | 3 | 3 | 3 | 5 | 1 | 3 |
| | | | 1 | | | | | | | | | | | | | | | | | | | | |
| | | | 1 | | | | | | | | | | | | | | | | | | | | |
| | | 1 | 1 | | | | | | | | | | | | | | | | | | | | |
| | | 1 | 1 | | | | | | | | | | | | | | | | | | | | |
| | | 1 | 1 | | | | | | | | | | | | | | | | | | | | |
| | | | 1 | | | | | | | | | | | | | | | | | | | | |
| | | | 1 | | | | | | | | | | | | | | | | | | | | |
| | | | 3 | | | | | | | | | | | | | | | | | | | | |
| | | | 4 | | | | | | | | | | | | | | | | | | | | |
| | | | 4 | | | | | | | | | | | | | | | | | | | | |
| | | | 4 | | | | | | | | | | | | | | | | | | | | |
| | | 3 | 1 | | | | | | | | | | | | | | | | | | | | |
| | | | 3 | | | | | | | | | | | | | | | | | | | | |
| | | 3 | 2 | | | | | | | | | | | | | | | | | | | | |
| | 3 | 2 | 1 | | | | | | | | | | | | | | | | | | | | |
| 3 | 3 | 3 | 1 | | | | | | | | | | | | | | | | | | | | |
| | | 17 | 1 | | | | | | | | | | | | | | | | | | | | |
| | | 15 | 2 | | | | | | | | | | | | | | | | | | | | |
| | | | 13 | | | | | | | | | | | | | | | | | | | | |
| | | | 9 | | | | | | | | | | | | | | | | | | | | |

24★ Three dice are arranged side by side. Seven faces are visible. What is the total of the other 11 sides?

25★★ How many triangles are there in the figure on the right?

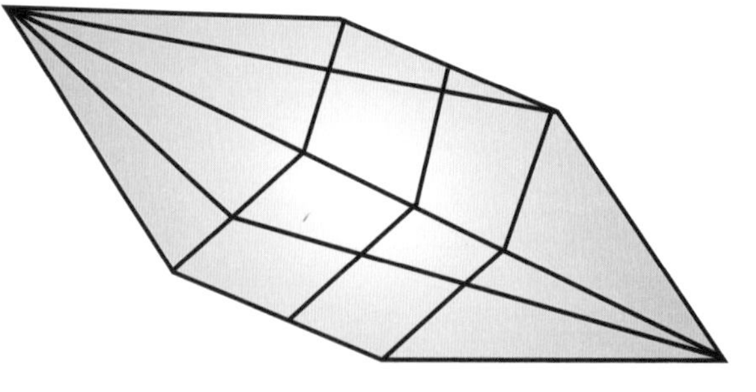

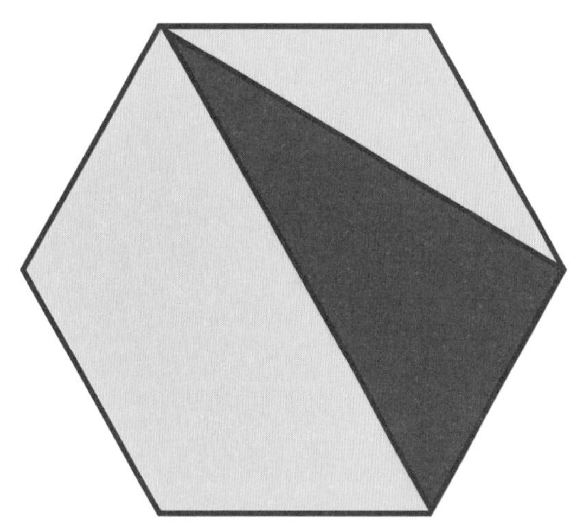

26★ Expressed as a fraction, what area of this hexagon is shaded?

27★ Can you spot the seven differences between these two pictures? Circle them in the drawing on the right.

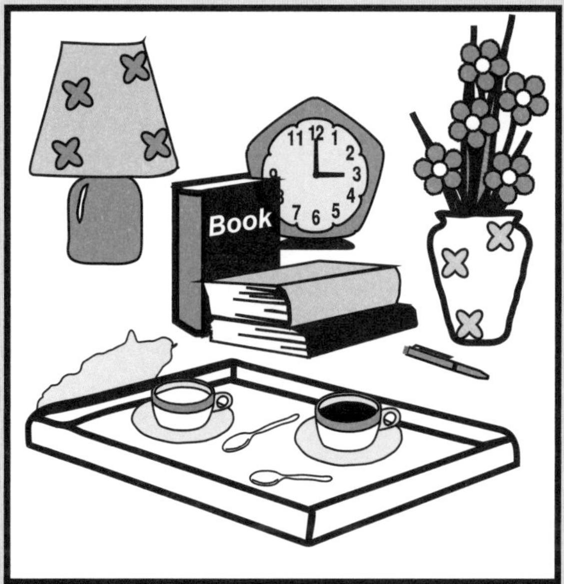


28★★ Which of the four boxed symbols completes the set?

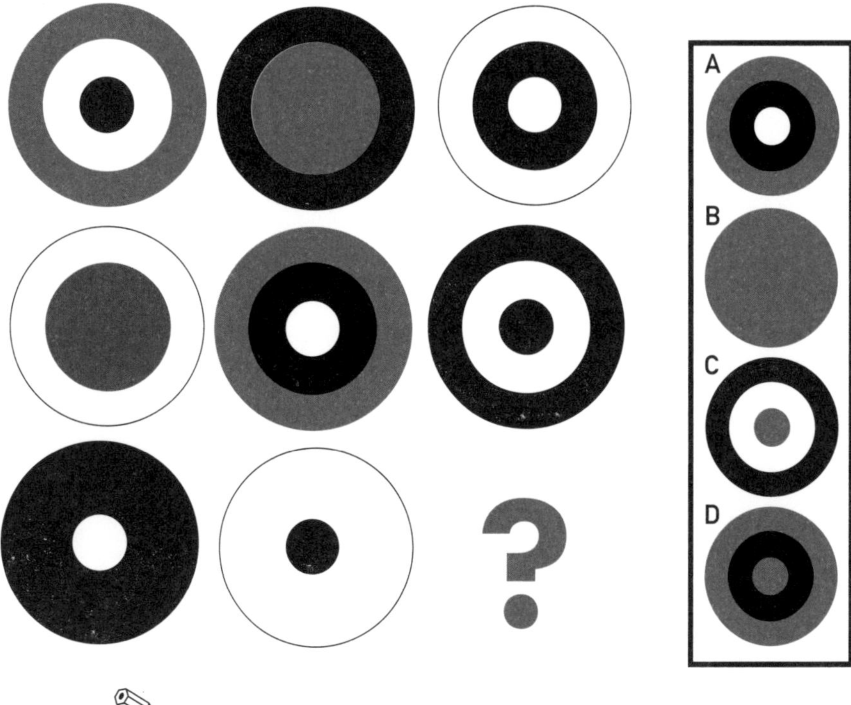


✎ ---------------------------------

**29★★★** What well-known geographical feature found on maps of the USA is represented by the following letters and symbols?
Think laterally…

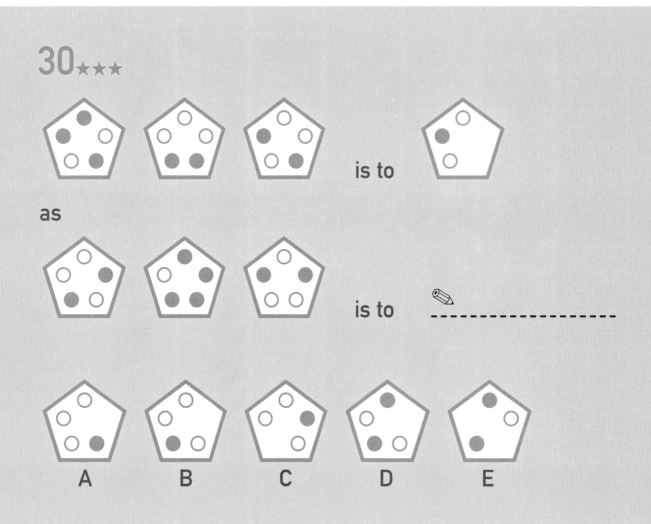

**30★★★**

is to

as

is to

A B C D E

**31** ★★ Complete this Japanese warehouse clearance puzzle, in which you, the sokoban (warehouse worker), have to shift the 'crates' (the circles) out through the exit. Place 5p coins on each of the crates and a pawn on the X to get you started.

(See page 175 for the rules.)

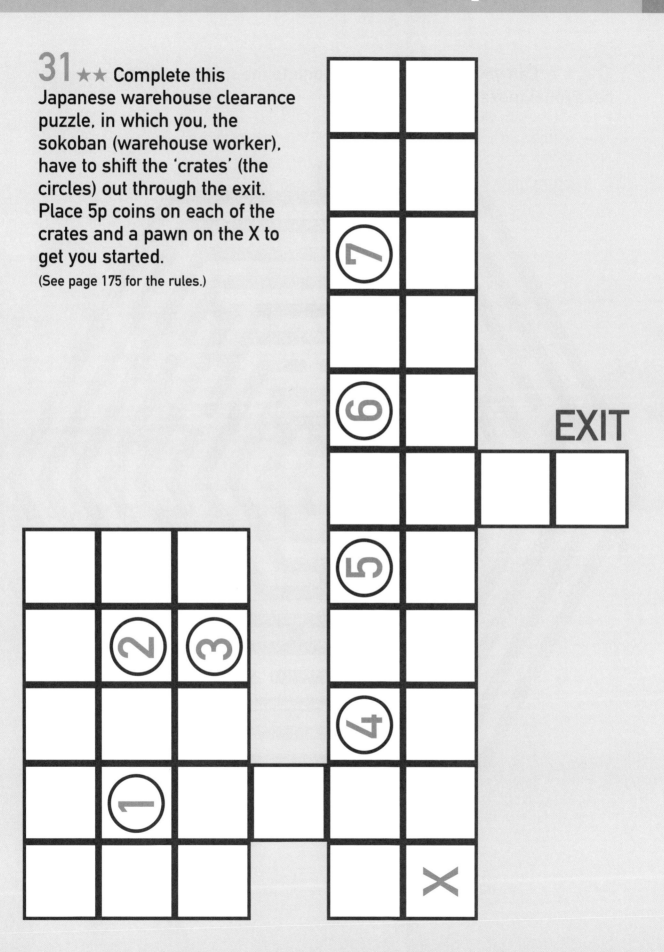

EXIT

7 6 5 4 2 3 1 X

**32★★** Can you find your way through to the middle of this hexagonal maze?

**33★★** Can you divide this picture by drawing two straight lines to produce three sections, each containing three nuts and five screws?

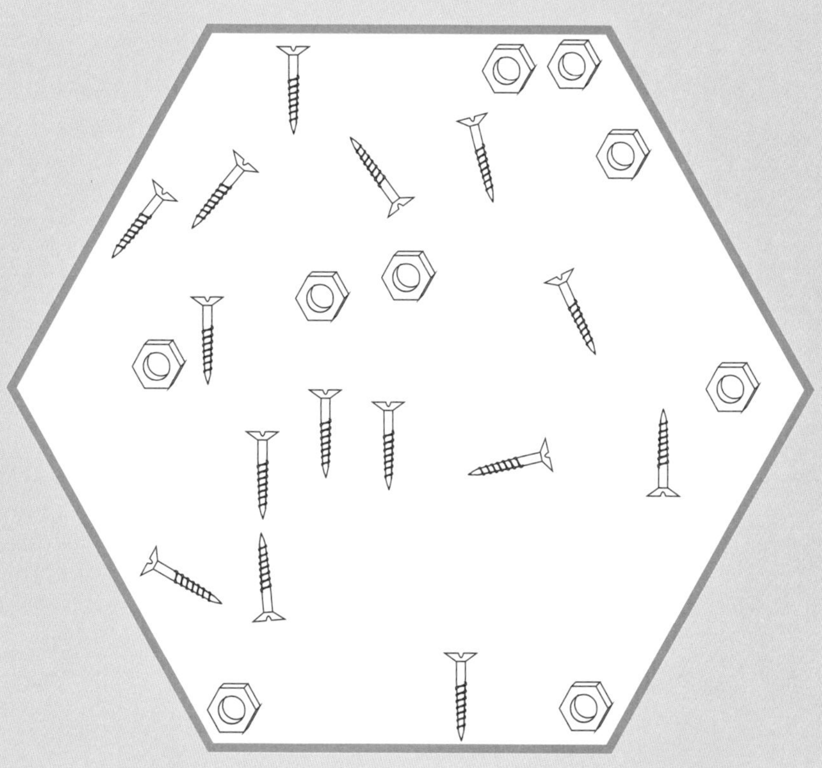

**34★** At first glance these fish may look the same, but one is slightly different. Which is the odd one out?

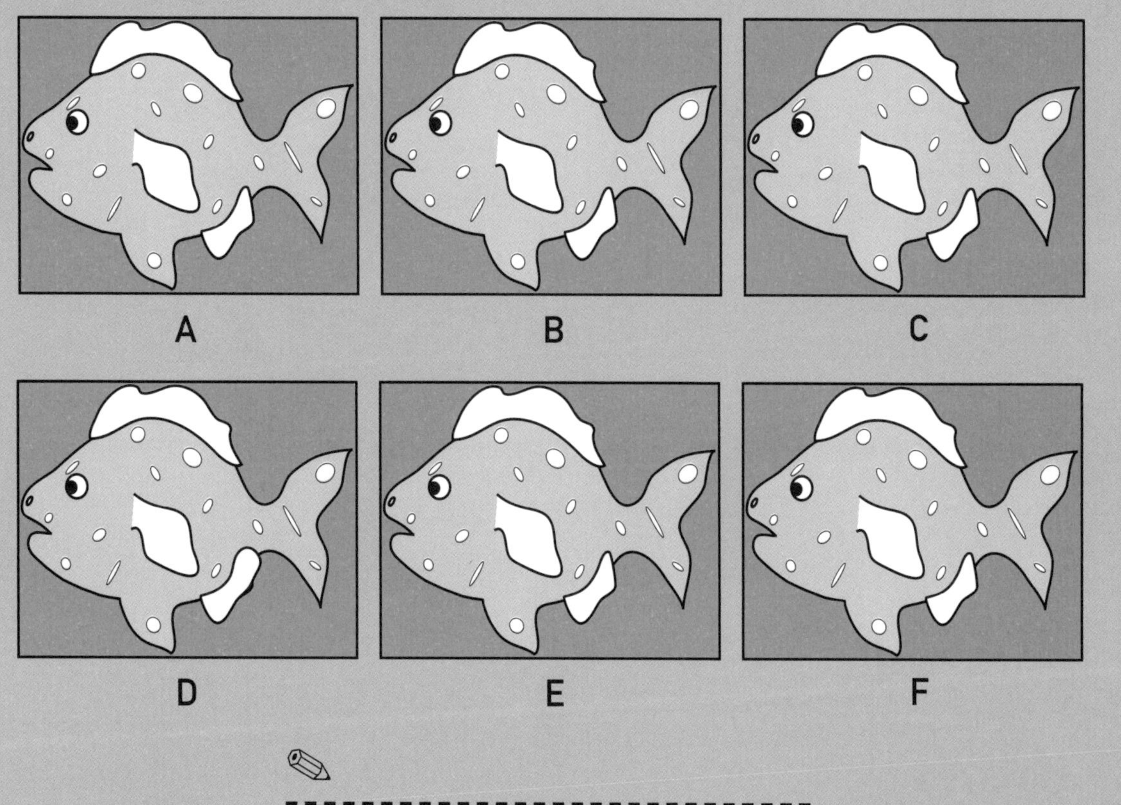


---------------------------------

35★★ Below are six shapes, each with a different number in the centre. Study the shapes for 1 minute then see if you can answer the questions on page 192.

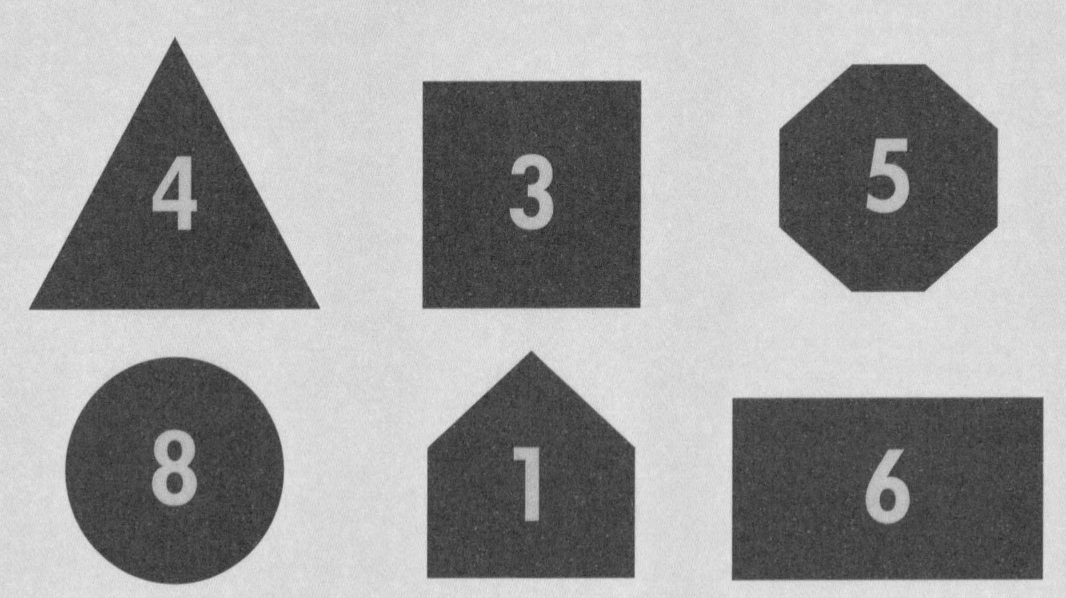


36★★ Solve the sequence to see if you're visually minded.

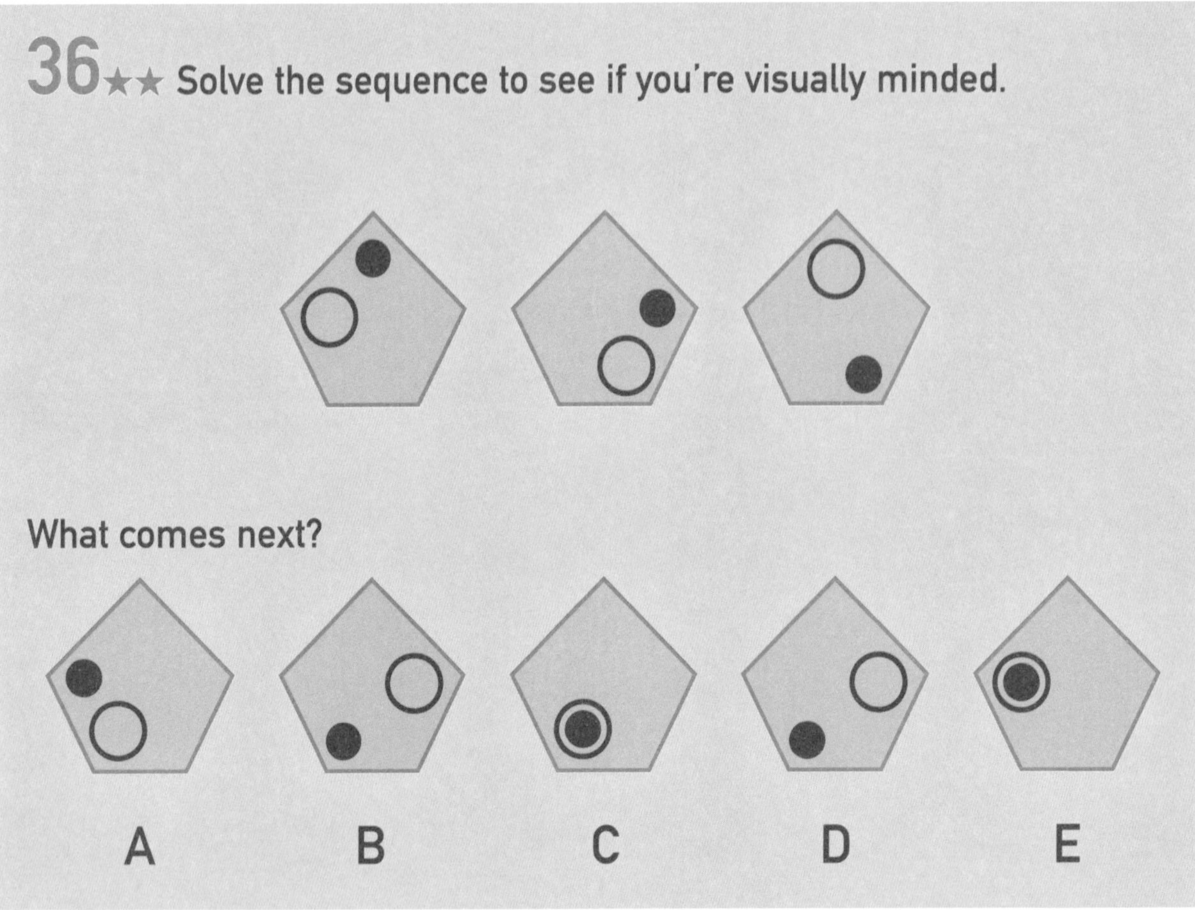

**37★** In the following group of dominoes, which one is missing?

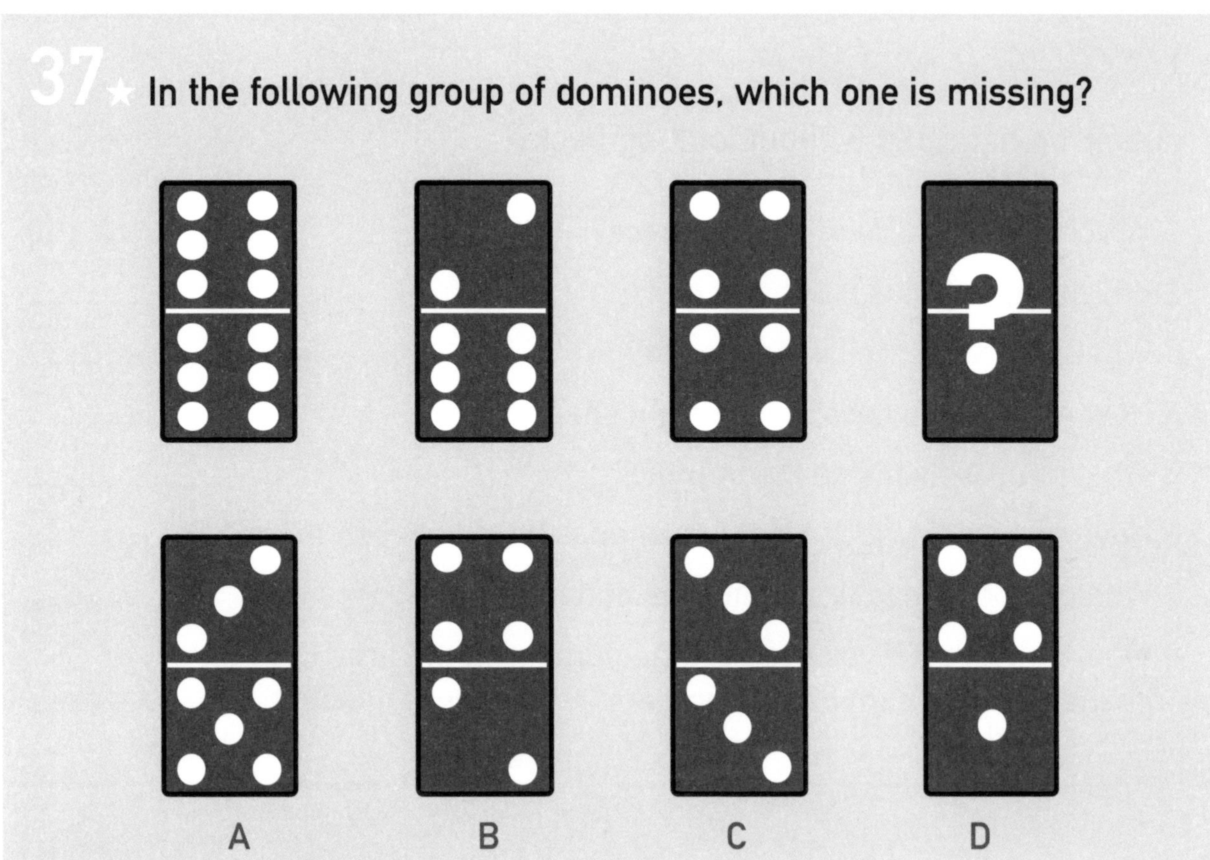


**38★★** How many revolutions must the large cog make to return all the cogs to their starting position?

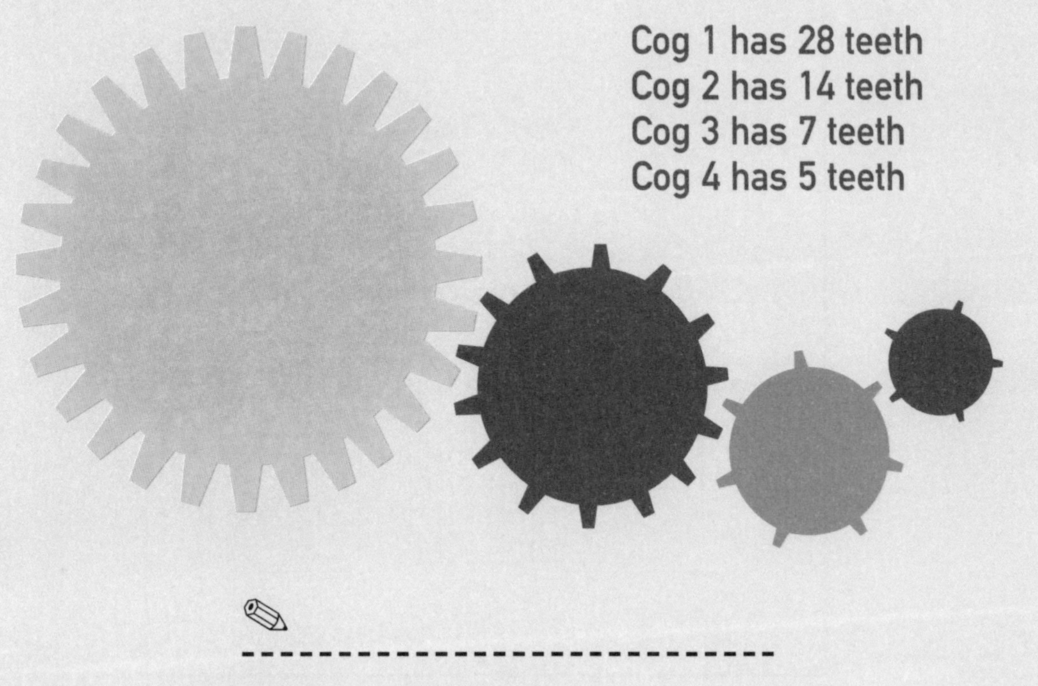

Cog 1 has 28 teeth
Cog 2 has 14 teeth
Cog 3 has 7 teeth
Cog 4 has 5 teeth

## 35 questions

Can you answer these questions to the puzzle on page 190 without looking back?

1 Which shape is first in the sequence? ----------

2 Which shape has a number 1 in it? ----------

3 What number is inside the square? ----------

4 How many sides does the top right shape have? ----------

5 What number is inside the triangle? ----------

6 How many sides do the last two shapes have between them? ----------

7 What shape comes first on the second row? ----------

8 What do you get if you subtract the number in the first shape from the sum of the numbers in the other shapes? ----------

## 39★

Using three different colours (or labelling the areas using three different symbols), shade in this picture so no two areas that share a border are the same colour.

40★ Which are the only two pieces that will fit together perfectly to form a blue copy of this white shape?

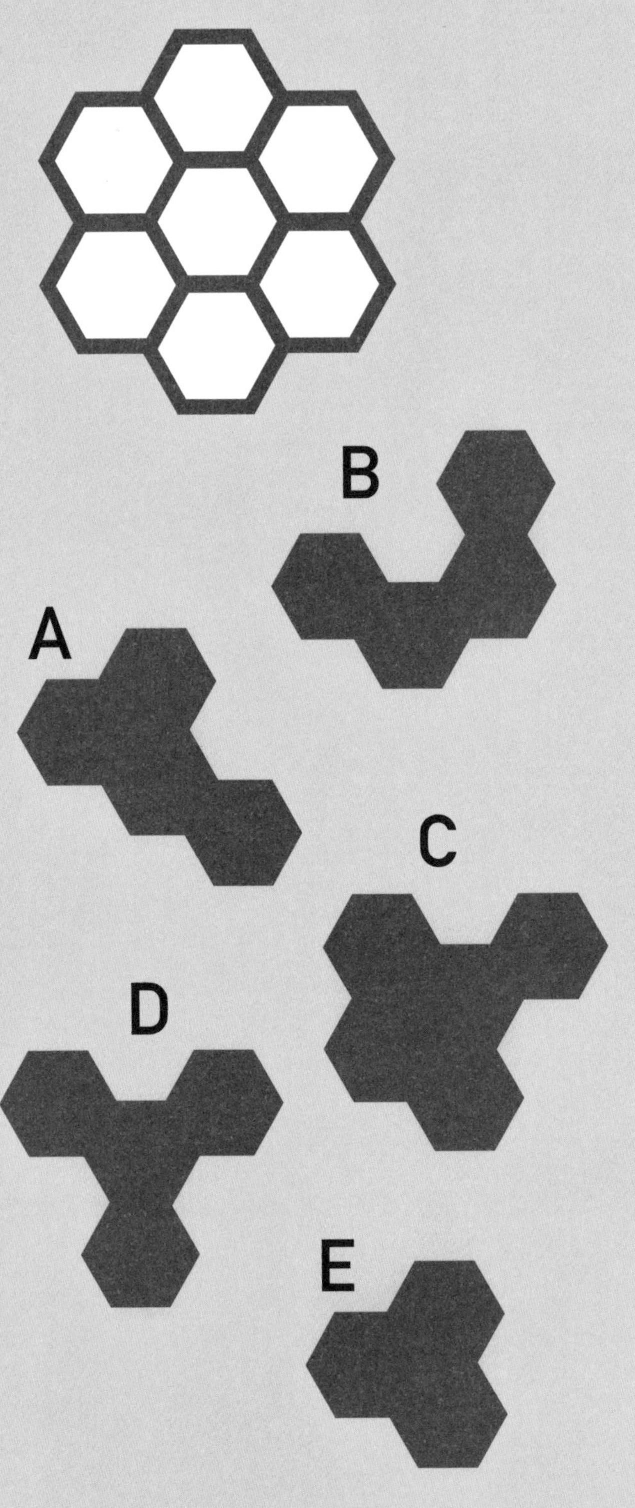


41★★ Can you find the link between these four items?

**42★★** When the shape on the right is folded to form a cube, which is the only one of the following that cannot be produced?

✎

A C B D

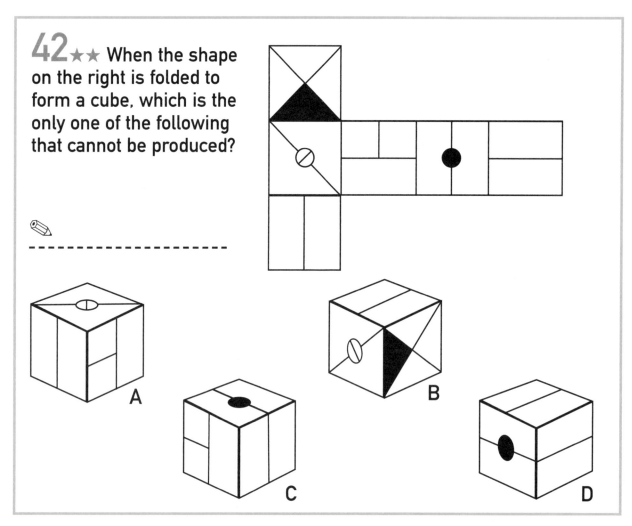

**43★** There is something wrong with one of these dice. Can you spot which one?

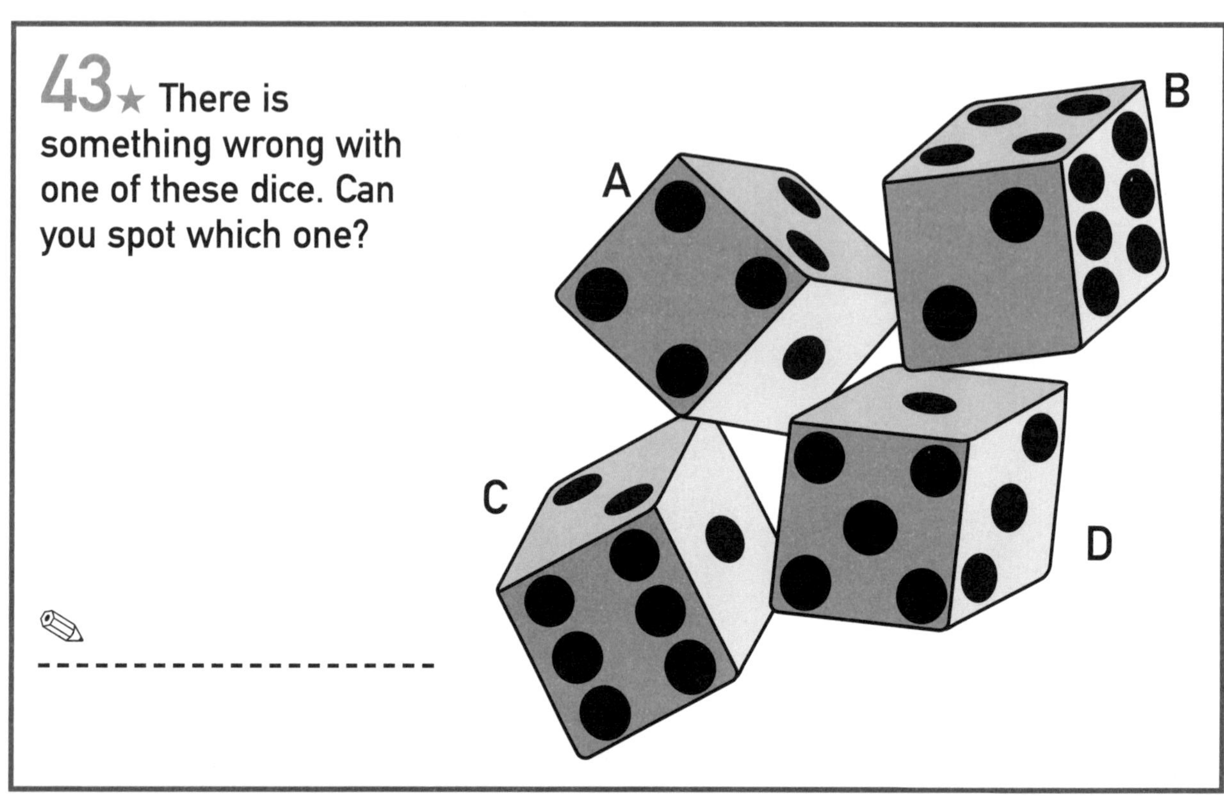


✎

**44**★★ How many squares are there altogether in this diagram? There may be many more than you at first think.

✎ ------------------------

**45**★★ Which of the four boxed figures completes the set?

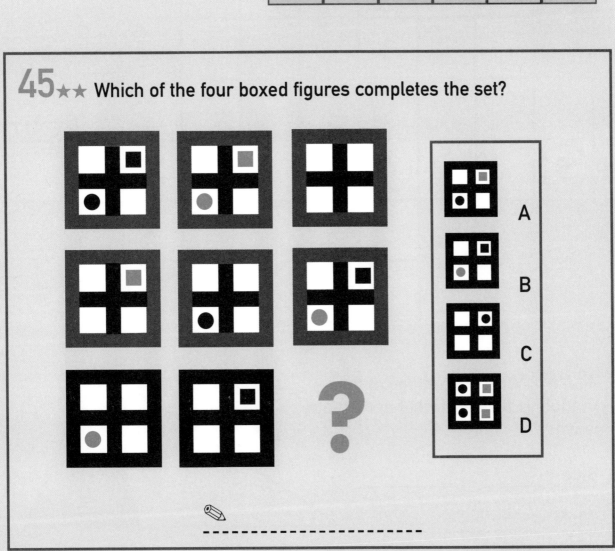

?

A

B

C

D

✎ ------------------------

**46★★** In this puzzle you are the sokoban (warehouse worker) and it's your job to move the 'crates' (the circles) out of the exit. Place some 5p coins on the circles and a pawn on the X to start. (See page 175 for the rules.)

**47★★** What percentage of the triangle is blue and what percentage is white?

Blue % ----------------------------

White % ----------------------------

48★★ How many revolutions must the large cog make to return all the cogs to their starting positions?

Cog 1 has 51 teeth
Cog 2 has 17 teeth
Cog 3 has 4 teeth
Cog 4 has 3 teeth

✎ ---------------

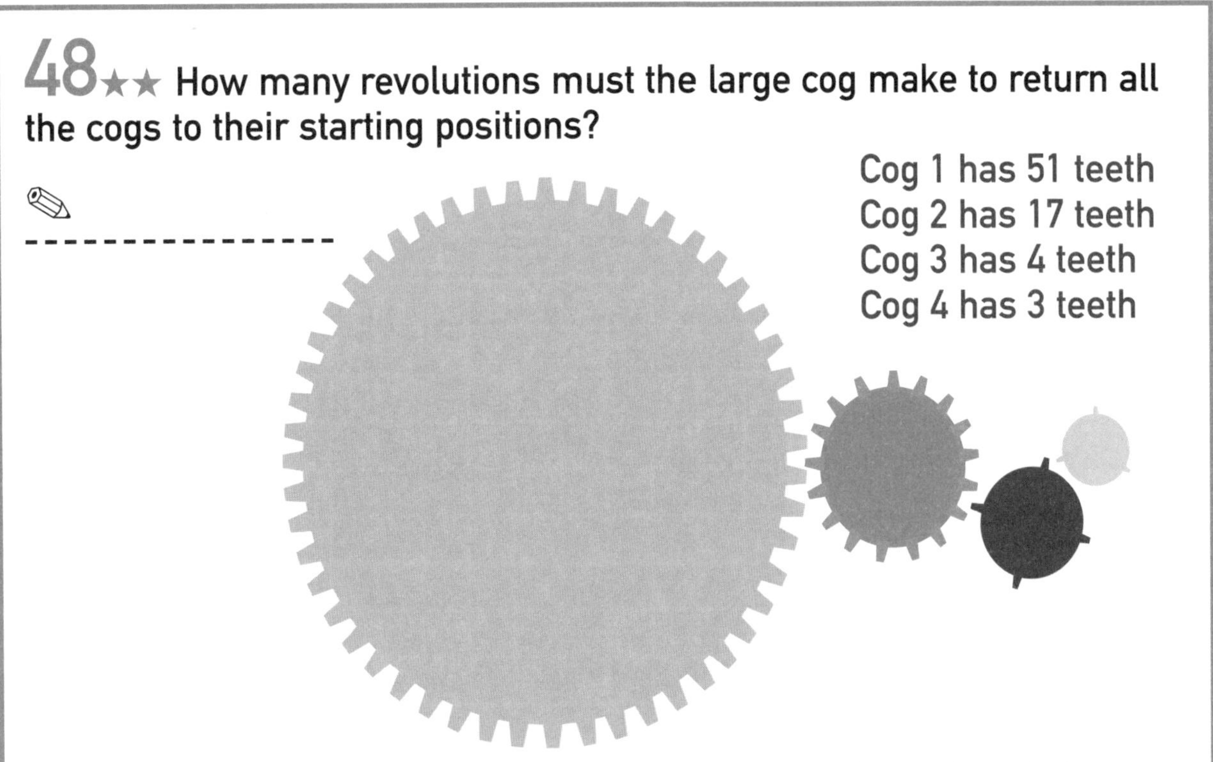

49★★★ Farmer Brown set his son a problem: to erect eight perfectly straight fences in a symmetrical pattern in the big field below, dividing it into five smaller fields, each containing two cows, three pigs and four sheep. How can the farmer's son achieve this?

**50**★★ **Can you complete this nonogram? Beware! It's not a jolly subject.** (See page 174 for details of how to solve these puzzles.)

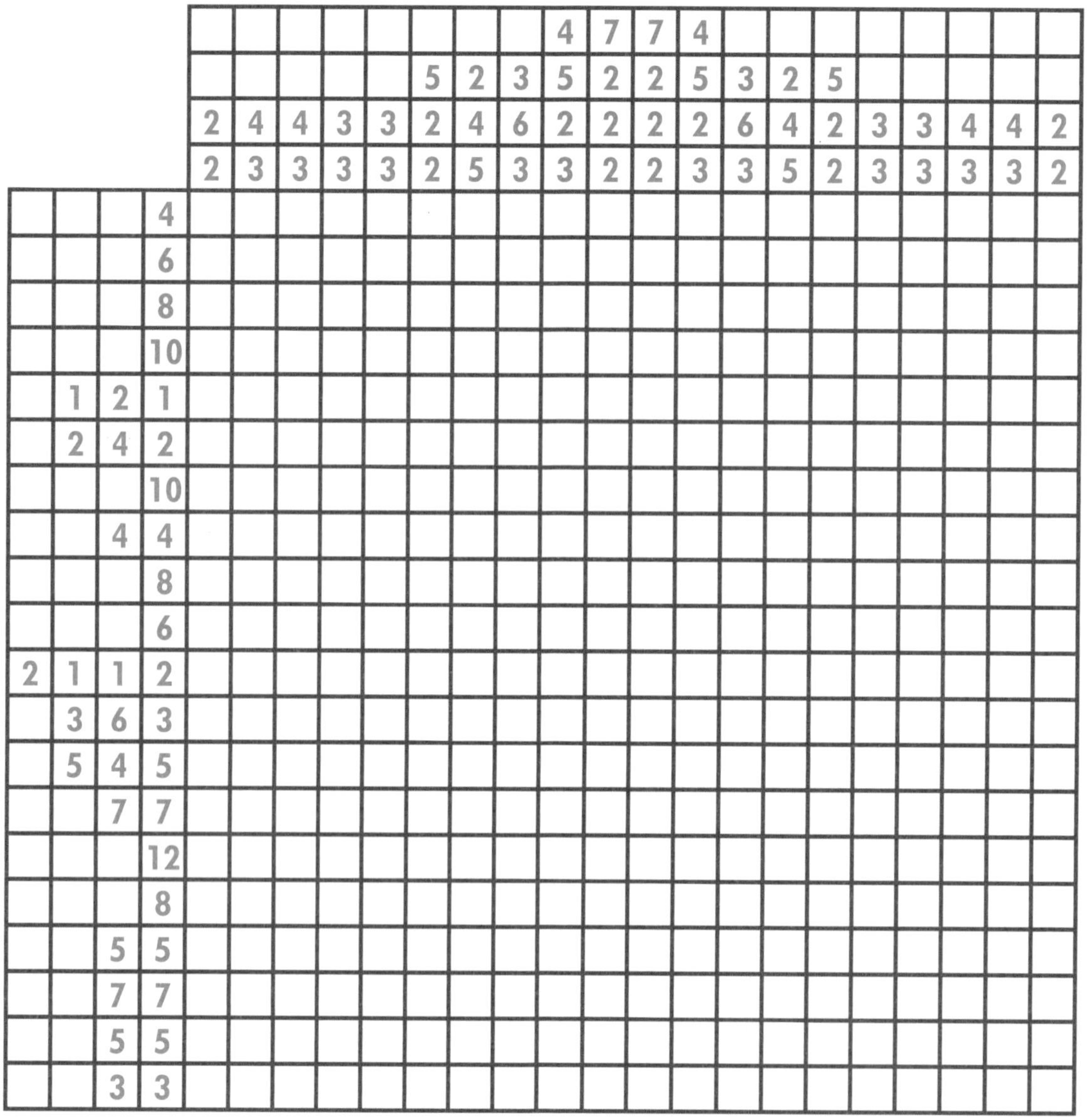

Column clues (top to bottom, columns left to right):

| 1 | 2 | 3 | 4 | 5 | 6 | 7 | 8 | 9 | 10 | 11 | 12 | 13 | 14 | 15 | 16 | 17 | 18 | 19 | 20 |
|---|---|---|---|---|---|---|---|---|---|---|---|---|---|---|---|---|---|---|---|
| | | | | | | | | 4 | 7 | 7 | 4 | | | | | | | | |
| | | | | | 5 | 2 | 3 | 5 | 2 | 2 | 5 | 3 | 2 | 5 | | | | | |
| 2 | 4 | 4 | 3 | 3 | 2 | 4 | 6 | 2 | 2 | 2 | 2 | 6 | 4 | 2 | 3 | 3 | 4 | 4 | 2 |
| 2 | 3 | 3 | 3 | 3 | 2 | 5 | 3 | 3 | 2 | 2 | 3 | 3 | 5 | 2 | 3 | 3 | 3 | 3 | 2 |

Row clues (rows top to bottom):

| Row | Clue |
|---|---|
| 1 | 4 |
| 2 | 6 |
| 3 | 8 |
| 4 | 10 |
| 5 | 1 2 1 |
| 6 | 2 4 2 |
| 7 | 10 |
| 8 | 4 4 |
| 9 | 8 |
| 10 | 6 |
| 11 | 2 1 1 2 |
| 12 | 3 6 3 |
| 13 | 5 4 5 |
| 14 | 7 7 |
| 15 | 12 |
| 16 | 8 |
| 17 | 5 5 |
| 18 | 7 7 |
| 19 | 5 5 |
| 20 | 3 3 |

**51**★ Take away just one of these three safety matches and leave no more than a match behind. Be prepared to groan when you work out the answer.

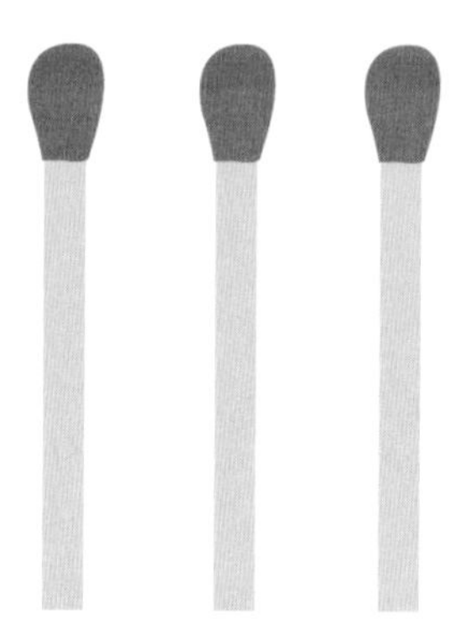

**52**★★ Miss Flannel would like a matching pair of bowls and pitchers for her newly decorated bedroom. Which two should she buy?

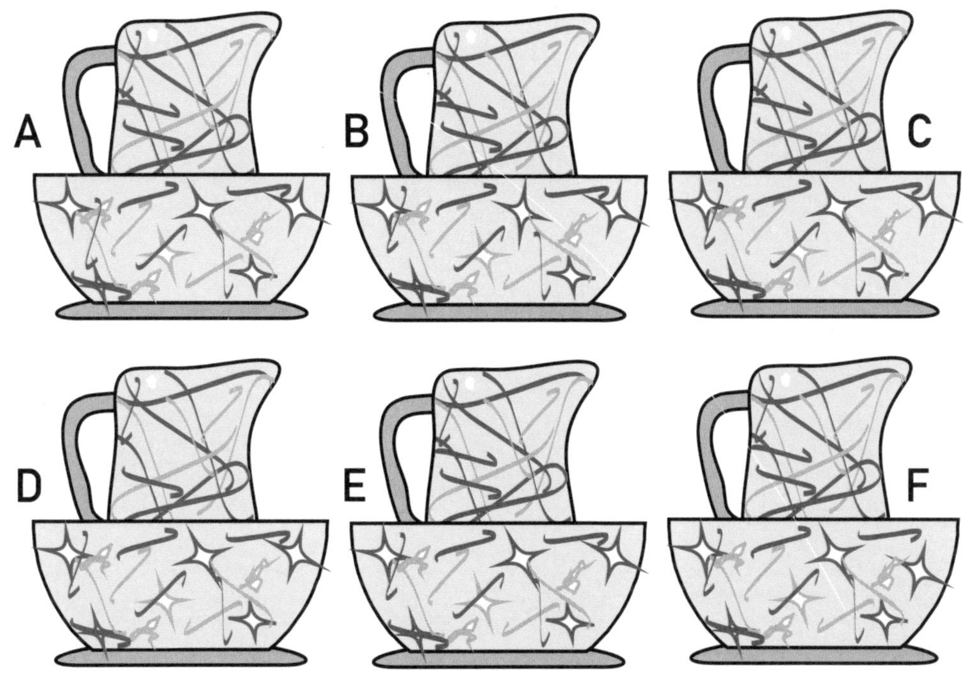


**53**★★ Can you spot the ten differences between these two pictures? Circle them in the lower drawing.

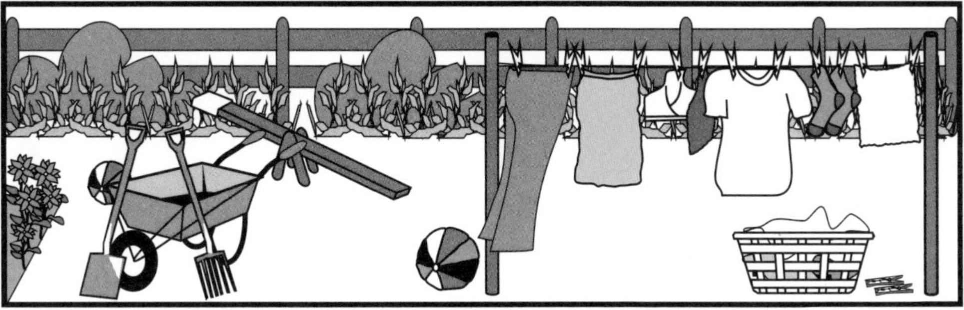

**54**★★★ A sum has been made from the upper faces of three dice… but it doesn't make sense. To make it work, you must roll each dice over in any direction by one quarter turn. No dice may be left in its original position. How many solutions are there, and what are they?

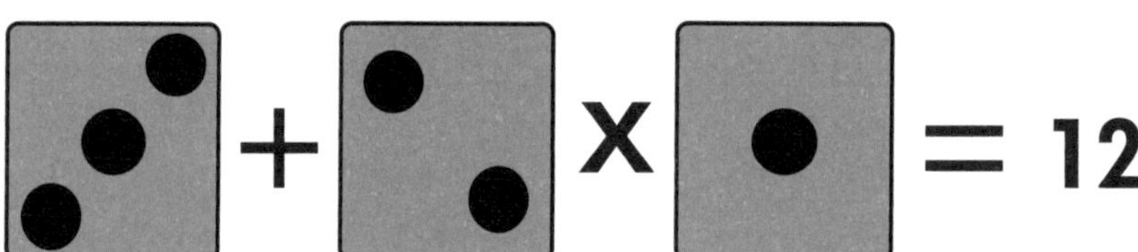


**55**★★★ Don't think about these questions too hard. Trust your initial instincts and see how many you answer correctly. Tick your answer.

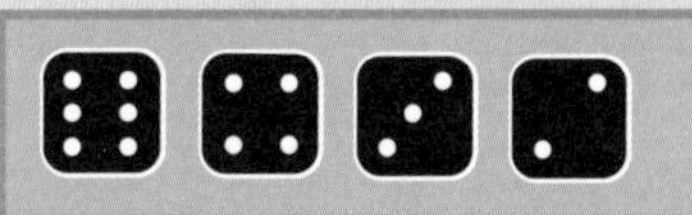

1 Do the reverse faces of these dice add up to 12?
YES
NO

2 Is this an unbeatable poker hand?
YES
NO

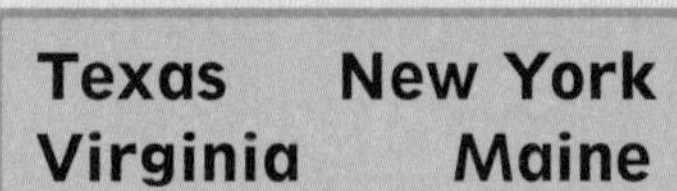


3 Do all these states have Atlantic coastlines?
YES
NO

4 This is your blackjack hand, have you bust?
YES
NO

| 90 | 142 |
|---|---|
| 166 | 78 |

5 Are any of these numbers divisible by 4?
YES
NO

| 316 | 305 |
|---|---|
| 911 | 280 |

6 Are these all model numbers of German cars?
YES
NO

| il | la |
|---|---|
| der | el |

7 Do all these words mean 'the'?
YES
NO

| Basketball team | Over |
|---|---|
| Colt 45 | Sextet |

8 Do all of these contain six?
YES
NO

## 56★ Can you solve the bubble problem?

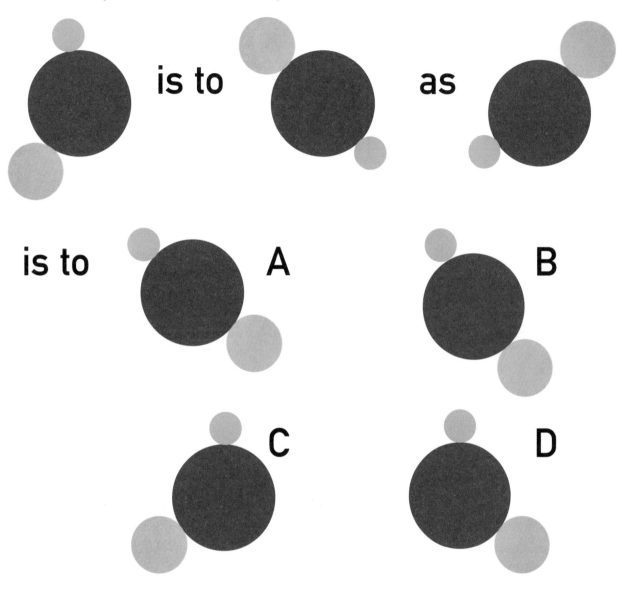

is to

as

is to

A

B

C

D

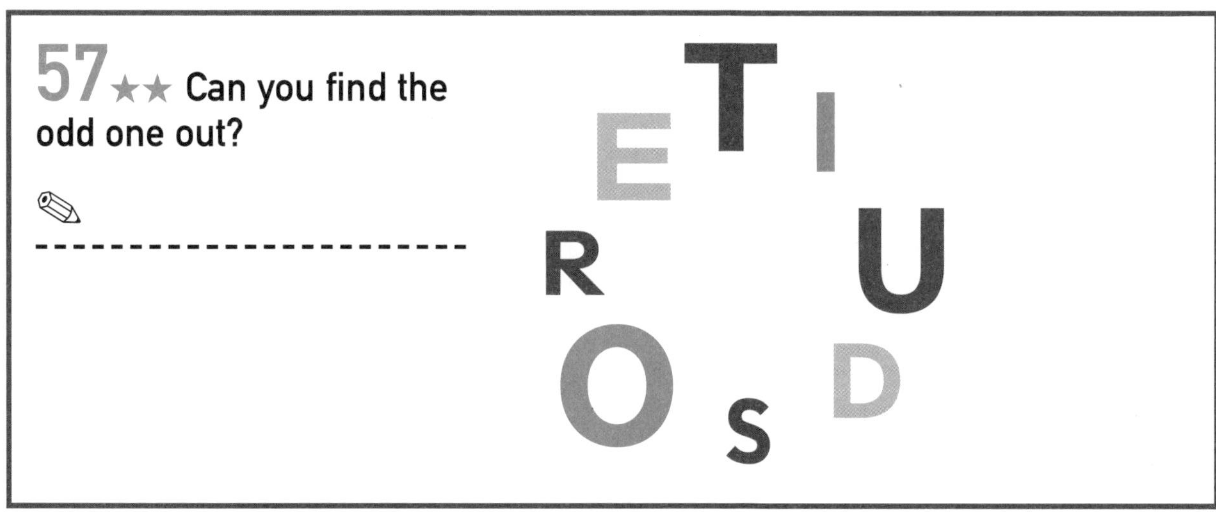

57★★ Can you find the odd one out?

**58★★** Which of the four boxed figures completes the set?

?

A

B

C

D

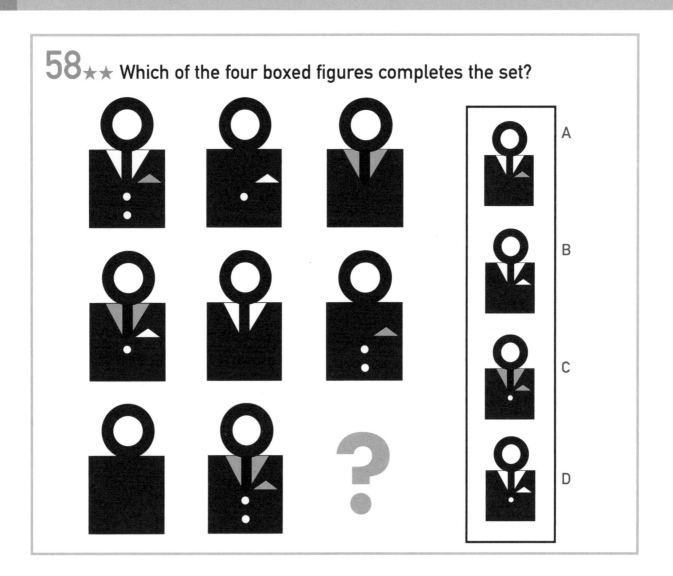

**59★★★** Here's a posy poser! One of these bunches of flowers doesn't fit into this group. Which is it?

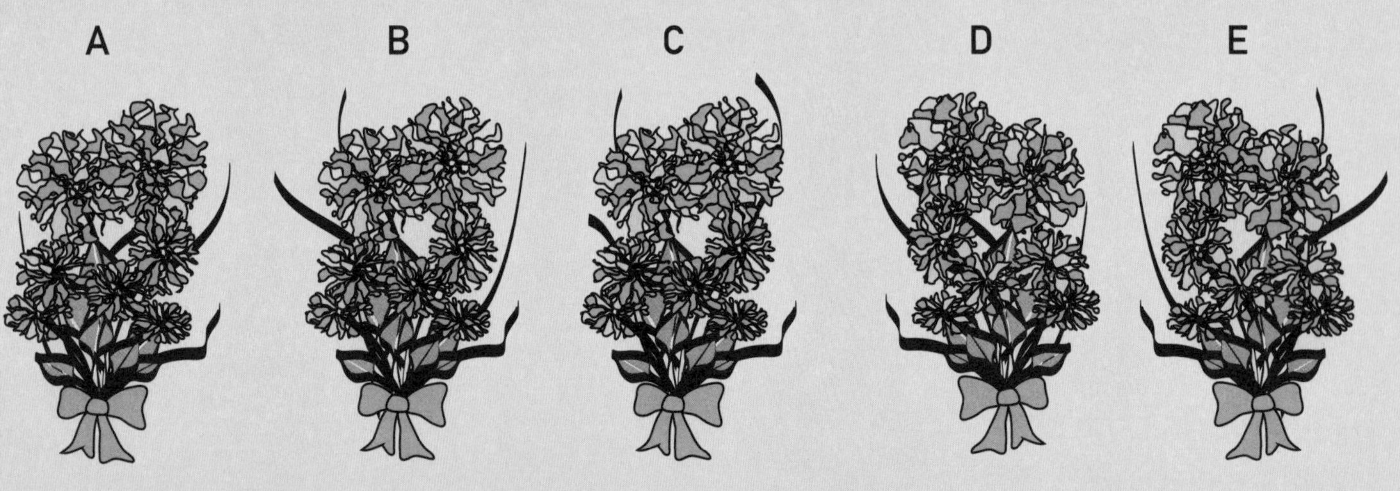

**60**★★★ These four counters are on a highly polished board. If you push any one of them (horizontally or vertically) they will keep moving until either they reach the edge of the board or hit another counter (but will not stop when they reach the star). For example, if you were to push 1 downwards it would move three squares then stop. The aim is to make any of the counters land on the star square in the centre. It is possible to do it in ten moves – how close can you get?

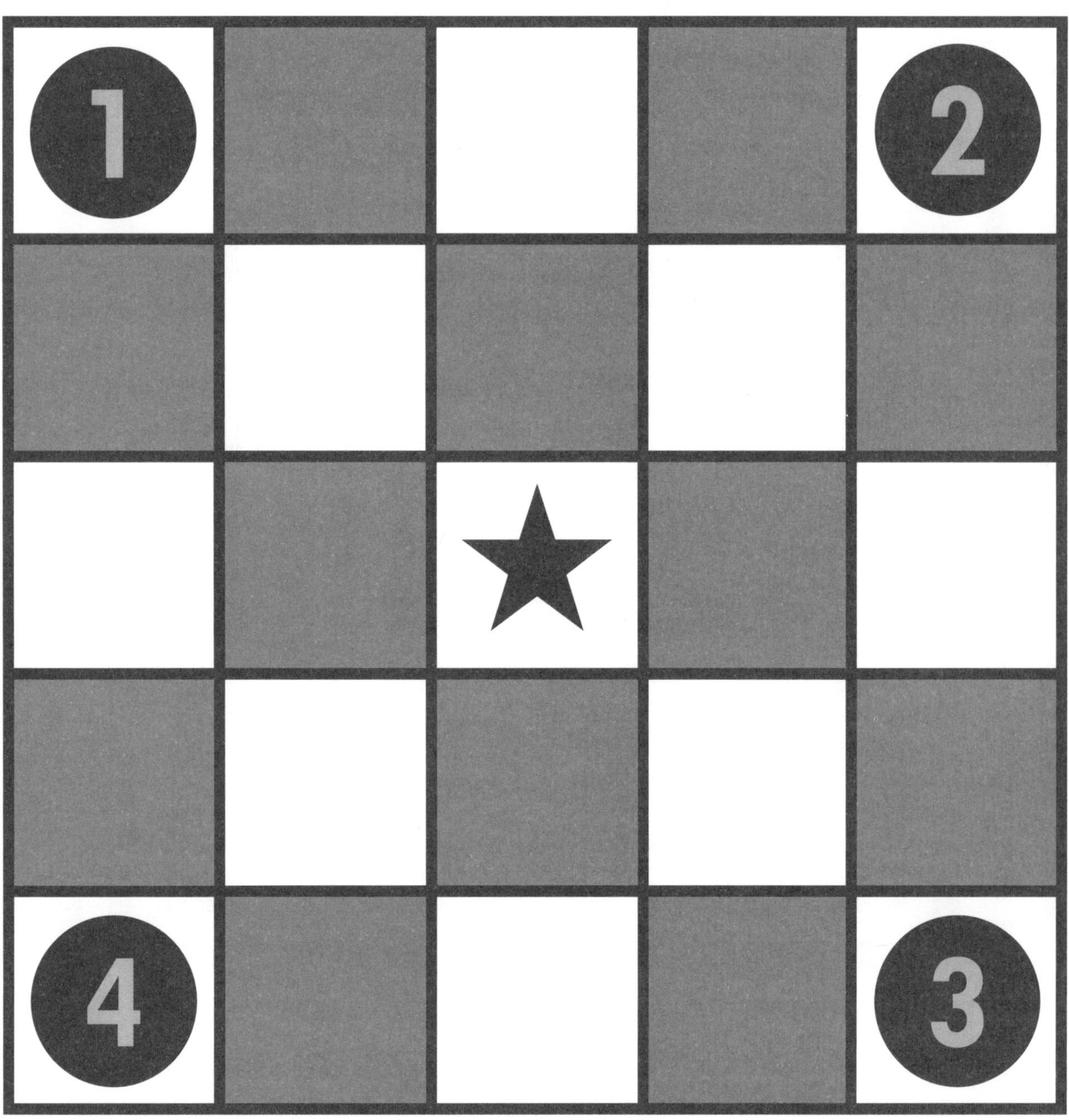

**61** ★★ Can you find your way through to the middle of this square maze to rescue the dog?

**62** ★★ Which of the four boxed figures completes the set?

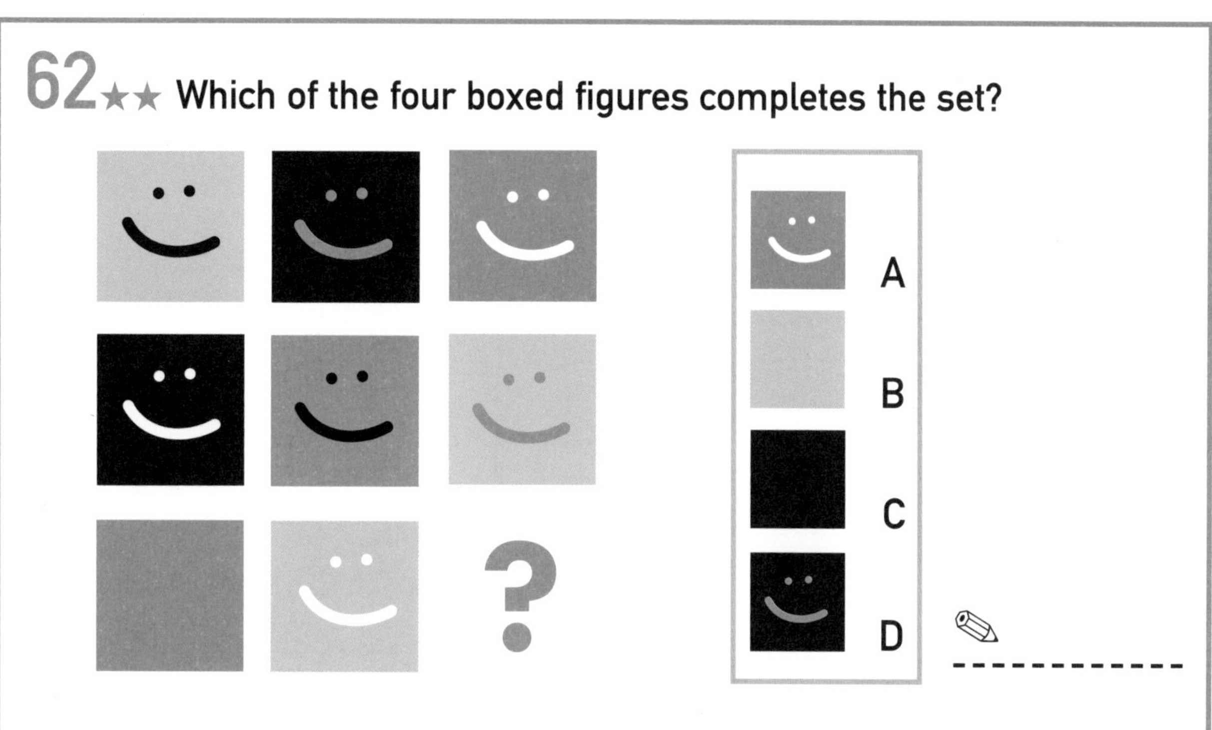


**63** ★★ Which are the only two pieces that will fit together perfectly to form a complete triangle?

**64** ★★ There are ten dominoes in this wall, but five have been masked out. Can you place the missing dominoes correctly, bearing in mind that each vertical line of four numbers (as well as the two end vertical lines of two numbers) adds up to eight?

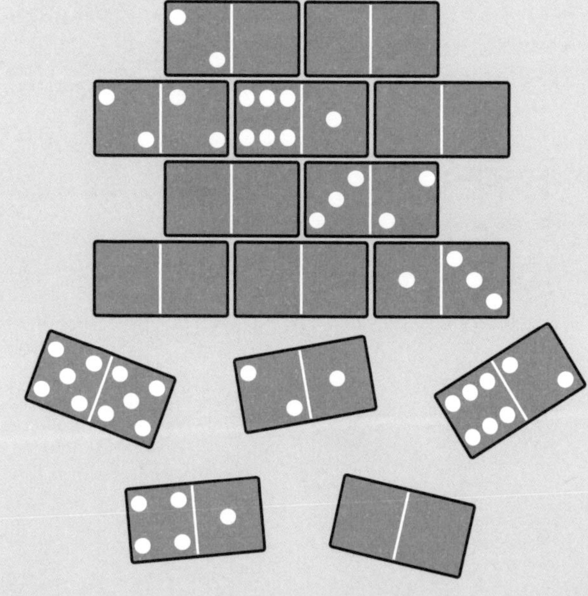

**65**★★ Study these shapes within shapes for 1 minute, then answer the questions on page 208 without looking back.

**66**★★★ Which shape should replace the question mark? Think laterally.

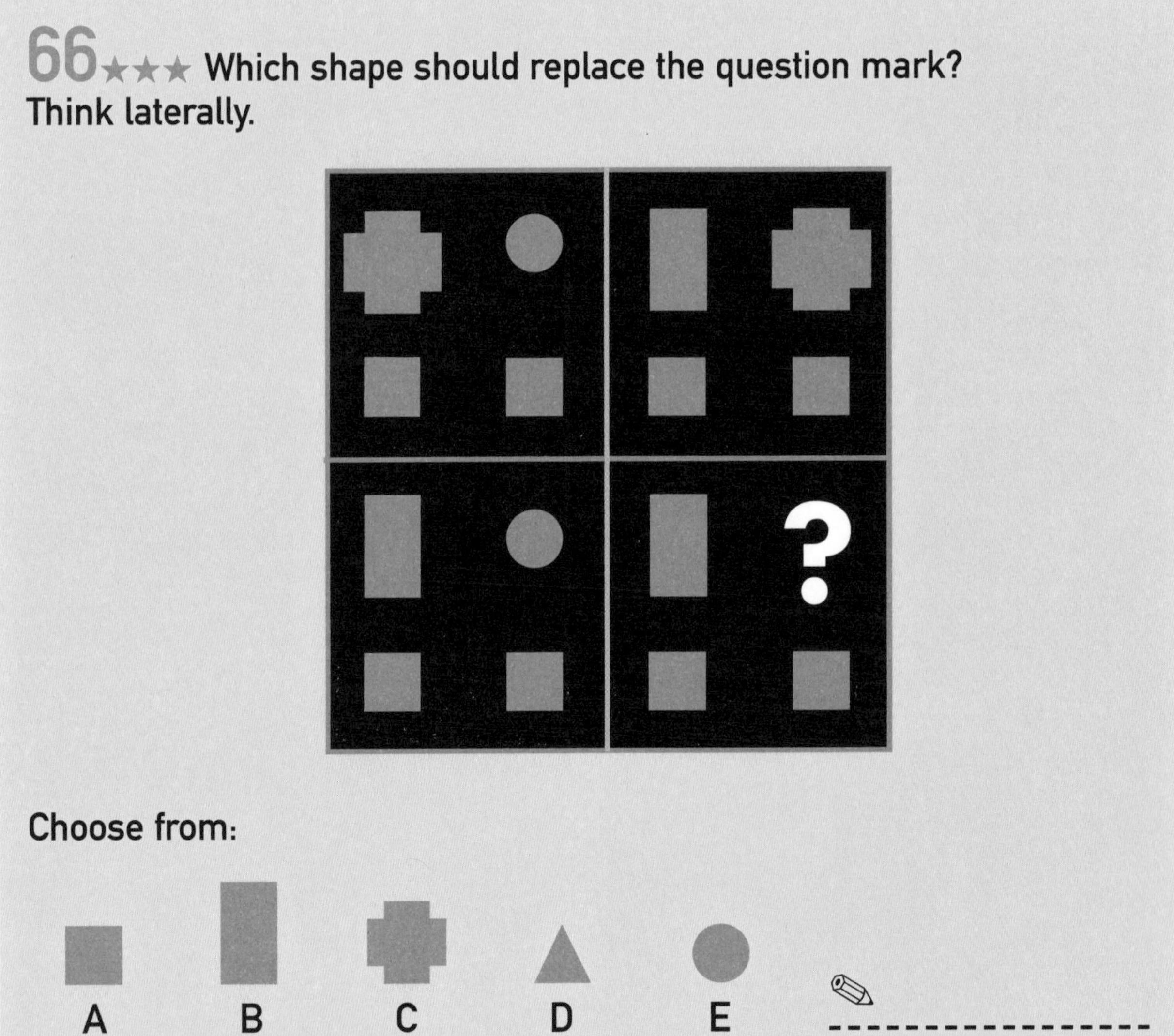

**67** ★★★ Which hexagon – A, B, C, D or E – should replace the question mark?

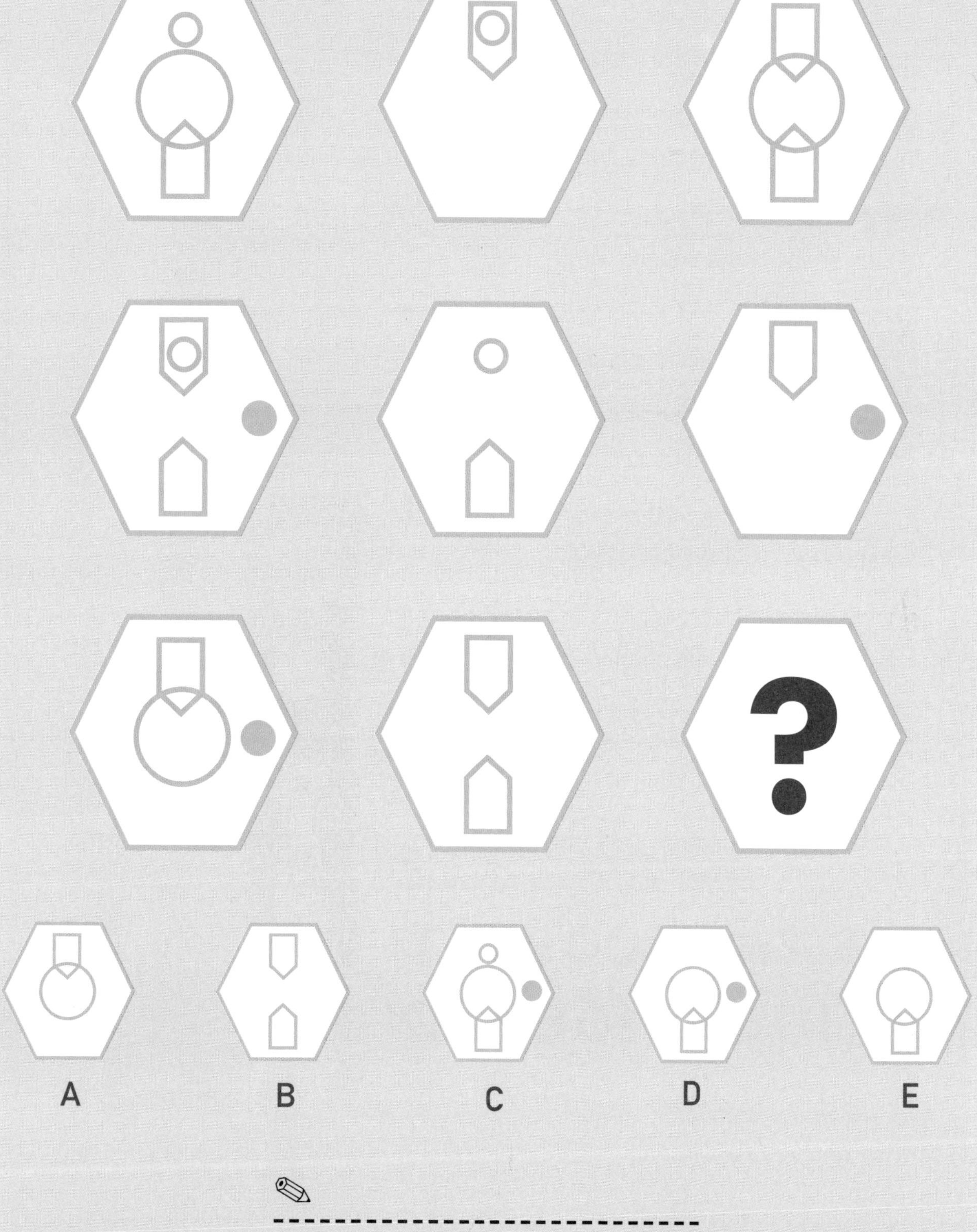


✎ ------------------------------

## 65 questions Can you answer these questions to the puzzle on page 206 without looking back?

1 Which shape lies in the middle of the shape in the centre?

✎ ------------------------------------

2 How many triangles are there altogether?

------------------------------------

3 There is one shaded circle. Which shape does it lie within?

------------------------------------

4 Which shape has a square within it?

------------------------------------

5 What outer shape lies second from the left?

------------------------------------

6 What's inside the shape second from the left?

------------------------------------

7 What shape is on the far right?

------------------------------------

8 How many four-sided shapes sit in the middle of other four-sided shapes?

------------------------------------

## 68★★ Can you crack this code? Singers ofTEN have such tricks!

**JIS THE IOOR'S TI WAS OFIO SOFIOED BY HIY**

----------------------------------------------------------------

**69★★★** How many revolutions must the large cog make to return all the cogs to their starting positions?

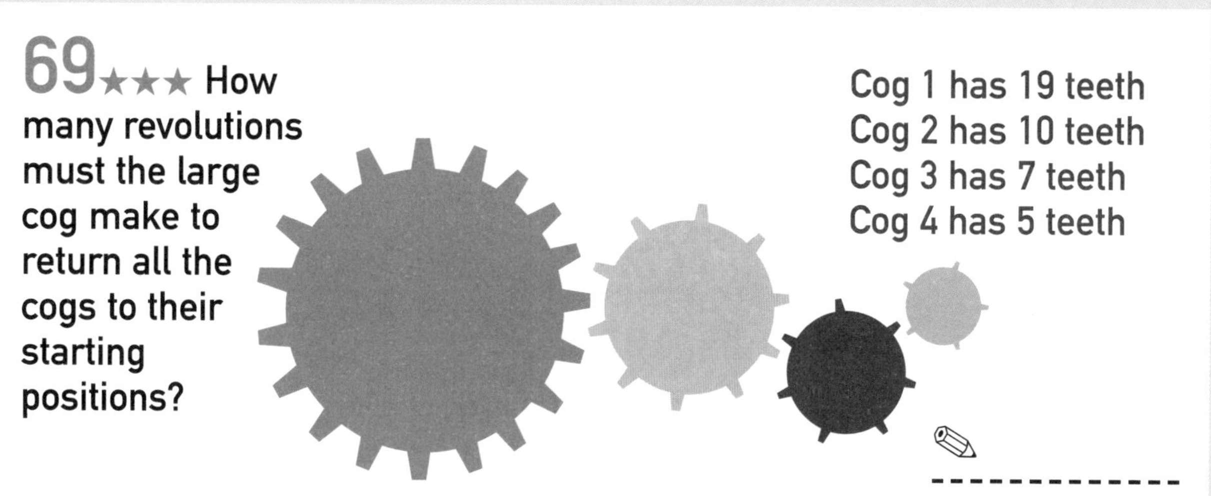

Cog 1 has 19 teeth
Cog 2 has 10 teeth
Cog 3 has 7 teeth
Cog 4 has 5 teeth

-------------

**70★★★ All aboard for this nonogram puzzle.** (See page 174 for details of how to do this type of puzzle.)

Column clues:

| | | | | | | | | | | | | | | | | | | | |
|---|---|---|---|---|---|---|---|---|---|---|---|---|---|---|---|---|---|---|---|
| | | | | 3 | | | | 3 | | | | | | | | | | | |
| | | 1 | 1 | 5 | 3 | | 3 | 5 | 1 | 3 | 3 | | 3 | 3 | 1 | 2 | | | |
| | | 1 | 5 | 2 | 5 | | 5 | 1 | 1 | 5 | 5 | 15 | 5 | 5 | 5 | 2 | | 2 | |
| 2 | 4 | 3 | 6 | 4 | 7 | 20 | 6 | 4 | 6 | 6 | 6 | 4 | 6 | 7 | 8 | 3 | 7 | 4 | 4 |

Row clues:

| | | | | | |
|---|---|---|---|---|---|
| | | | | 1 | 1 |
| | | | | 5 | 5 |
| | | | | 5 | 5 |
| | | | | | 13 |
| | | | | 1 | 1 |
| | | | | 1 | 1 |
| | | | | 6 | 6 |
| | | | | 6 | 6 |
| | | | | 6 | 6 |
| | | | | 6 | 6 |
| | | | | 15 | 2 |
| | | | 1 | 1 | 4 |
| 2 | 1 | 1 | 1 | 1 | 1 |
| | | | 7 | 1 | 6 |
| | | | | 1 | 16 |
| | 3 | 3 | 3 | 3 | 2 |
| | | | | | 17 |
| | | | | | 16 |
| | | | | | 14 |
| | | | | | 12 |

**71** ★★ Can you discover which windmill is the odd one out?

A B C

D E F

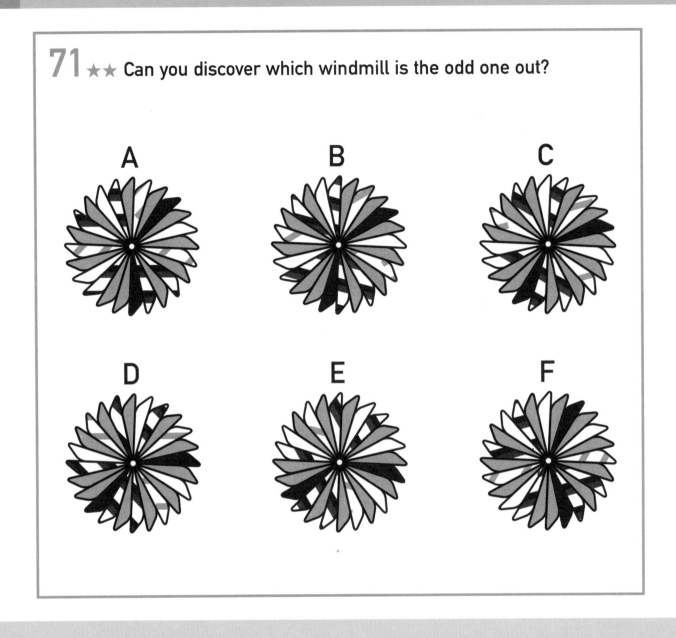

**72** ★★ Can you crack the code and discover where you might find a Swiss spy?

3 1322 15 34

**73** ★★★ Don't think about these questions too hard. Trust your instincts and see how many you can circle correctly.

Sloth Vanity
Pride Lust

1 Are these four of the Seven Deadly Sins?
YES
NO

Rash Duty Many Do
Weedy Sand Say Duet

2 Are these all anagrams of days of the week?
YES
NO

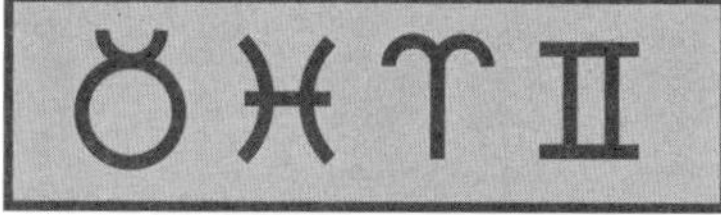

3 Do these astrological signs each have four legs?
YES
NO

1904 1932
1984 1996

4 Were these Olympic Games all held in the USA?
YES
NO

5 Do these keyboard symbols all begin with 'A'?
YES
NO

3 7
9 11

6 Is 101 divisible by any of these numbers?
YES
NO

Texas New York
Georgia Maine

7 Do all these state capitals begin with 'A'?
YES
NO

Au Ag
Cu Fe

8 Are all these chemical elements metals?
YES
NO

**74** ★★ Using three different colours (or labelling the areas using three different symbols), shade in the diagram so no two areas that share a border are the same colour.

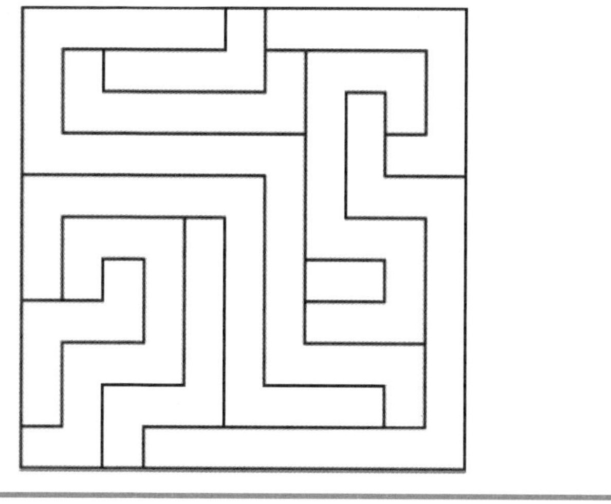

**75**★★★ Can you figure out how to solve this Japanese sokoban (warehouse worker) puzzle and push the 'crates' (the circles) out through the exit (in this one you can use either of the two exits marked to remove a crate)? Place coins on each of the crates, and a pawn on the X to get you started. (See page 175 for the rules.)

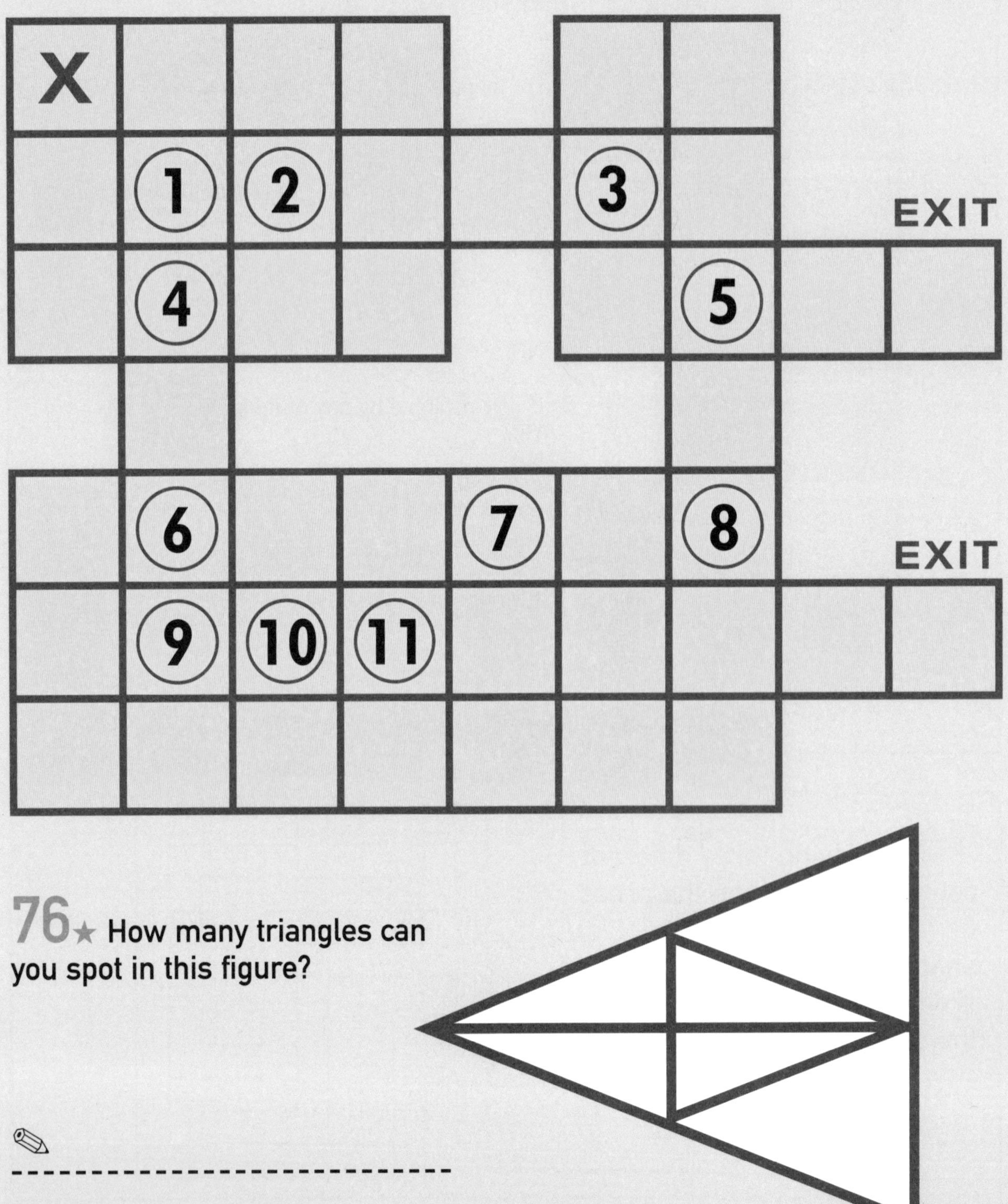


**76**★ How many triangles can you spot in this figure?

✎ ------------------------------

## 77 ★★ What is the value of the missing domino?

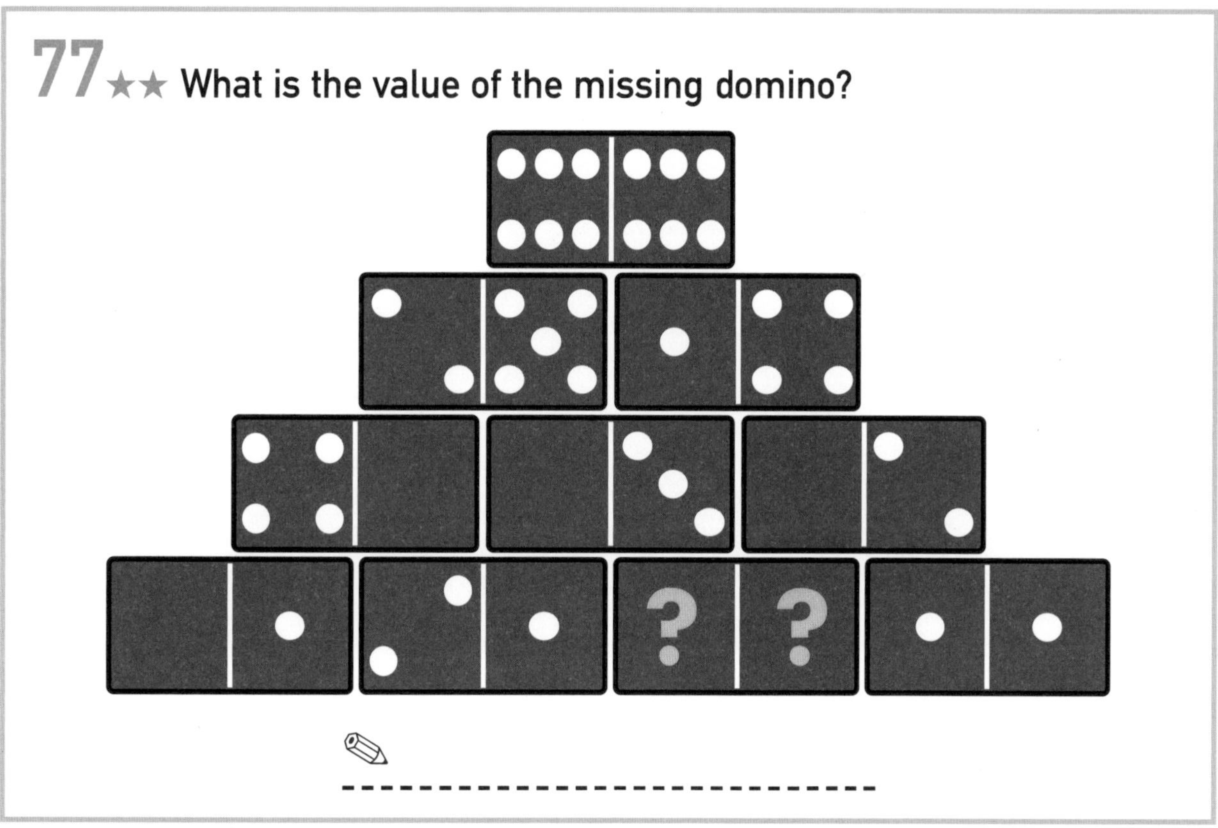


✎ ____________________________

## 78 ★★★ At first glance, these spinning tops may look the same, but only two are identical. Which is the matching pair?

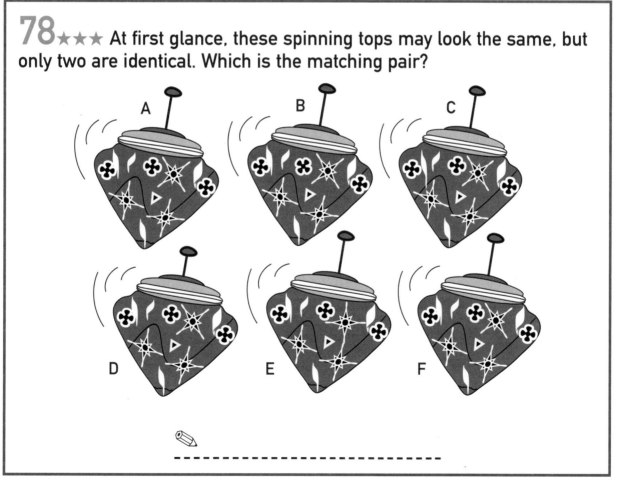

A B C

D E F

✎ ____________________________

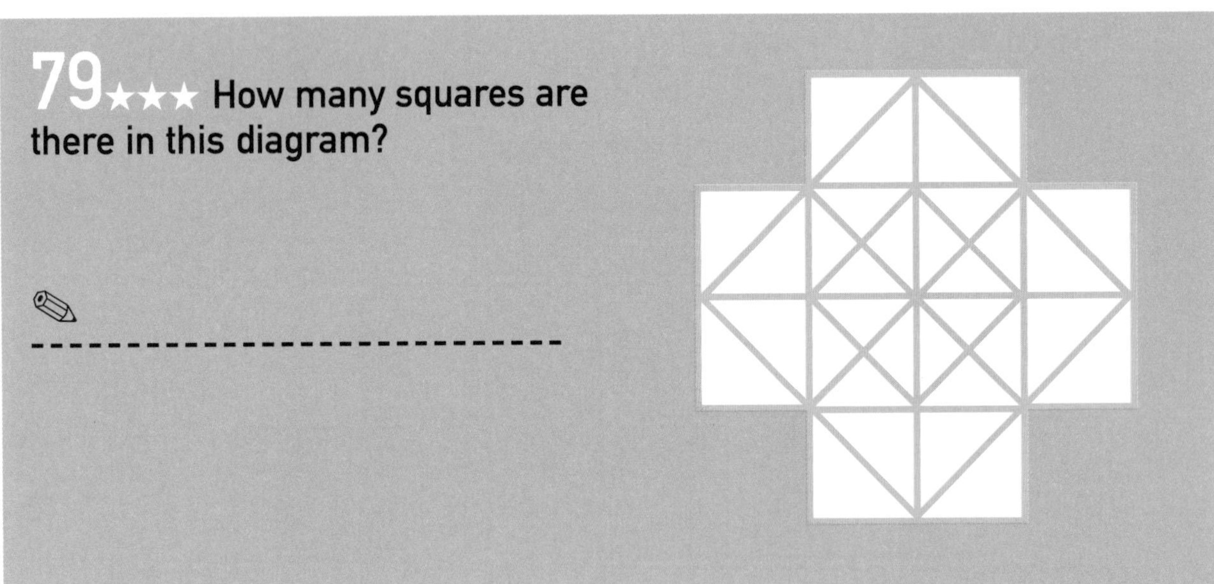

**79★★★** How many squares are there in this diagram?

✎ ------------------------------

**80★★** When the shape below is folded to form a cube, which if any of the following can be produced?

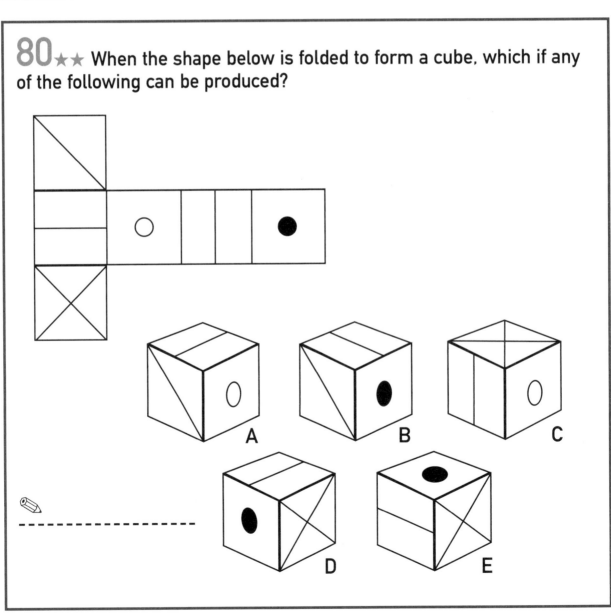

✎ --------------------

81★★★ Take away the two sticks indicated by the arrows and then rearrange the two remaining sticks to leave a capital H. Think laterally.

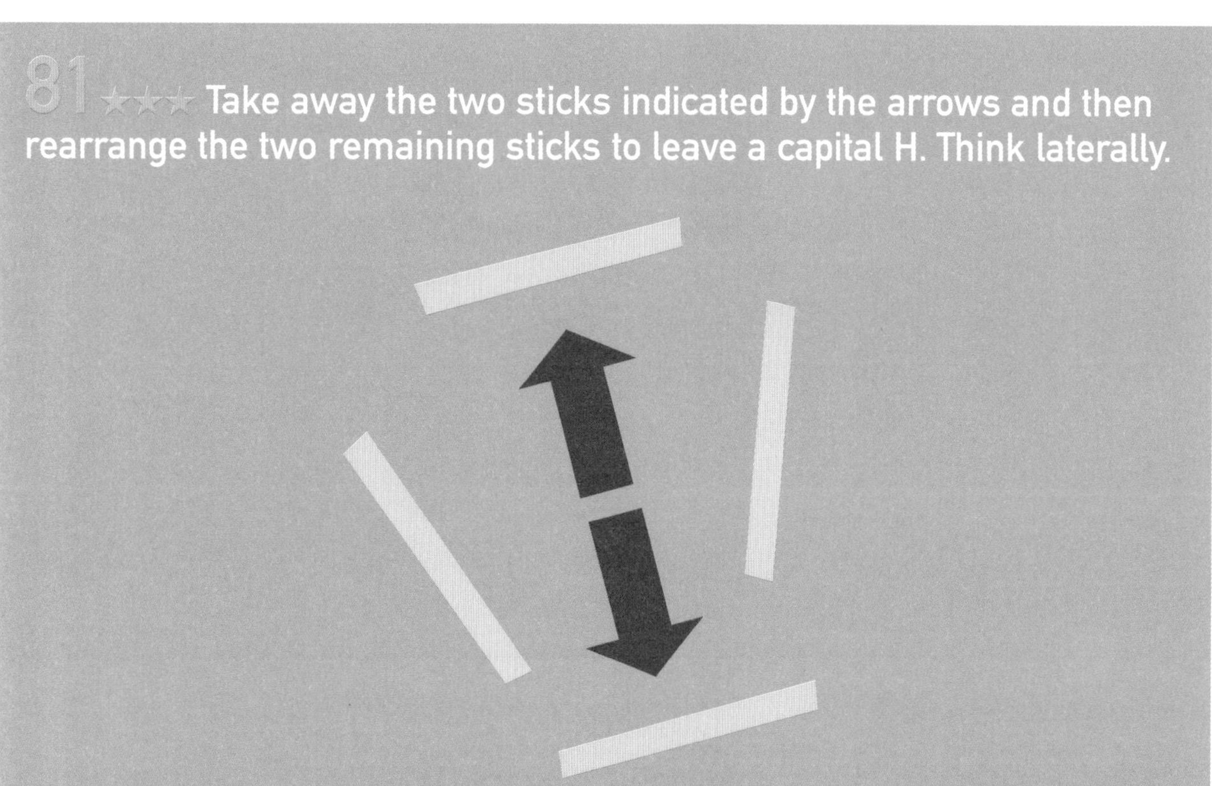

82★★ Can you spot the ten differences between these two pictures? Circle them in the drawing on the right.

**83** ★★★ Crack the code to find out where you might uncover a *French* spy.

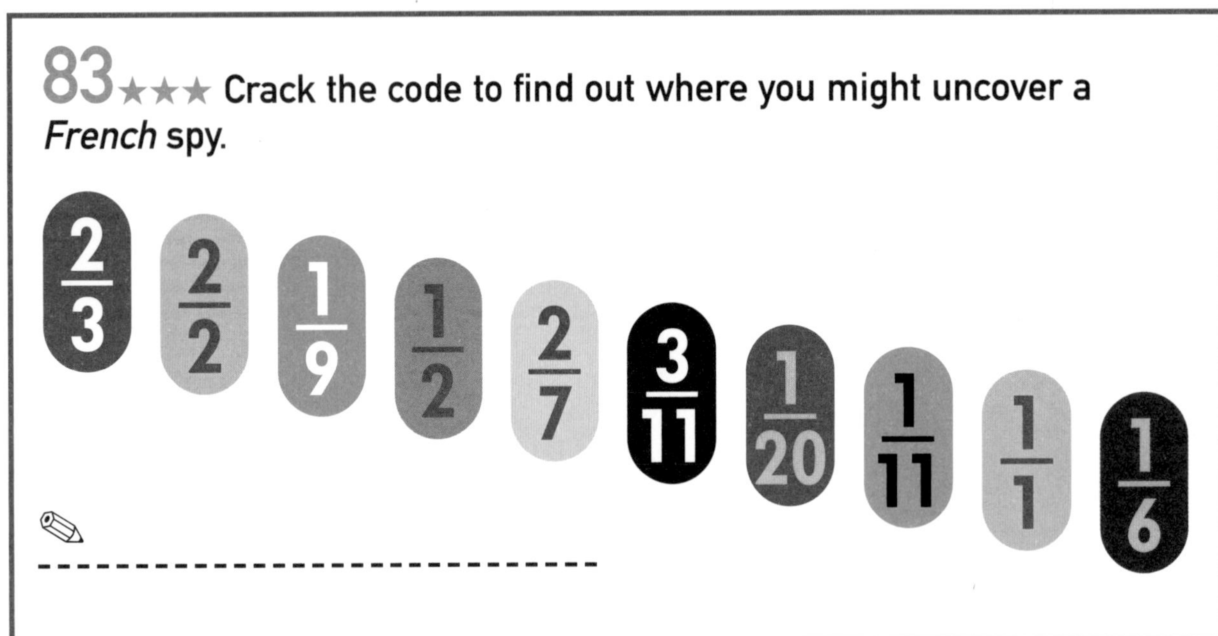


✎ ____________________________

**84** ★★★ Can you solve this visual conundrum?

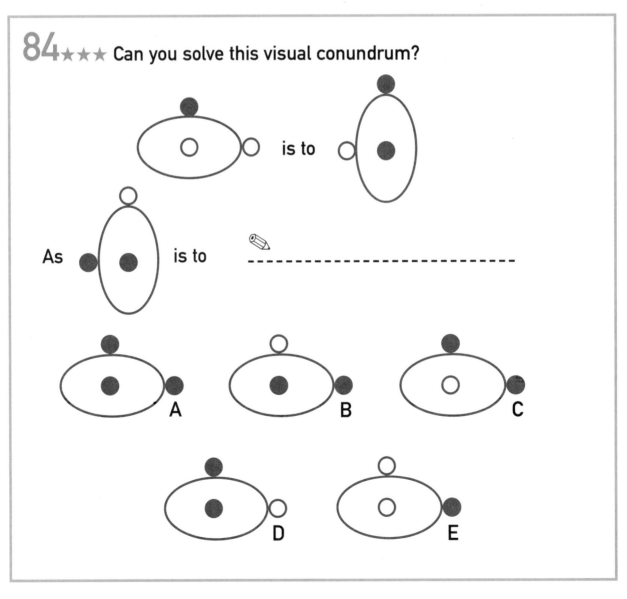

is to

As is to ✎ ____________________________

A B C

D E

**85** ★★★ Someone has started to build a wall. Can you finish the task, by putting into position the remaining seven dominoes? Bear in mind, however, that in each horizontal row there must be six different groups of spots, which together add up to the total to the right of each row; and in each vertical column, there must be three different groups of spots, which add up to the total at the base of each column.

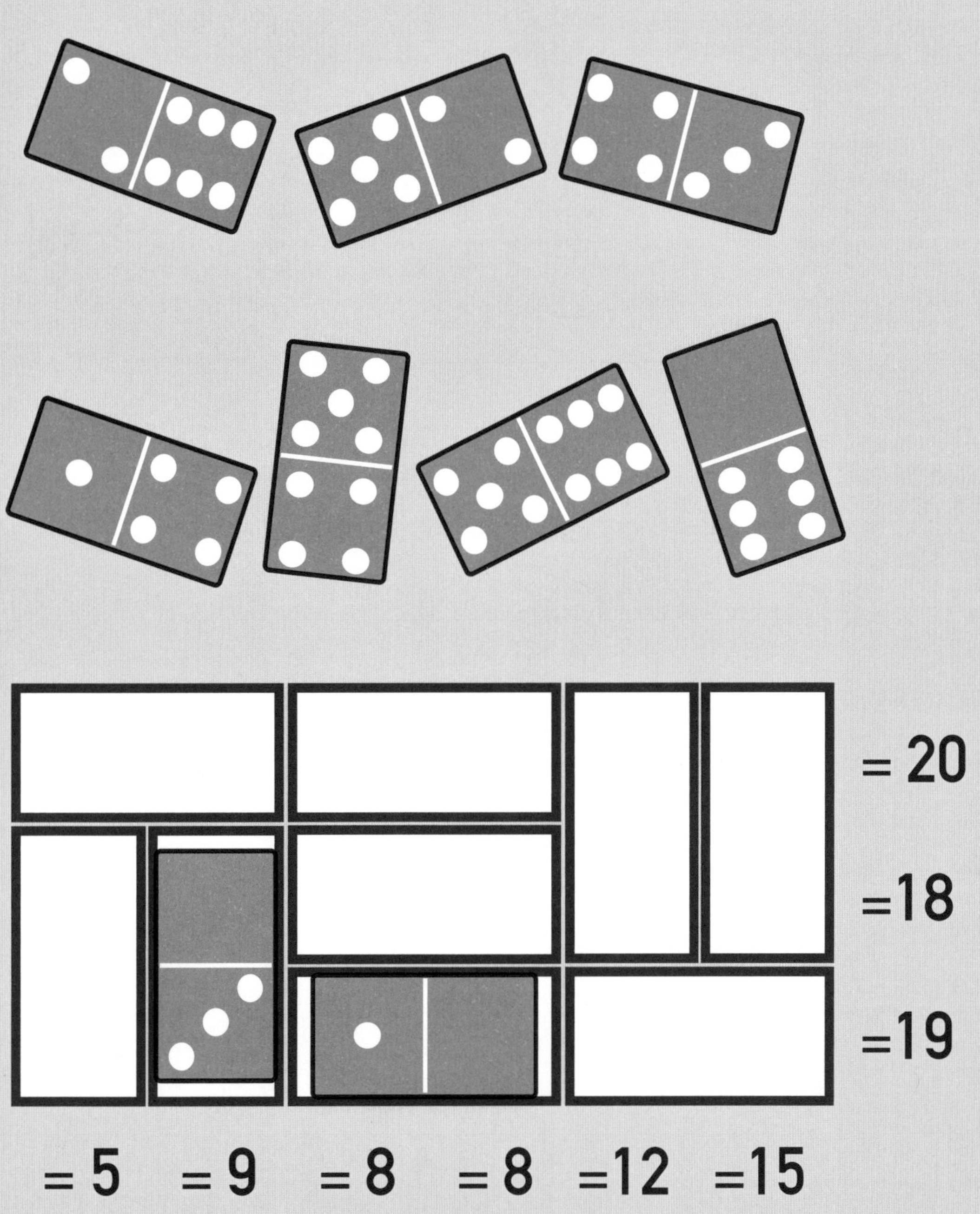

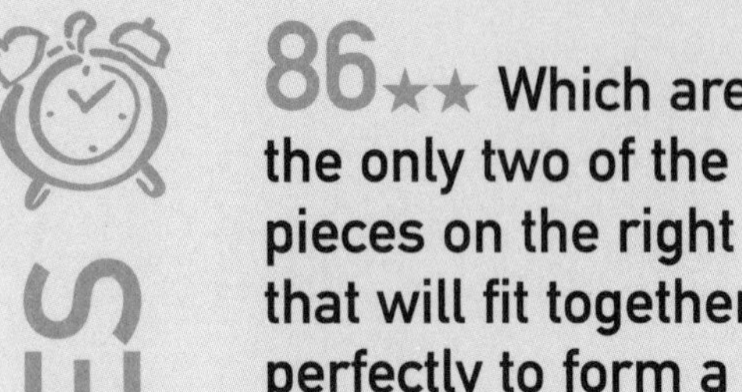

5 MINUTES

**86** ★★ Which are the only two of the pieces on the right that will fit together perfectly to form a cube made up of 27 smaller cubes?

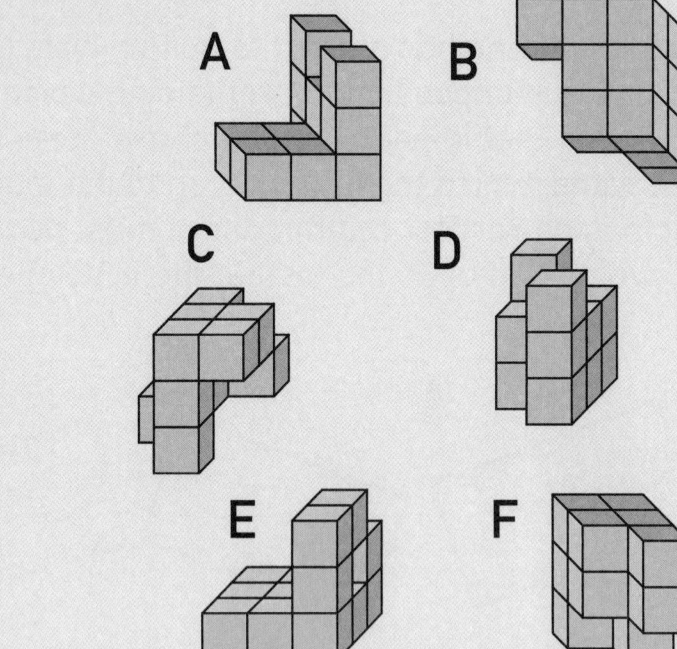


**87** ★★ Which of the four boxed figures completes the set?

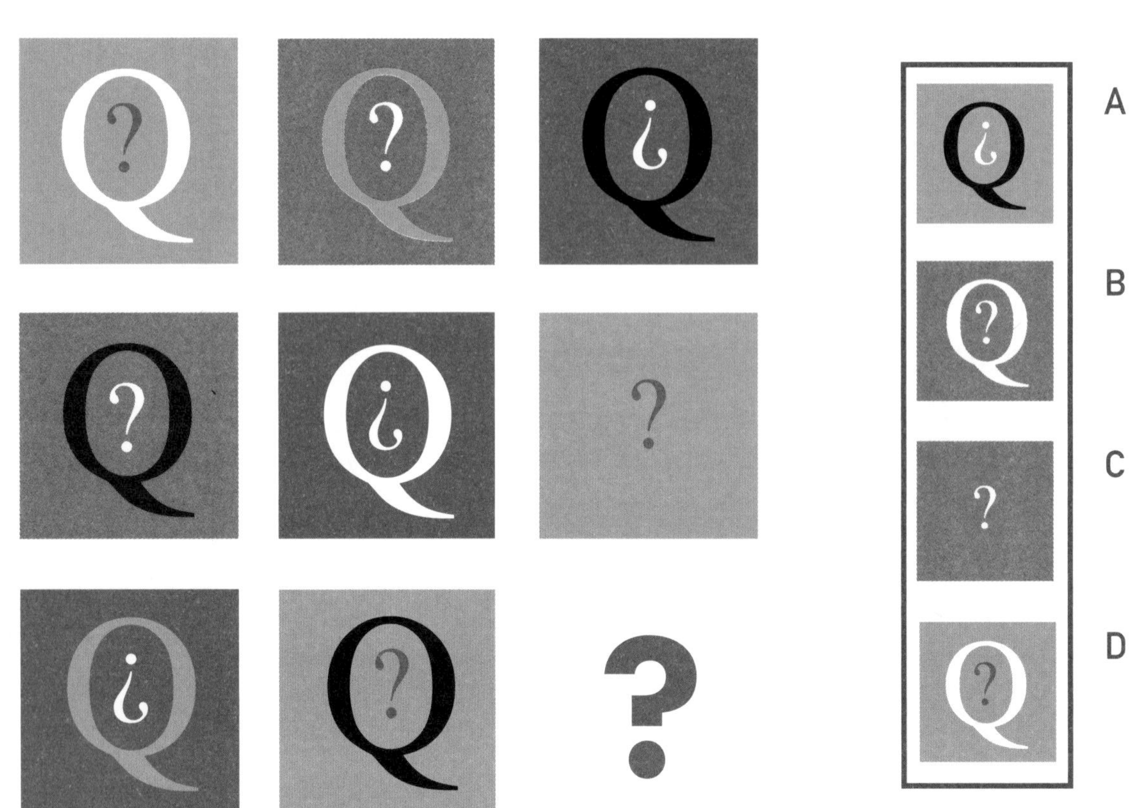

**88** ★★★ When the shape below is folded to form a cube, which is the only one of the following that *cannot* be produced?

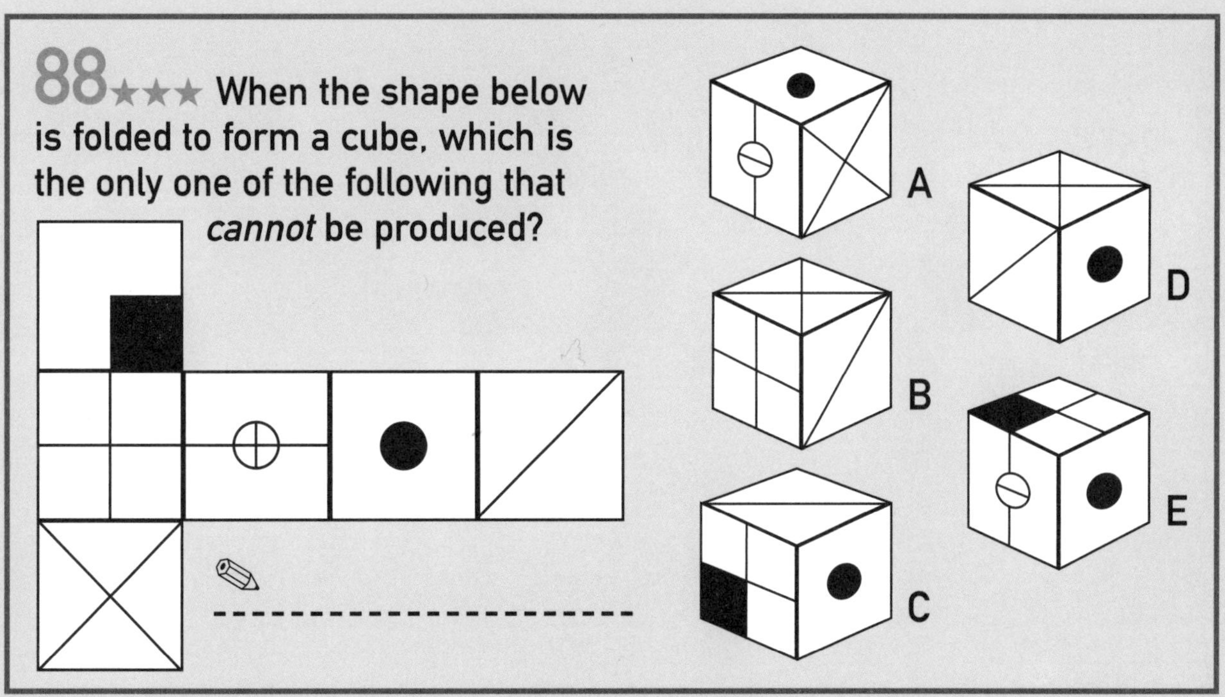


---------------------

**89** ★★★ How many differences can you spot between these two pictures? Circle them in the drawing on the right.

# take a

Word puzzles are the most familiar of all the challenges in this book. People have pondered riddles since antiquity – and there are some fine examples here.

You'll also find yourself pulling words in every direction – unravelling them in anagrams, searching for them in grids, defining them, and disentangling them from cunning codes. We hope you'll discover how much fun it is to wrestle with letters and words. What is certain is that when you reach this section's end you won't be at a loss for them...

★ easy ★★ medium ★★★ hard

# letter

# warm-up...

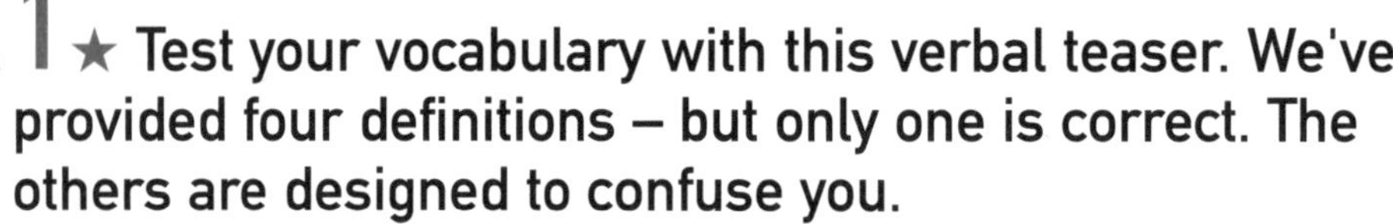

1★ Test your vocabulary with this verbal teaser. We've provided four definitions – but only one is correct. The others are designed to confuse you.

**Puny**

**Small horse** **Jokey**
**Smelly** **Feeble**

✎ ---------------------------------

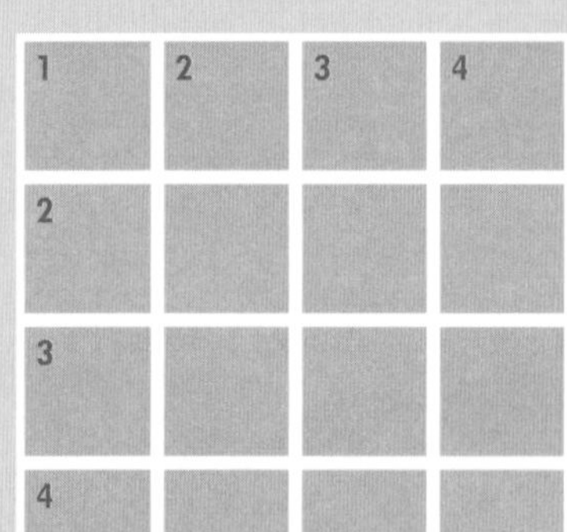

2★ Each answer is a four-letter word. When entered in the grid, a magic square will be formed in which each word reads the same across as down.

1 **Story**
3 **Heather**
2 **Very dry**
4 **Border**

3★ Test your word power. What is the opposite of **premeditated**?

**Influenced** **Rushed**
**Contrived** **Desirable**
**Accidental**

✎ ---------------------------------

**4★** Which word, when tagged onto the first word, will form another word, and when placed in front of the second word will also form another word?

**page ( ________ ) hem**

**5★** Find the word in this strange anagram.

**Not bay?**  ________

**6★** Which is the odd word out and why?

Schmaltzy

Feudalism

Yachtsmen

Sparkling

Brainwave

Lethargic

 ________

**7★** Just one set of the following letters is an anagram of a five-letter word. Can you discover which it is?

RHUED

GEROC

YRFOM

KERCA

MECUN

FEBLO

 ________

Turn the page for word puzzles aplenty...

# How to solve logic problems

Problems with grids. In these puzzles the trick is to deduce what is known for sure from the information given. Each type of item correlates with exactly one of every other item (in this example, one boy dates one girl at one location). The grid covers every possible combination once.

| | Bella | Deborah | Kath | Bowling | Cinema | Park |
|---|---|---|---|---|---|---|
| David | ✕ | | | | | |
| Steve | ✕ | ✕ | | | ✕ | |
| Terry | | | | | | |
| Bowling | | | | | | |
| Cinema | | ✓ | | | | |
| Park | | | ✕ | | | |

The clues will enable you to fill in the obvious valid and invalid combinations, and from there you can deduce further information. In this example, if Deborah went to the cinema ✓ but Steve did not ✕, Steve cannot have dated Deborah (new ✕ deduced).

As Bella did not date Steve either ✕, he must have dated Kath (new ✓ deduced) and so on.

**8★★ Five friends enjoyed a day out at the Newmarket racecourse last Saturday, each placing a bet on a horse in a different race – and winning! What is the name of the horse on which each racegoer placed his or her stake, at what time did the race start and how much did he or she win?**

1 The friend who placed a bet on Champion won £1 less than whoever put money on Deliberator in the race that began at 4 o'clock.

2 Arthur (who won £4 more than Roger) placed his money on a horse that ran half an hour later than Roger's choice.

3 Kathleen, who placed a bet on Post Pipper, won more than whoever placed a bet on Showman.

4 Leveller won £5 for one lucky punter.

5 Frank put his money on a horse that ran half an hour later than another.

| | HORSE | | | | | RACE TIME | | | | | WINNINGS | | | | |
|---|---|---|---|---|---|---|---|---|---|---|---|---|---|---|---|
| | Champion | Deliberator | Leveller | Post Pipper | Showman | 2pm | 2.30pm | 3pm | 4pm | 4.30pm | £5 | £6 | £9 | £10 | £14 |
| Arthur | | | | | | | | | | | | | | | |
| Debbie | | | | | | | | | | | | | | | |
| Frank | | | | | | | | | | | | | | | |
| Kathleen | | | | | | | | | | | | | | | |
| Roger | | | | | | | | | | | | | | | |
| £5 | | | | | | | | | | | | | | | |
| £6 | | | | | | | | | | | | | | | |
| £9 | | | | | | | | | | | | | | | |
| £10 | | | | | | | | | | | | | | | |
| £14 | | | | | | | | | | | | | | | |
| 2pm | | | | | | | | | | | | | | | |
| 2.30pm | | | | | | | | | | | | | | | |
| 3pm | | | | | | | | | | | | | | | |
| 4pm | | | | | | | | | | | | | | | |
| 4.30pm | | | | | | | | | | | | | | | |

**9★** Which word can be found in the following anagram?

**Ciao! Ms**  ________________________________

**10★★** Answer the clues to find eight answers. These letters can than be transferred into the main grid to give you a comical quotation and the name of the comic to whom it is attributed.

| | | | | | | | | | |
|---|---|---|---|---|---|---|---|---|---|
| 1D | 2B | 3A | 4G | 5C | 6D | | 7G | 8E | 9C |
| | 10F | 11C | 12D | 13C | | 14G | 15F | | 16E |
| 17C | | 18F | 19E | 20G | 21H | 22A | | 23B | 24H |
| 25G | | 26E | 27G | 28A | 29H | 30H | 31B | 32D | |
| 33G | 34B | 35H | 36G | 37F | 38H | 39F | | 40D | 41H |
| 42H | 43E | | | | | | | | |

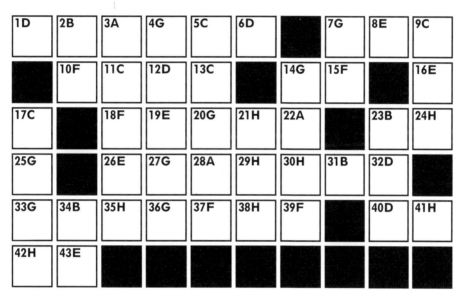

A Recently stolen or smuggled — _ _ _ (22 28 3)

B Engage for work — _ _ _ _ (23 2 34 31)

C Shabby and untidy — _ _ _ _ _ (9 11 5 13 17)

D A cherished desire — _ _ _ _ _ (32 6 1 12 40)

E Exercises evaluating knowledge — _ _ _ _ _ (8 43 19 16 26)

F A throng or clique — _ _ _ _ _ (37 15 39 18 10)

G Opinions that are worth a penny? — _ _ _ _ _ _ _ _ (20 7 14 36 33 4 27 25)

H Final path of an aircraft while landing — _ _ _ _ _ _ _ _ (41 29 30 42 35 24 21 38)

**11** For this wordfinder puzzle, you must find words of three letters or more by travelling horizontally, vertically or diagonally to adjacent letters. Each letter may be used once only in each new word. Plurals and well-known proper names are allowed.

| Y | L | N |
|---|---|---|
| A | I | E |
| T | R | C |

TARGET

★ 20 words
★★ 30 words
★★★ 35 words

**12★** The dice blocks each have a six-letter word written on them, but unfortunately you can see only three sides. When you have solved the clues, the first column will reveal a ten-letter word.

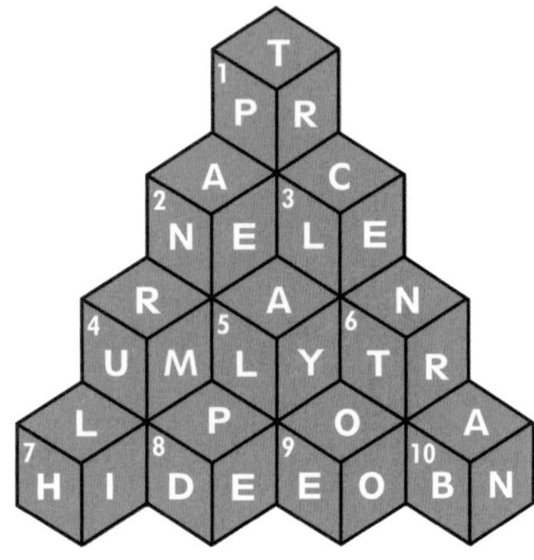


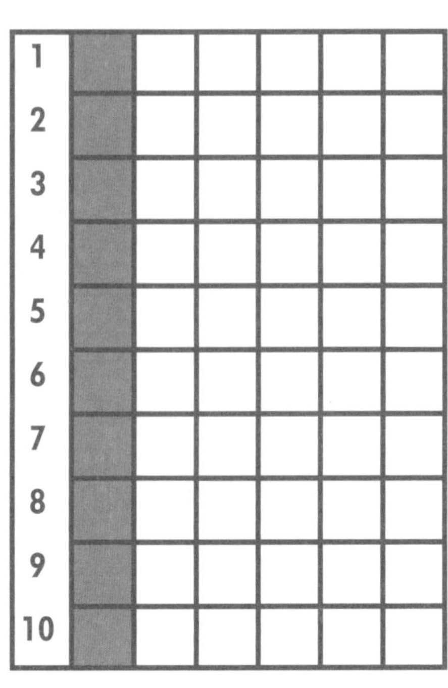


CLUES

1 Allow
2 Highly decorative
3 Royal home
4 Games official
5 Recently
6 Deer's horn
7 Excite
8 Obstruct
9 Resist
10 Within reach

13★★ Place all the words from the list below into the grid. Will they fit? If you do it right they will.

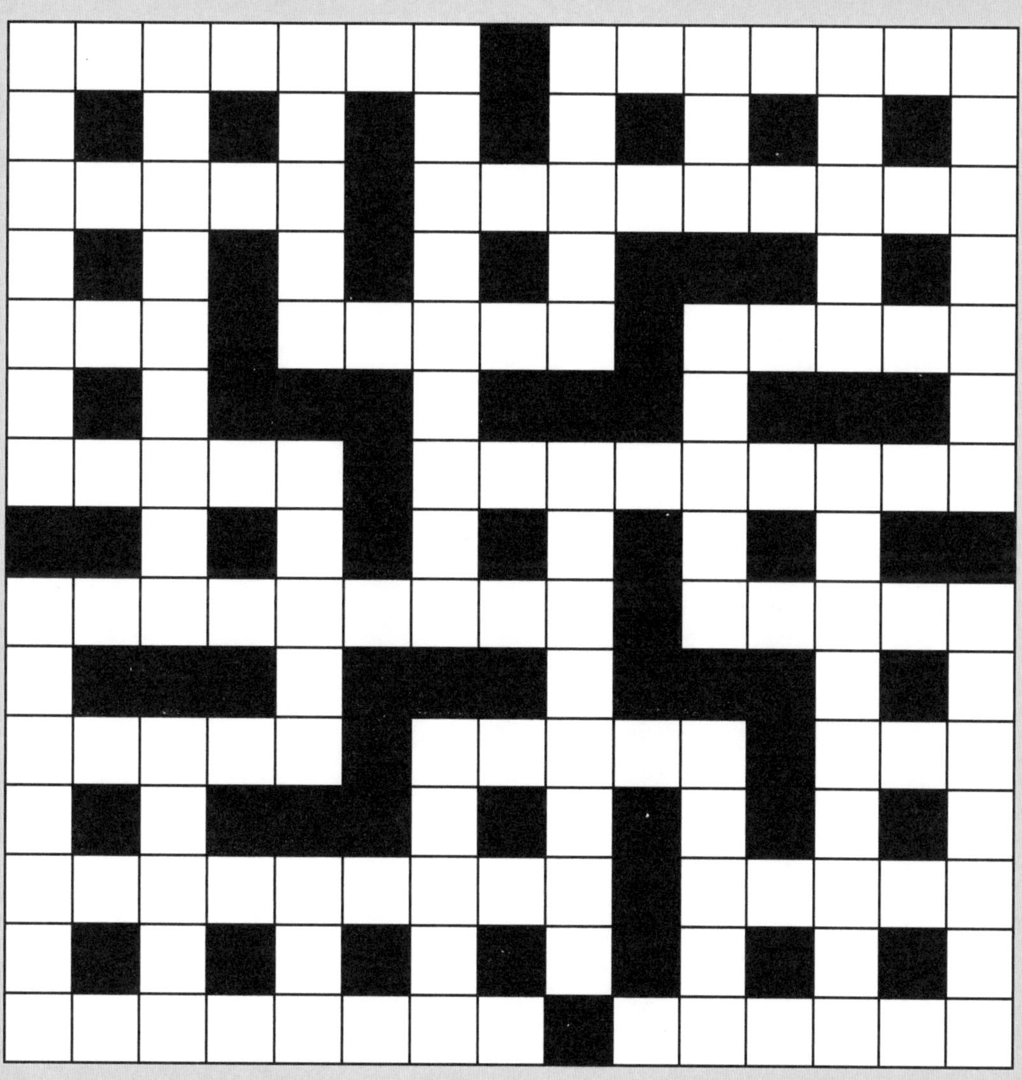

3-LETTER WORDS
AIR
INK
INN
SIR

5-LETTER WORDS
CHOIR
CLAPS
DEPTH
DRIVE
ERROR
GROWN
IDEAS
NAMES
OILED
OLDER
OPERA
RACES
RADIO
REINS
SAVED
STAIR

7-LETTER WORDS
CHOKING
COWBOYS
ENTERED
HARNESS
RESTORE
SHRINKS
SPONGES
WEIGHTS

9-LETTER WORDS
CUSTOMERS
HURRICANE
INCORRECT
REPLACING
SPIRITUAL
UNCOVERED
WELL-KNOWN
WINDMILLS

**14★** Test your vocabulary with this verbal teaser. We've provided four definitions – but only one is correct. The others are designed to confuse you.

**Tureen**

**Tall building** | **Large dish**
**Small coin** | **Pointed beard**

**15★★** What is the opposite of meteoric?

**Transient** | **Meticulous** | **Mellow**
**Steady** | **Esoteric**

**16★** Can you spot the following birds in the grid? They may be found across, down or diagonally in any direction.

| | | | | | | | | | | | | | |
|---|---|---|---|---|---|---|---|---|---|---|---|---|---|
| T | O | U | C | A | N | P | L | B | H | C | N | I | F |
| O | R | A | N | G | E | V | A | E | L | G | A | E | N |
| R | A | Q | W | S | M | T | R | K | F | J | W | C | T |
| R | Z | H | U | D | U | C | K | L | X | V | S | Y | U |
| A | G | E | L | O | Y | P | J | I | B | O | V | E | T |
| P | L | A | X | V | U | W | A | K | W | S | T | E | R |
| R | U | Q | T | E | R | N | M | L | Z | I | X | S | P |
| D | E | V | Y | L | G | Q | I | O | W | P | R | E | Y |
| L | H | J | F | N | K | O | U | R | N | D | A | J | B |
| W | N | C | H | E | L | U | O | I | O | X | V | N | C |
| A | S | J | W | H | A | B | N | S | R | D | E | F | M |
| C | L | A | R | J | I | O | Y | N | E | C | N | V | N |
| A | O | Y | H | N | R | Q | Z | L | H | K | L | O | B |
| M | Z | C | B | K | S | H | A | U | T | Z | V | B | C |

CONDOR
DOVE
DUCK
EAGLE
EMU
FINCH
GOOSE
HERON
JAY
KIWI
LARK
MACAW
MOA
OWL
PARROT
RAVEN
ROBIN
SWAN
TERN
TOUCAN

**17★** Change warm into cold by altering one letter at a time.

**WARM**

_______________ District

_______________ Joker

_______________ Twine

**COLD**

**18★★** Place all the pieces into the grid so that a valid crossword is formed. Remember that crossword grids possess half-turn symmetry. The coloured blocks will also help.

| N | E | E | | | | | | |
|---|---|---|---|---|---|---|---|---|
| O | ■ | X | | | | | | |
| B | U | T | | | | | | |
| | | | | | | | | |
| | | | | | | | | |
| | | | | | | | | |
| | | | | | | | | |
| | | | | | | | | |
| | | | | | | | | |

**19★** Which word is hidden in this anagram?

**Be loud**

## 20★ Solve the clues provided to complete the pyramid. When you've done that, the 14 letters in the pyramid can be arranged to make a single word (clue: movie art).

### CLUES

1 Belonging to me
2 Food covered in pastry crust
3 Suspend
4 Thespian

✎ ------------------

## 21★ 18 words ★★ 22+ words

**In this alphabetical quiz, we take you through an A to Z of answers, each of which has all but one letter missing. How many can you reconstruct?**

| | |
|---|---|
| Scientific equipment | A _ _ A _ A _ _ _ |
| Blown spheres | B _ B B _ _ _ |
| It preys on your mind | C _ _ _ C _ _ _ C _ |
| United we stand, ___ we fall | D _ _ _ D _ D |
| St ___, US hospital drama | E _ _ E _ _ E _ E |
| The golden anniversary | F _ F _ _ _ _ _ |
| Swimmers wear them | G _ G G _ _ _ |
| A vital statistic | H _ _ _ H _ |
| Type of police parade | I _ _ _ _ I _ I _ _ _ I _ _ |
| A feeling of envy | J _ _ _ _ _ _ _ |
| Rap with the knuckles | K _ _ _ K |
| Without exaggeration | L _ _ _ _ _ L L _ |
| Embalmed body | M _ M M _ |
| A golfer's favourite hole? | N _ N _ _ _ _ N _ _ |
| The other side | O _ _ O _ _ _ _ O _ |
| Marionette | P _ P P _ _ |
| In a line, like its five vowels? | Q _ _ _ _ _ _ _ |
| Store of water | R _ _ _ R _ _ _ R |
| Don't run with them | S _ _ S S _ _ S |
| You go to a doctor for it | T _ _ _ T _ _ _ T |
| That's odd | U _ U _ U _ _ |
| Clear in the memory | V _ V _ _ |
| Native American dwelling | W _ _ W _ _ |
| Newton-John's favourite disco | X _ _ _ _ _ |
| The day before | Y _ _ _ _ _ _ _ Y |
| Jagged line | Z _ _ Z _ _ |

**22**★★ No fewer than five newly wedded couples moved into Newcomer Street on different days last week. Every man moved in on the same day as his wife, so can you discover who is married to whom, the number of the house in which they have taken up residence and when they moved in? (See page 224 for tips on how to solve this puzzle.)

1 Of Andrew (who didn't move into Newcomer Street on Friday) and Fred: one lives at No 10 and the other is married to Barbara.

2 Diane (who lives at an odd-numbered house) moved to the street later in the week than Samuel and his wife, but earlier in the week than Martin and his wife (who isn't Lucy).

3 Of William and Lucy's husband: one lives at No 14 and the other moved into Newcomer Street earlier in the week than the couple who moved into No 10.

4 Fred and his wife moved in the day before the couple who live at No 32.

5 The couple who moved in on Thursday live at either No 14 or No 17. Pauline and her husband didn't move in on Wednesday.

| | WIFE | | | | | HOUSE NO | | | | | DAY | | | | |
|---|---|---|---|---|---|---|---|---|---|---|---|---|---|---|---|
| | Barbara | Diane | Lucy | Pauline | Tina | 10 | 14 | 17 | 21 | 32 | Monday | Tuesday | Wednesday | Thursday | Friday |
| Andrew | | | | | | | | | | | | | | | |
| Fred | | | | | | | | | | | | | | | |
| Martin | | | | | | | | | | | | | | | |
| Samuel | | | | | | | | | | | | | | | |
| William | | | | | | | | | | | | | | | |
| Monday | | | | | | | | | | | | | | | |
| Tuesday | | | | | | | | | | | | | | | |
| Wednesday | | | | | | | | | | | | | | | |
| Thursday | | | | | | | | | | | | | | | |
| Friday | | | | | | | | | | | | | | | |
| No 10 | | | | | | | | | | | | | | | |
| No 14 | | | | | | | | | | | | | | | |
| No 17 | | | | | | | | | | | | | | | |
| No 21 | | | | | | | | | | | | | | | |
| No 32 | | | | | | | | | | | | | | | |

**23**★★ The answer to each clue is a five-letter word. When entered in the correct order in the grid the words form a magic square in which each word reads the same both across and down. The clues are given in no particular order.

CLUES

Room aboard a ship

Clergyman

Nimble

Bring up to date

Reflection

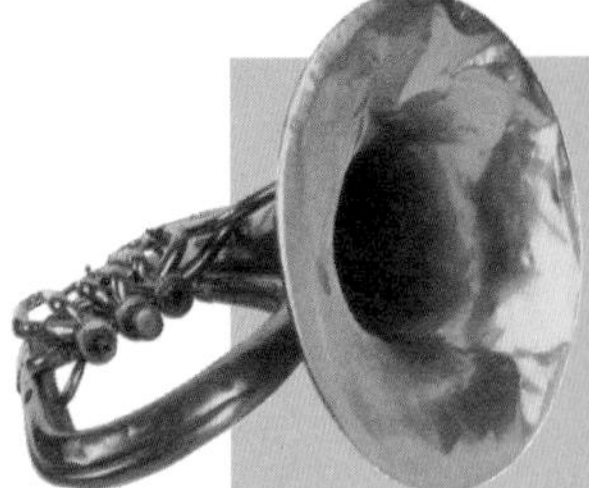

**24★** Can you spot the following musical terms and instruments in the grid? They may be found across, down or diagonally in any direction.

| Q | I | K | W | A | E | B | N | Z | I | T | H | E | R |
|---|---|---|---|---|---|---|---|---|---|---|---|---|---|
| E | M | F | G | C | N | J | T | C | P | S | P | V | A |
| L | W | T | R | I | F | L | E | K | Y | U | Z | D | T |
| G | X | V | S | H | A | L | L | O | W | L | U | R | I |
| U | Y | P | J | W | L | K | U | N | U | F | C | B | U |
| B | A | N | J | O | E | W | A | T | C | H | X | H | G |
| Q | O | R | K | Y | N | V | E | U | E | N | P | R | A |
| D | E | O | W | P | R | A | H | S | T | E | A | D | Y |
| K | Q | H | V | L | N | F | I | I | U | B | W | J | L |
| E | Z | Y | U | T | R | U | M | P | E | T | H | G | L |
| W | A | J | I | K | L | U | N | I | A | Z | E | Q | A |
| S | T | A | R | S | R | U | L | P | N | T | P | A | R |
| A | V | L | A | D | O | C | L | E | F | I | C | B | G |
| E | N | T | E | R | T | A | I | N | T | E | M | P | O |

BANJO
BUGLE
CELLO
CLEF
CODA
DRUM
FLUTE
GUITAR
HARP
HORN
LARGO
LUTE
MINIM
PIANO
PIPE
TEMPO
WALTZ
ZITHER

**25★★** Place the tiles in the grid to form a magic square, in which the words read the same across as down.

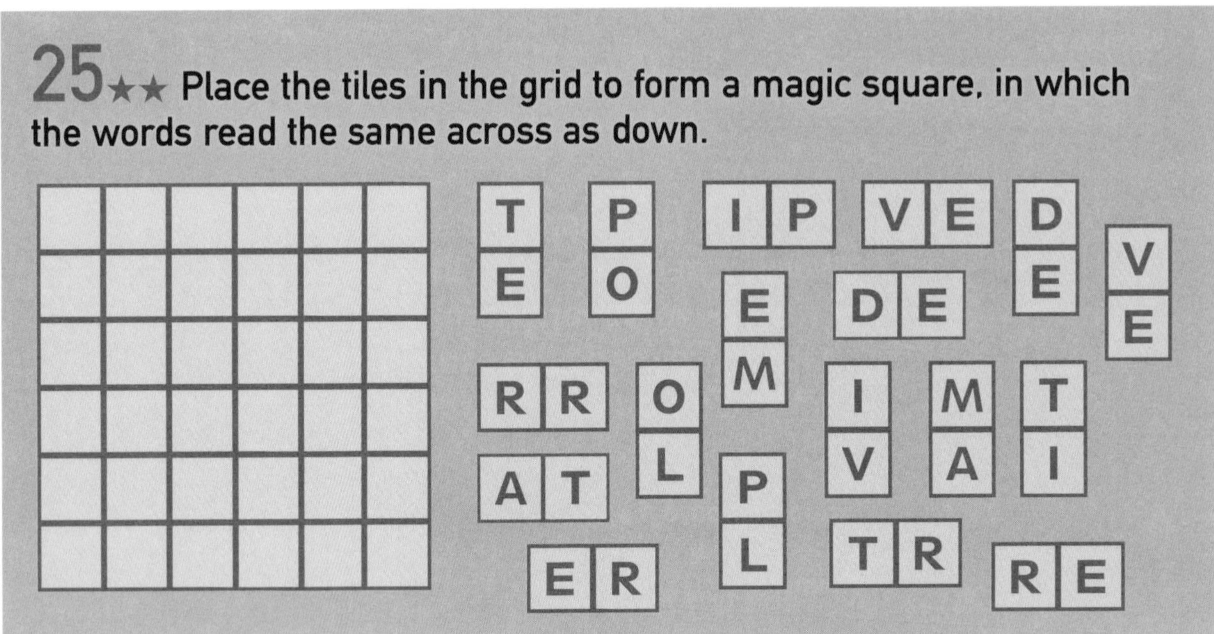

**26**★★★ A letter-fit puzzle with a twist. Every word is five letters long, so what goes where? That's for you to work out. (We've placed one word on the grid to get you started.)

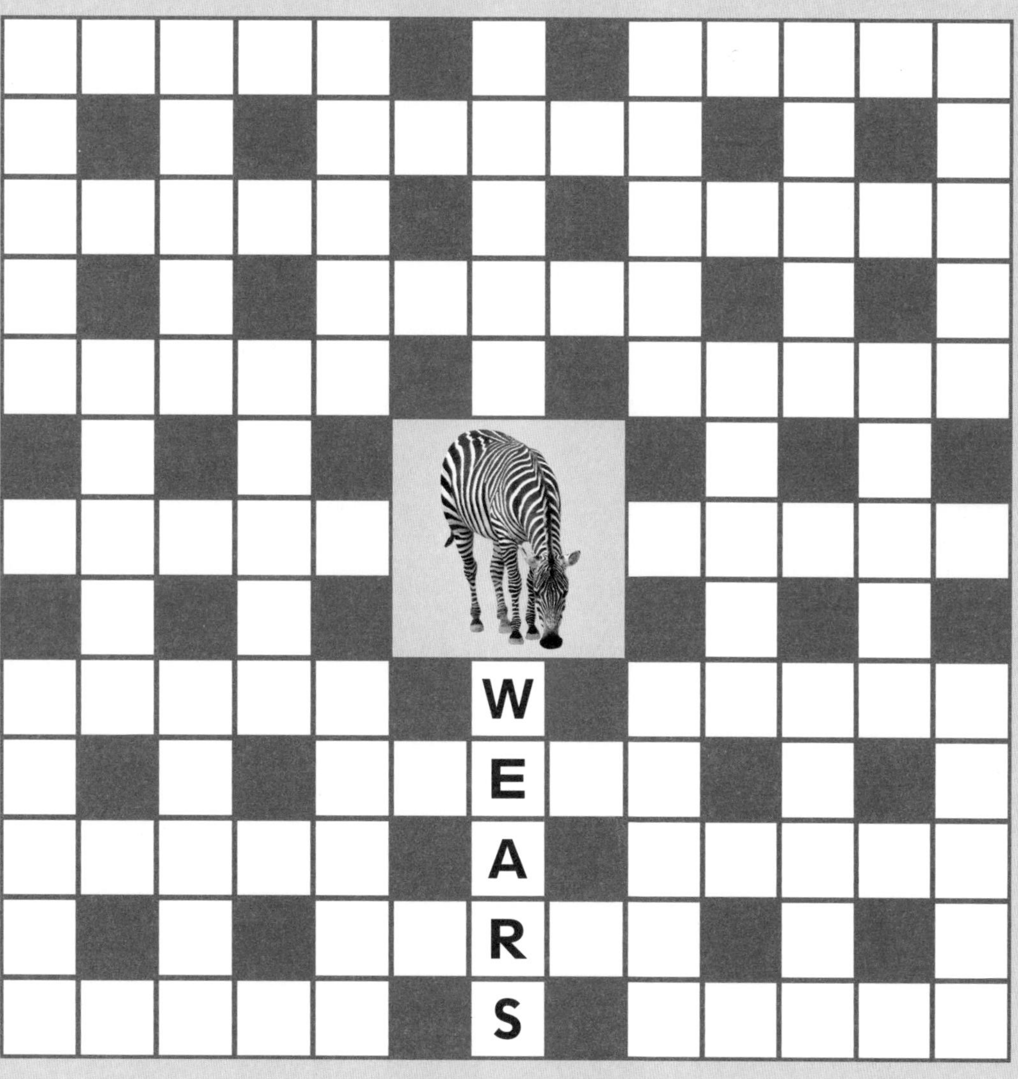

AGAIN
AGING
ANGER
APRON
DENSE
DISKS
DRAMA
EIGHT
EMPTY
ENEMY
FABLE
GATES
GLIDE
GREAT
GREEN
IDEAS
ITEMS
LOYAL
OTHER
RANGE
RAZOR
REEDS
REFER
RHYME
ROADS
STEER
SUGAR
TIDAL
TOWEL
TREAT
URGED
USING
~~WEARS~~
WHEAT
WIPED
ZEBRA

**27★** Just one of the sets of letters below is an anagram of a five-letter word. Find the word.

LUBRA OPRDA UGRNA NETDR HEDCN

✎ ------------------------------------------------

**28★** Which word, when tagged onto the first word will form one word, and when placed in front of the second word will also form another word?

**can ( ________ ) sure**

**29★** Answers in this word square read the same across as down.

| 1 | 2 | 3 | 4 |
|---|---|---|---|
| 2 | | | |
| 3 | | | |
| 4 | | | |

CLUES

1 **We need to ___ the bathroom walls**
2 **The ___ is part of the eye**
3 **The footballer walked with a ___**
4 **You can ___ a ship on the horizon**

**30★★** Which is the odd word out? Circle your answer.

| | |
|---|---|
| **Tin** | **Sieve** |
| **Minim** | **Linen** |
| **Militia** | **Avoid** |

## 31

For this wordfinder puzzle, you must find words of three letters or more by travelling horizontally, vertically or diagonally to the adjacent letters. Each letter may be used once only in each new word. Plurals and well-known proper names are allowed here.

| | | |
|---|---|---|
| I | S | L |
| N | E | A |
| T | R | V |

**TARGET**
★ 20 words
★★ 30 words
★★★ 35 words

✎
_______________
_______________
_______________
_______________
_______________

## 32★★

Each of the six people in this puzzle started collecting stamps in a different month, and each has chosen to collect stamps from just one particular country. Can you discover each philatelist's full name, the month in which the collection was started and the country issuing the stamps he or she collects? (See page 224 for tips on how to solve this puzzle.)

| | SURNAME | | | | | | MONTH | | | | | | COUNTRY | | | | | |
|---|---|---|---|---|---|---|---|---|---|---|---|---|---|---|---|---|---|---|
| | Frost | Grant | MacDonald | Marks | Quiller | Willis | January | February | April | May | July | August | Australia | Britain | France | Japan | Spain | USA |
| Amelia | | | | | | | | | | | | | | | | | | |
| Christian | | | | | | | | | | | | | | | | | | |
| Daphne | | | | | | | | | | | | | | | | | | |
| David | | | | | | | | | | | | | | | | | | |
| Gina | | | | | | | | | | | | | | | | | | |
| Hugh | | | | | | | | | | | | | | | | | | |
| Australia | | | | | | | | | | | | | | | | | | |
| Britain | | | | | | | | | | | | | | | | | | |
| France | | | | | | | | | | | | | | | | | | |
| Japan | | | | | | | | | | | | | | | | | | |
| Spain | | | | | | | | | | | | | | | | | | |
| USA | | | | | | | | | | | | | | | | | | |
| January | | | | | | | | | | | | | | | | | | |
| February | | | | | | | | | | | | | | | | | | |
| April | | | | | | | | | | | | | | | | | | |
| May | | | | | | | | | | | | | | | | | | |
| July | | | | | | | | | | | | | | | | | | |
| August | | | | | | | | | | | | | | | | | | |

1 Mr Quiller collects French stamps and began his collection two months earlier than Miss Marks, but later than Gina (who isn't collecting British stamps).

2 Daphne started her collection the month before the man who collects Spanish stamps.

3 The most recently started stamp collection isn't Hugh's. Neither Gina nor Hugh collects Japanese stamps.

4 The person surnamed Willis started collecting later than Christian, but earlier than whoever collects stamps from the USA.

5 The person surnamed Frost started collecting stamps three months later than David Grant.

**33** ★★★ Solve the clues to find the answers. These letters can then be transferred into the main grid to give you a financial quote and the name of the American entertainer who said it.

| 1C | | 2J | 3B | 4C | 5F | | 6J | 7A | | 8D |
|---|---|---|---|---|---|---|---|---|---|---|
| | 9K | 10F | 11A | 12F | 13H | | 14J | 15E | 16H | 17A |
| | 18B | 19A | 20B | 21A | | 22B | 23A | 24J | 25G | |
| 26H | 27I | 28F | | 29C | 30G | 31I | 32D | 33F | | 34D |
| 35D | | 36D | 37H | 38I | | 39K | 40A | 41H | | 42A |
| 43E | 44J | 45G | 46E | | 47E | 48G | 49D | | 50J | 51G |
| | 52A | 53K | 54H | | 55A | 56J | 57C | 58I | | 59A |
| 60D | | 61D | 62G | 63H | | 64K | 65K | 66E | 67J | |

**34** ★★★ Which pair of letters are the odd ones out?

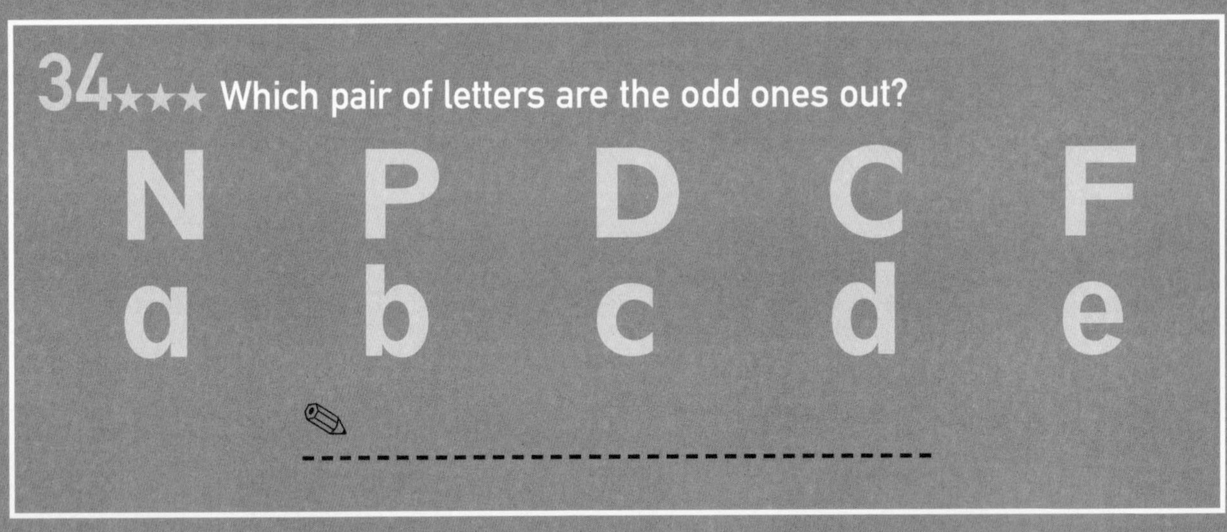

A Middle Eastern resident (11)

42 11 21 23 7 17 59 55 19 40 52

B Masonry partition (4)

18 3 22 20

C Biblically, let it be (4)

1 29 57 4

D Make prettier (8)

61 32 8 49 60 34 35 36

E Overactive (5)

15 47 66 46 43

F Fortunate (5)

10 28 12 5 33

G Witchcraft from Haiti (6)

45 30 48 25 51 62

H Type of weapon that fits on another weapon (7)

63 16 26 37 41 13 54

I A very useful computer command! (4)

38 31 58 27

J Dutifully complying with instructions (8)

44 2 56 50 6 67 24 14

K Doggy (5)

9 65 53 39 64

35★★ Crack this code to reveal a short, familiar saying.

JGTG VQFCA, IQPG VQOQTTQY

---------------------------------

## 36★ Change need to want by solving three clues. One letter only is altered at each step.

NEED

_______________ Useless plant

_______________ Make way

_______________ Magician's stick

WANT

## 38★★ Solve the clues provided to fill out the word pyramid. When the pyramid is complete, the 15 letters can be arranged into one word (clue: something mathematical).

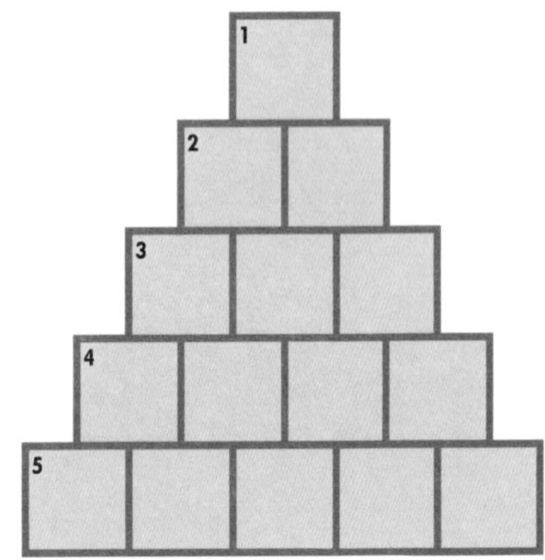

CLUES

1 The Roman numeral for 1000 (1)

2 Expression of refusal (2)

3 Spasmodic twitching of muscles (3)

4 Group of three (4)

5 Big (5)

## 37★★ The dice blocks each have a six-letter word written on them, but unfortunately you can see only three sides. When you have solved the clues, the first column will reveal a word.

CLUES

1 Front runner
2 Gas, symbol O
3 Root vegetable
4 Get
5 Distress call
6 Supernatural
7 Prosper
8 Breathe in
9 Spoken
10 Sign up

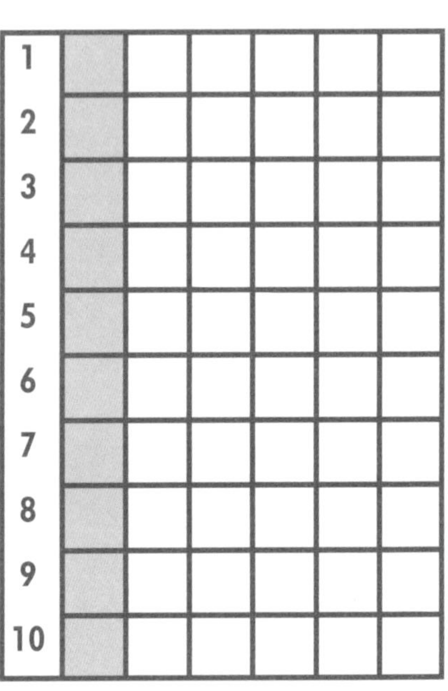

**39★** Can you spot the following capital cities in the grid? They may be found across, down or diagonally in any direction.

| | | | | | | | | | | | | | |
|---|---|---|---|---|---|---|---|---|---|---|---|---|---|
| A | N | A | V | A | H | T | S | G | H | E | N | O | W |
| T | O | R | O | N | T | O | B | V | I | E | N | N | A |
| Q | B | T | S | F | D | C | G | N | M | P | J | M | R |
| O | S | U | T | Q | P | Z | R | T | O | O | I | L | S |
| Y | I | L | P | A | K | W | E | X | T | L | M | H | A |
| U | L | P | R | E | W | B | C | R | I | Z | S | L | W |
| R | O | I | A | N | I | A | N | S | O | T | K | O | U |
| K | S | T | Y | V | I | X | M | J | G | M | C | N | Y |
| D | A | S | L | R | A | L | L | W | U | S | E | D | C |
| U | E | S | O | F | I | A | D | R | O | A | J | O | S |
| B | L | L | V | W | Q | R | A | M | Y | T | U | N | E |
| L | B | U | S | R | L | U | B | A | K | W | I | J | L |
| I | T | E | W | D | S | B | L | A | O | S | W | U | K |
| N | A | I | R | O | B | I | A | N | T | P | L | I | Q |

| | |
|---|---|
| CAIRO | OSLO |
| DUBLIN | OTTAWA |
| HAVANA | PARIS |
| KABUL | QUITO |
| LIMA | ROME |
| LISBON | SOFIA |
| LONDON | TOKYO |
| MOSCOW | VIENNA |
| NAIROBI | WARSAW |

**40★** What does that word mean? We've provided four definitions – but only one is correct. The other three are designed to confuse you.

ENDEAVOUR

**Consume** **Confusion**
**Conclusion** **Attempt**

✎ ------------------------------

**41★** Which word, when tagged onto the first word, will form another word, and when placed in front of the second word will form another word?

**bar(________________)say**

**42**★★ Can you squeeze these words into the grid? One's been positioned to get you started.

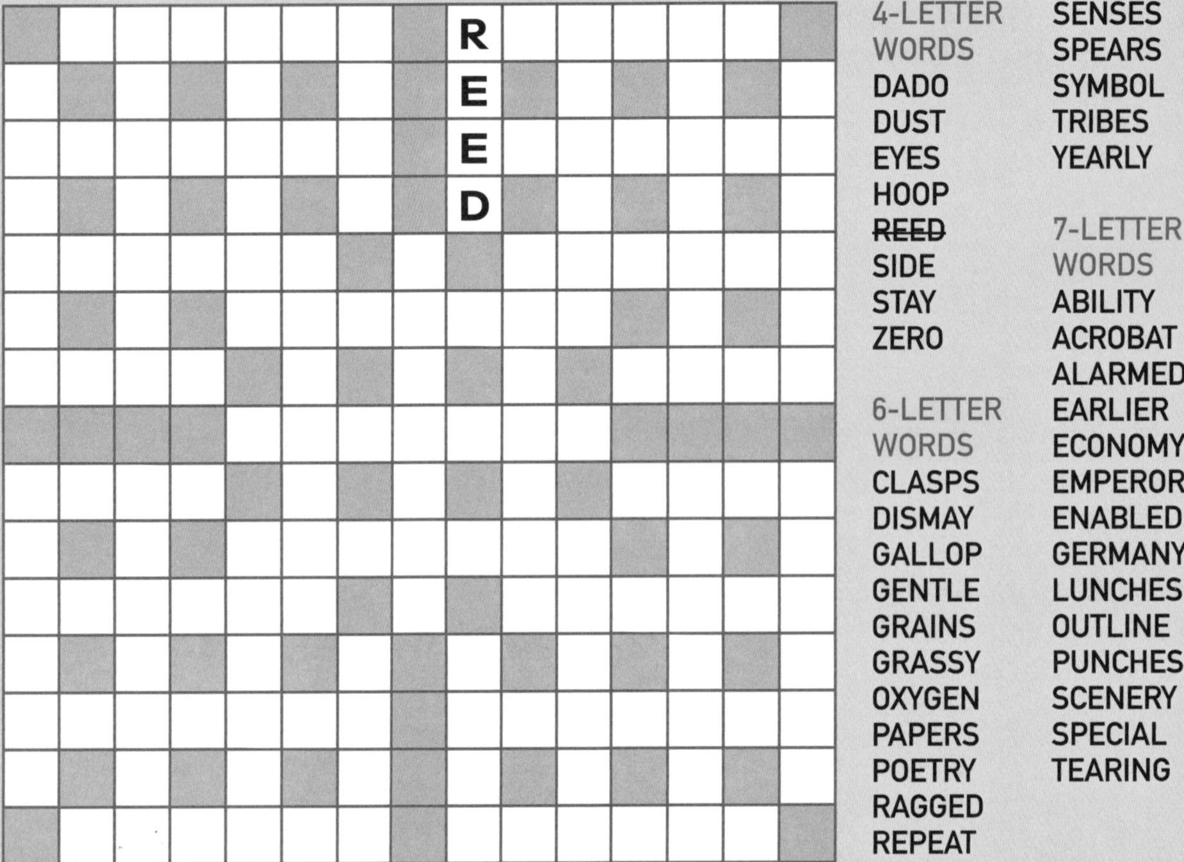


4-LETTER WORDS
DADO
DUST
EYES
HOOP
~~REED~~
SIDE
STAY
ZERO

6-LETTER WORDS
CLASPS
DISMAY
GALLOP
GENTLE
GRAINS
GRASSY
OXYGEN
PAPERS
POETRY
RAGGED
REPEAT
SENSES
SPEARS
SYMBOL
TRIBES
YEARLY

7-LETTER WORDS
ABILITY
ACROBAT
ALARMED
EARLIER
ECONOMY
EMPEROR
ENABLED
GERMANY
LUNCHES
OUTLINE
PUNCHES
SCENERY
SPECIAL
TEARING

**43**★ Test your vocabulary with this verbal teaser. We've provided four definitions, but only one is correct. Can you spot it?

**NOUGAT**

**Confectionery**

**Toothache**

**Zero**

**Turkish dignitary**

\-----------------------------------

**44★★** Which of these is the correct definition of the word at the top?

TORPID

Very hot

Frightening

Bullfighter

Sluggish

**45★** Find the word that links the pair of words below.

back (.........) some

**46★** Can you find the six-letter word contained in this anagram?

air sob

**47★★** Solve the clues, adding a letter at a time, and complete the pyramid.

**CLUES**

| | |
|---|---|
| Neuter pronoun (2) | _ _ |
| Small unit (3) | _ _ _ |
| Wound (4) | _ _ _ _ |
| Snapper (5) | _ _ _ _ _ |
| Sharp to the taste (6) | _ _ _ _ _ _ |
| Bird (7) | _ _ _ _ _ _ _ |

**48** In this wordfinder puzzle, try to find words of three letters or more by travelling horizontally, vertically or diagonally to adjacent letters. Each letter may be used only once in each new word. Plurals and well-known proper names are allowed.

TARGET
★ 15 words
★★ 23 words
★★★ 28 words

| | | |
|---|---|---|
| S | N | O |
| P | I | C |
| M | A | H |

**49** ★★ Can you spot these transport-related terms in the grid? They may be found across, down or diagonally in any direction. One word in the list doesn't appear in the grid. Which one is it?

| | | | | | | | | | | | | | |
|---|---|---|---|---|---|---|---|---|---|---|---|---|---|
| Y | E | T | T | J | K | L | N | Y | M | F | H | G | W |
| A | H | S | T | C | G | V | X | R | Q | Z | B | A | C |
| C | L | G | K | A | F | H | M | R | E | D | I | L | G |
| H | O | R | N | Z | B | W | P | E | L | N | B | O | X |
| T | T | V | A | I | C | E | L | F | J | Z | H | D | T |
| D | W | R | S | E | D | A | N | K | R | C | W | N | L |
| Q | Y | H | A | A | N | P | X | C | I | P | G | O | H |
| A | X | V | L | I | B | A | Z | E | L | T | U | G | L |
| Q | M | N | E | C | N | P | J | H | R | G | F | E | Y |
| I | A | Z | E | R | H | T | N | A | V | A | V | S | W |
| G | F | O | H | E | T | S | M | V | B | S | H | L | E |
| F | Q | T | W | F | U | E | L | H | U | H | O | U | R |
| M | C | N | A | P | D | Y | J | B | L | I | X | A | T |
| C | A | R | R | O | T | O | M | S | K | P | O | E | J |

BUS
CAR
DINGHY
FERRY
FUEL
GLIDER
GONDOLA
JET
PEDAL
RAFT
SEDAN
SHIP
TAXI
TRAIN
TRAM
TUG
VAN
WAGON
WHEEL
YACHT

**50**★★★ Can you solve this straightforward cryptogram in which each letter of the alphabet has been substituted for another? The last five letters are the name of the Greek author.

PFCBZPK ZP CBH OVVOZYN FV AOP
ZN TFYCBR FV KYHOC OPEZHCR. LUOCF

---

**51**★★ Place all the pieces into the grid so that a valid crossword is formed. Remember that crossword grids possess half-turn symmetry. The coloured blocks will also help in this regard.

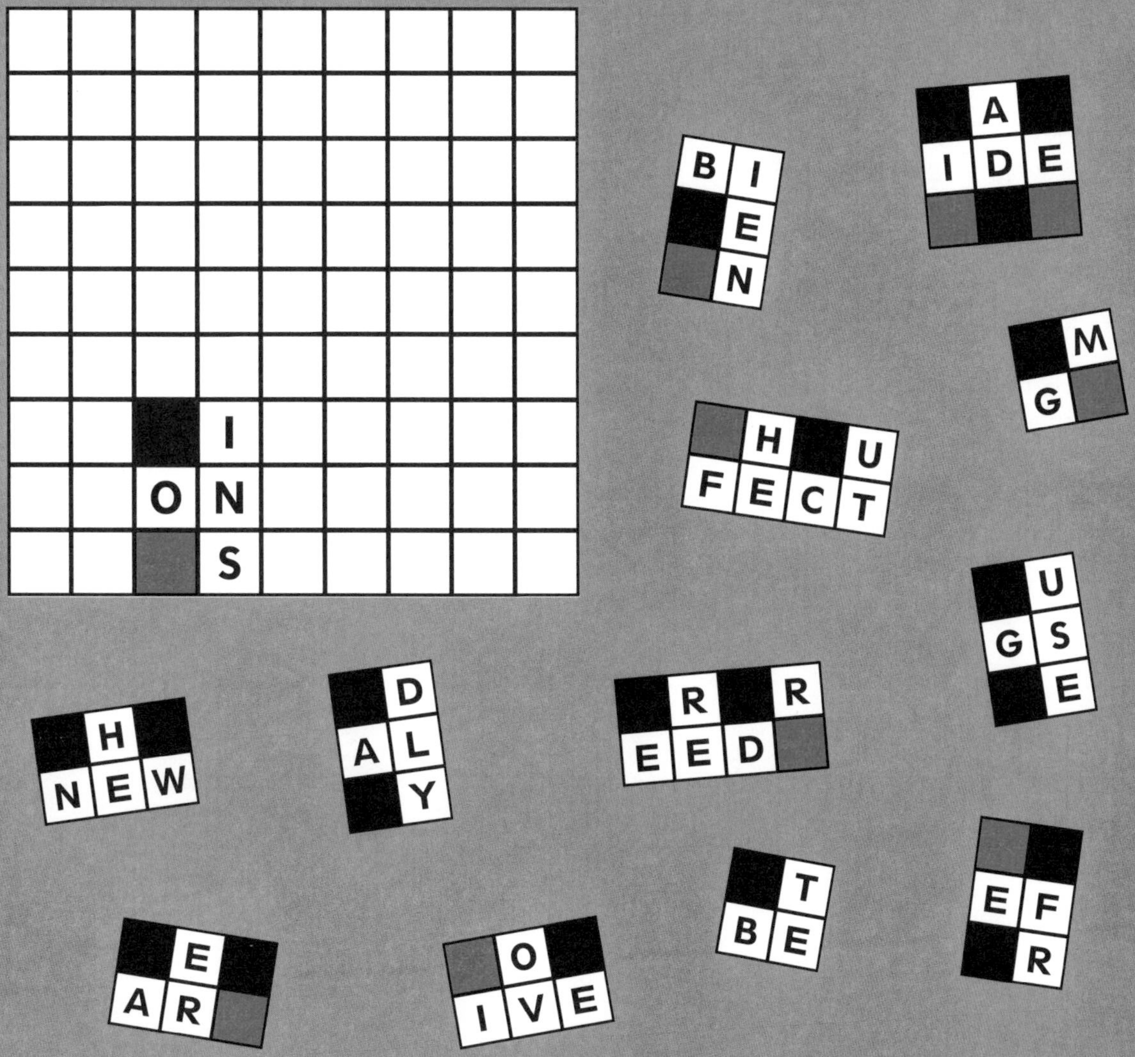

**52★★** Just one of the sets of letters below is an anagram of a six-letter English word. Can you find the word?

HURCOL
LEACBN
LERDCA
YRCOLT
KCEGIL
BUREFT

✎ ----------------------------

**53★★★** Can you solve the code? There are only seven letters in the message.

SVQAR TBCIN PZXTR
TIEFG IWVCD FYXBK
MTCDO QRAIZ

✎ ----------------------------

**54★** Can you change dine to feed by altering a single letter at a time?

DINE

✎ --------------- Very good

--------------- Retrieve

--------------- Ward off

FEED

**55★** Find the word that links this pair of words

chain ( --------------- ) way

**56** ★★★ A man goes into a grocery store in downtown San Francisco and asks the shopkeeper if he has any **n*e**u*. The shopkeeper replies: 'I don't have any, man. Get out!' What *did* the man ask for? There is a clue in that rude reply.

---

**57** ★ Which word is hidden in the anagram below?

**Then cram**

---

**58** ★★★ Fill in the missing letters to leave a well-known scientific figure. Beware! This is a word puzzle with a clever twist.

_ _ S _ _ U _ _ _ _ E _ _ _ _ _ E _ _ E _ _ _ _ N _ _ _ R _ _ E (1543 – 1816)

---

**59** ★★★ Which is the odd word out?

**Calculator**
**Stings**
**Aromatic**
**Attendant**
**Argued**
**Oratorio**
**Taciturn**
**Balloonist**
**Decapitate**

## 60★★ Six estate agents have sold flats in different blocks today. Find out the price and location of each of the flats they sold, together with the name of the purchaser in every case. (See page 224 for tips on how to solve this puzzle.)

1 Proffitts sold a flat at a price £5000 lower than the one (either in Lofty Reach or Cloudy View) bought by Mr Bishop.

2 The flat sold by Sellmore's was more expensive than that sold by Hearth & Home, which, in turn, was more expensive than that found in Grande Vista.

3 The flat in Happy Heights cost less than the one bought by Miss Walters.

4 Either Shark & Co or Hearth & Home sold the flat at a price £5000 lower than the one in Lofty Reach. Mrs Cairn's new flat cost more than the one in Lofty Reach.

5 The flat in Cloudy View cost more than the penthouse flat purchased by Ms Dimarco, but £5000 less than that sold by Sayle & Sons.

6 The flat in Sky Scraper isn't the one sold by Grinn & Bearitt, which achieved a higher price than the one in Tall Towers, which was purchased by either Miss Walters or Mr Bishop.

7 The flat bought by Mr Brown cost less than that sold by Shark & Co.

| | PRICE | | | | | | LOCATION | | | | | | PURCHASER | | | | | |
|---|---|---|---|---|---|---|---|---|---|---|---|---|---|---|---|---|---|---|
| | £73,000 | £78,000 | £83,000 | £88,000 | £93,000 | £98,000 | Cloudy View | Grande Vista | Happy Heights | Lofty Reach | Sky Scraper | Tall Towers | Mr Bishop | Mr Brown | Mrs Cairn | Ms Dimarco | Mr Goring | Miss Walters |
| Grinn & Bearitt | | | | | | | | | | | | | | | | | | |
| Hearth & Home | | | | | | | | | | | | | | | | | | |
| Proffitts | | | | | | | | | | | | | | | | | | |
| Sayle & Sons | | | | | | | | | | | | | | | | | | |
| Sellmore's | | | | | | | | | | | | | | | | | | |
| Shark & Co | | | | | | | | | | | | | | | | | | |
| Mr Bishop | | | | | | | | | | | | | | | | | | |
| Mr Brown | | | | | | | | | | | | | | | | | | |
| Mrs Cairn | | | | | | | | | | | | | | | | | | |
| Ms Dimarco | | | | | | | | | | | | | | | | | | |
| Mr Goring | | | | | | | | | | | | | | | | | | |
| Miss Walters | | | | | | | | | | | | | | | | | | |
| Cloudy View | | | | | | | | | | | | | | | | | | |
| Grande Vista | | | | | | | | | | | | | | | | | | |
| Happy Heights | | | | | | | | | | | | | | | | | | |
| Lofty Reach | | | | | | | | | | | | | | | | | | |
| Sky Scraper | | | | | | | | | | | | | | | | | | |
| Tall Towers | | | | | | | | | | | | | | | | | | |

## 61★★ Test your vocabulary with this verbal teaser. We've provided four definitions, but only one is correct. Can you find it?

**SLEIGHT**

**Trickery  Trivial  Insult  Sledge**

✎ ----------------------------------------

## 62★

Each answer is a four-letter word. When entered in the grid, a magic square will be formed in which each word reads the same across as down.

| 1 | 2 | 3 | 4 |
|---|---|---|---|
| 2 | | | |
| 3 | | | |
| 4 | | | |

1 He __ __ __ __ his wallet on the train

2 She plays the __ __ __ __ in an orchestra

3 He is the __ __ __ __ winner in the competition

4 The ants __ __ __ __ in the garden

## 63★★

Place every word in the list onto the grid provided.

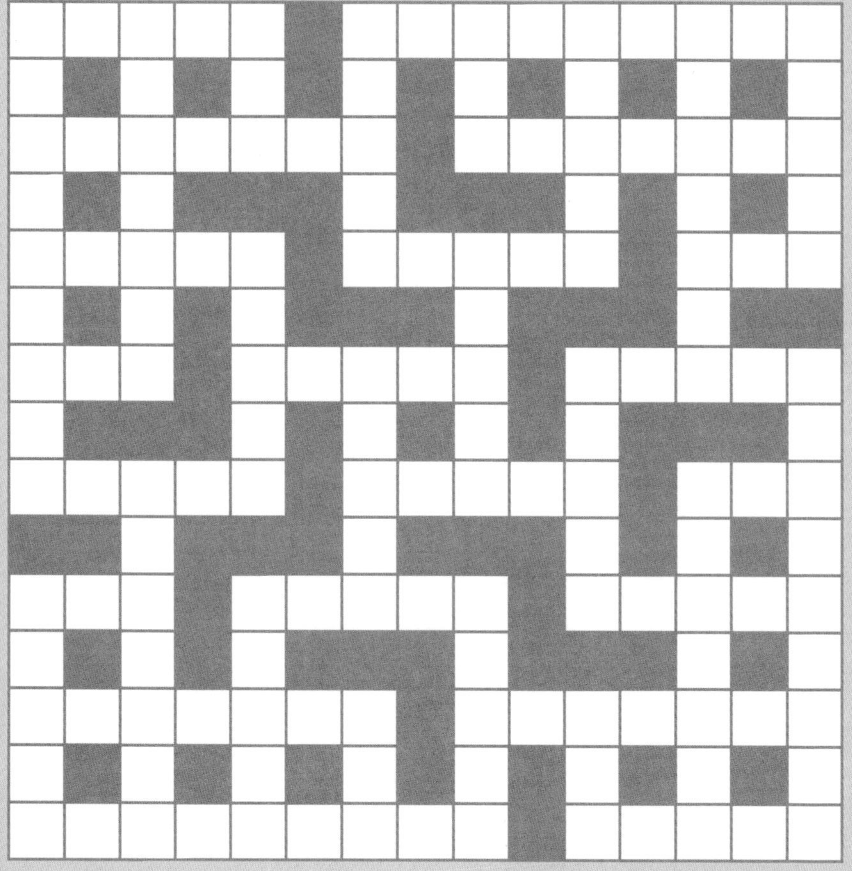

3-LETTER WORDS
CUT
ERR
EYE
JET
MUM
RAN
SKI
WAS

5-LETTER WORDS
ASKED
ATTIC
CARED
COURT
DROVE
DUCKS
EARTH
ERROR
EXTRA
HOURS
MERCY
RIGID
STAYS
STEER
STUNS
TASTY
TIRED
UNTIE
UPSET
YOURS

7-LETTER WORDS
AMERICA
BADGERS
BARRIER
REMOVED
THICKER
THUNDER
UPRIGHT
WHOEVER

9-LETTER WORDS
ABANDONED
ENJOYABLE
SUBTRACTS
YESTERDAY

**64★★** Change trim into neat by altering a single letter at a time.

**TRIM**

✎ _______________ Vehicle

_______________ Group

_______________ Nipple

**NEAT**

**65★★** Test your vocabulary with this verbal teaser. We've provided four definitions, but only one is correct. Can you find it?

**ONYX**

**Large antelope**

**Semi-precious stone**

**Greek god**

**Inner ear**

✎ ____________________

**66★** Each answer is a four-letter word. When entered in the grid, a magic square will be formed in which each word reads the same across and down.

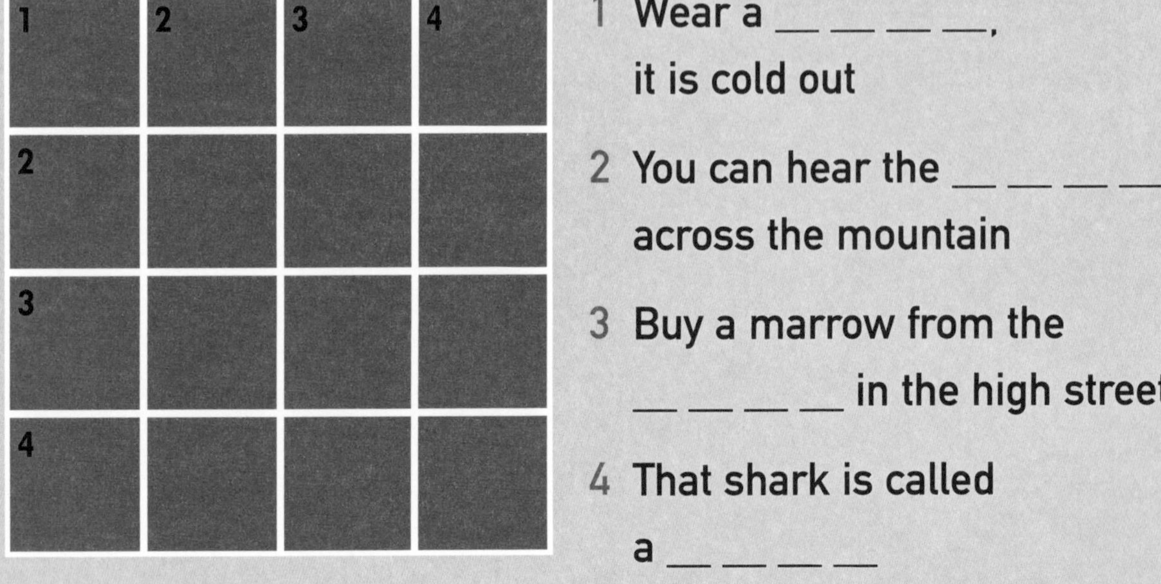


1 Wear a __ __ __ __, it is cold out

2 You can hear the __ __ __ __ across the mountain

3 Buy a marrow from the __ __ __ __ in the high street

4 That shark is called a __ __ __ __

## 67★★ 

The dice blocks below each have a six-letter word written on them, but unfortunately you can only see three sides. When you have solved the clues, the first column of the grid will reveal a word.

CLUES

1 Opportunity
2 Clothing
3 Religious reading
4 Deep ravine
5 Father of Saturn
6 Foam
7 Busy
8 Vibration
9 Article
10 Cure

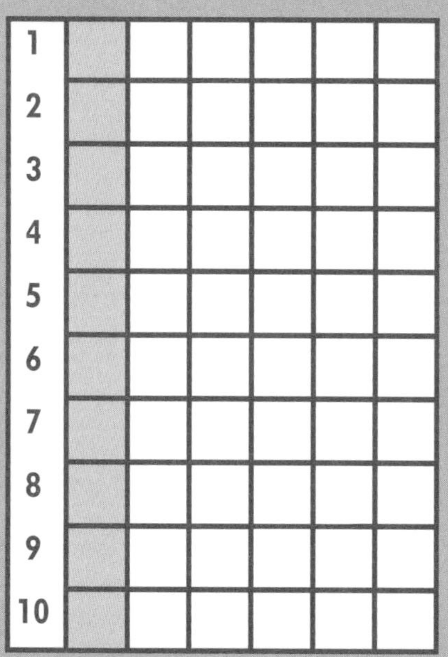


## 68★

Place the tiles in the crossword. The words formed will read the same across as down.

CLUES

1 **Arrived**

2 **Measure of space**

3 **Cries as a cat**

4 **Simple**

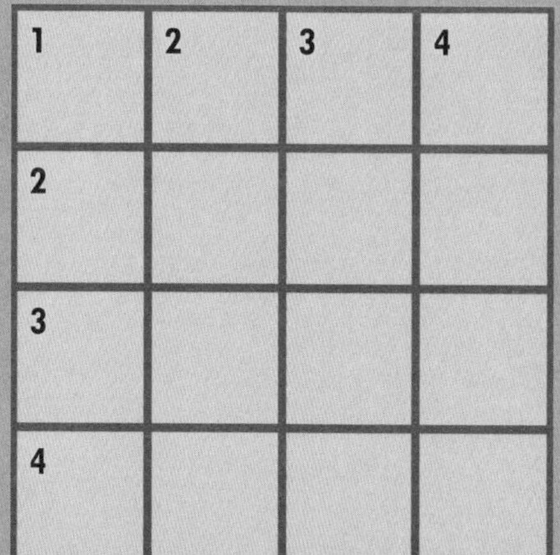


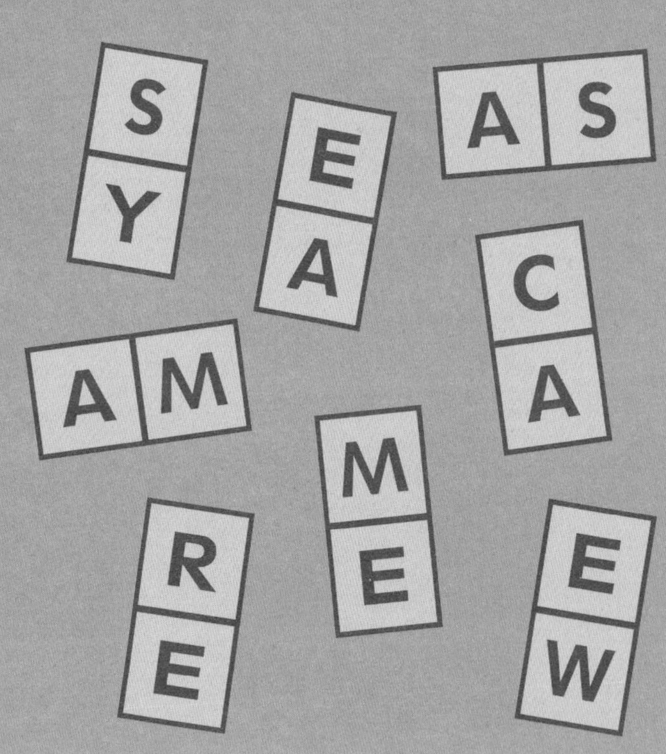

69★★ The dice blocks each have a six-letter word written on them, but unfortunately you can only see three sides. When you have solved the clues, the first column will reveal a word or phrase.

CLUES

1 Chalice
2 Colour
3 Unit of time
4 Goad
5 Onslaught
6 Flower part
7 Objective
8 Exempt
9 Settlement
10 Yield

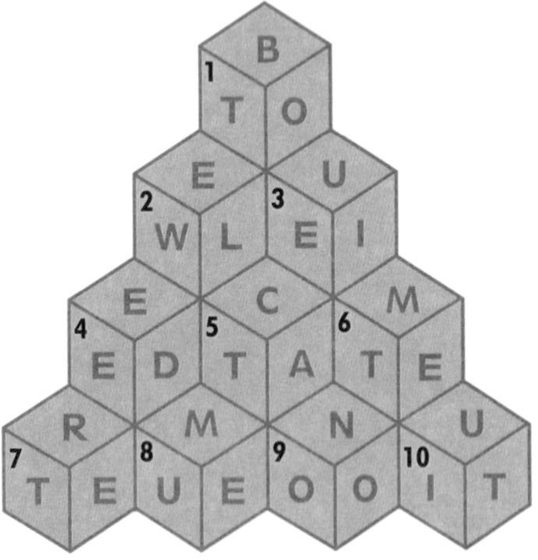

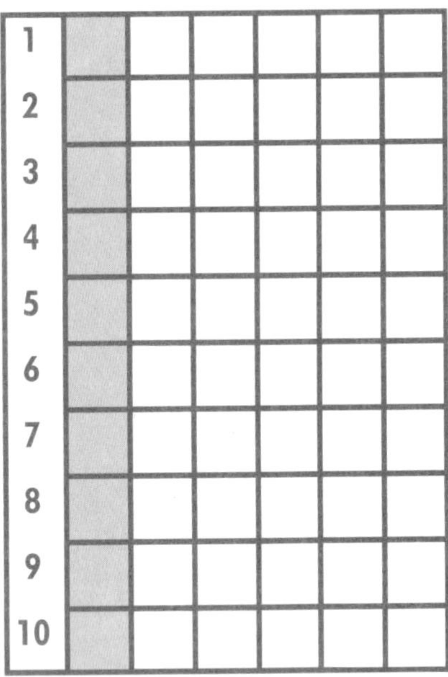

70★★ Place all the pieces onto the grid so that a valid crossword is formed. Remember that crossword grids possess half-turn symmetry. The coloured blocks will also help.

**71** ★★ Which of these anagrams makes a word?

ELRUAL
ESMMIO
GNORAO
VAPTIR
URBTBE
VESORR

**72** ★★ Get from hake to ling, changing just one letter each time.

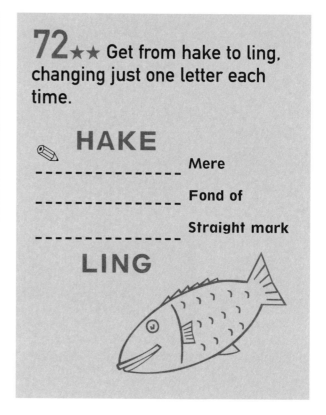

HAKE
_______________ Mere
_______________ Fond of
_______________ Straight mark
LING

**73** ★★★ What is this riddle referring to?

A dozen Royals gathered round,
Entertained by two who clowned.
Each king there had servants ten,
Though none of them were also men.
The lowest servant sometimes might
Defeat the King in a fair fight.
A weapon stout, a priceless jewel,
The beat of life, a gardener's tool.
What are we talking about here?

## 74★

Can you spot the following weights and measures in the grid? They may be found across, down or diagonally in any direction.

| | | | | | | | | | | | | | |
|---|---|---|---|---|---|---|---|---|---|---|---|---|---|
| E | R | T | E | M | M | A | R | G | D | R | I | L | L |
| I | L | S | N | V | K | U | V | R | W | B | G | R | E |
| R | E | U | S | E | C | H | K | A | E | J | O | A | B |
| O | N | T | O | M | P | Q | Y | I | N | I | Z | H | I |
| L | O | R | W | J | I | P | I | N | T | W | N | I | C |
| A | C | C | O | U | N | T | W | O | S | P | R | E | E |
| C | A | R | A | T | B | D | N | V | H | U | J | K | D |
| Y | E | L | L | I | Q | X | P | R | N | M | F | T | L |
| G | A | O | S | B | K | M | O | V | E | D | B | W | F |
| F | V | U | Z | U | A | L | Y | X | W | P | R | U | A |
| A | B | L | S | C | R | E | E | N | K | R | V | I | T |
| M | A | O | R | X | W | E | L | L | N | Z | E | T | H |
| J | P | E | G | E | H | F | N | C | O | T | S | A | O |
| K | L | Z | Q | T | Y | P | E | S | T | H | E | R | M |

ACRE
AMP
CALORIE
CARAT
CUBIT
DECIBEL
DENIER
ERG
FATHOM
GRAIN
GRAM
JOULE
KNOT
METRE
OHM
PINT
REAM
THERM
TON
VOLT

## 75 & 76

For these wordfinder puzzles, you must trace out words of three letters or more by travelling horizontally, vertically or diagonally to adjacent letters.

Each letter may be used once only in any one word. Plurals and well-known proper names are allowed.

| | | |
|---|---|---|
| O | M | L |
| D | R | Y |
| A | N | T |

TARGET
★ 18 words
★★ 25 words
★★★ 30 words

| | | |
|---|---|---|
| S | T | P |
| E | A | R |
| U | Q | O |

TARGET
★ 27 words
★★ 38 words
★★★ 50 words

**77★** Test your vocabulary with this verbal teaser. We've provided explanations – but only one definition is correct. The other three are designed to confuse you!

**Eider**

**Concept**

**Type of duck**

**Breed of dog**

**Ill-will**

**78★★** Which is a word? Just one of the following sets of letters is an anagram of a five-letter word. Can you find the word?

L E G T N

O L C R E

T C O H E

L U D I B

M E U D O

H I N W L

✎ ---------------------------

**79★** Find the word that links the pair of words below.

fountain (____________) knife

**80★★★** Which is the odd word out?

Estate Shaven

Atoned Talent

Averse Tenser

Enters

✎ ---------------------------

**81** ★ Test your vocabulary with this verbal teaser. We've provided four definitions, but only one is correct. Can you find it?

**CODDLE**

**Pamper** **Mob**

**Young cod** **Conundrum**

**82** ★★ Can you spot the following weather-related words in the grid? They may be found across, down or diagonally in any direction. One word in the list doesn't appear in the grid. Which one is it?

| | | | | | | | | | | | | | |
|---|---|---|---|---|---|---|---|---|---|---|---|---|---|
| O | M | N | U | B | J | K | W | A | H | G | A | L | E |
| B | R | I | G | H | T | Q | F | D | U | O | L | C | S |
| L | O | Q | N | T | R | E | V | P | D | C | I | K | G |
| Y | T | X | N | Z | U | Q | E | V | X | L | S | W | H |
| M | S | P | V | T | Q | L | F | L | O | O | D | G | T |
| O | Q | X | I | U | L | R | T | K | S | E | N | E | O |
| W | N | B | P | S | C | S | J | U | O | L | I | A | H |
| Y | E | L | D | R | A | I | N | Z | N | C | W | F | P |
| S | E | F | K | R | J | N | M | O | F | E | H | K | G |
| U | V | B | U | S | Y | H | G | E | W | L | Q | Z | P |
| L | J | Y | U | O | N | B | M | M | V | E | U | I | L |
| T | E | R | Y | U | X | B | L | I | X | U | T | Q | F |
| R | O | A | M | L | D | A | F | S | P | H | N | O | M |
| Y | L | L | I | H | C | H | E | T | S | U | G | J | G |

BRIGHT
CALM
CHILLY
DRY
FLOOD
FOG
GALE
GUST
HAIL
HOT
ICE
MIST
RAIN
SHOWER
SLEET
SNOW
STORM
SULTRY
SUNNY
WIND

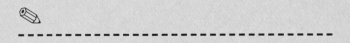

**83**★★ Can you find the word in this anagram?

# Rain clad

**84**★★ Place all the pieces into the grid so that a valid crossword is formed. Remember that crossword grids possess half-turn symmetry. The coloured blocks will also help.

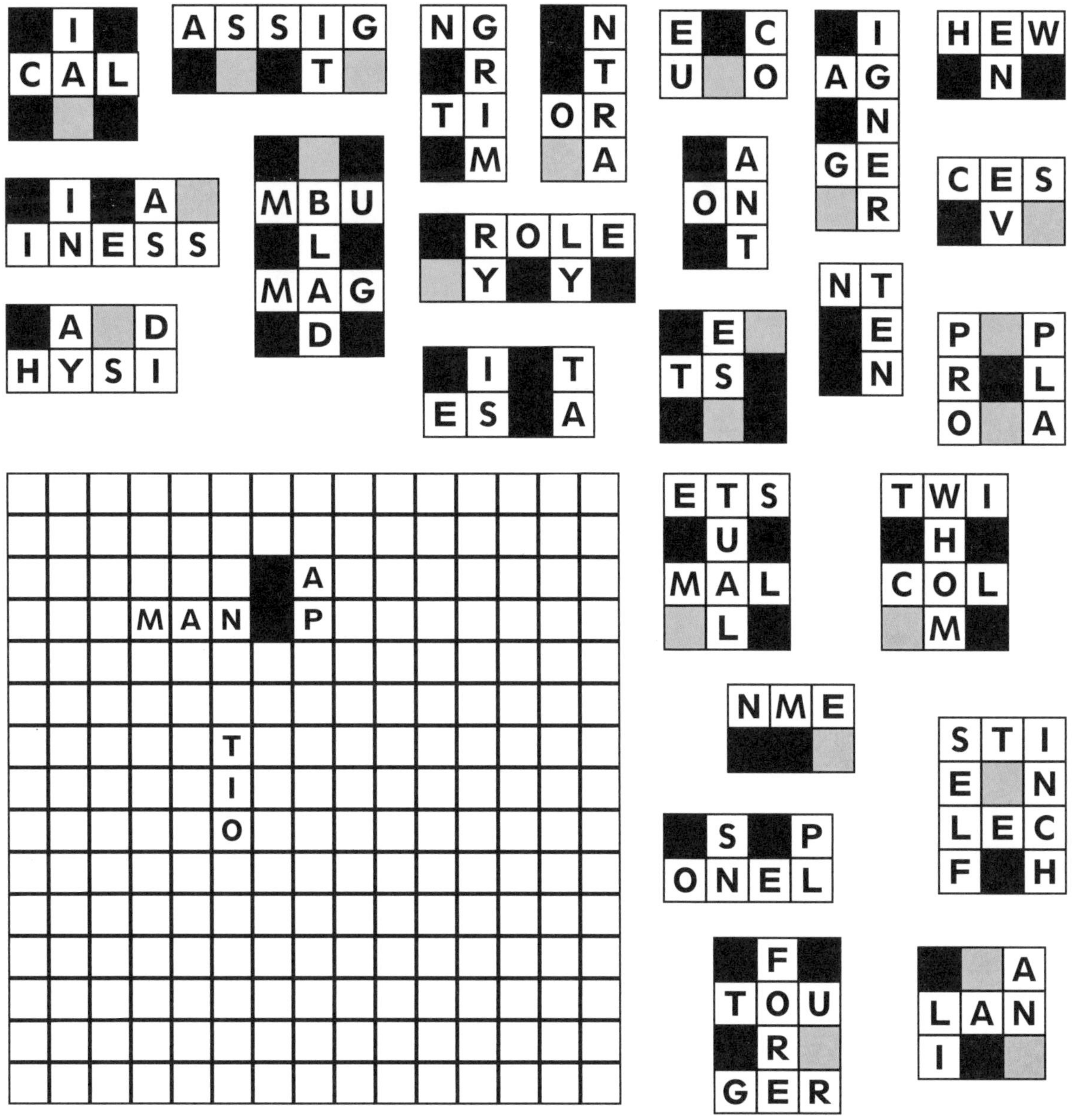

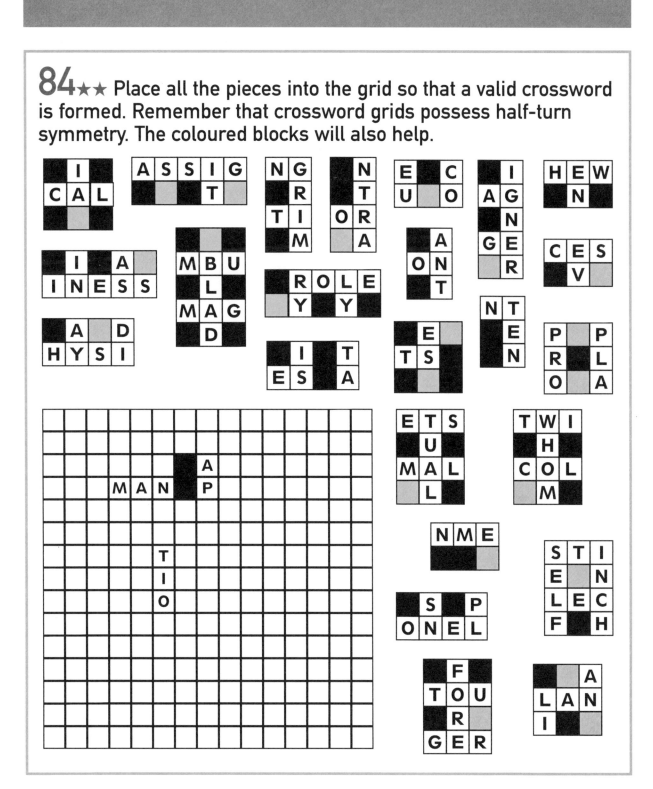

**85★★** The wooden blocks each have a six-letter word written on them, but unfortunately you can only see three sides. When you have solved the clues, the first column will reveal a word.

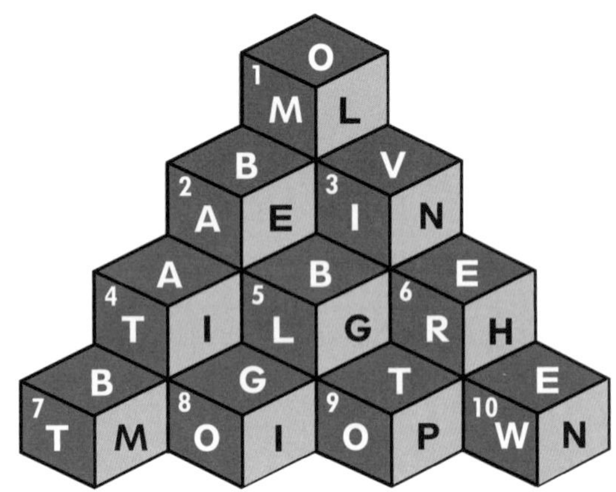


CLUES
1 Conventional
2 Flaming
3 Hallucination
4 Baby
5 Worldwide
6 Symbol of Sagittarius
7 Wood
8 Overlook
9 Choice
10 Relative

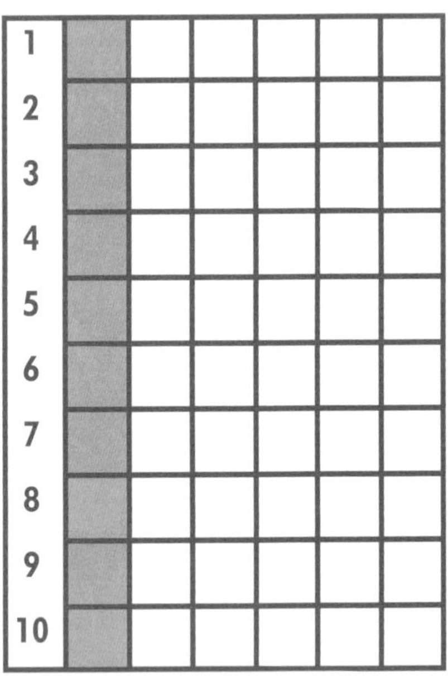


**86★** There are two ways to solve this magic square, in which the grid reads the same across or down. Answer the clues or fit in the tiles below.

CLUES
1 Identical
2 Afresh
3 Only
4 Sheep

E R

E W

S A

N E

M E

A M

E S

W E

**87★★** In which famous children's story are the following characters found? Think laterally to find the answer.

Colin Drew

Diana Len

---

**88★** Which is the odd word out?

Bayonet Pioneer

Colonel Wronged Honesty

---

**89★★** Believe it or not, the word LIFELINE is concealed in this grid only once. Can you locate it? It may be read across, down or diagonally in any direction.

| | | | | | | | | | | | | | |
|---|---|---|---|---|---|---|---|---|---|---|---|---|---|
| L | I | F | E | N | E | L | E | F | I | L | L | L | E |
| E | N | I | L | N | I | N | L | N | N | E | I | I | L |
| N | E | I | E | F | I | L | I | N | E | F | F | F | F |
| N | N | F | E | E | E | L | F | L | L | I | E | E | E |
| E | I | L | F | I | N | E | L | I | E | F | E | L | N |
| N | E | I | I | N | I | I | F | F | F | I | N | I | L |
| I | L | I | F | E | L | I | L | E | I | L | L | N | E |
| L | I | I | E | I | E | F | I | E | L | E | E | N | F |
| E | L | I | F | E | L | I | F | L | F | F | F | E | E |
| F | E | E | I | E | I | N | E | I | I | I | I | N | N |
| E | F | I | L | E | F | I | L | E | F | I | L | E | F |
| L | I | I | I | E | I | I | I | N | I | E | E | L | L |
| I | L | I | F | E | L | I | N | I | L | I | F | E | L |
| N | N | I | E | F | E | E | I | L | E | L | E | N | L |

30 MINUTES

| 1A | 2G | 3C | 4J | | 5K | 6F | 7C | 8J | 9A | | 10F |
|---|---|---|---|---|---|---|---|---|---|---|---|
| 11F | | 12C | 13D | 14B | | 15J | 16L | 17G | 18J | | 19D |
| 20C | | 21F | 22K | 23B | | 24L | 25A | 26D | 27L | 28A | 29A |
| | 30E | 31G | 32J | 33G | | 34G | 35K | | 36C | 37L | |
| 38F | 39D | 40G | 41D | 42I | 43G | 44G | | 45L | 46G | 47E | 48F |
| 49L | 50G | 51H | 52F | 53H | 54D | | 55J | 56D | | 57C | 58D |
| 59G | | 60C | 61K | 62D | | 63A | 64F | 65J | 66I | 67H | 68J |
| 69A | 70L | | 71K | | 72E | 73J | 74K | 75B | 76K | 77K | 78H |
| 79L | 80J | | 81D | 82A | 83G | 84I | 85L | 86C | 87L | 88I | 89J |

**90**★★★ Solve the clues to find the answers. These letters can then be transferred into the main grid to give you a piece of timely advice from a writer. The writer's name appears after the quotation.

A Disturbed (8)
82 25 63 9 29 1 69 28

B Up to the present time (3)
14 23 75

C Clearly apparent (8)
3 12 86 36 20 7 60 57

D A remarkable development or trend (10)
81 58 26 54 56 62 41 13 19 39

E The momentary present (3)
72 47 30

F Locate exactly (8)
6 52 11 48 10 38 64 21

G Impossible to undo (12)
31 46 50 59 40 44 83 43 2 34 33 17

H An implement used for a task (4)
51 53 78 67

I Otherwise known as a castle (4)
42 66 88 84

J Sharing the activities of a group (11)
15 89 68 73 32 65 80 18 4 8 55

K Buildings housing groups of religious followers (8)
71 22 61 74 77 76 35 5

L A mental position from which things are viewed (10)
87 16 24 37 70 45 49 85 27 79

1 HOUR

## 91 ★★★ Each of the six families in this puzzle consists of a father, mother, son and daughter whose names and surnames begin with five different letters of the alphabet. Can you discover the make-up of each family? (See page 224 for tips on how to solve this puzzle.)

1 Bella's son's forename begins with the same letter as that of Kevin's mother.

2 Mrs King's forename begins with the same letter as that of Sharon's son.

3 Billy's mother's forename begins with the same letter as Jean's son.

4 Sean's mother's forename begins with the same letter as that of he who is married to the woman whose forename begins with the same letter as that of Larry's son.

5 Jerry's surname starts with a different letter from that of Jean's son's forename.

6 Liam's mother's forename begins with the same letter as that of the Bates boy.

7 Ricky's mother's forename begins with the same letter as that of Lynne's son.

8 The forename of the Bates boy begins with a different letter from Brenda's surname.

9 Mrs Race's forename begins with a different letter from that of Rachel's son.

10 The forename of the King boy begins with the same letter as the forename of the woman married to Steve.

# the ultimate

These puzzles are so devilishly hard that the usual star ratings do not apply – all are three stars plus.

Whether you start here or work your way up through other sections building confidence as you go, the goal is the same – to surmount this Everest of brain rackers. Here you will find puzzles that promise to give your intelligence the most rigorous challenge it's ever had – the hardest cryptic crosswords, the most fiendish lateral thinking puzzles, the trickiest logic grids, the most maddening mazes.

Only the bravest applicants need apply... So put on your thinking cap, and let's get started...

# challenge

# warm-up...

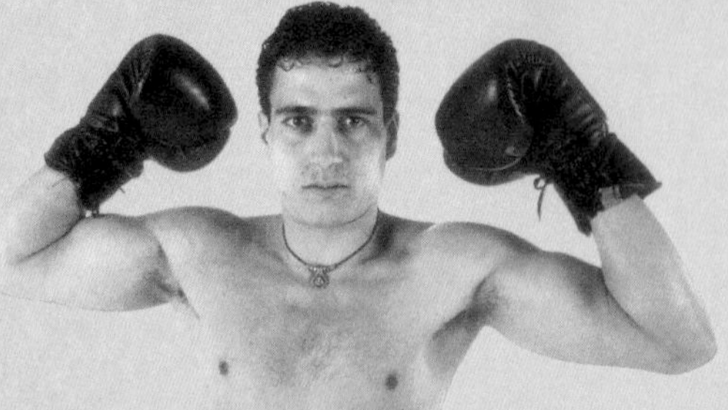

**1** What can be driven, but has no wheels? And can be sliced, but still remains whole?

**2** Each block in this pyramid is the total of the two blocks below it. Find all the numbers, given that only the digits from 1 to 6 inclusive are used, and there are no negative numbers or fractions.

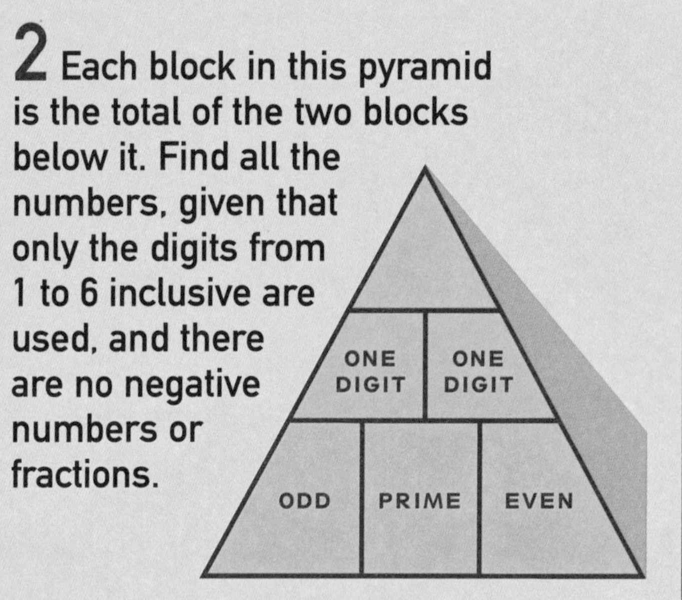


**3** Can you find a single hidden word in this anagram?

**Vintage riots**

**4** To complete this difficult wordfinder puzzle trace out words of four letters or more by travelling horizontally, vertically or diagonally to adjacent letters. Each letter that appears may be used only once in any single word. Plurals and well-known proper names are allowed.

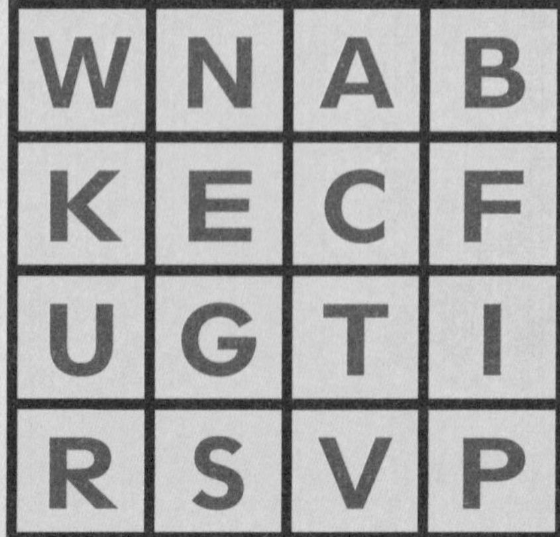


Target:
★ 18 words
★★ 25 words
★★★ 30 words

**5** Spell out a ten-letter word, moving through each circle once only. Clue: it's the longest of three.

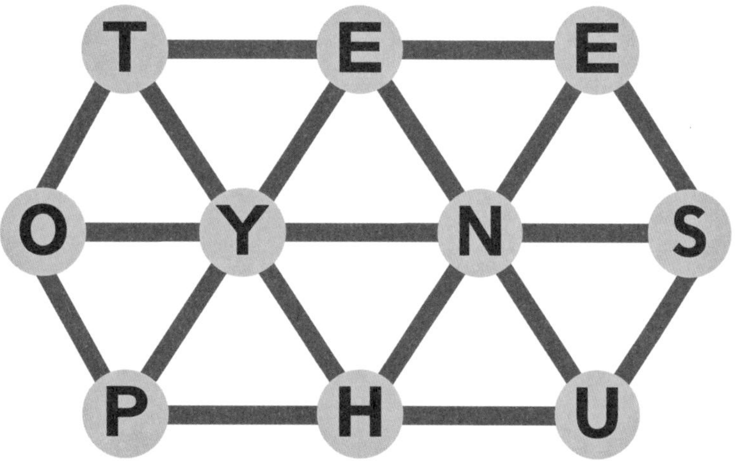


**6** What comes next?

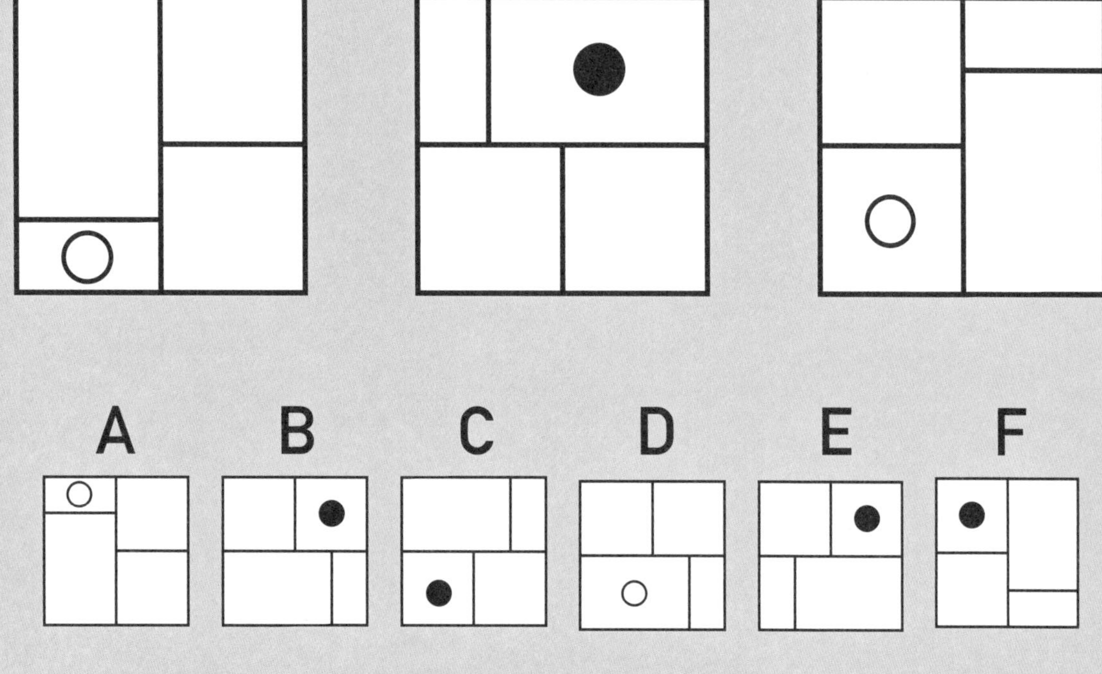


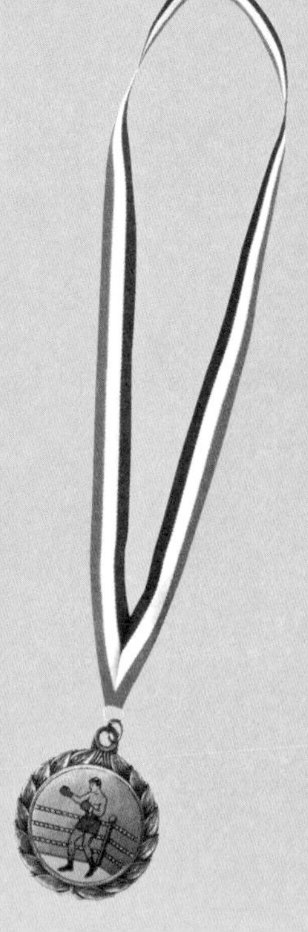

Go for gold!

**7** Can you work out the height of line AB (the triangle is not drawn to scale)?

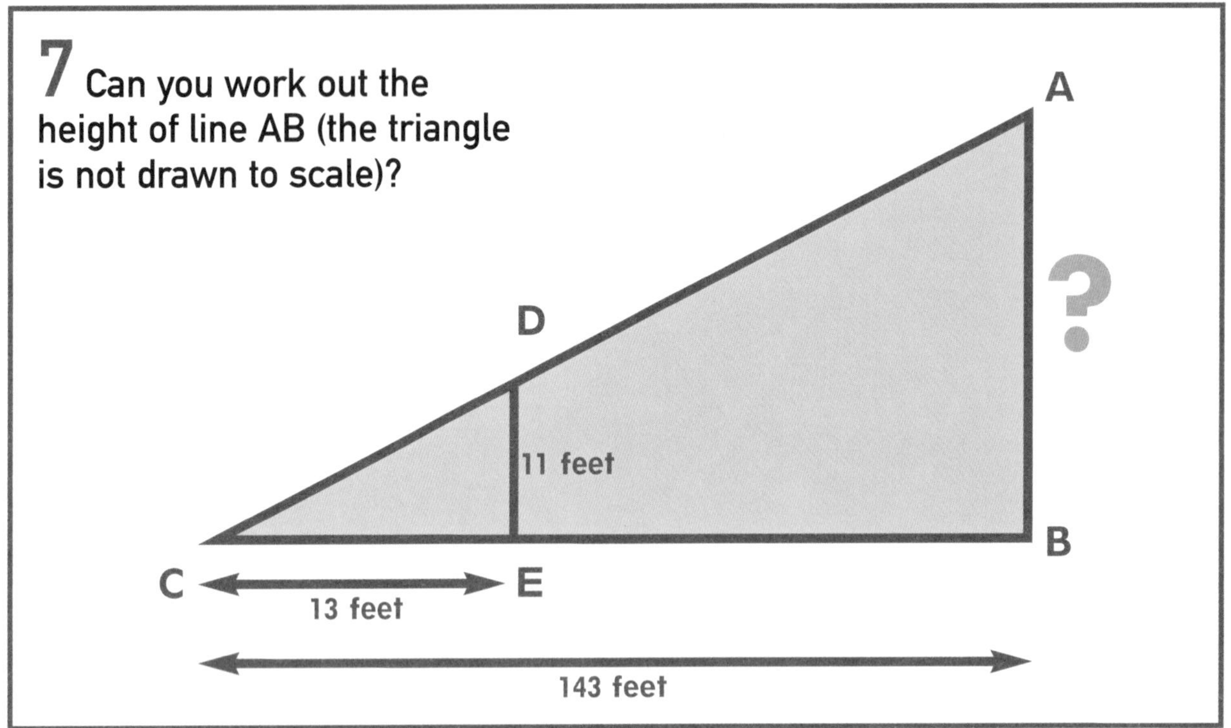


**8** Test your vocabulary with this verbal teaser. We've provided four definitions – but only one is correct. The others are designed to confuse you.

# Furze

Hoarse
Coarse
Gorse
Norse

**9** Can you solve this riddle to get two familiar entities?

One falls but never breaks.
The other breaks but never falls.
They are never seen together.
What are they?

10

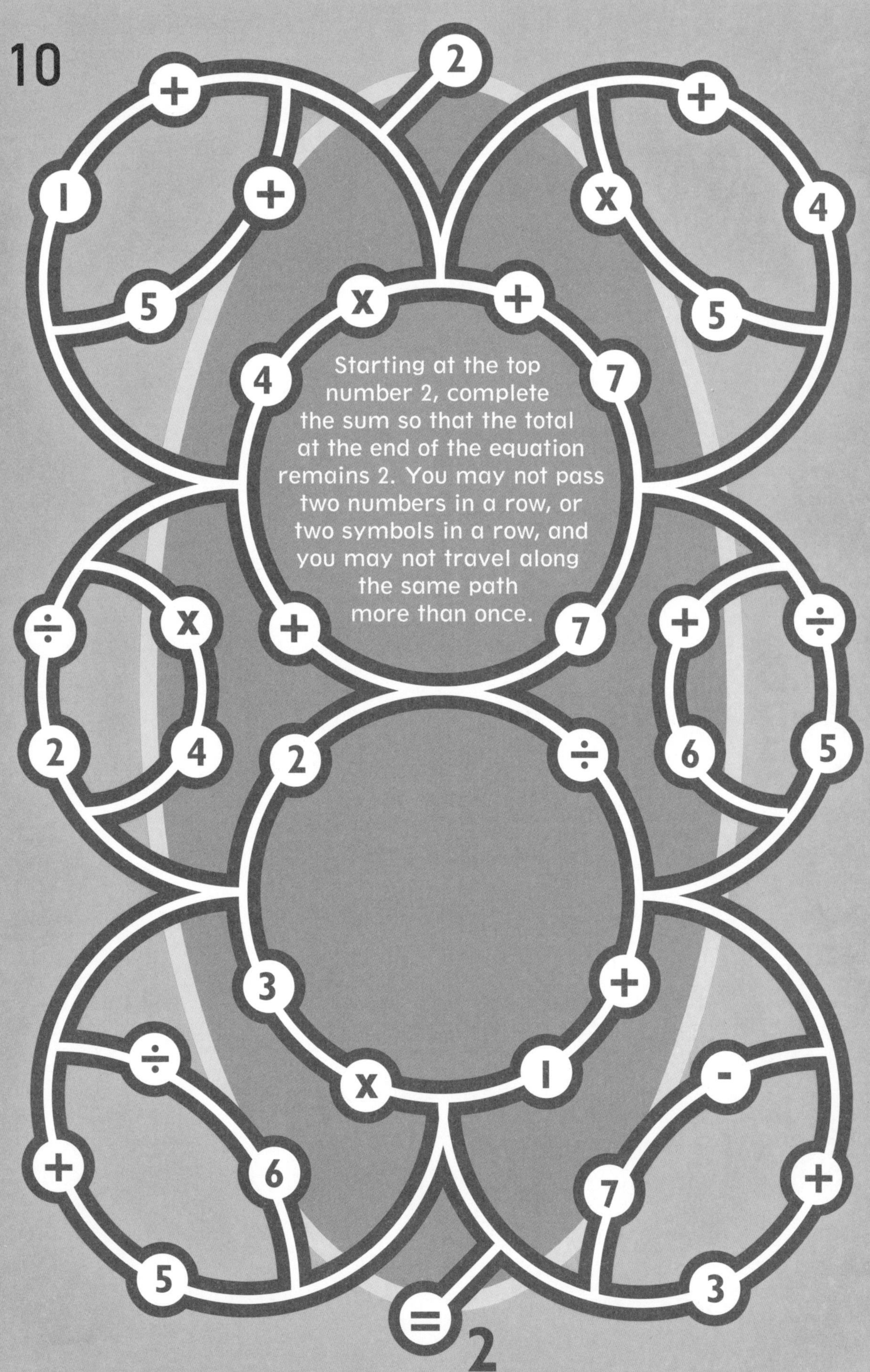
2
+
+
+
I
x
4
5
5
x
+
4
7
Starting at the top number 2, complete the sum so that the total at the end of the equation remains 2. You may not pass two numbers in a row, or two symbols in a row, and you may not travel along the same path more than once.
÷
x
+
÷
+
7
2
4
2
÷
6
5
3
+
x
I
÷
-
+
6
7
+
5
3
=
2

**11** Find the odd word out.

Dotterel

Pomfret

Phalarope

Guacharo

Lorikeet

**12** Which of the following is the opposite of dreamy?

**Expressive**

**Pessimistic**

**Vague**

**Pragmatic**

**Dismal**

**13** Planets A and B are in orbit around the same sun. Planet A takes five years to make one complete orbit, while planet B takes four years. Currently, planet A, planet B and the sun are all in the same line. How long will it be before this situation occurs once again?

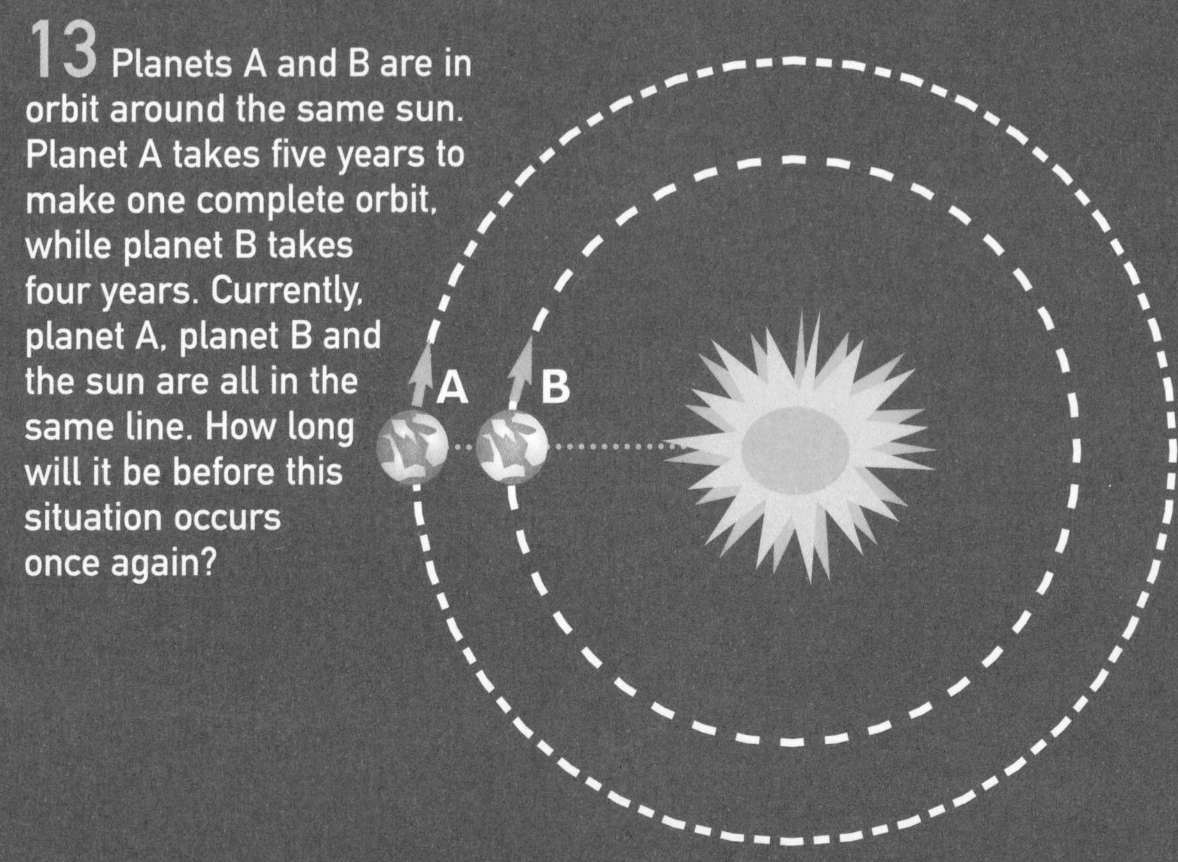

# How to solve logic problems

In these puzzles the trick is to deduce what is known for sure from the information given. Each type of item correlates with exactly one of every other item (in this example, one boy dates one girl at one location). The grid covers every possible combination once.

The clues will enable you to fill in the obvious valid and invalid combinations, and from there you can deduce further information.

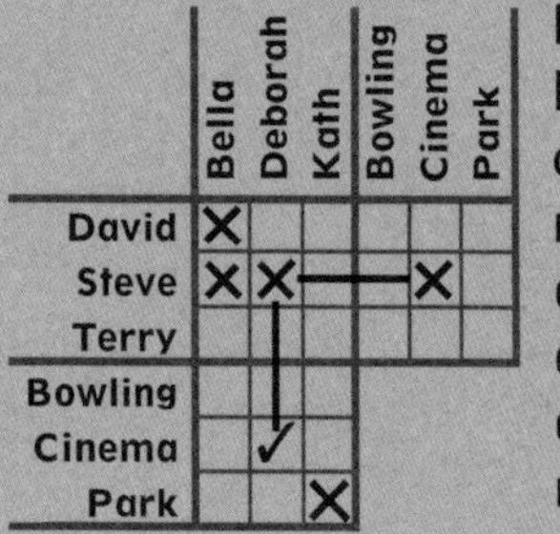


In this example, if Deborah went to the cinema ✓, but Steve did not ✗, Steve cannot have dated Deborah (new ✗, deduced). As Bella did not date Steve either ✗, he must have dated Kath (new ✓, deduced), etc.

## 14

Each of the six schoolgirls assembled below attends a different school, where the colour of the uniform is different from the others. Can you identify all six girls in terms of their names, ages, the name of the school they attend and the colour of their uniforms?

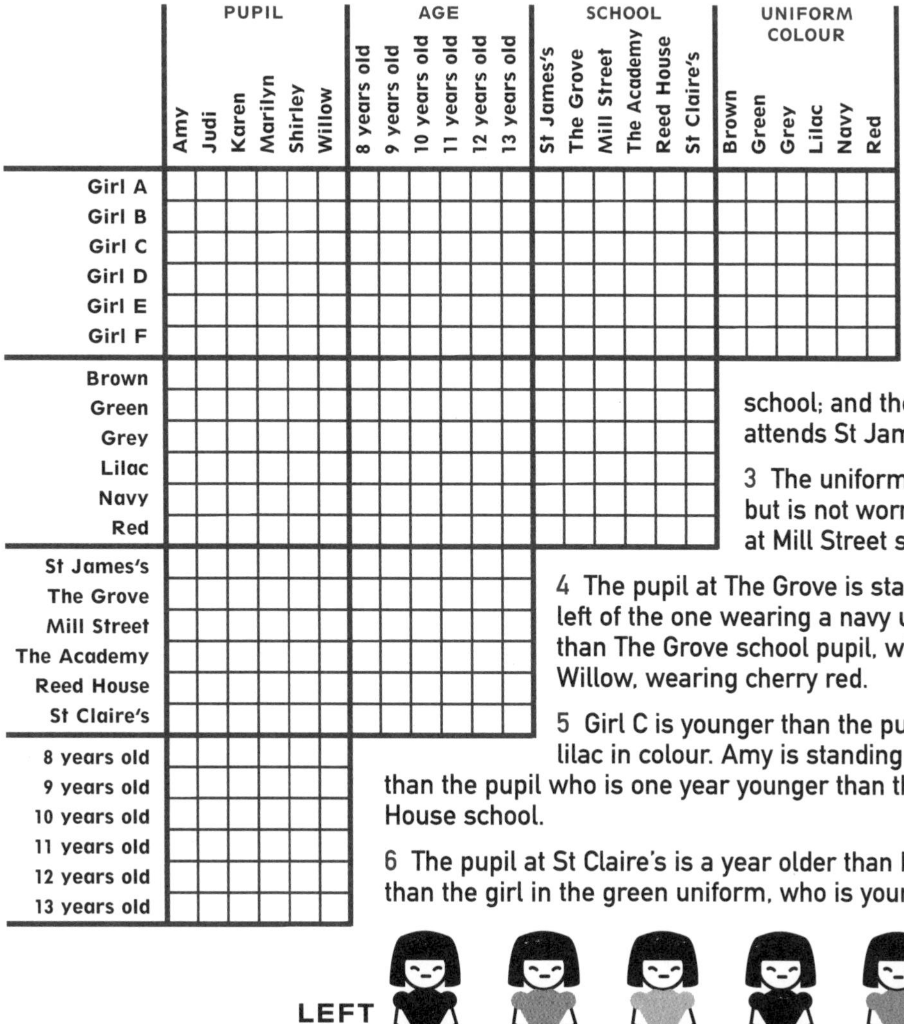

| | PUPIL | | | | | | AGE | | | | | | SCHOOL | | | | | | UNIFORM COLOUR | | | | | |
|---|---|---|---|---|---|---|---|---|---|---|---|---|---|---|---|---|---|---|---|---|---|---|---|---|
| | Amy | Judi | Karen | Marilyn | Shirley | Willow | 8 years old | 9 years old | 10 years old | 11 years old | 12 years old | 13 years old | St James's | The Grove | Mill Street | The Academy | Reed House | St Claire's | Brown | Green | Grey | Lilac | Navy | Red |
| Girl A | | | | | | | | | | | | | | | | | | | | | | | | |
| Girl B | | | | | | | | | | | | | | | | | | | | | | | | |
| Girl C | | | | | | | | | | | | | | | | | | | | | | | | |
| Girl D | | | | | | | | | | | | | | | | | | | | | | | | |
| Girl E | | | | | | | | | | | | | | | | | | | | | | | | |
| Girl F | | | | | | | | | | | | | | | | | | | | | | | | |
| Brown | | | | | | | | | | | | | | | | | | | | | | | | |
| Green | | | | | | | | | | | | | | | | | | | | | | | | |
| Grey | | | | | | | | | | | | | | | | | | | | | | | | |
| Lilac | | | | | | | | | | | | | | | | | | | | | | | | |
| Navy | | | | | | | | | | | | | | | | | | | | | | | | |
| Red | | | | | | | | | | | | | | | | | | | | | | | | |
| St James's | | | | | | | | | | | | | | | | | | | | | | | | |
| The Grove | | | | | | | | | | | | | | | | | | | | | | | | |
| Mill Street | | | | | | | | | | | | | | | | | | | | | | | | |
| The Academy | | | | | | | | | | | | | | | | | | | | | | | | |
| Reed House | | | | | | | | | | | | | | | | | | | | | | | | |
| St Claire's | | | | | | | | | | | | | | | | | | | | | | | | |
| 8 years old | | | | | | | | | | | | | | | | | | | | | | | | |
| 9 years old | | | | | | | | | | | | | | | | | | | | | | | | |
| 10 years old | | | | | | | | | | | | | | | | | | | | | | | | |
| 11 years old | | | | | | | | | | | | | | | | | | | | | | | | |
| 12 years old | | | | | | | | | | | | | | | | | | | | | | | | |
| 13 years old | | | | | | | | | | | | | | | | | | | | | | | | |

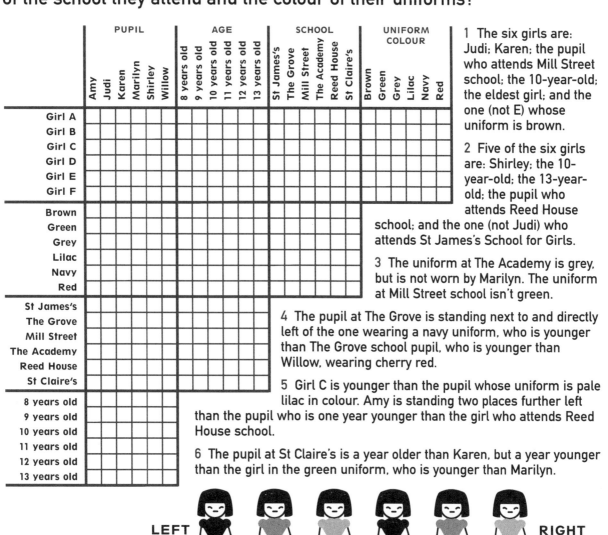

1 The six girls are: Judi; Karen; the pupil who attends Mill Street school; the 10-year-old; the eldest girl; and the one (not E) whose uniform is brown.

2 Five of the six girls are: Shirley; the 10-year-old; the 13-year-old; the pupil who attends Reed House school; and the one (not Judi) who attends St James's School for Girls.

3 The uniform at The Academy is grey, but is not worn by Marilyn. The uniform at Mill Street school isn't green.

4 The pupil at The Grove is standing next to and directly left of the one wearing a navy uniform, who is younger than The Grove school pupil, who is younger than Willow, wearing cherry red.

5 Girl C is younger than the pupil whose uniform is pale lilac in colour. Amy is standing two places further left than the pupil who is one year younger than the girl who attends Reed House school.

6 The pupil at St Claire's is a year older than Karen, but a year younger than the girl in the green uniform, who is younger than Marilyn.

LEFT A B C D E F RIGHT

15 Each block in this pyramid is the total of the two blocks below it. Can you deduce all the missing numbers?

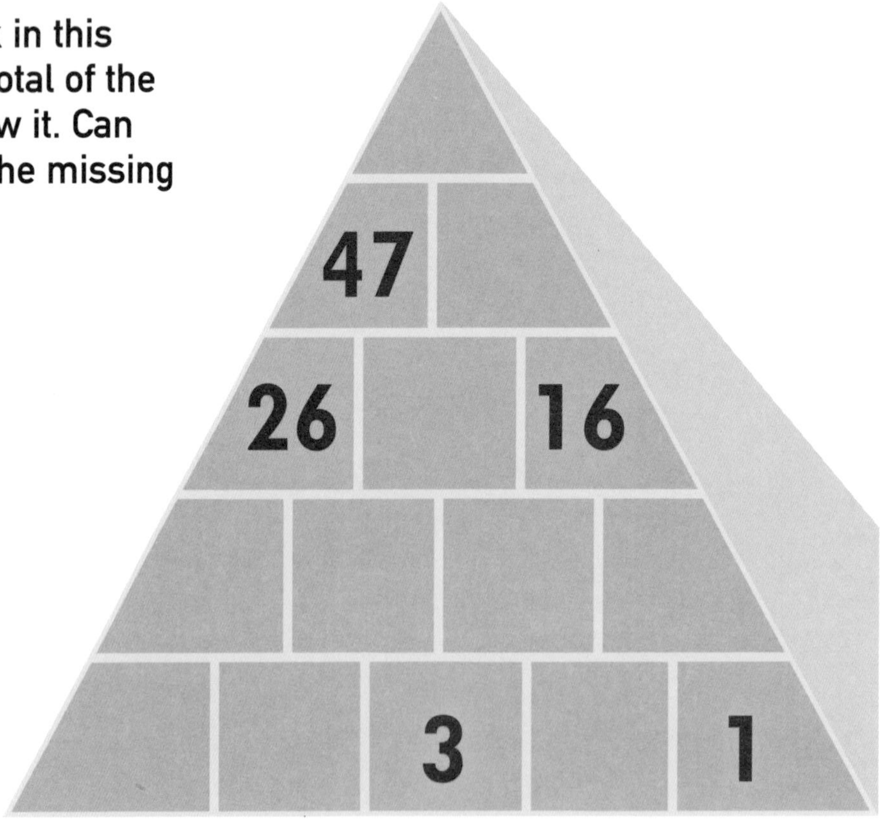

16 What is green and has an 'H' at each end? Clue: use a bit of lateral thinking.

17 How many revolutions must the large cog make to return all the cogs to their starting positions?

Cog 1 has 11 teeth
Cog 2 has 8 teeth
Cog 3 has 7 teeth
Cog 4 has 4 teeth

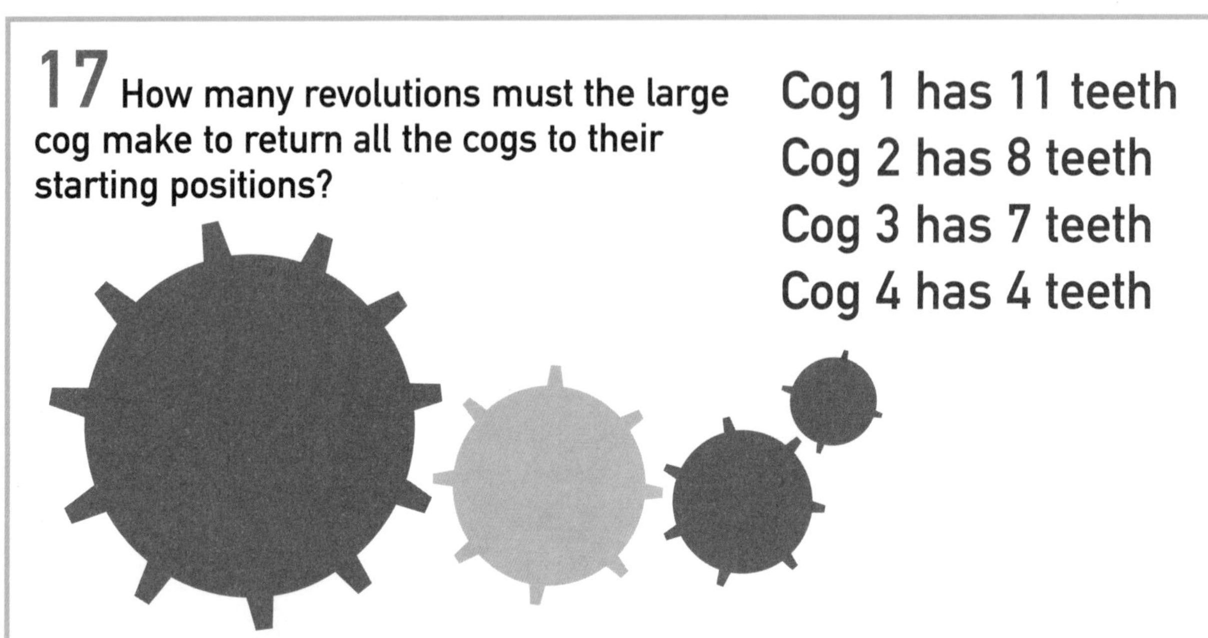

**18** Watch the birdie! Can you find 32 birds in this wordsearch? We have provided scrambled versions of their names to assist you.

| | | | | | | | | | | | | | | | |
|---|---|---|---|---|---|---|---|---|---|---|---|---|---|---|---|
| C | V | L | L | I | B | R | O | Z | A | R | M | T | K | T | R |
| A | V | O | C | E | T | F | L | A | M | I | N | G | O | S | I |
| Y | R | A | N | A | C | M | G | R | E | B | E | N | T | R | Y |
| P | U | G | W | Y | E | R | E | D | N | A | G | O | E | K | E |
| I | P | D | O | R | C | G | H | I | L | E | R | T | S | E | K |
| G | W | B | L | O | O | O | Y | C | B | K | S | C | N | K | R |
| E | I | I | U | S | S | B | C | K | I | O | J | P | O | N | U |
| O | N | N | L | D | E | E | K | K | O | R | H | O | M | S | T |
| N | A | I | I | I | G | H | S | R | A | C | T | K | E | R | C |
| T | N | U | P | D | T | E | Y | U | N | T | N | S | D | O | R |
| G | E | G | B | Z | O | E | R | I | O | I | I | R | O | D | A |
| T | A | N | K | F | R | Y | F | I | T | R | A | E | N | N | V |
| M | G | E | J | P | R | F | R | R | G | Z | G | I | L | O | E |
| A | L | P | S | W | A | C | A | M | Z | A | B | X | N | C | N |
| T | E | O | Q | H | P | M | B | U | N | O | R | A | M | Y | I |
| C | H | I | C | K | E | N | B | C | R | C | U | R | L | E | W |

| | | | |
|---|---|---|---|
| TCAOEV | EULCWR | ELESTKR | PNUIENG |
| URBAGRGIDE | LEGEA | WMCAA | OPNEIG |
| ZZBURAD | AFOGNMLI | MGIPAE | EVNRA |
| YCNAAR | GENDAR | ATIMNR | AILOLZRBR |
| HIAFCCNHF | ESOOG | ERIMLN | BIORN |
| ENHCKIC | OSGNGIL | YOSEPR | ORRETSO |
| TCEIKALCO | EEGRB | HTROCIS | OKRTS |
| DOCNOR | GUESOR | RPTRAO | ERTYKU |

**19** Spell out a ten-letter word, passing through each letter once only. Clue: he starts but never wins.

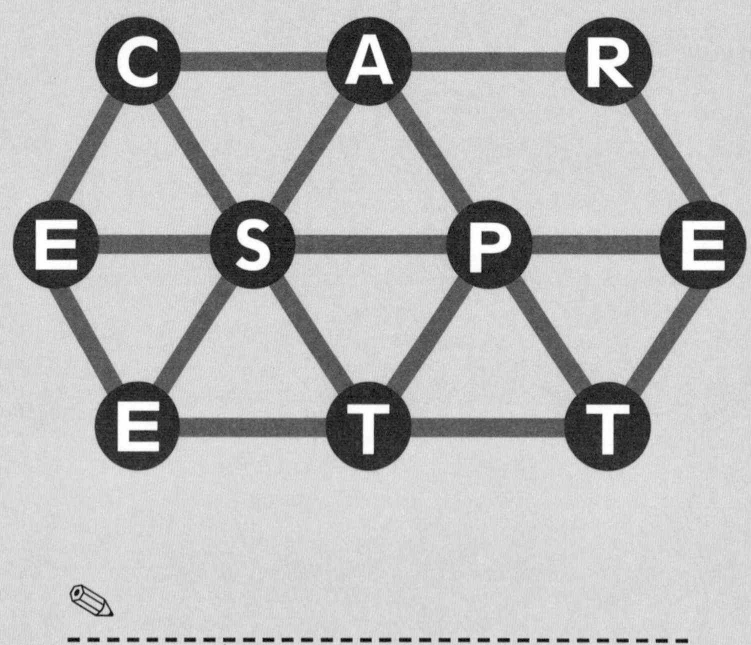


**20** Discover the surnames of five fashion designers by picking one letter from each shape in the order indicated by the numbers (one letter from box 1, one from box 2 etc.).

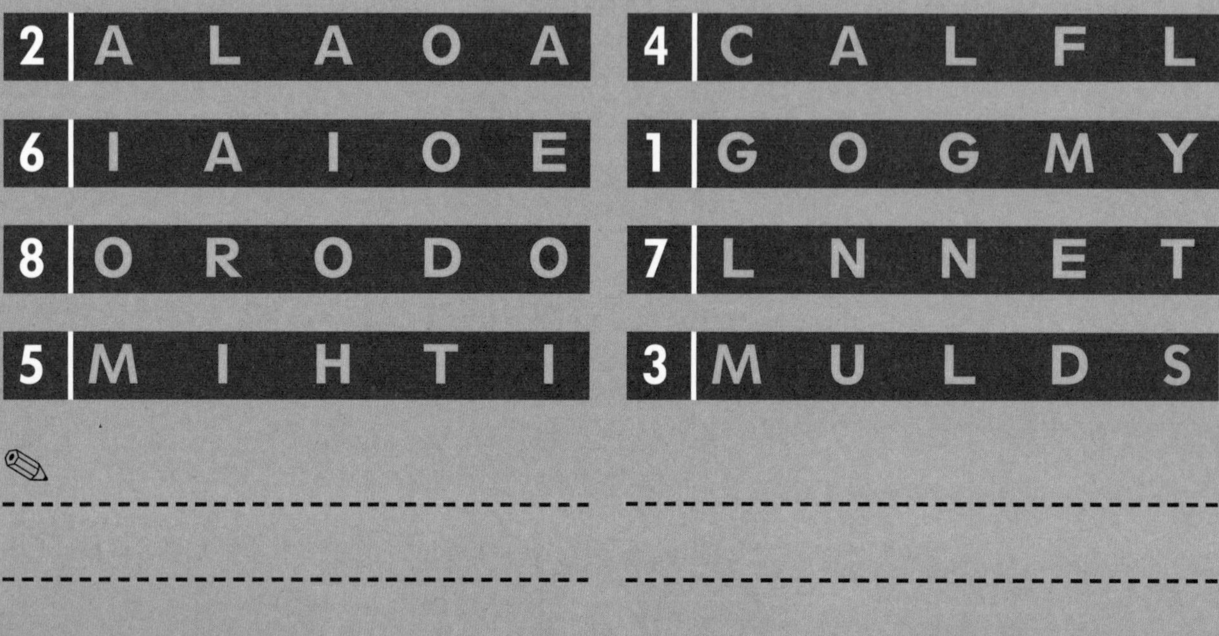

**21** Sharpen your pencil and your wits for this cryptic conundrum.

ACROSS

1 Nautical rope found back in docks (5)
4 Right has nothing to fight (5)
8 Pluck the zebra's ears initially (there's little inside) (6)
9 Sword made of thin, flexible metal (4)
10 Angel is about to grow stuff on old envelope (7,3)
12 Divorce wrecked nice desire (6,4)
14 Rotate number in tin (4)
16 Medical pediatrician centre (6)
17 Big man – foot and a yard (5)
18 She's a gem (5)

DOWN

2 Team leader has staff population (11)
3 Arranged opera in the outdoors (4,3)
5 Some of the toffee's sour (3)
6 A tailor must have this – a good fit (11)
7 I led back to the sandwich shop (4)
11 The French follow grain cartilage (7)
13 Leave former computers (4)
15 Eccentric seed (3)

**22** To solve this puzzle you need to be wise to the time differences between different countries. It assumes GMT is standard and ignores any local adjustments for summertime.

I flew from Nuuk on a six-hour flight to Istanbul. I stayed there for exactly half a day. Then I flew to Helsinki, which took three hours. I then had to wait two hours for a ferry to Copenhagen, which lasted 11 hours. If I left Greenland at 2am on Monday, what day and time did my ferry arrive in Copenhagen?

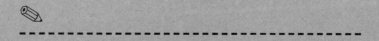

## 23

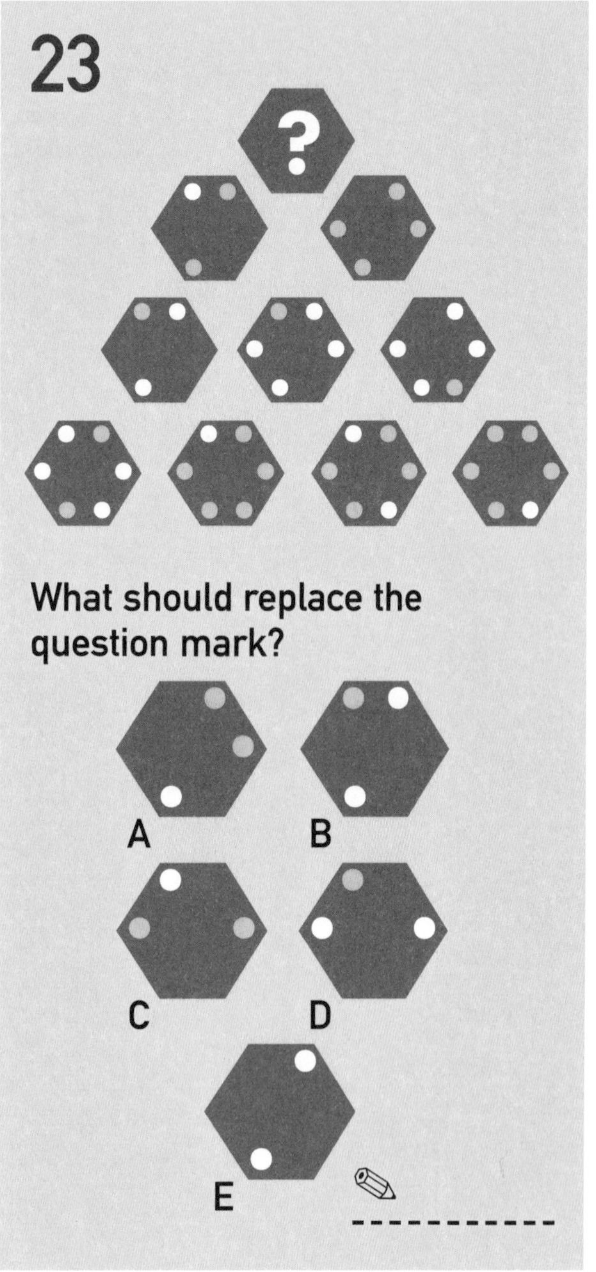


What should replace the question mark?

## 24

When the shape below is folded to form a cube, which is the only one of the following that can be produced?

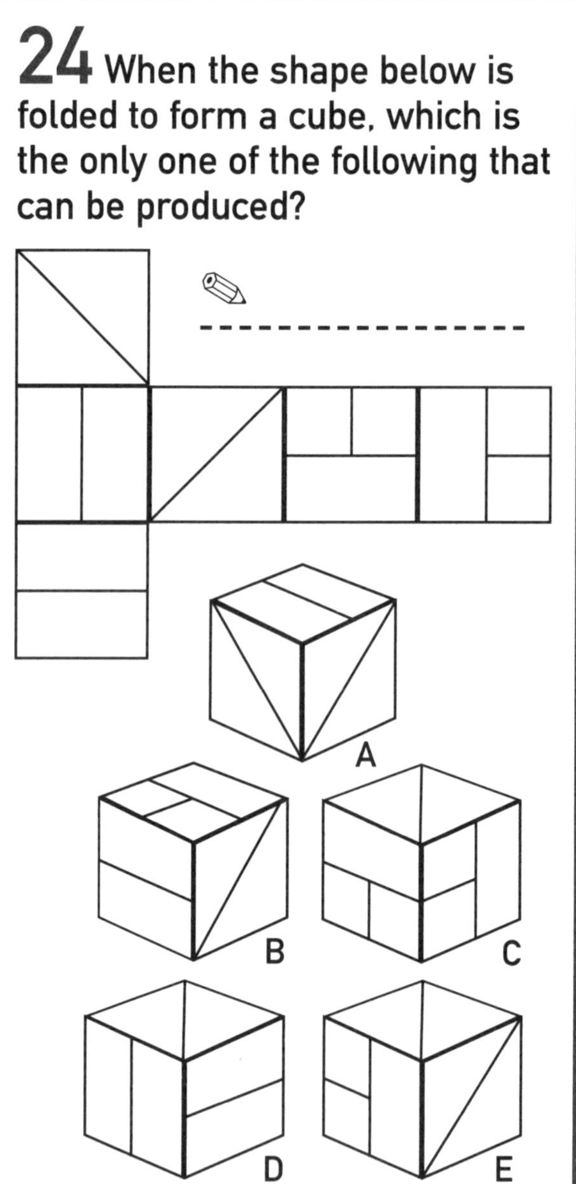


## 25

Which is the right definition of the word? Only one answer is correct – the others are designed to confuse you.

**Incus**

- River in India
- Bone in the ear
- Pain in the neck
- Reflection in water

**26** Planets C and D are in orbit around the same sun. Planet C takes eight years to make one complete orbit, while planet D takes five years. Currently, planet B is on the line connecting planet C and the sun. How long will it be before this situation occurs once again?

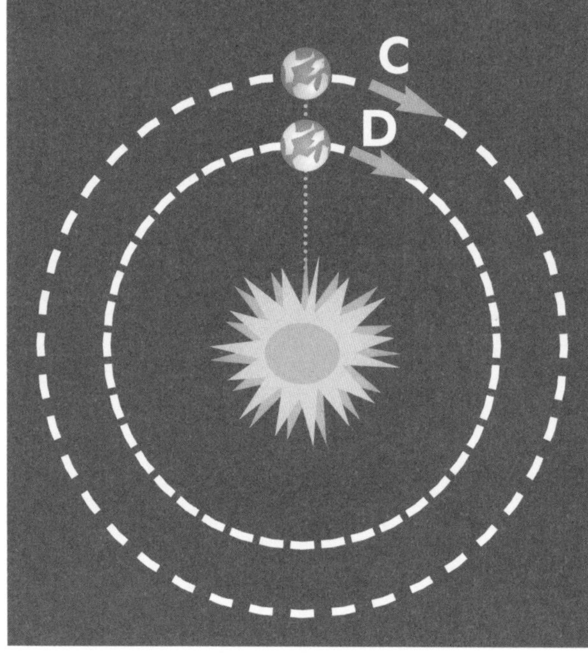


**27** Which of these is the odd word out?

Galliot

Pinnace

Cordoba

Trireme

Felucca

**28** Each block in this pyramid is the total of the two blocks below it. Can you find all the missing numbers?

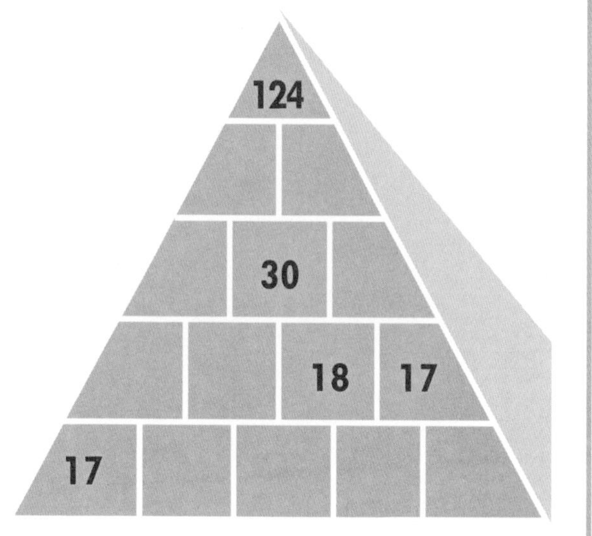

## 29

I got it in a forest but didn't want it.

Once I had it, I couldn't see it.

The more I searched for it, the less I liked it.

I took it home in my hand because I could not find it.

What was it?

## 30

What is the opposite of hoarse?

Discordant

Soft

Audible

Soporific

Mellifluous

## 31

How many revolutions must the large cog make to return all of the cogs to their starting positions?

Cog 1 has 8 teeth

Cog 2 has 7 teeth

Cog 3 has 4 teeth

Cog 4 has 3 teeth

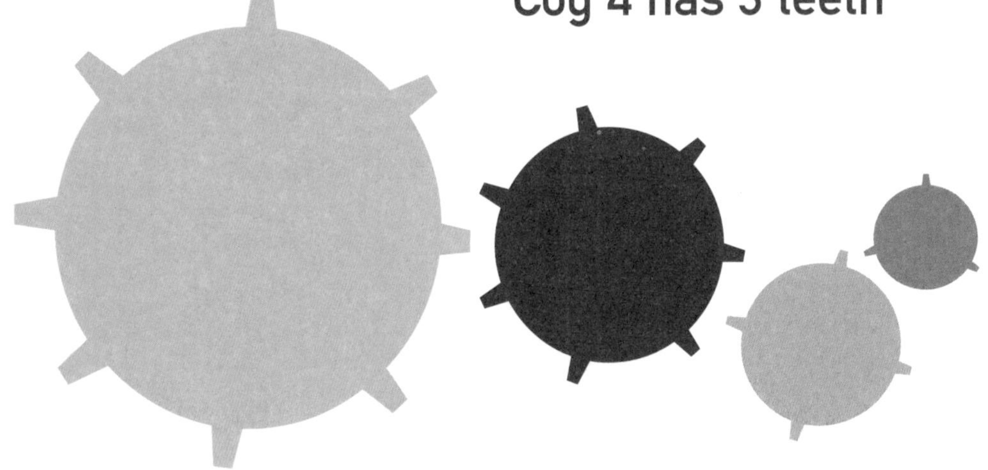

**32** A train is travelling in the direction AB. A passenger walks from one side of the carriage in the direction AC. In what direction is he actually walking relative to the earth: 1, 2, 3 or 4?

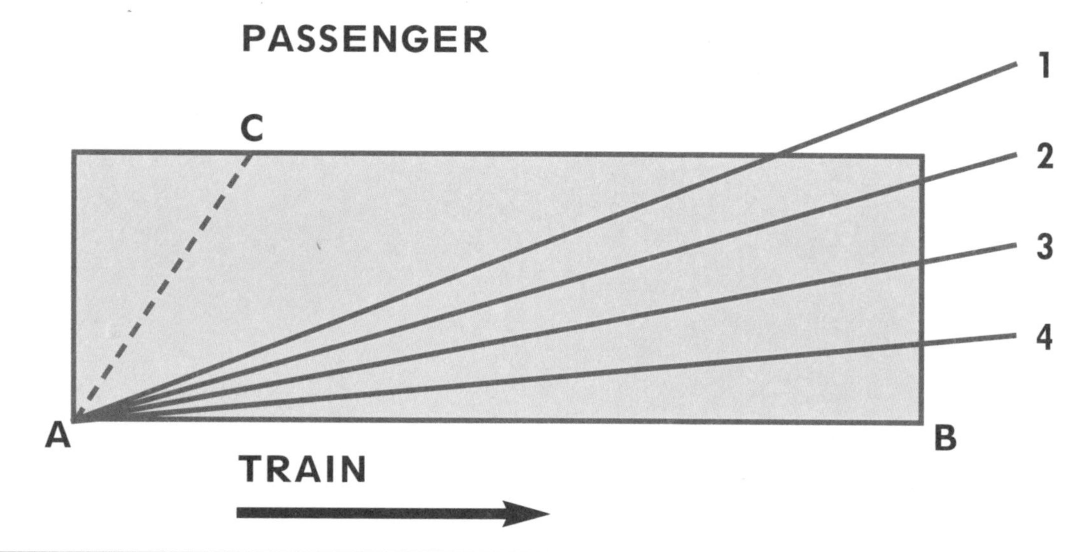


**33**

If Emma is [flags],

what is Lord Nelson trying to say with these flags?

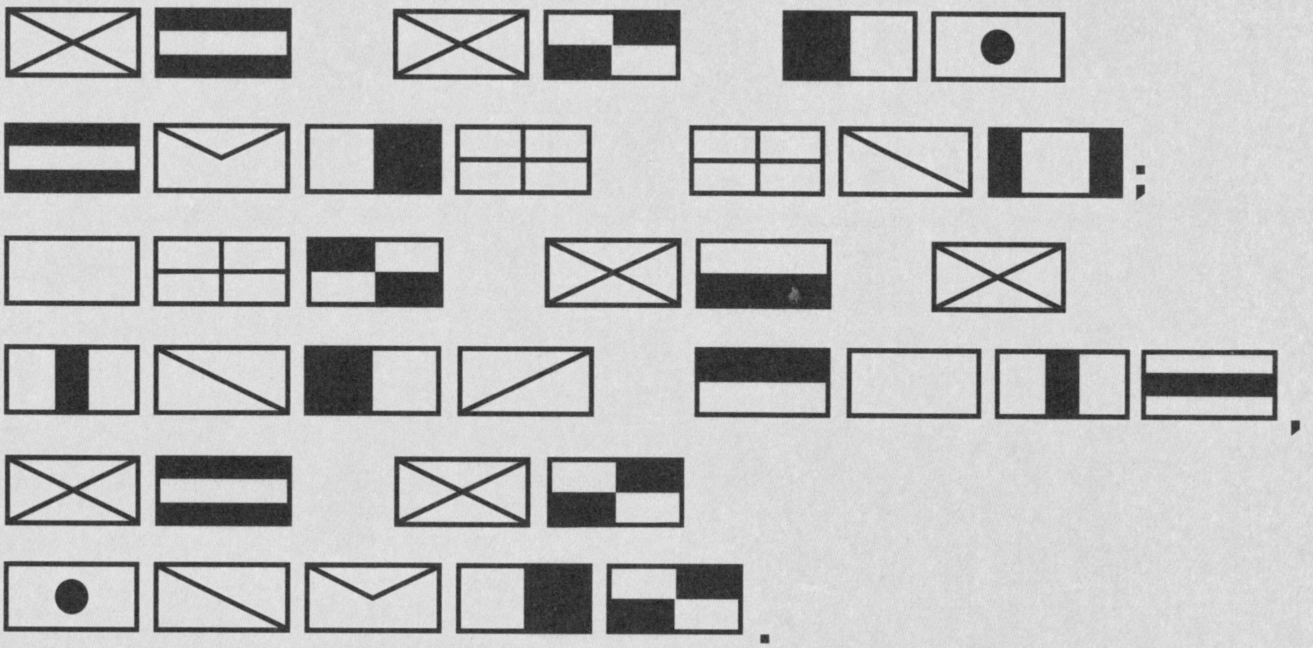

**34** Can you unravel this anagram to find a 12-letter word?

✎ ---------------------------

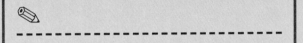

**35** Which 12-letter word can be found within this anagram?

✎ ---------------------------

**36** To solve this puzzle you need to be wise to the time differences between different countries. It assumes GMT is standard and ignores any local adjustments for summertime.

One Sunday afternoon at 3, Jambyn in Ulan Bator rang his friend Fidel in Manila and spent an hour telling him a topical joke! Fidel then spent half an hour translating the joke and e-mailed his friend Jenny in New Zealand. Jenny read the joke two hours after Fidel e-mailed it. Eleven hours later, Jenny was at her office, where she spent one hour writing a letter (including the joke) to her mother Helen on holiday in Bilbao. The letter took three and a half days to reach Helen, by which time the joke wasn't funny at all!

On what day and at what time did the letter reach Jenny's mother?

**37** Hic! Can you find 30 assorted drinks in this wordsearch grid? The words can be hidden horizontally, vertically, diagonally, backwards or forwards. We have provided 'letter cocktails' of their names to help you find them.

| B | H | G | N | I | L | S | H | I | G | H | B | A | L | L | S | U |
|---|---|---|---|---|---|---|---|---|---|---|---|---|---|---|---|---|
| A | E | E | R | G | N | O | H | C | U | O | S | O | U | C | P | D |
| E | T | N | D | M | A | N | H | A | T | T | A | N | X | I | P | B |
| E | B | E | E | A | I | A | P | E | R | I | T | I | F | D | A | U |
| B | A | O | D | D | Y | R | E | T | S | I | N | A | P | E | N | T |
| I | O | A | L | A | I | R | H | A | S | K | A | O | P | R | H | T |
| G | S | U | M | L | C | C | R | G | O | S | I | I | D | L | C | E |
| D | B | V | R | O | I | S | T | E | X | C | L | R | T | H | S | R |
| P | A | E | E | B | N | N | U | I | H | S | O | Q | S | U | P | M |
| E | L | R | A | N | O | T | G | M | N | C | R | R | E | C | W | I |
| L | Q | M | J | H | G | N | I | E | A | E | Z | R | D | S | H | L |
| U | V | O | A | E | C | A | R | L | R | R | T | Z | O | I | O | K |
| J | Q | U | R | H | E | O | P | H | L | R | I | O | B | D | A | F |
| S | K | T | P | P | T | L | M | M | A | A | L | E | W | E | E | L |
| O | S | H | A | N | D | Y | I | H | A | O | D | A | D | C | K | V |
| S | O | D | A | V | L | A | C | N | N | H | W | O | Y | A | H | L |
| T | E | R | A | L | C | C | C | G | G | N | C | D | D | R | M | Y |

ANOLMTADLOI
PRAFIEIT
IETNECNEBDI
GNLOBIREL
BNUROBO
EUTMBKRLTI
VLAOSDAC
MHNCAPEGA
RTHUSAEERC
RDCYEHAER

CDRIE
CAERLT
OCRALID
AGNJELIDRE
GHHLIBLA
LUJEP
KHICRS
RMDAEIA
AMATTANHN
OMACH

MCAESUDT
ONLOGO
ELIRSPN
ERANITS
PCNAPSHS
DSYHNA
RDSEACI
NGSIL
COSOGUNH
HUVTEMRO

**38** Starting at the top left number 7, complete a sum as you travel through the maze so that the total at the end of the equation remains 7. You may not pass two numbers in a row, or two symbols in a row, and you may not travel along the same path more than once.

**39** How many revolutions must the large cog make to return all the cogs to their starting positions?

Cog 1 has 13 teeth
Cog 2 has 7 teeth
Cog 3 has 6 teeth
Cog 4 has 3 teeth

**40** Which is the right definition of the word? Only one answer is correct – the others are designed to confuse you!

**ENERVATE**

Energize Enfranchise
Endanger Enfeeble

**41** Can you identify the missing letter? Think laterally.

**RE-EMPT**

Choose from:

**N, O, P, Q, R**

**42** Discover the surnames of five actresses by picking one letter from each shape in the order indicated by the numbers (so, one letter from box 1, one from box 2 and so on).

| | | | | | |
|---|---|---|---|---|---|
| 4 | F | C | M | D | I |
| 2 | L | F | H | O | R |
| 7 | A | R | E | T | O |
| 1 | G | B | G | P | T |

| | | | | | |
|---|---|---|---|---|---|
| 5 | P | F | K | B | F |
| 8 | N | G | H | R | N |
| 6 | I | S | E | F | M |
| 3 | I | E | O | L | A |

**43** Each block in this pyramid is the total of the two blocks below it. Can you find all the missing numbers?

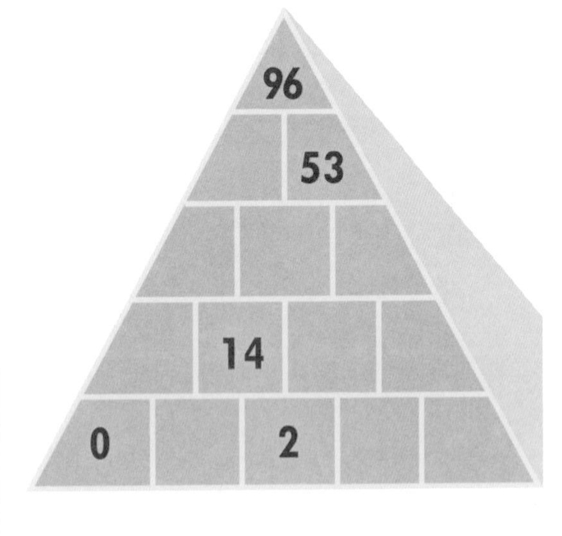


**44** Cuba is the same number of hours ahead of Samoa and behind Germany. That number is two hours less than the time difference between Germany and Japan. Fill in the blank clocks.

**45** Can you crack this cryptic crossword?

ACROSS

3 Lines for X and V are examples of serial communication (3-8)
7 Kings who imagine there's no one North-Eastern (4)
8 Develop part-diatribe comedy (6)
10 Hard criminal (5)
11 Upset medium risk to look smug (5)
13 Ship-shape gybe on the past events (6)
14 ...or that shirt's not right when altered (4)
15 Two spaces are legally worthless (4,3,4)

DOWN

1 Two coils of fried vegetable pancake (6,4)
2 Some meagre beast that's like a loon (5)
4 Alternatively, a Conservative speech (7)
5 Crazy need for action of train (10)
6 Prone to fib (3)
9 Spoil can one's mixed with dry vermouth? (7)
12 Like a very small 13-year-old, perhaps (5)
13 Prohibit degree number (3)

**46** The six people in this puzzle are each learning two different languages. Every student has two lessons on one evening per week and no one has a lesson on the same evening as anyone else. What is each person's full name, on which evening are his or her lessons and which two languages (one European and one other) is he or she learning to speak?

(See page 267 for tips on how to complete logic puzzles.)

| | SURNAME | | | | | | EVENING | | | | | | EUROPEAN | | | | | | OTHER | | | | | |
|---|---|---|---|---|---|---|---|---|---|---|---|---|---|---|---|---|---|---|---|---|---|---|---|---|
| | Agnew | Burstow | Fitzpatrick | Holmes | Killick | Morris | Monday | Tuesday | Wednesday | Thursday | Friday | Saturday | Dutch | French | German | Greek | Italian | Spanish | Burmese | Cantonese | Hebrew | Hindi | Kurdish | Swahili |
| Clifford | | | | | | | | | | | | | | | | | | | | | | | | |
| Kay | | | | | | | | | | | | | | | | | | | | | | | | |
| Mike | | | | | | | | | | | | | | | | | | | | | | | | |
| Rosa | | | | | | | | | | | | | | | | | | | | | | | | |
| Sandy | | | | | | | | | | | | | | | | | | | | | | | | |
| Terry | | | | | | | | | | | | | | | | | | | | | | | | |
| Burmese | | | | | | | | | | | | | | | | | | | | | | | | |
| Cantonese | | | | | | | | | | | | | | | | | | | | | | | | |
| Hebrew | | | | | | | | | | | | | | | | | | | | | | | | |
| Hindi | | | | | | | | | | | | | | | | | | | | | | | | |
| Kurdish | | | | | | | | | | | | | | | | | | | | | | | | |
| Swahili | | | | | | | | | | | | | | | | | | | | | | | | |
| Dutch | | | | | | | | | | | | | | | | | | | | | | | | |
| French | | | | | | | | | | | | | | | | | | | | | | | | |
| German | | | | | | | | | | | | | | | | | | | | | | | | |
| Greek | | | | | | | | | | | | | | | | | | | | | | | | |
| Italian | | | | | | | | | | | | | | | | | | | | | | | | |
| Spanish | | | | | | | | | | | | | | | | | | | | | | | | |
| Monday | | | | | | | | | | | | | | | | | | | | | | | | |
| Tuesday | | | | | | | | | | | | | | | | | | | | | | | | |
| Wednesday | | | | | | | | | | | | | | | | | | | | | | | | |
| Thursday | | | | | | | | | | | | | | | | | | | | | | | | |
| Friday | | | | | | | | | | | | | | | | | | | | | | | | |
| Saturday | | | | | | | | | | | | | | | | | | | | | | | | |

1 The student surnamed Holmes has lessons either the evening before or the evening after the student learning both Italian and either Hindi or Burmese.

2 Hebrew lessons are later in the week than those taken by Sandy, whose lessons are the evening after those in Swahili.

3 The student surnamed Killick has lessons later in the week than the person learning Greek.

4 Hindi lessons are the evening before those taken by the student surnamed Fitzpatrick, but later in the week than German lessons.

5 The student surnamed Agnew takes lessons later in the week than the one learning Dutch.

6 Rosa's lessons are earlier in the week than those taken by Mike, who isn't the student learning Greek. Clifford's lessons are earlier in the week than those taken by the student surnamed Burstow.

7 Either Italian or French is being studied alongside Kurdish, the lessons for which are earlier in the week than those taken by the student surnamed Morris, who isn't the person learning Spanish.

8 Burmese lessons are earlier in the week than those taken by Terry, but later in the week than those taken by the youngest student, whose surname is either Burstow or Killick.

9 Kay (whose surname isn't Fitzpatrick) is learning French and takes lessons later in the week than the student learning Cantonese.

**47** Which is the right definition of the word? Only one answer is correct – the others are designed to confuse you!

# Plumbago

- Leisure vehicle
- Rheumatism
- Blue flower
- Red brick

**48** Spell out a ten-letter word, moving through each circle once only. Clue: originally, it was as long as Lent.

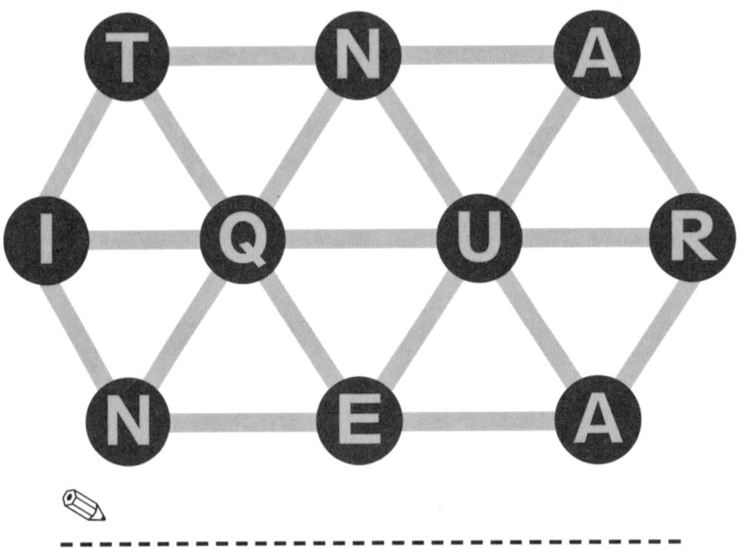


**49** What comes next?

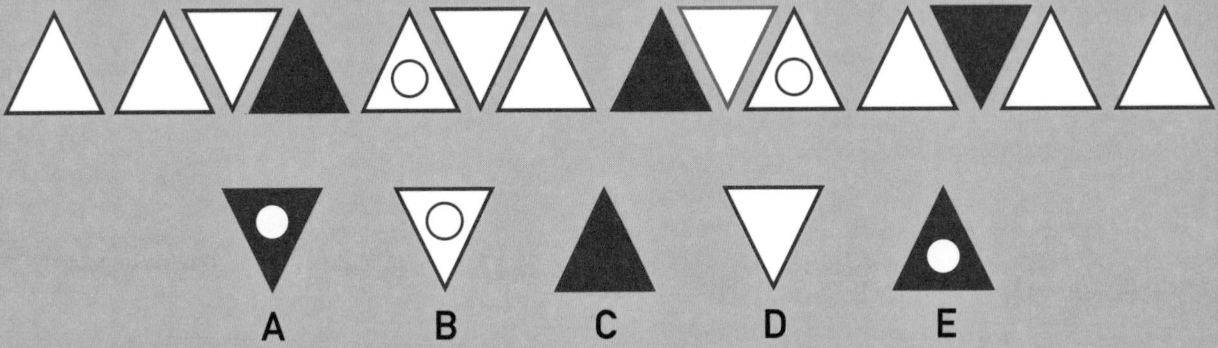

**50** Which of these is the odd word out?

Macaque

Dromedary

Dugong

Chervil

Ichneumon

---

**51** Gerald arrives at his local railway station to catch the Waterloo train, which departs hourly at exactly five minutes past the hour.

Thinking he might have just missed it, he looks up at the station clock and sees that the hour and minute hands are coincident between 1 and 2.

Rather surprisingly, he then knows that he hasn't missed his train. If the clock is correct, how does he know?

---

**52** What word is hidden in this anagram?

Glycerine fit

---

**53** Calculate the angle at x.

x

**54**

When I am filled I can
point the way.
When I am empty,
nothing moves me.
I have two skins, one
without and one within.

What am I?

**55** What is the opposite of parsimonious?

**Cosmopolitan**
**Lavish**
**Bipartisan**
**Casual**
**Quiescent**

**56** Planets E and F are in orbit around the same sun. Planet E takes ten years to make one complete orbit, while planet F takes nine years. Currently, planet F is 60 degrees further into its orbit than planet E. How long will it be before planet F lies on a line connecting planet E and the sun?

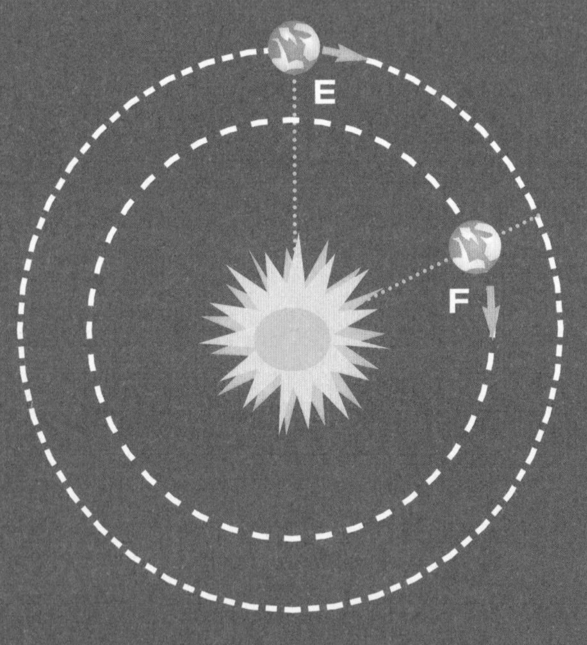


**57** For this difficult wordfinder puzzle, you must trace out words of five letters or more by travelling horizontally, vertically or diagonally to adjacent letters. Each letter may be used only once for any one word. Plurals and well-known proper names are allowed.

| X | E | C | H |
|---|---|---|---|
| S | A | R | U |
| G | O | T | F |
| N | I | L | D |

TARGET
★ 45 words
★★ 55 words
★★★ 65 words

**58** Every one of the six women in this puzzle went on holiday, moved to a new town, became engaged and started a new job this year. However, the four months in which each woman did so are all different and none begins with the same letter as that of her name. Can you discover the facts? (See page 267 for tips on logic grids.)

| | HOLIDAYED | | | | | | MOVED | | | | | | ENGAGED | | | | | | NEW JOB | | | | | |
|---|---|---|---|---|---|---|---|---|---|---|---|---|---|---|---|---|---|---|---|---|---|---|---|---|
| | January | February | March | August | September | October | January | February | March | August | September | October | January | February | March | August | September | October | January | February | March | August | September | October |
| Alison | | | | | | | | | | | | | | | | | | | | | | | | |
| Frances | | | | | | | | | | | | | | | | | | | | | | | | |
| Jane | | | | | | | | | | | | | | | | | | | | | | | | |
| Mandy | | | | | | | | | | | | | | | | | | | | | | | | |
| Olivia | | | | | | | | | | | | | | | | | | | | | | | | |
| Suzanne | | | | | | | | | | | | | | | | | | | | | | | | |
| NEW JOB January | | | | | | | | | | | | | | | | | | | | | | | | |
| NEW JOB February | | | | | | | | | | | | | | | | | | | | | | | | |
| NEW JOB March | | | | | | | | | | | | | | | | | | | | | | | | |
| NEW JOB August | | | | | | | | | | | | | | | | | | | | | | | | |
| NEW JOB September | | | | | | | | | | | | | | | | | | | | | | | | |
| NEW JOB October | | | | | | | | | | | | | | | | | | | | | | | | |
| ENGAGED January | | | | | | | | | | | | | | | | | | | | | | | | |
| ENGAGED February | | | | | | | | | | | | | | | | | | | | | | | | |
| ENGAGED March | | | | | | | | | | | | | | | | | | | | | | | | |
| ENGAGED August | | | | | | | | | | | | | | | | | | | | | | | | |
| ENGAGED September | | | | | | | | | | | | | | | | | | | | | | | | |
| ENGAGED October | | | | | | | | | | | | | | | | | | | | | | | | |
| MOVED January | | | | | | | | | | | | | | | | | | | | | | | | |
| MOVED February | | | | | | | | | | | | | | | | | | | | | | | | |
| MOVED March | | | | | | | | | | | | | | | | | | | | | | | | |
| MOVED August | | | | | | | | | | | | | | | | | | | | | | | | |
| MOVED September | | | | | | | | | | | | | | | | | | | | | | | | |
| MOVED October | | | | | | | | | | | | | | | | | | | | | | | | |

1 The name of the woman who started a new job in March begins with a different letter from that of the month in which a new job was started by the woman who moved house in August.

2 Olivia's holiday was in a month beginning with a different letter from that of the name of the woman (who took her holiday in October) whose name starts with a different letter from that of the month when a new job was started by whoever got engaged in September.

3 The woman who holidayed in January moved in the same month as a new job was started by the woman who moved in March.

4 The woman who started a new job in September moved in the same month as a new job was started by whoever moved house in October.

5 The woman who moved house in August started a new job in the same month as the removal month chosen by whoever started a new job in February.

6 The name of the woman who moved in January begins with the same letter as the month when a holiday was taken by someone who didn't move in August. Whoever started a new job in January moved in the same month as a new job was started by the woman who moved in September.

7 The woman who holidayed in September started a new job in the same month as the removal month chosen by the woman who started her new job in August.

8 Mandy moved in the same month as a new job was started by whoever holidayed in January. The woman whose new job began in March moved in a month that begins with the same letter as that of the name of the woman whose new job began in the same month as Alison's holiday.

9 The woman who holidayed in February moved in a different month from the month in which a new job was started by the woman who moved in February.

**59** Each block in this pyramid is the total of the two blocks below it. Can you find all the missing numbers?

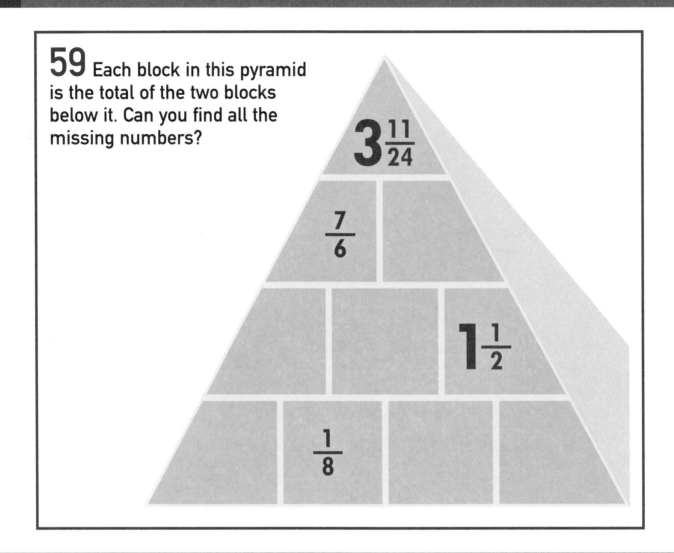

| | | | |
|---|---|---|---|
| | $3\frac{11}{24}$ | | |
| $\frac{7}{6}$ | | | |
| | | $1\frac{1}{2}$ | |
| | $\frac{1}{8}$ | | |

**60** You are going on a long journey, it seems! Can you work out your instructions from the cryptic message below?

PERCH ACE ATTIC ETON

FRIED HAYFORK APE HORNET

THERE ALE WAIST HEY SHONE

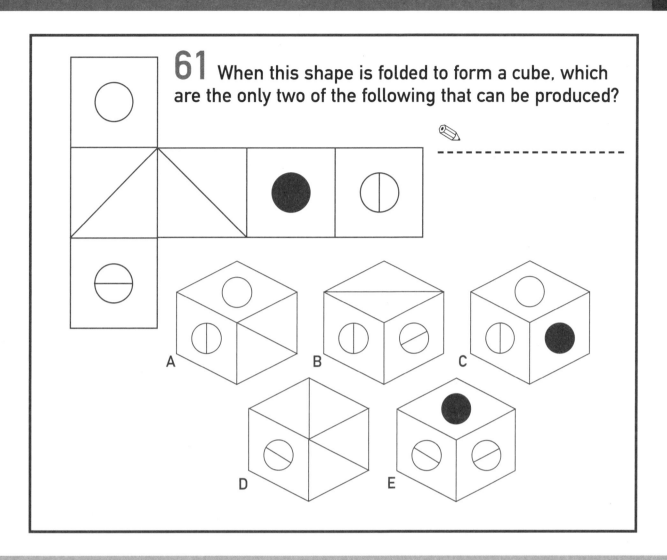

**61** When this shape is folded to form a cube, which are the only two of the following that can be produced?

✎ ____________________

A B C D E

**62** Discover the surnames of five golfers by picking a letter from each shape in the order indicated by the numbers.

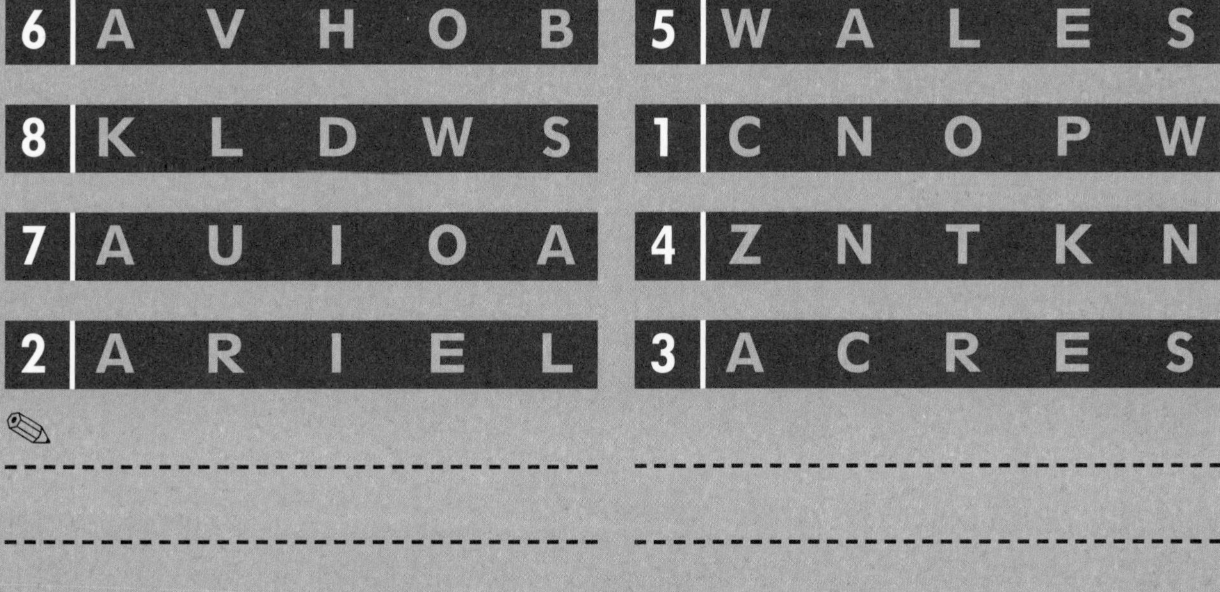


✎ ____________________

**63** Can you solve this riddle?

I live above a star, but I'm useful here on earth.

I have eleven neighbours, each one of different worth.

I am visited in sequence, first, last or in between.

PQRS are my initials – now tell me what I mean.

**64** How many degrees do the internal angles add up to?

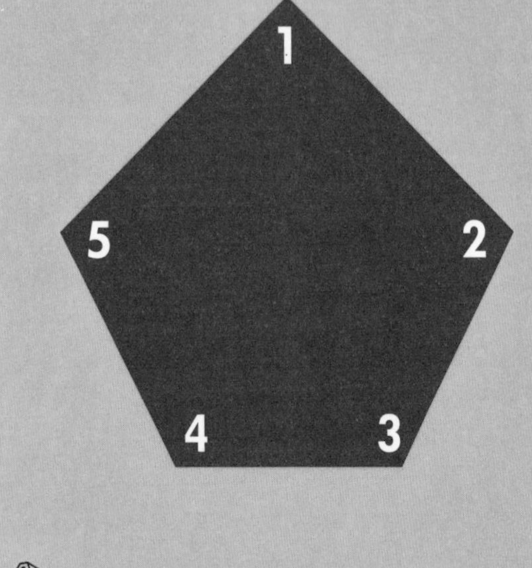


**65** Which is the odd one out in this list?

Canapes

Muscatel

Recurring

Whelks

Skinned

**66** Spell out a ten-letter word, moving through each circle once only. Clue: dislike E.T.?

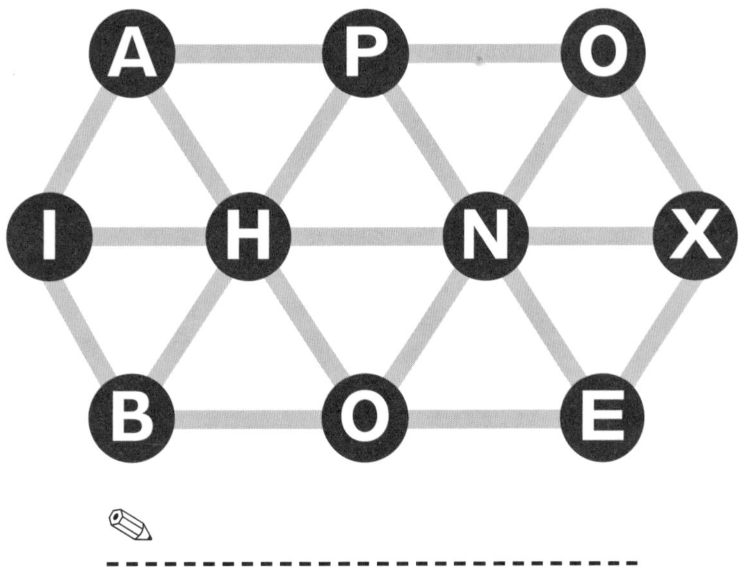


✎ ______________________________

**67** If Sir Percy KBE starts at the top left-hand square of the chessboard, which palace will he move to?

**68** For this difficult wordfinder puzzle, you must trace out words of five letters or more by travelling horizontally, vertically or diagonally to adjacent letters. Each letter may be used only once for any one word. Plurals and well-known proper names are allowed.

| U | S | L | M |
|---|---|---|---|
| O | Y | A | B |
| R | E | I | F |
| X | T | D | C |

✎ ------------------------------

----------------------------------------

----------------------------------------

----------------------------------------

Target:

★ 14 words
★★ 20 words
★★★ 27 words

**69** When the shape on the right is folded to form a cube, which are the only two of the following that can be produced?

✎ ------------------------------

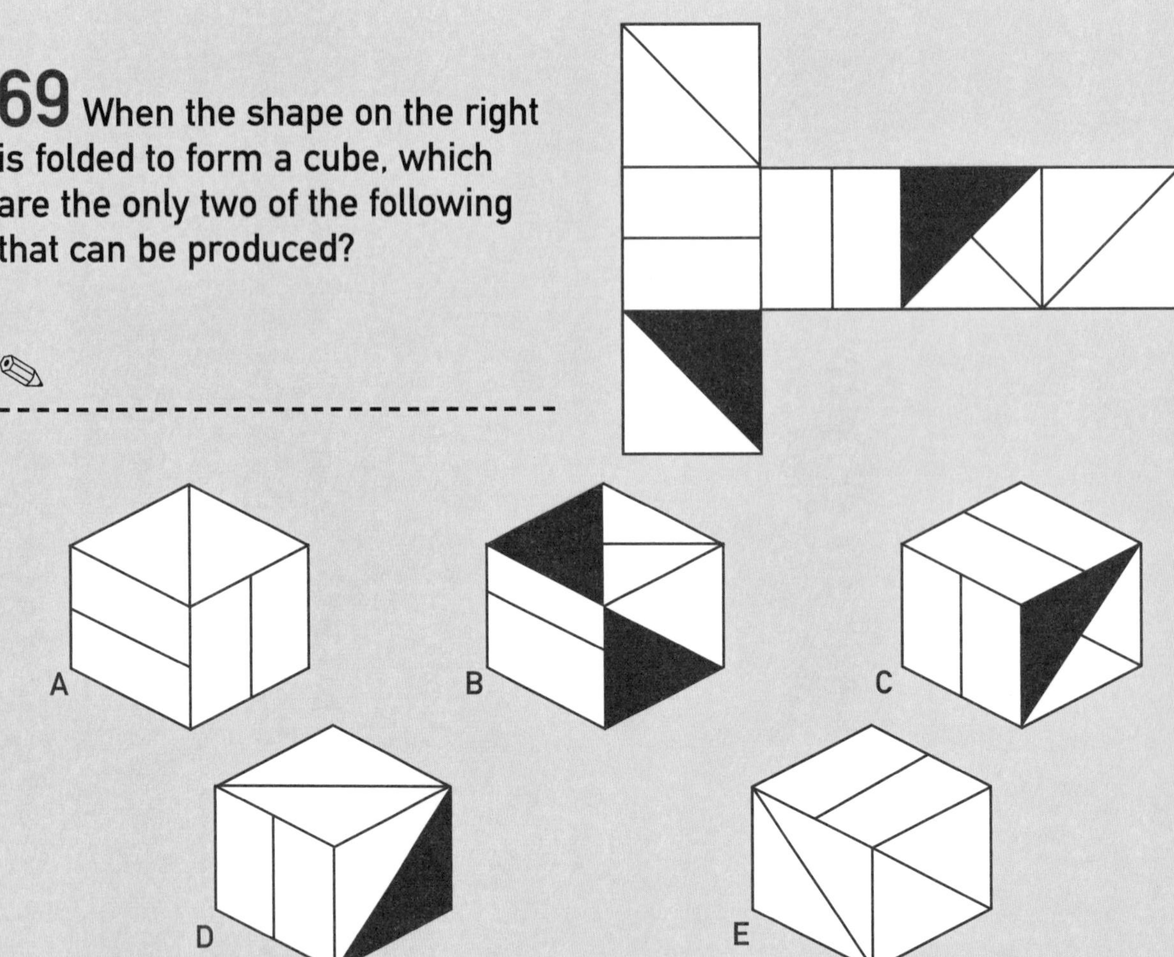

**70** Can you complete this gridless logic puzzle? (Tip: it may be helpful to cross out clues from which no new information can be deduced.)
The eight men in this puzzle each sent and received one card on St Valentine's Day. Unfortunately, the woman to whom each man had sent his card actually sent a card to one of the other seven men!
To whom did every man and woman send a card?

1 George sent a card to the woman who sent a card to Clive, who sent a card to Zoë.

2 Selina sent a card to the man who sent a card to the woman who sent a card to David.

3 Zoë sent a card to the man who sent a card to the woman who sent a card to the man who sent a card to Xenia. George received a card from the woman who received a card from Bob, whose card was from Xenia.

4 Edward received a card from the woman who received a card from the man who received a card from Venetia, who didn't get one from Frank.

5 Frank received a card from the woman who received a card from the man who received a card from Tanya.

6 Hank sent a card to the woman who sent a card to the man who sent a card to Ursula.

7 Andrew sent a card to the woman who sent a card to Hank. The man who sent a card to Yolande received one from Ursula. The man who sent a card to Xenia received one from Wilma.

| MAN | Sent a card to: |
|---|---|
| | |
| | |
| | |
| | |
| | |
| | |
| | |
| | |

| WOMAN | Sent a card to: |
|---|---|
| | |
| | |
| | |
| | |
| | |
| | |
| | |
| | |

**71** Each block in this pyramid is the total of the two blocks below it. Which number should replace the question mark?

| | | | |
|---|---|---|---|
| 112 | | | |
| | | | |
| | | 11 | |
| 3 | ? | 7 | 4 |

**72** An ex-cellent puzzle. All the words to be found contain an X. To make it harder, several letters have been missed off the grid.

| S | L |  | E | E | Z | E | E | C | E | X |  | A |  | S | T |
|---|---|---|---|---|---|---|---|---|---|---|---|---|---|---|---|
| B |  | X | X | X | H | X | L | X | X | J | W | S | T | E | T |
|  | G |  | Y | T |  | T |  | L | P | M |  | X |  | S | C |
| X | R | N | E | E | I |  | N | B | E | E | O | J | D | N | A |
| C | J | X | I | R |  | N |  | O | D | D | C | E |  | E |  |
| I | I | N | A | N | T | D | C | T | I | A | T | T | Z |  | E |
| T | T |  | M |  | I | X | E | T |  | S |  | C | K | X |  |
| E | N | T |  | L | H | A | E | R | I |  | O | T | C | E | O |
| D | E |  | E |  | N | Q | L | X |  | C |  | L | X | Q | I |
| L | L | B | X | X | M | E | E | P | N | L | A | Y | P | E | T |
|  | L |  | P | P | P | I | X | W | X | I | P | E | S | X | P |
| E |  | H | O | A | U | R | R | A |  | E | G | X | S | O | E |
| B | C |  | R | N | J | F | E | E | M |  | Q | C | E | T | C |
| O | X | E | T | D | G | N |  | S |  | I | G | U |  | I |  |
| W | E | D | O | L | P |  | E | A | S | X | N | S | X |  | E |
| A | L | E | X | T |  | N |  | I | V | E | E | E |  | X | Z |

EXACT
EXAMINE
EXAMPLE
EXCELLENT
EXCEPTION
EXCESS
EXCITEDLY
EXCLAIMED
EXCUSE
EXHAUST
EXHIBIT
EXISTED
EXIT
EXOTIC
EXPAND
EXPECT
EXPEDITION
EXPENSES
EXPERIMENT
EXPERT
EXPLAINING
EXPLODE
EXPLORE
EXPLOSION
EXPORT
EXPRESS
EXTEND
EXTENSIVE
EXTERNAL
EXTINCT
EXTRA
EXTREME

**73** Can you unravel this anagram?

## Optical moons

**74** What is the opposite of halcyon?

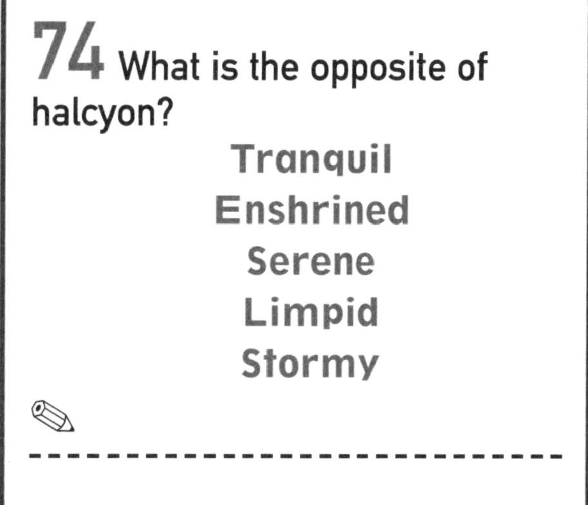


**75** On 28 February 2000, US Olympic swimmer Doug Musselman decided to cross the Bering Strait. At 3pm the same day Doug left from Alaska, swimming westward. Ten hours later, the tired swimmer reached Uelen in Russia.

What date and time was it when he arrived?

**76** Planets G and H are orbiting the same sun but their orbits are not in the same geometrical plane. Planet G takes 28 years to complete one orbit, while Planet H takes 20 years. Currently, all three bodies are on the same connecting line. How long will it be before this situation occurs again?

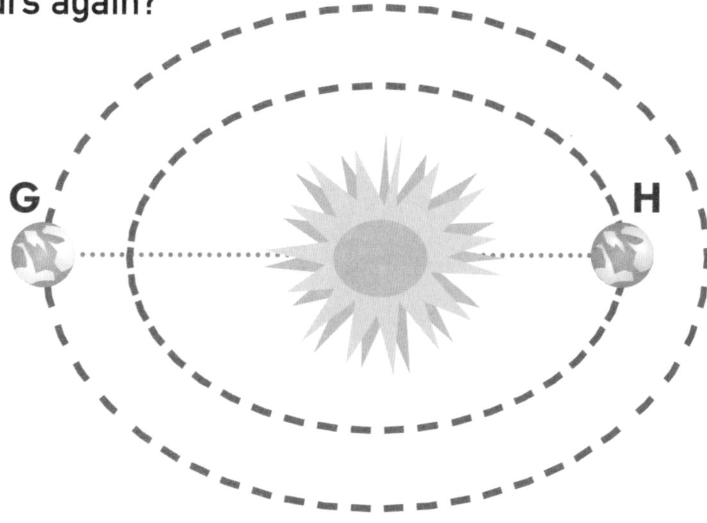

**77** What is the opposite of sepulchral?

Lugubrious
Riotous
Cheerful
Romantic
Funereal

**78** Spell out a ten-letter word moving through each circle once only. Clue: the first biblical murder.

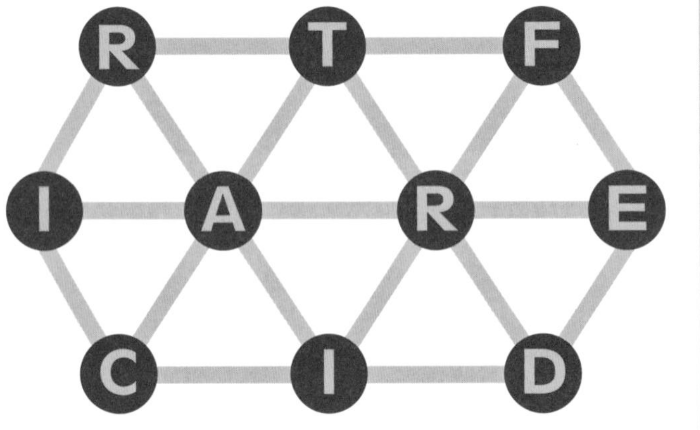


**79** Each line and symbol that appears in the four outer circles, right, is transferred to the central circle according to these rules:

If a line or symbol occurs in the outer circles:
- once: it is transferred
- twice: it is possibly transferred
- three times: it is transferred
- four times: it is not transferred

Which of the circles, A, B, C, D or E, should appear at the centre of the diagram above?

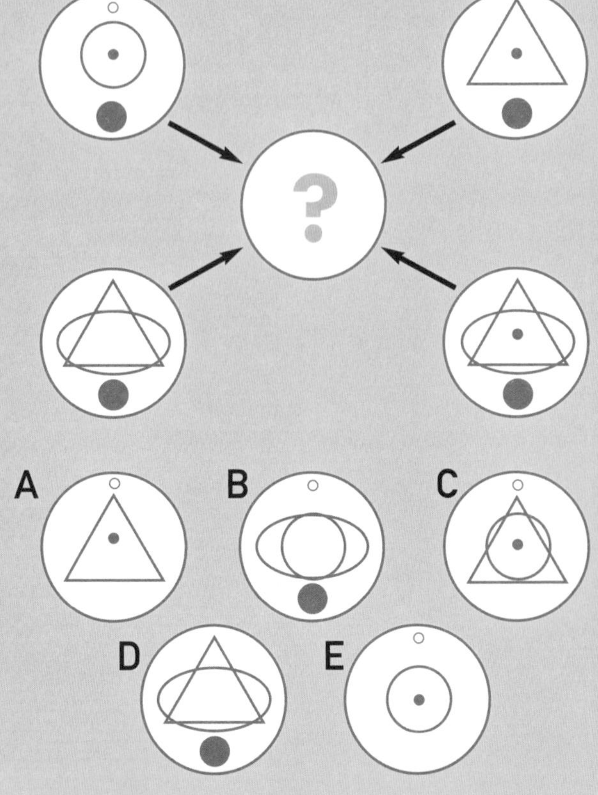

**80** Can you crack this code? If you do, you'll discover what Albert Einstein was saying here.

**1+5−9+17−17+13+2−12+1+5−3+4−9+14−12−3+1+15−1+1−3−13 = ?**

---------------------------------------------------

**81** Can you solve this lateral teaser?

Having first put down some money, I then toss the dice. Next I add the number to the score and find that the sum total, coincidentally, is what?

**82** Discover the surnames of five inventors by picking a letter from each shape in the order indicated by the numbers.

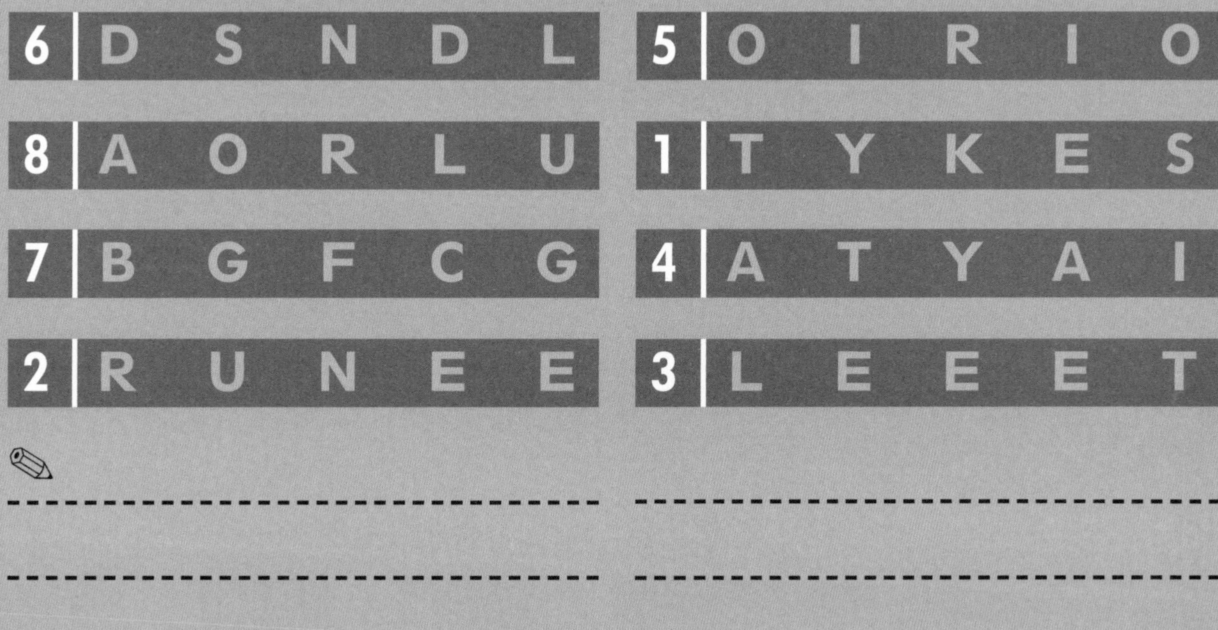

**83** Place all the numbers in this list on the square to replace the question marks, so that all the sides add up to the same total.

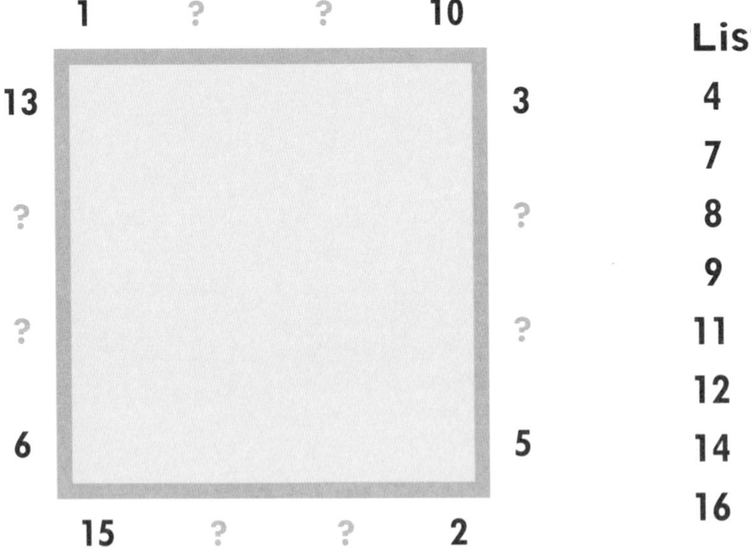


**84** Planets J and K are orbiting different suns. Planet J takes 25 years to orbit its sun, while planet K takes 28 years. The two orbits join at one point. Currently, planet J is at that point and planet K is 90 degrees away. How long will it be before the two planets collide?

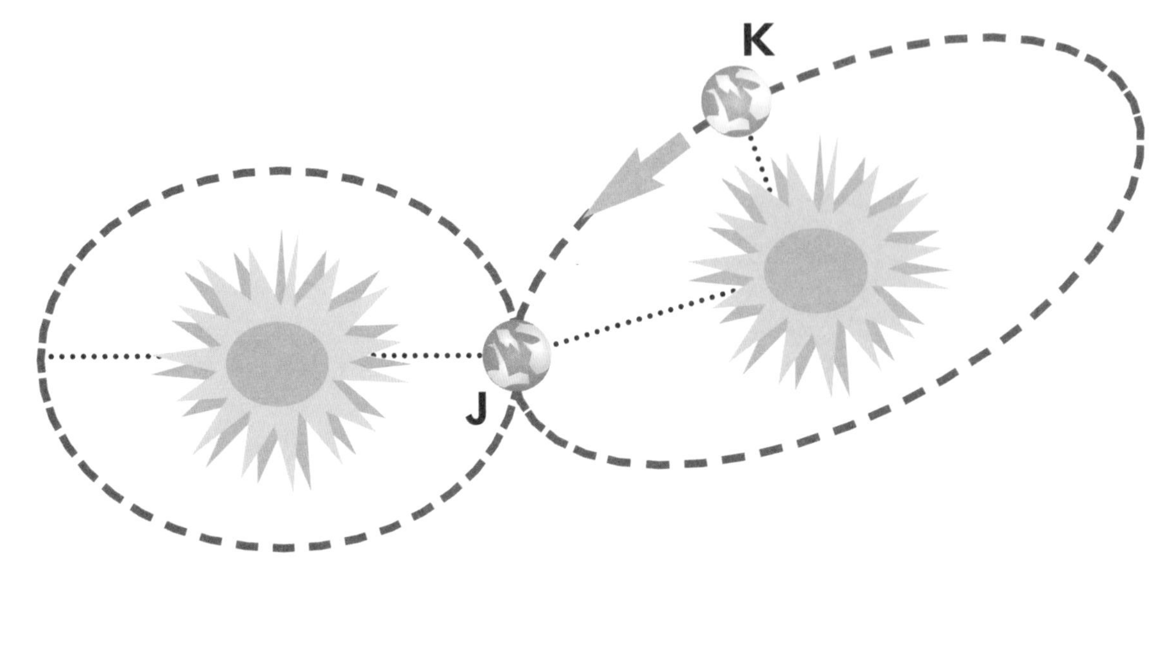

**85** Each block in this pyramid is the total of the two blocks below it. Find all the missing numbers.

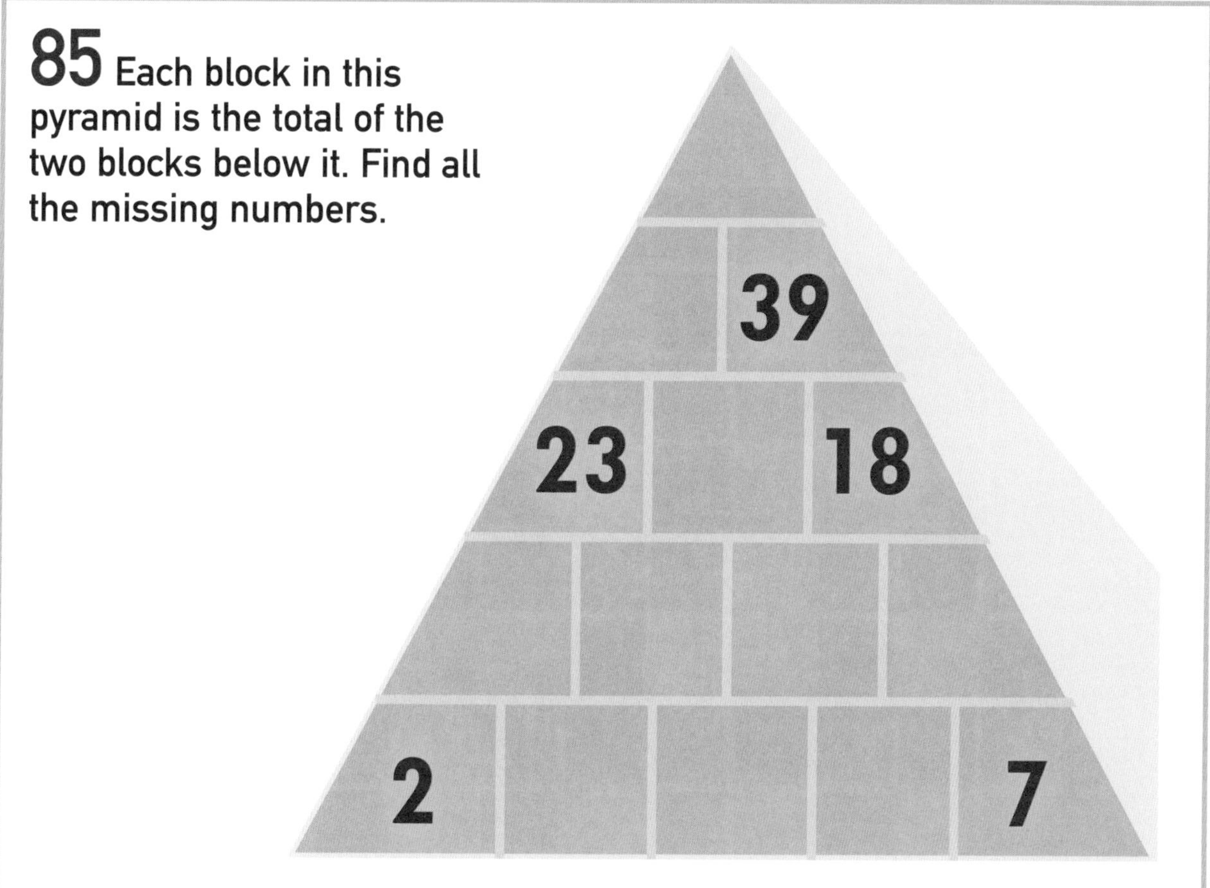


**86** Six friends in six different countries go online at the same time to chat. For Andrew, who is not in Greece, it's 1pm, for Caroline it is 9½ hours later. Dave's in Pakistan, Elizabeth's in El Salvador. Brian is 3 hours behind Dave. Fiona is 2½ hours ahead of Caroline. Brian is not in Chile or Sri Lanka. It is 1am in Brunei. One friend goes online at 10pm, another at 11am. Can you work out which friend is online in which country at what local time?

Andrew ----------------------------------------

Brian ----------------------------------------

Caroline ----------------------------------------

Dave ----------------------------------------

Elizabeth ----------------------------------------

Fiona ----------------------------------------

1 HOUR

**87** The challenge here is to complete this brainracker of a cryptic crossword in under an hour.

**ACROSS**

1 Obvious Freudian instinct in competition? (7)

8 In study, nothing gurus revise is absurd (11)

9 Sounds like he was a gardener (3)

10 Make more agreeable by adding four points to 10 (7)

12 Hares to define how far you can hear (7)

15 Cover over fish (3)

16 However, is 0 or 1 smaller? (11)

17 Improve computer rating from B to A (7)

**DOWN**

2 Give recent upheaval of deputy (10)

3 Eats, expires around middle of lunch (5)

4 Brass and steel mettle (5)

5 Tidy genie involved in colouring T-shirts (3-6)

6 Run out and supply baby? (6-4)

7 Gelatine appears in mirror (9)

11 Wife loves romance (3)

13 Oh, reverse ram to make more intense (3,2)

14 His and her square successor (5)

1 HOUR

## 88 Can you solve this gridless logic puzzle? (See page 267 for tips.)

In the country of Inflatia, the currency is virtually worthless, so it takes a lot of cash to buy even the cheapest item. Consequently, the women of Inflatia have extremely large purses! In order to bring you this puzzle, we carried out a survey among the first six women encountered in the capital, asking how many Inflatian dollars and pennies each had in her purse (each of which was a different colour from anyone else's). Can you discover the results of our survey?

**Dollars:** 10,300; 10,400; 10,500; 10,700; 10,800; 10,900.
**Pennies:** 10; 20; 40; 60; 70; 90.

1 Ruby had 20 fewer pennies than Mrs Macey.
2 The blue purse contained more pennies than the brown purse, which isn't Ms Vale's.
3 Lena had 40 pennies in her purse, which contained 100 dollars more than Pamela's.
4 Miss Rosenberg's purse is either black or white.
5 Miss Lestrange had either 10 more or 10 fewer pennies than were in the pink purse.
6 Ann had 200 dollars more than the woman with the black purse, who had either 10 more or 10 fewer pennies than Hannah.
7 The green purse contained either 20 more or 20 fewer pennies than that owned by Ann, who isn't Miss Lestrange.
8 Ruby isn't Ms Vale, whose purse contained either 70 or 90 pennies, as well as 100 fewer dollars than the white purse.
9 Ms Watson hadn't exactly 10,700 Inflatian dollars in her purse. Mrs Macey's purse is either green or pink.
10 Mrs Franks had 100 dollars less than Mrs Macey, but more dollars than Daphne.

| Respondent | Surname | Dollars | Pennies | Purse |
|---|---|---|---|---|
| | | | | |
| | | | | |
| | | | | |
| | | | | |
| | | | | |
| | | | | |

# answers

Who topped the class at hot topics?

Who went cross-eyed completing simply crosswords?

Who figured out number know-how?

Who was put to the test in testing trivia?

Who saw the way through eye see?

Who took a chance on take a letter?

Who battled out at the ultimate challenge?

The answers lie in the pages that follow...

1
Tiger Woods
Martina Hingis
Nasser Hussain
David Beckham
Steve Waugh
Jonah Lomu
Andre Agassi
Sonia O'Sullivan
Jonathan Edwards
Michael Schumacher

2
MANDELSON RESIGNS FROM CABINET

3
Britney Spears

4
Peggy (Mitchell) from *EastEnders*

5
ELEMENTARY (my dear Watson) – words attributed to Sherlock Holmes

6
1 19 September 1985 – In Mexico City earthquake kills thousands.
2 22 January 1901 – Queen Victoria dies at Osborne, Isle of Wight.
3 1 May 1931 – President Hoover opens Empire State Building.
4 13 April 1980 – Spaniard Severiano Ballesteros becomes youngest ever winner of the US Masters.
5 1 August 1976 – Champion driver Niki Lauda escapes death in inferno.
6 1 June 1957 – In Britain, ERNIE draws the first Premium Bond prizes.
7 18 November 1991 – Shi'ite Muslim faction in Lebanon free Terry Waite.
8 20 July 1969* – Neil Armstrong is first man to step on the moon.
*In the USA, from where the Apollo mission was controlled. In the UK, the moon landing was approximately 3am BST on 21 July.

7
NASA reveals Earth's near miss.
(Each number is the alphabetical position of the letter it represents, so that 1=A, 2=B, 3=C, etc.)

8
1 'Pure and Simple'
2 75
3 The third Saturday in June
4 *Battlefield Earth*
5 Bateman
6 Total eclipse of the Moon
7 Sir Alec Guinness
8 *The League of Gentlemen*
9 Joanne Kathleen
10 The time and date were 01:01:01 on 01/01/01
11 L'Oréal
12 *Hidden Dragon*
13 Chief Inspector of Schools for England and Wales
14 Donald Dewar
15 Pristina

9
A Bloodhound
B Weimaraner
C Shih Tzu
D Standard poodle

All featured in the film *Best in Show*, as revealed in the boxed letters.

10

| | |
|---|---|
| France | 1998 |
| Uruguay | 1950 |
| Italy | 1982 |
| Brazil | 1994 |
| Argentina | 1978 |
| England | 1966 |

11
Mike Tyson

12

| | | | | | | | | | | | | | |
|---|---|---|---|---|---|---|---|---|---|---|---|---|---|
| U | C | L | N | P | S | K | E | N | N | E | D | Y | B |
| N | O | I | T | C | E | L | E | D | F | N | R | R | V |
| A | N | W | L | Z | T | T | O | L | L | A | B | U | M |
| M | G | Y | U | C | A | B | H | K | M | E | N | N | J |
| I | R | E | U | R | N | O | X | I | N | A | O | N | E |
| N | E | L | H | V | E | P | R | C | D | K | I | I | S |
| T | S | G | W | Q | S | P | L | A | R | E | T | N | U |
| R | S | P | J | K | Y | I | M | R | N | U | A | G | O |
| R | E | A | G | A | N | S | G | T | E | O | N | M | H |
| L | U | C | Y | T | K | V | D | E | L | H | I | A | E |
| R | E | V | O | O | H | C | E | R | S | P | M | T | T |
| F | U | N | S | U | T | W | I | U | O | G | O | E | I |
| T | R | U | M | A | N | V | B | K | L | F | N | J | H |
| W | O | M | E | N | O | T | G | N | I | H | S | A | W |

13
1 20 October 1973 – Fantastic Opera House in Sydney opened to the public.
2 23 August 1926 – Movie idol Rudolph Valentino dies at age 31.
3 11 February 1990 – Nelson Mandela freed after 26 years in jail.
4 17 April 1969 – Voting age lowered from 21 to 18 in Britain.
5 13 July 1985 – Live Aid concerts in London and Philadelphia raise millions for famine relief.
6 2 October 1950 – *Peanuts* comic strip makes its debut.
7 18 May 1980 – Long-dormant Mount St Helens erupts.
8 14 November 1940 – Coventry Cathedral destroyed in Blitz.

14

Isadora most enjoyed gymnastics (clue 5), thus the Japanese woman who stayed at the Harriot and enjoyed judo (clue 2) is Chloë. Eric, who enjoyed the swimming, is American (1).

The Swedish person who enjoyed the high jump isn't Dan (3), so must be Tom. Thus Dan enjoyed the tennis. Dan stayed at the Milton (3), so (4) the Peruvian who stayed at the Blitz is Isadora. Dan is from India. Tom stayed at the Madison (4) and Eric at the Charlton Hotel.

Thus:
Chloë – Japanese – Harriot – judo;
Dan – Indian – Milton – tennis;
Eric – American – Charlton – swimming;
Isadora – Peruvian – Blitz – gymnastics;
Tom – Swedish – Madison – high jump.

15

| | | | | | | |
|---|---|---|---|---|---|---|
| 1 | W | E | A | L | T | H |
| 2 | A | V | E | N | U | E |
| 3 | L | I | K | E | L | Y |
| 4 | L | A | R | I | A | T |
| 5 | S | T | A | B | L | E |
| 6 | T | R | E | N | C | H |
| 7 | R | A | T | I | O | N |
| 8 | E | X | C | E | E | D |
| 9 | E | D | I | B | L | E |
| 10 | T | A | N | K | E | R |

16

Queen Mother and One Hundred (the Queen Mother's 100th birthday was in August 2000).

17

CHERNOBYL (deactivated in December 2000)

18

(Gordon) Brown

19

1 Nigel Spexx
2 Z
3 'Riting has a new voyss'
4 4.6 kilos
5 *Dog Eared and Dirty*
6 Orly
7 33-1
8 No. 5412
9 Camilla Goodread
10 Contacious

20

All Saints
Shaggy
Westlife
Eminem
Stereophonics
Robbie Williams
Craig David
Manic Street Preachers
R. Kelly
Aerosmith

21

The missing politician is George W. Bush.

| | | | | | | | | | | |
|---|---|---|---|---|---|---|---|---|---|---|
| M | I | S | S | | | | T | A | N | G |
| A | | | C | A | T | C | H | | | R |
| K | | | A | | | | O | | | E |
| E | V | E | R | | P | U | R | S | U | E |
| R | | R | | | R | | | C | | D |
| | F | O | R | B | I | D | D | E | N | |
| A | | D | | | C | | | N | | A |
| N | E | E | D | L | E | | S | E | A | L |
| G | | | A | | | | H | | | A |
| E | | | T | E | M | P | O | | | R |
| R | O | S | E | | | | W | A | R | M |

| | | | | | | | | | |
|---|---|---|---|---|---|---|---|---|---|
| | | H | | Q | | A | | M | |
| O | N | E | H | U | N | D | R | E | D |
| | E | R | I | E | | D | O | N | E |
| | V | | T | E | D | I | O | U | S |
| O | A | K | | N | I | C | K | | K |
| | D | I | A | M | E | T | E | R | |
| | A | L | T | O | | | R | O | D |
| | | N | E | T | S | | Y | E | W |
| Y | E | S | | H | A | Y | | | I |
| | L | | R | E | L | E | A | R | N |
| B | E | T | | R | O | A | R | E | D |
| | C | I | A | | O | R | I | E | L |
| E | T | C | | U | N | S | A | F | E |

22

The combination is 81. Correct years for false answers:

B The *Exxon Valdez* oil tanker runs aground in Alaska (1989)
E The Berlin Wall falls (1989)
H Eire appoints its first female president (1990)
K Nelson Mandela freed after 27 years (1990)
N Mike Tyson becomes youngest ever heavyweight champion (1986)

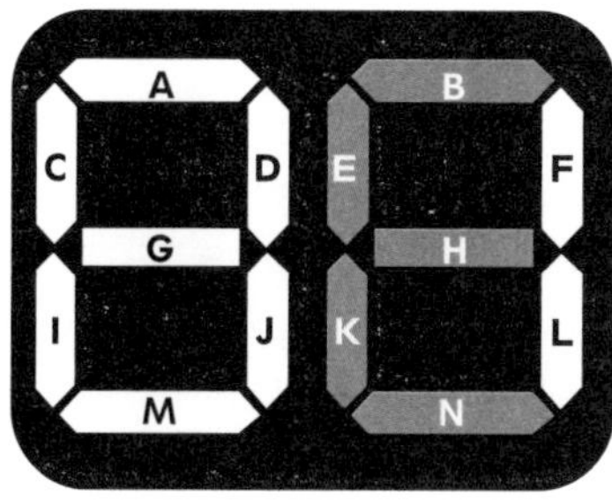

23 Quotation attributed to Victor Borge, the pianist.

| W | H | E | N |  | A | N |  | O | P | E | R | A |  |
|---|---|---|---|---|---|---|---|---|---|---|---|---|---|
| S | T | A | R |  | S | I | N | G | S |  | H | E | R |
|  | H | E | A | D |  | O | F | F |  | S | H | E |  |
| U | S | U | A | L | L | Y |  | I | M | P | R | O | V |
| E | S |  | H | E | R |  | A | P | P | E | A | R | A |
| N | C | E |  |  |  |  |  |  |  |  |  |  |  |

A Won
B Greatness
C Piranhas
D Useful
E Hash
F Forehead
G Happy
H Mercenaries
I Overlap

24
Said in March 2001, on the destruction of the MIR space station.

|  |  | T | H | E |  | B | E | S | T |  |
|---|---|---|---|---|---|---|---|---|---|---|
| F | I | R | E | W | O | R | K | S |  | I |
|  | H | A | V | E |  | E | V | E | R |  |
| S | E | E | N |  | I |  | D | O |  | N |
| O | T |  | T | H | I | N | K |  | I |  |
| W | I | L | L |  | S | E | E |  | A | N |
| Y | T | H | I | N | G |  | L | I | K | E |
|  | I | T |  | A | G | A | I | N |  |  |

A Benefits
B Shake
C However
D Retrieve
E Nightingale
F Kinky
G Wide
H National
I Hostilities

25
The missing wizard is Harry Potter.

| P | A | P | E | R | B | A | C | K | Y | D | K | N | I |
|---|---|---|---|---|---|---|---|---|---|---|---|---|---|
| A | K | R | A | M | R | E | T | A | W | E | C | U | M |
| L | O | B | O | L | D | F | A | C | E | A | A | R | P |
| F | Y | R | A | N | O | I | T | C | I | D | B | T | R |
| Y | B | O | O | K | S | H | O | P | H | L | D | N | I |
| H | P | A | R | T | C | I | L | A | T | I | R | I | N |
| P | A | P | E | R | Y | R | O | T | S | N | A | R | T |
| A | R | T | T | T | I | T | L | E | P | E | H | P | S |
| R | A | Y | P | R | X | E | D | N | I | E | P | U | I |
| G | G | P | A | C | O | P | Y | R | N | S | T | B | L |
| O | R | E | H | V | O | L | U | M | E | I | N | L | E |
| P | A | R | C | O | L | U | M | N | E | V | I | I | V |
| Y | P | R | O | O | F | R | E | A | D | E | R | S | O |
| T | H | G | I | R | Y | P | O | C | T | R | P | H | N |

26
1 Britney Spears 1981
2 Barbra Streisand 1942
3 Cher 1946
4 Robbie Williams 1974
5 Michael Jackson 1958
6 Elton John 1947

27

| 1 c | 6 c | 11 c |
|---|---|---|
| 2 c | 7 b | 12 a |
| 3 d | 8 a | 13 b |
| 4 b | 9 b | 14 c |
| 5 a | 10 d | 15 c |

28
A Raven
B Bald eagle
C Toucan
D Ostrich

The raven is the connection with the 2001 Super Bowl (the Baltimore Ravens won the final, beating the New York Giants 34-7).

29
Michael Douglas (married Catherine Zeta-Jones, shown). Their first child is named Dylan.

30
A Hamburger, USA
B Caviar, the Russian Federation
C Sushi, Japan
D Spaghetti, Italy

The Russian Federation won the most silver medals (the USA won the most medals overall).

31
Nicole Kidman (shown) split from actor husband Tom Cruise. They last starred together in *Eyes Wide Shut*, directed by Stanley Kubrick.

32

The missing singer is Madonna.

| C | R | E | A | M |  | A | C | T | O | R |
|---|---|---|---|---|---|---|---|---|---|---|
| R |  |  |  | A |  | B |  | E |  | A |
| A |  | P | A | R | T | Y |  | R |  | N |
| T |  | R |  | R |  | S | H | R | U | G |
| E | N | E | M | Y |  | S |  | I |  | E |
|  |  | D |  |  |  |  |  | F |  |  |
| F |  | I |  | A |  | S | T | I | L | L |
| L | O | C | A | L |  | C |  | E |  | E |
| O |  | T |  | T | R | E | N | D |  | M |
| U |  | E |  | E |  | N |  |  |  | O |
| R | O | D | E | R |  | T | A | L | O | N |

33

1 14 November 1963 – Volcanic island of Surtsey appears off coast of Iceland.
2 10 November 1989 – Bulldozers begin to demolish the Berlin Wall.
3 10 February 1942 – 'Chatanooga-Choo-Choo' by Glenn Miller sells a million.
4 5 July 1980 – Bjorn Borg wins Wimbledon trophy for 5th time.
5 10 March 1969 – James Earl Ray sentenced to 99 years for murder of Martin Luther King.
6 11 May 1981 – Musical *Cats*, based on T.S. Eliot's playful poems, opens.
7 21 June 1919 – German fleet scuttled off Scapa Flow.
8 24 January 1986 – Spacecraft, *Voyager II*, encounters Uranus.

34

The female owners of the elkhound and bulldog don't include Miss Barker (clue 4).

The owner of the bulldog isn't Ms Pooch (clue 1), so must be Mrs Walker, and Ms Pooch's Blue Desire II is an elkhound. Miss Barker calls her dog Bo-Bo (4). The Skye terrier known as Fleece isn't Mr Yapp's (2), so must be Mr Leash's dog. Mr Yapp doesn't own the beagle (2), so must own the Rottweiler, with the registered name of Loxwood Rose (3). Miss Barker owns the beagle.

Du Barry Lace alias Max (3) belongs (by elimination) to Mrs Walker. Sweet Loyalty isn't a beagle (5), so must be the Skye terrier. Royal Debate is the beagle. Sam is a Rottweiler (5) and Lucy an elkhound.

Thus:

Miss Barker – beagle – Bo-Bo – Royal Debate;
Mr Leash – Skye terrier – Fleece – Sweet Loyalty;
Ms Pooch – elkhound – Lucy – Blue Desire II;
Mrs Walker – bulldog – Max – Du Barry Lace;
Mr Yapp – Rottweiler – Sam – Loxwood Rose.

35

1 2001 was the 40th anniversary of the first manned space flight. (1961)
2 2004 is the 92nd anniversary of the sinking of the *Titanic*. (1912)
3 2002 is the 39th anniversary of the assassination of John F. Kennedy. (1963)
4 2003 is the 75th anniversary of the first talking film. (1928)
5 2001 was the 225th anniversary of American Independence. (1776)

36

The combination is 53. Correct years for false answers:

D Jackson Pollock begins 'Action Painting' technique (1948)
E Russian dog Laika launched into space (1957)
I Première of animated film *Snow White and the Seven Dwarfs* (1938)
K Ian Fleming, creator of James Bond, dies (1964)

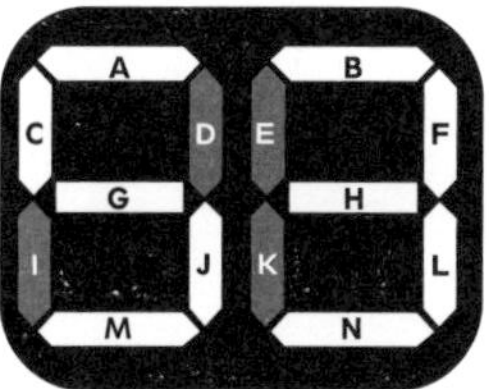


37

(Russell) Crowe

38

PALINDROME (2002 is a palindromic year)

39

Yasser Arafat
Gordon Brown
Jacques Chirac
Al Gore
William Hague
Vaclav Havel
Robert Mugabe
Vladimir Putin
Ariel Sharon
Ann Widdecombe

40

| 1 | B | A | N | D | I | T |
|---|---|---|---|---|---|---|
| 2 | R | E | V | E | A | L |
| 3 | I | G | N | I | T | E |
| 4 | T | A | T | T | O | O |
| 5 | A | U | G | U | S | T |
| 6 | W | A | I | T | E | R |
| 7 | A | R | T | E | R | Y |
| 8 | R | E | S | U | L | T |
| 9 | D | I | S | C | U | S |
| 10 | S | T | R | E | A | M |

41
FLIES INSPIRE HEARING AID TECHNOLOGY
Each number indicates the alphabetical position of the letter it represents plus one – so that 2=A, 3=B, 4=C, etc.

42
The missing film is *Chocolat*.

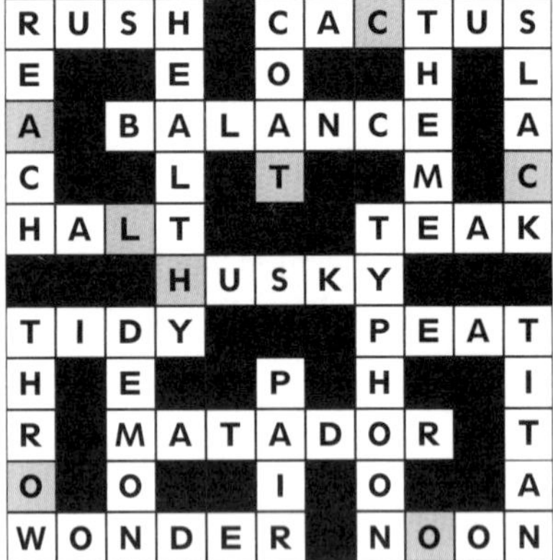


43
A space station (Mir)

| | | | | | | | | | |
|---|---|---|---|---|---|---|---|---|---|
| | S | | S | | | T | | | |
| A | P | H | I | S | | I | S | L | E |
| | E | A | R | P | I | E | C | E | S |
| | A | H | E | A | D | | O | U | T |
| F | R | A | N | C | O | | R | | |
| | M | | | E | L | A | P | S | E |
| G | E | R | M | S | | P | I | E | R |
| | N | O | R | T | H | P | O | L | E |
| | | U | S | A | | L | | V | |
| K | E | G | | T | O | E | C | A | P |
| | T | H | E | I | R | | A | G | E |
| | N | E | R | O | | G | L | E | N |
| B | A | N | A | N | A | | M | S | S |

44
1 10 April
2 Dawn French (in *A Midsummer Night's Dream*)
3 John Savident
4 Martin Bell
5 Jack 'The Hat' McVitie
6 Consignia
7 Pakistan and Sri Lanka
8 Steps
9 Cambridge
10 4 August 2000
11 *Mamma Mia*
12 Sir Paddy Ashdown
13 Gianluca Vialli
14 Denzil, Xavier
15 Nike

45
1 Wobbly Wednesday
2 55 points (20+35)
3 76
4 Down (by 57)
5 Gelapsipan
6 Gravestone
7 Sluggino
8 October
9 2740
10 Belgium

46
'This is delicious! I highly recommend winning.'
(In this code, each letter is represented by its counterpart in the alphabet when reading backwards, so that Z=A, Y=B, X=C, etc.)

47
A Craig Phillips
B Prince Harry
C Vanessa Feltz
D George Orwell

The link is Big Brother (Craig Phillips won the *Big Brother* TV challenge in 2000, Vanessa Feltz appeared in *Celebrity Big Brother*, and George Orwell invented Big Brother, in his book *Nineteen Eighty-Four*). Prince Harry is the odd one out because he's the *little* brother of Prince William.

48
1 2001 was the 55th birthday of Liza Minnelli. (1946)
2 2004 is the 27th anniversary of Elvis Presley's death. (1977)
3 2002 is the 43rd anniversary of Billie Holiday's death. (1959)
4 2003 is the 53rd birthday of Stevie Wonder. (1950)
5 2002 is the 67th birthday of Woody Allen. (1935)

49

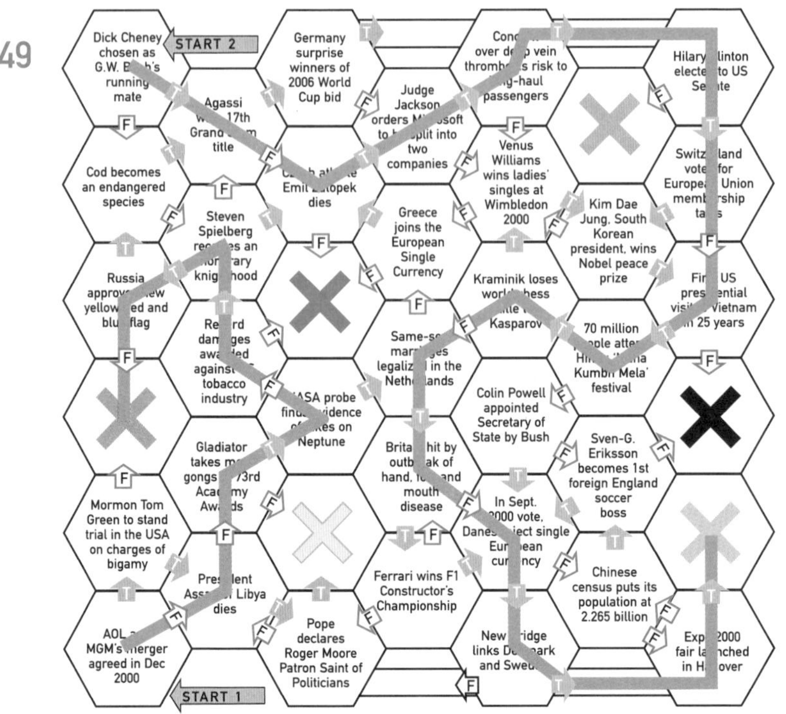

49 (continued)
Correct versions of false statements:
- AOL and Time Warner's merger agreed in Dec 2000
- President Assad of Syria dies
- NASA probe finds evidence of lakes on Mars
- Russia approves new white, red and blue flag
- Agassi wins 7th Grand Slam Title
- Switzerland votes against European Union membership talks
- Kasparov loses world chess title to Kraminik
- Britain hit by outbreak of foot and mouth disease

Unused false answers:
- Pope declares Thomas More Patron Saint of Politicians
- Chinese census puts its population at 1.265 billion

50

| | |
|---|---|
| Conchita Martinez | 1994 |
| Jana Novotna | 1998 |
| Arthur Ashe | 1975 |
| Virginia Wade | 1977 |
| Pat Cash | 1987 |
| Andre Agassi | 1992 |

51
Ogden Nash

52

| | | | | | | |
|---|---|---|---|---|---|---|
| 1 | J | O | I | N | E | D |
| 2 | A | M | O | U | N | T |
| 3 | D | O | U | B | L | E |
| 4 | E | N | T | I | R | E |
| 5 | J | O | G | G | E | R |
| 6 | A | N | O | I | N | T |
| 7 | G | I | N | G | E | R |
| 8 | G | O | S | S | I | P |
| 9 | E | X | P | E | R | T |
| 10 | R | E | P | E | A | T |

53
Monday's contestant who won £90,000 but failed in the subject of wildlife wasn't Damian (clue 3), Bella, Jack or Lavinia (clue 2) or Hilary (4), so must have been Frank. Damian took part on Tuesday and failed in languages (3). Saturday's contestant wasn't Jack or Hilary (2) or Bella (4), so must have been Lavinia. Thus, Friday's was Jack (2).
Bella appeared on Thursday (4) and Hilary on Wednesday. The person who won £70,000 and failed in TV (5) wasn't Bella or Jack (2) or Hilary (4), so must have been Lavinia. Jack won less than Bella (2) and Hilary (4), so (2) Jack won £40,000 and Bella £45,000. The person who failed in geography won £60,000 (1), so is Hilary, and Damian won £55,000. Jack didn't fail in art (5), so must have failed in history. Bella failed in the subject of art.
Thus:
Bella – Thursday – art – £45,000;
Damian – Tuesday – languages – £55,000;
Frank – Monday – wildlife – £90,000;
Hilary – Wednesday – geography – £60,000;
Jack – Friday – history – £40,000;
Lavinia – Saturday – TV – £70,000.

54
*Adrian Mole: The Cappuccino Years*
*Return of the Naked Chef*
*Scarlet Feather*
*The Beatles Anthology*
*The Blind Assassin*
*Delia's Chocolate Collection*
*Marrying the Mistress*
*Harry Potter and the Prisoner of Azkaban*
*Hannibal*
*'Tis*

55
1 9 January 1972 – The liner *Queen Elizabeth* destroyed by fire in Hong Kong.
2 14 August 1945 – Japan surrenders to the Allies, ending the Pacific War.
3 12 July 1998 – Brazil lose 3-0 to France in soccer World Cup Final.
4 11 July 1975 – Chinese archaeologists unearth Terracotta army.
5 25 January 1924 – Chamonix hosts first Winter Olympics.
6 9 November 1988 – Kasparov beats Karpov to become World Chess Champion.
7 7 June 1982 – Graceland, home of Elvis Presley, opens to the public.
8 25 July 1978 – Baby Louise Brown is first test-tube baby.

56
Cathy Freeman (the athlete who lit the Olympic flame)

57
(Bill) Clinton

58
Dame Barbara Cartland

59
Brooklyn (the child of Victoria Beckham, aka Posh Spice, and David Beckham)

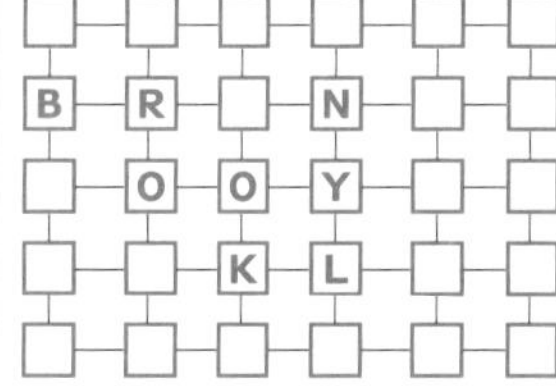

## 60

Hoddle (Glenn)

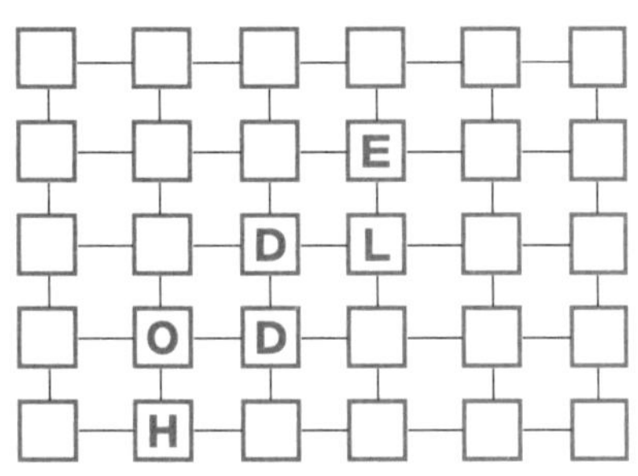


## 61

The leftover letters, when rearranged, give Julia Roberts.

## 62

*The Weakest Link*

## 63

Correct versions of false statements:

- Cyclist Chris Boardman retires after new one-hour event record
- Portugal re-elects President Sampaio
- Ariel Sharon wins February 2001 Israel PM elections
- Cambridge wins 147th University Boat Race on Thames course
- Jean Chrétien, Canadian PM, wins a third term
- Donald Campbell's *Bluebird* craft recovered from Coniston Water
- Bank of Japan cuts interest rates to 0%
- Sea link between China and Taiwan restored after 51 years

Unused false answers:

- Earthquake, 6.8 on Richter scale, hits Washington State
- Thale cress becomes first plant to be genetically coded
- Bangladesh wins Test-playing status for world cricket

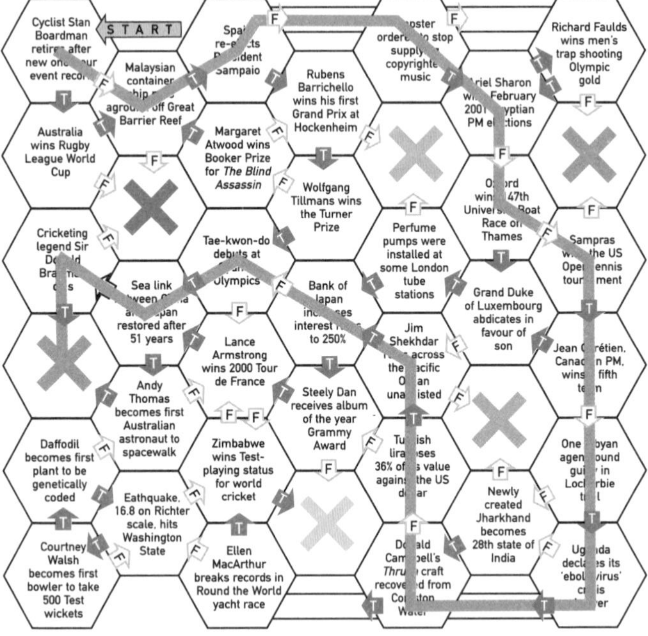


## 64

Tiger (Woods)

## 65

| | | |
|---|---|---|
| 1 | Hovercraft | 1955 |
| 2 | Laser | 1960 |
| 3 | Diesel engine | 1892 |
| 4 | Telephone | 1876 |
| 5 | Rubik's cube | 1975 |
| 6 | Electric light bulb | 1879 |

## 66

'If you grow up in the suburbs of anywhere, a dream like this seems kind of vaguely ludicrous and completely unattainable.' (It is written in reverse.)

## 67

Eminem

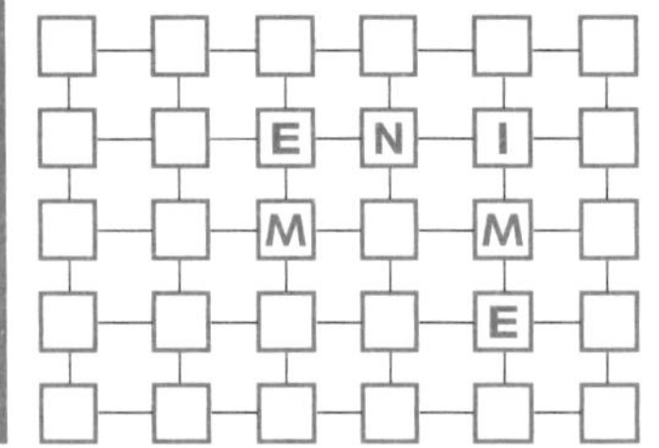


## 68

| | | | | | | |
|---|---|---|---|---|---|---|
| 1 | S | T | O | R | M | Y |
| 2 | I | N | V | E | N | T |
| 3 | X | E | R | X | E | S |
| 4 | N | O | V | I | C | E |
| 5 | A | S | C | E | N | D |
| 6 | T | R | O | P | H | Y |
| 7 | I | N | C | O | M | E |
| 8 | O | R | C | H | I | D |
| 9 | N | U | T | M | E | G |
| 10 | S | T | U | P | I | D |

## 69

Solution: J.K. Rowling

| B | I | B | L | E |  | T | R | O | O | P |
|---|---|---|---|---|---|---|---|---|---|---|
| R |  |  |  | A |  | O |  | B |  | I |
| A |  | S | I | G | H | T |  | J |  | S |
| S |  | P |  | L |  | A | V | E | R | T |
| S | N | A | R | E |  | L |  | C |  | E |
|  |  | G |  |  |  |  |  | T |  |  |
| S |  | H |  | G |  | W | H | I | R | L |
| C | L | E | A | R |  | E |  | V |  | A |
| R |  | T |  | A | L | I | K | E |  | R |
| A |  | T |  | V |  | R |  |  |  | G |
| P | R | I | Z | E |  | D | R | A | K | E |

## 70

MADONNA WEDS GUY RITCHIE IN DORNOCH

## 71

Vladimir Putin

## 72

1 The Limpix
2 Three
3 Ohio
4 War and Peace
5 45.28 metres
6 Simone Rockstone
7 Billy 'Flop' Nelson
8 23
9 Silver
10 Ramon Caverara

## 73

1 Philip Trainset
2 25.6
3 Giggle
4 Hurrah!, Toenail or Gotlotnot
5 Earplug
6 Four hours
7 15-3
8 Barnstormers
9 1975–8
10 20 years

## 74

Remember throughout that each yacht finished in three different positions (clue 1). The 1st yacht in the first leg wasn't *Chrysalis* (clue 2), *Hawk Moth* or *Imago* (4) or *Mayfly IV* (6), so must be either *Red Admiral* or *Swallowtail*. If it was *Swallowtail*, then *Mayfly IV* was 1st in the second leg (3), which isn't possible (6), so the 1st yacht in the first leg was *Red Admiral*. Thus *Red Admiral* was 2nd in the second leg (5).

The 2nd yacht in the first leg wasn't *Chrysalis* (2), *Swallowtail* (3), *Hawk Moth* or *Imago* (4), so must be *Mayfly IV*. The 3rd yacht in the first leg wasn't *Chrysalis* (2), so must be (4) *Swallowtail*. Thus *Mayfly IV* was 3rd in the second leg (3) and *Imago* was 3rd in the third. *Imago* was 6th in the first leg (5), so (2) *Chrysalis* was 5th and *Hawk Moth* 4th.

*Red Admiral* was either 4th or 5th in the third leg (6) and *Mayfly IV* was 5th or 6th. Thus (2) *Chrysalis* was 1st and *Hawk Moth* 2nd in the third leg. The 6th in the second leg wasn't *Chrysalis* (2), so (4) must be *Swallowtail*. The 6th in the third leg wasn't *Red Admiral* (6), so must be *Mayfly IV*.

By elimination, *Chrysalis* was 4th in the second leg, so (6) *Red Admiral* was 5th in the third and *Swallowtail* 4th in the third. *Imago* was 1st in the second leg (2) and *Hawk Moth* was 5th.

Thus (first leg – second leg – third leg):
*Chrysalis* – fifth – fourth – first;
*Hawk Moth* – fourth – fifth – second;
*Imago* – sixth – first – third;
*Mayfly IV* – second – third – sixth;
Red Admiral – first – second – fifth;
*Swallowtail* – third – sixth – fourth.

## 75

'The Dome should be delighted. It's the first time they've had people so keen to get in.'
(In this code, each letter is represented by its counterpart in the alphabet when reading backwards, so that Z=A, Y=B, X=C, etc.

## 76

1 *The Godfather* 1972
2 *Titanic* 1997
3 *Toy Story* 1995
4 *M*A*S*H* 1970
5 *Bugsy Malone* 1976
6 *The Blair Witch Project* 1999

## 77

'Mick is a wonderful man but a terrible husband.'
(This time each letter has been replaced by one above and to its immediate left on a standard keyboard.)

## 78

'If we don't succeed, we run the risk of failure.'
(Each letter in the words spoken has been replaced by one to its immediate left on a standard keyboard.)

79

Chris Tarrant

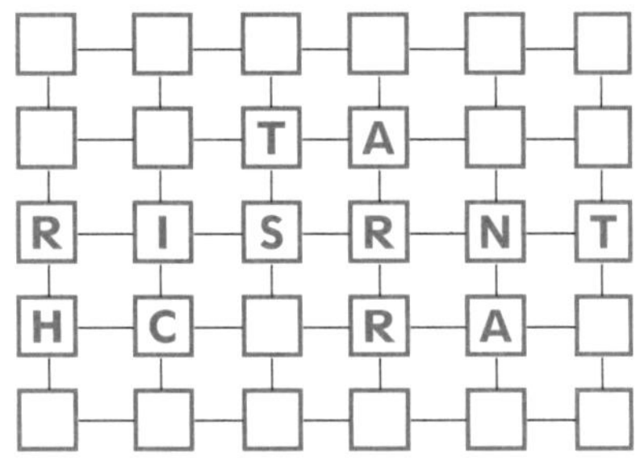


80

1 2001 was the 7th anniversary of Nelson Mandela becoming president of South Africa (1994)
2 2002 is the 23rd anniversary of Margaret Thatcher becoming British prime minister (1979)
3 2001was the 10th anniversary of Boris Yeltsin becoming president of the Russian Federation (1991)
4 2003 is the 10th anniversary of Bill Clinton becoming president of the USA (1993)
5 2002 is the 36th anniversary of Mrs Indira Gandhi becoming prime minister of India (1966)

81

| | |
|---|---|
| 1 b | 6 b |
| 2 b | 7 a |
| 3 c | 8 d |
| 4 d | 9 c |
| 5 c | 10 a |

82

The combination is 47. Correct years for false answers:

A The world's first railway timetable is published (1839)
E Ulysses Grant becomes 18th US president (1868)
H Painter Gustav Klimt dies (1918)
I The first liquid fuel rocket is launched (1926)
K The first edition of *The Reader's Digest* is published (1922)
M Joseph Hansom patents a 'safety cab' (1834)
N Pope Pius XI denounces the USSR (1924)

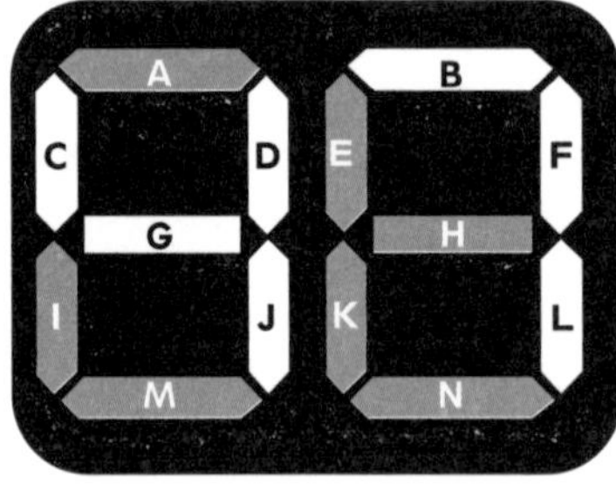


83

1 Ronald Reagan 1980
2 Jimmy Carter 1976
3 F.D. Roosevelt 1932
4 John F. Kennedy 1960
5 Bill Clinton 1992
6 Dwight D. Eisenhower 1952

1

2

3

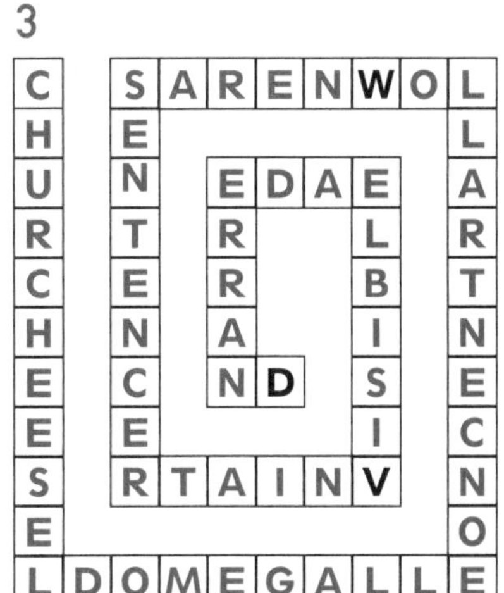

1 Church
2 Cheese
3 Seldom
4 Omega
5 Galleon
6 Once
7 Central
8 Allow
9 Owner
10 Erase
11 Sentence
12 Certain
13 Invisible
14 Leader
15 Errand

4

The anagram is Argentina.

| M | I | X | E | D |   | F | A | T | A | L |
|---|---|---|---|---|---|---|---|---|---|---|
| A |   |   |   | I |   | R |   | A |   | A |
| J |   | G | R | A | C | E |   | R |   | S |
| O |   | R |   | R |   | S | H | A | R | E |
| R | E | A | D | Y |   | H |   | N |   | R |
|   |   | T |   |   |   |   |   | T |   |   |
| S |   | I |   | A |   | M | O | U | N | D |
| P | A | T | C | H |   | O |   | L |   | I |
| L |   | U |   | E | X | T | R | A |   | R |
| I |   | D |   | A |   | O |   |   |   | T |
| T | R | E | A | D |   | R | I | S | K | Y |

5

6

The anagram is Copacabana.

| C | E | N | T |   | P | E | R | M | I | T |
|---|---|---|---|---|---|---|---|---|---|---|
| H |   |   | R |   | L |   |   | A |   | H |
| E |   | C | A | B | A | R | E | T |   | E |
| A |   |   | I |   | N |   |   | C |   | F |
| T | O | O | L |   |   |   | S | H | U | T |
|   |   |   | E | A | R | T | H |   |   |   |
| N | E | A | R |   |   |   | O | A | T | H |
| O |   | L |   |   | S |   | R |   |   | E |
| V |   | I | M | I | T | A | T | E |   | A |
| E |   | E |   |   | A |   | E |   |   | R |
| L | I | N | G | E | R |   | N | E | A | T |

7

|   | E |   | U |   |   |   | S |   | M |   |
|---|---|---|---|---|---|---|---|---|---|---|
| E | X | I | S | T | S |   | A | G | E | D |
|   | P |   | E |   | T |   | L |   | A |   |
|   | L | I | D |   | R | O | M | A | N |   |
|   | O |   |   |   | E |   | O |   | I |   |
| F | R | I | G | H | T | E | N | I | N | G |
|   | A |   | R |   | C |   |   |   | G |   |
|   | T | E | E | T | H |   | I | L | L |   |
|   | I |   | E |   | E |   | D |   | E |   |
| B | O | R | N |   | S | P | L | A | S | H |
|   | N |   | S |   |   |   | E |   | S |   |

8

| 2 | x | 6 | + | 3 | − | 5 | = | 10 |
|---|---|---|---|---|---|---|---|---|
| x |   | + |   | x |   | − |   |   |
| 5 | − | 2 | + | 6 | x | 3 | = | 27 |
| − |   | − |   | − |   | x |   |   |
| 3 | x | 5 | + | 2 | − | 6 | = | 11 |
| + |   | x |   | + |   | + |   |   |
| 6 | − | 3 | + | 5 | x | 2 | = | 16 |
| = |   | = |   | = |   | = |   |   |
| 13 |   | 9 |   | 21 |   | 14 |   |   |

9

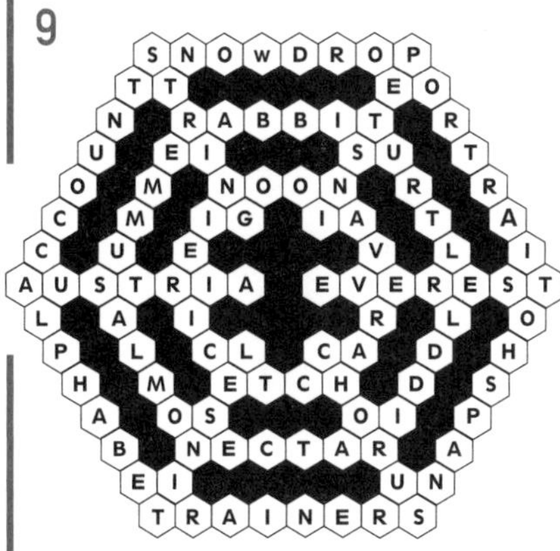

10

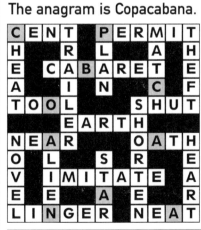

ACROSS
9 Remain (stay)
14 Large house (mansion)
5 Tug (pull)
21 Phobia (fear)
7 Plenty (ample)
2 School group (class)
15 Insect (moth)
11 Finished (done)
23 First appearance (debut)
6 Noisy (loud)
22 Shortly (soon)
18 Animal skin (pelt)
20 Stadium (arena)

DOWN
1 Corrosion (rust)
2 Stiff mud (clay)
19 Glance (look)
18 Beyond (past)
3 Snow vehicle (sled)
4 Wreck (ruin)
17 Difficult (hard)
8 Sea journey (passage)
16 Undo (open)
12 Small weight (ounce)
10 Allow in (admit)
9 Tempest (storm)
13 Build (erect)

| | R | | C | L | A | S | S | | R | |
|---|---|---|---|---|---|---|---|---|---|---|
| P | U | L | L | | | | L | O | U | D |
| | S | | A | M | P | L | E | | I | |
| S | T | A | Y | | A | | D | O | N | E |
| T | | D | | | S | | | U | | R |
| O | | M | A | N | S | I | O | N | | E |
| R | | I | | | A | | | C | | C |
| M | O | T | H | | G | | P | E | L | T |
| | P | | A | R | E | N | A | | O | |
| F | E | A | R | | | | S | O | O | N |
| | N | | D | E | B | U | T | | K | |

## 11

| O | T | H | E | R | S | | A | G | E | D |
|---|---|---|---|---|---|---|---|---|---|---|
| C | | I | | A | | A | | R | | I |
| C | A | B | I | N | | R | O | A | D | S |
| U | | E | | C | | M | | N | | A |
| P | U | R | C | H | A | S | E | D | | P |
| A | | N | | | | | | F | | P |
| T | | A | S | S | O | C | I | A | T | E |
| I | | T | | E | | R | | T | | A |
| O | L | I | V | E | | E | T | H | E | R |
| N | | N | | S | | P | | E | | E |
| S | I | G | N | | P | E | E | R | E | D |

## 12

| H | O | N | I | A | R | A | | D | E | A | T | H |
|---|---|---|---|---|---|---|---|---|---|---|---|---|
| A | | | M | | | T | | I | | R | | I |
| N | | A | P | P | R | O | V | E | | R | | L |
| D | | | O | | | M | | T | H | E | F | T |
| S | H | A | R | K | S | | F | | | S | | |
| O | | | T | | A | T | L | A | N | T | I | S |
| M | | E | | | T | | O | | | S | | C |
| E | M | P | L | O | Y | E | R | | K | | | H |
| | | S | | | R | | A | D | A | G | I | O |
| C | H | I | P | S | | Z | | | I | | | O |
| A | | L | | C | H | I | N | E | S | E | | N |
| T | | O | | A | | N | | | E | | | E |
| S | O | N | A | R | | C | H | A | R | T | E | R |

## 13

The anagram is Shakespeare.

## 14

1 Broken
2 Enough
3 Ghost
4 Stalemate
5 Terrible
6 Lesson
7 Onset
8 Eternal
9 Altar
10 Arrive
11 Venom
12 Omitted
13 Educate
14 Teaspoon

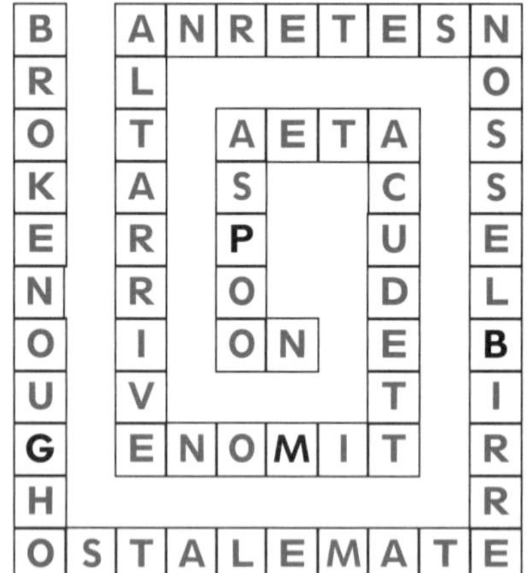

## 15

| | | | | | | F | | H | | V |
|---|---|---|---|---|---|---|---|---|---|---|
| | | | | | C | A | M | E | R | A |
| | | | | | | K | | R | | S |
| | | | | | R | E | P | E | A | T |
| | | | | | | | R | | X | |
| | | | | | | C | O | M | E | T |
| | | | | | | A | D | O | | R |
| | | | C | O | M | B | | A | T | E |
| A | S | I | A | | | L | I | T | H | E |
| | U | | S | I | R | E | N | | A | |
| A | N | N | U | L | | | N | E | W | S |
| | R | | A | L | T | O | | P | | O |
| P | I | L | L | | A | B | S | O | R | B |
| | S | | T | A | C | O | | C | U | E |
| R | E | L | Y | | T | E | T | H | E | R |

## 16

| | | | W | | B | | | | X | |
|---|---|---|---|---|---|---|---|---|---|---|
| S | I | G | H | T | U | N | S | E | E | N |
| | N | | E | | T | | E | | N | |
| E | D | D | Y | | T | I | P | T | O | E |
| | E | | | | E | | I | | P | |
| | C | O | C | K | R | O | A | C | H | |
| | I | | R | | B | | | | O | |
| A | S | H | O | R | E | | T | U | B | A |
| | I | | O | | A | | O | | I | |
| E | V | E | N | I | N | G | S | T | A | R |
| | E | | | | S | | S | | | |

## 17

## 18

| P | | R | A | L | A | E | R | E | C |
|---|---|---|---|---|---|---|---|---|---|
| R | | M | | | | | | | U |
| O | | Y | | G | N | I | D | | D |
| T | | S | | A | | | A | | E |
| E | | T | | L | | | E | | R |
| S | | E | | L | | | L | | E |
| T | | R | | O | N | | B | | H |
| R | | Y | | | | | U | | C |
| A | | A | C | H | T | R | O | | A |
| N | | | | | | | | | E |
| G | E | M | I | N | I | G | N | I | T |

1 Protest
2 Strange
3 Gemini
4 Ignite
5 Teacher
6 Reduce
7 Cereal
8 Alarm
9 Mystery
10 Yacht
11 Trouble
12 Leading
13 Gallon

## 19

| G | I | B | L | E | T | S |  | T | O | K | Y | O |
|---|---|---|---|---|---|---|---|---|---|---|---|---|
| Y |  | U |  | P |  | C |  | T |  | I |  | D |
| P | U | B | L | I | C | H | O | L | I | D | A | Y |
| S |  | O |  | C |  | L |  |  |  | S |  | S |
| Y | E | N |  | E | D | E | L | W | E | I | S | S |
|  |  | I |  | N |  | P |  | H |  | N |  | E |
| H | E | C | A | T | E |  | F | I | L | T | H | Y |
| I |  | P |  | R |  | E |  | T |  | H |  |  |
| B | A | L | D | E | A | G | L | E |  | E | A | R |
| B |  | A |  |  |  | G |  | F |  | H |  | U |
| E | I | G | H | T | A | N | D | A | H | A | L | F |
| R |  | U |  | U |  | O |  | N |  | L |  | U |
| T | H | E | F | T |  | G | A | G | G | L | E | S |

## 20

| D | A | S | H |  | C | A | N | T | E | R |
|---|---|---|---|---|---|---|---|---|---|---|
| O |  |  | Y |  | H |  |  | I |  | U |
| N |  | A | G | A | I | N | S | T |  | L |
| O |  |  | I |  | C |  |  | L |  | E |
| R | A | R | E |  |  |  | D | E | A | R |
|  |  |  | N | O | I | S | E |  |  |  |
| R | I | C | E |  |  |  | L | A | S | T |
| O |  | A |  |  | P |  | I |  |  | O |
| U |  | B | I | O | L | O | G | Y |  | W |
| G |  | I |  |  | O |  | H |  |  | E |
| H | O | N | E | S | T |  | T | O | I | L |

## 21

|  |  | P | O | S | T | C | A | R | D |  |
|---|---|---|---|---|---|---|---|---|---|---|
| M |  | A |  | E |  | O |  | A |  | V |
| A | S | S | E | T |  | L | A | P | S | E |
| R |  | T |  | T |  | A |  | I |  | R |
| S | T | E | W | E | D |  | I | D | E | S |
| U |  |  |  | R |  | R |  |  |  | A |
| P | A | L | E |  | D | E | P | A | R | T |
| I |  | E |  | S |  | P |  | C |  | I |
| A | B | A | F | T |  | A | U | R | A | L |
| L |  | R |  | A |  | S |  | I |  | E |
|  | U | N | A | B | A | T | E | D |  |  |

## 22

| P | R | O | S | E |  | C |  | A |  | B |  | E |
|---|---|---|---|---|---|---|---|---|---|---|---|---|
| A |  | K |  |  | C | H | I | L | D | R | E | N |
| E | M | A | I | L |  | A |  | L |  | O |  | Z |
| L |  |  | D | I | C | T | I | O | N | A | R | Y |
| L |  | R |  | G |  |  |  | Y |  | D |  | M |
| A | M | E | T | H | Y | S | T |  | I | S | L | E |
|  |  | C |  | T |  | H |  | F |  | I |  |  |
| S | E | T | H |  | C | Y | L | I | N | D | E | R |
| C |  | A |  | C |  |  |  | X |  | E |  | A |
| R | I | N | G | L | E | A | D | E | R |  |  | T |
| I |  | G |  | O |  | S |  | D | O | U | B | T |
| B | U | L | G | A | R | I | A |  | L |  |  | A |
| E |  | E |  | K |  | A |  | L | E | M | O | N |

## 23

ACROSS
9 Infant (child)
13 Between (through)
14 Fortunate (lucky)
1 Seashore (beach)
5 Join (connect)
15 Twelve (dozen)
3 Clutch (grasp)
11 Winch (hoist)
8 Weary (tired)
7 Weighty (heavy)

DOWN
5 Roman vehicle (chariot)
1 Turn red (blush)
6 Taint (tarnish)
10 Soiled (dirty)
3 Welcome (greet)
9 Christmas song (carol)
11 Hunting dog (hound)
4 Beg (plead)
2 Convenient (handy)
12 Teach (train)

| 1B | E | A | C | 2H |  | 3G | R | A | S | 4P |
|---|---|---|---|---|---|---|---|---|---|---|
| L |  |  |  | A |  | R |  |  |  | L |
| U |  | 5C | O | N | N | E | C | 6T |  | E |
| S |  | H |  | D |  | E |  | A |  | A |
| 7H | E | A | V | Y |  | 8T | I | R | E | D |
|  |  | R |  |  |  |  |  | N |  |  |
| 9C | H | I | L | 10D |  | 11H | O | I | S | 12T |
| A |  | O |  | I |  | O |  | S |  | R |
| R |  | 13T | H | R | O | U | G | H |  | A |
| O |  |  |  | T |  | N |  |  |  | I |
| 14L | U | C | K | Y |  | 15D | O | Z | E | N |

## 24

The anagram is Jingle Bells.

| T | E | N | O | R |  | B | E | L | O | W |
|---|---|---|---|---|---|---|---|---|---|---|
| H |  |  |  | O |  | R |  | U |  | A |
| O |  | P | E | A | C | E |  | B |  | T |
| N |  | R |  | S |  | A | G | R | E | E |
| G | H | O | S | T |  | D |  | I |  | R |
|  |  | J |  |  |  |  |  | C |  |  |
| R |  | E |  | B |  | S | T | A | R | T |
| E | X | C | E | L |  | T |  | T |  | O |
| B |  | T |  | A | B | A | T | E |  | U |
| E |  | O |  | N |  | F |  |  |  | G |
| L | U | R | E | D |  | F | A | I | T | H |

## 25

| A | C | H | E |  | A | F | F | O | R | D |
|---|---|---|---|---|---|---|---|---|---|---|
| I |  | E |  |  |  | R |  | R |  | A |
| D | E | A | T | H | D | U | T | I | E | S |
| E |  | V |  | E |  | I |  | G |  | H |
|  | S | Y | M | P | A | T | H | I | Z | E |
| A |  | W |  | A |  | T |  | N |  | R |
| S | T | E | N | T | O | R | I | A | N |  |
| T |  | I |  | I |  | E |  | L |  | E |
| H | I | G | H | T | R | E | A | S | O | N |
| M |  | H |  | I |  |  |  | I |  | V |
| A | T | T | E | S | T |  | O | N | L | Y |

## 26

|  |  |  | H |  | U |  |  |  | M |  |
|---|---|---|---|---|---|---|---|---|---|---|
|  |  | B | I | G | D | I | P | P | E | R |
|  | C |  | P |  | D |  | L |  | S |  |
| W | H | I | P |  | E | L | A | P | S | E |
|  | I |  | O |  | R |  | S |  | E |  |
| S | N | I | D | E |  | S | T | I | N | G |
|  | A |  | R |  | D |  | I |  | G |  |
| S | T | O | O | G | E |  | C | H | E | F |
|  | O |  | M |  | U |  | A |  | R |  |
| S | W | E | E | T | C | O | R | N |  |  |
|  | N |  |  |  | E |  | T |  |  |  |

## 27

|  | E | L | I | M | I | N | A | T | E |  |
|---|---|---|---|---|---|---|---|---|---|---|
|  |  | E |  | A |  | A |  | R |  |  |
| D | R | A | W | S |  | T | R | U | C | E |
| E |  | S |  | H |  | I |  | S |  | A |
| C | I | T | E |  | D | O | C | T | O | R |
| I |  |  |  | S |  | N |  |  |  | T |
| M | I | N | U | T | E |  | G | A | S | H |
| A |  | O |  | A |  | O |  | S |  | E |
| L | A | T | E | R |  | P | I | T | O | N |
|  |  | E |  | V |  | T |  | I |  |  |
|  | A | D | V | E | R | S | A | R | Y |  |

## 28

1 Macabre
2 Remain
3 Nadir
4 Robust
5 Stamina
6 Ancestry
7 Yield
8 Dismantle
9 Lethal
10 Altitude
11 Expand
12 Danger

28 (grid)

| M | | I | D | L | E | I | Y | R | T |
|---|---|---|---|---|---|---|---|---|---|
| A | | S | | | | | | | S |
| C | | M | | D | N | A | P | | E |
| A | | A | | A | | | X | | C |
| B | | N | | N | | | E | | N |
| R | | T | | G | | | D | | A |
| E | | L | | E | R | | U | | N |
| M | | E | | | | | T | | I |
| A | | T | H | A | L | T | I | | M |
| I | | | | | | | | | A |
| N | A | D | I | R | O | B | U | S | T |

29

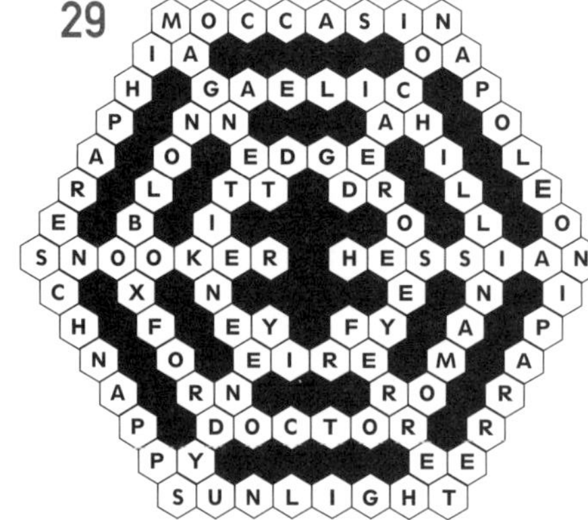


30

| | B | R | A | C | K | I | S | H | | W |
|---|---|---|---|---|---|---|---|---|---|---|
| A | | O | | O | | O | | I | | A |
| G | R | O | S | S | | T | I | G | H | T |
| G | | M | | M | | A | | H | | E |
| R | U | S | T | I | C | | S | T | I | R |
| E | | E | | C | O | G | | E | | L |
| S | U | R | E | | P | R | A | N | C | E |
| S | | V | | O | | O | | S | | V |
| I | C | I | N | G | | W | H | I | T | E |
| O | | C | | L | | T | | O | | L |
| N | | E | L | E | P | H | A | N | T | |

31

| | W | | G | | G | | | | S | | O | | S | |
|---|---|---|---|---|---|---|---|---|---|---|---|---|---|---|
| S | A | L | I | V | A | | C | A | R | A | P | A | C | E |
| | L | | O | | N | | O | | I | | P | | R | |
| E | L | E | V | A | T | O | R | | L | O | O | F | A | H |
| | A | | A | | R | | P | | A | | S | | W | |
| T | H | A | N | K | Y | O | U | | N | E | E | D | L | E |
| | S | | N | | | | S | | K | | | | Y | |
| | | H | I | P | P | O | C | R | A | T | E | S | | |
| | O | | | | E | | H | | | | X | | A | |
| S | T | Y | M | I | E | | R | E | L | A | T | I | V | E |
| | T | | A | | R | | I | | A | | E | | A | |
| S | O | R | R | E | L | | S | O | M | B | R | E | R | O |
| | M | | T | | E | | T | | I | | N | | I | |
| W | A | T | E | R | S | K | I | | N | U | A | N | C | E |
| | N | | N | | S | | | | A | | L | | E | |

32
The anagram is Bruce Willis.

| W | I | L | D | | E | X | P | A | N | D |
|---|---|---|---|---|---|---|---|---|---|---|
| R | | | E | | A | | | B | | E |
| O | | O | S | T | R | I | C | H | | N |
| N | | | C | | N | | | O | | I |
| G | L | U | E | | | | D | R | U | M |
| | | | N | E | R | V | E | | | |
| G | O | L | D | | | | P | I | C | K |
| U | | E | | | O | | O | | | A |
| E | | G | L | I | M | P | S | E | | Y |
| S | | A | | | I | | I | | | A |
| S | I | L | E | N | T | | T | A | L | K |

33

| S | H | O | R | T | A | G | E | | S | T | A | N | D | A | R | D |
|---|---|---|---|---|---|---|---|---|---|---|---|---|---|---|---|---|
| A | | | E | | | R | | S | | H | | | E | | | E |
| C | L | O | C | K | | A | L | T | E | R | | S | P | O | O | N |
| R | | | U | | | C | | A | | I | | | E | | | T |
| E | | | P | | L | E | G | I | B | L | E | | N | | | A |
| D | A | T | E | D | | F | | N | | L | | I | D | E | A | L |
| | R | | R | | | U | | | | E | | | A | | B | |
| | M | | A | | A | L | L | E | G | R | O | | B | | L | |
| S | Y | S | T | E | M | | | R | | | M | E | L | T | E | D |
| P | | | E | | A | M | I | A | B | L | E | | E | | | R |
| E | | S | | | Z | | M | | A | | G | | | S | | A |
| C | H | O | I | C | E | | P | | N | | A | N | T | H | E | M |
| T | | R | | | | P | R | I | D | E | | | | O | | A |
| A | R | R | I | V | E | | O | | A | | O | C | C | U | L | T |
| T | | Y | | | X | | V | | G | | C | | | T | | I |
| O | | | B | | P | R | E | S | E | N | T | | S | | | S |
| R | E | C | E | D | E | | | A | | | E | X | T | E | N | T |
| | X | | S | | L | A | R | G | E | S | T | | R | | A | |
| | I | | T | | | S | | | | Q | | | E | | M | |
| S | T | A | S | H | | S | | H | | U | | A | N | G | E | L |
| E | | | E | | G | E | N | E | R | A | L | | G | | | I |
| A | | | L | | | M | | A | | N | | | T | | | T |
| R | E | P | L | Y | | B | O | R | E | D | | S | H | O | R | T |
| C | | | E | | | L | | T | | E | | | E | | | L |
| H | Y | D | R | O | G | E | N | | T | R | I | A | N | G | L | E |

## 34

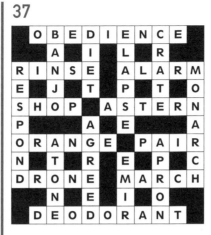

| | | | | | | C | | S | | F |
|---|---|---|---|---|---|---|---|---|---|---|
| | | | | | G | U | I | T | A | R |
| | | | | | | R | | E | | E |
| | | | | | H | E | L | M | E | T |
| | | | | | | | A | | W | |
| | | | | | B | A | W | L | E | D |
| | | | | | | R | | A | | E |
| | T | | I | | L | O | A | T | H | E |
| S | H | A | R | P | | S | P | E | A | R |
| | R | | R | U | P | E | E | | L | |
| M | I | N | I | M | | | D | E | F | Y |
| | L | | G | A | I | T | | V | | I |
| U | L | N | A | | D | E | L | E | T | E |
| | E | | T | O | L | L | | N | I | L |
| E | D | G | E | | E | L | A | T | E | D |

## 35

| E | C | O | N | O | M | Y | | E | M | U |
|---|---|---|---|---|---|---|---|---|---|---|
| | H | | O | | I | | C | | U | |
| | O | U | T | S | K | I | R | T | S | |
| | L | | A | | E | | E | | E | |
| M | E | L | B | A | | O | D | I | U | M |
| | S | | I | | | | E | | M | |
| S | T | A | L | E | | I | N | E | P | T |
| | E | | I | | K | | T | | I | |
| | R | E | T | E | N | T | I | V | E | |
| | O | | Y | | E | | A | | C | |
| A | L | P | | R | E | P | L | I | E | D |

## 36

| | C | | S | | F | | S | | E | | C | |
|---|---|---|---|---|---|---|---|---|---|---|---|---|
| S | H | I | N | T | O | | P | O | N | C | H | O |
| | R | | E | | X | | A | | F | | A | |
| B | Y | T | E | | T | A | S | M | A | N | I | A |
| | S | | Z | | R | | M | | N | | N | |
| C | A | M | E | R | O | N | | S | T | E | R | N |
| | N | | | | T | | S | | | | E | |
| A | T | L | A | S | | K | U | M | Q | U | A | T |
| | H | | N | | S | | N | | U | | C | |
| W | E | S | T | W | A | R | D | | A | N | T | E |
| | M | | L | | R | | I | | R | | I | |
| E | U | R | E | K | A | | A | C | T | I | O | N |
| | M | | R | | H | | L | | Z | | N | |

## 37

| | O | B | E | D | I | E | N | C | E | |
|---|---|---|---|---|---|---|---|---|---|---|
| | | A | | I | | L | | R | | |
| R | I | N | S | E | | A | L | A | R | M |
| E | | J | | T | | P | | T | | O |
| S | H | O | P | | A | S | T | E | R | N |
| P | | | | A | | E | | | | A |
| O | R | A | N | G | E | | P | A | I | R |
| N | | T | | R | | E | | P | | C |
| D | R | O | N | E | | M | A | R | C | H |
| | | N | | E | | I | | O | | |
| | D | E | O | D | O | R | A | N | T | |

## 38

| 5 | + | 6 | x | 3 | – | 9 | = | 24 |
|---|---|---|---|---|---|---|---|---|
| x | | + | | x | | – | | |
| 3 | x | 9 | + | 6 | – | 5 | = | 28 |
| + | | x | | – | | x | | |
| 9 | – | 3 | x | 5 | + | 6 | = | 36 |
| – | | – | | + | | + | | |
| 6 | – | 5 | + | 9 | x | 3 | = | 30 |
| = | | = | | = | | = | | |
| 18 | | 40 | | 22 | | 27 | | |

## 39

| A | C | R | O | P | H | O | B | I | A | | A | R | O | U | S | E |
|---|---|---|---|---|---|---|---|---|---|---|---|---|---|---|---|---|
| | A | | P | | | | A | | N | | R | | B | | O | |
| F | L | O | U | N | D | E | R | | H | O | M | E | S | P | U | N |
| | Y | | S | | Y | | C | | Y | | C | | C | | T | |
| S | P | Y | | S | E | C | O | N | D | T | H | O | U | G | H | T |
| | S | | S | | I | | D | | R | | A | | R | | P | |
| C | O | M | M | O | N | D | E | N | O | M | I | N | A | T | O | R |
| | | | A | | G | | | | U | | R | | N | | L | |
| S | P | A | S | M | | S | W | I | S | H | | E | T | H | E | R |
| | R | | H | | A | | I | | | | R | | I | | | |
| B | I | C | A | R | B | O | N | A | T | E | O | F | S | O | D | A |
| | M | | N | | U | | D | | E | | L | | M | | I | |
| F | E | E | D | I | N | G | B | O | T | T | L | E | | U | S | E |
| | R | | G | | D | | R | | A | | O | | P | | T | |
| F | A | I | R | G | A | M | E | | N | O | N | M | E | T | A | L |
| | T | | A | | N | | A | | U | | | | A | | F | |
| N | E | S | B | I | T | | K | I | S | S | O | F | L | I | F | E |

## 40

| | N | | C | | | | S | | A | |
|---|---|---|---|---|---|---|---|---|---|---|
| | A | P | O | P | H | T | H | E | G | M |
| | K | | F | | O | | A | | O | |
| B | E | E | F | | I | N | V | E | R | T |
| | D | | E | | P | | I | | A | |
| | | H | E | R | O | I | N | E | | |
| | K | | B | | L | | G | | E | |
| L | A | U | R | E | L | | F | U | N | D |
| | Y | | E | | O | | O | | T | |
| P | A | L | A | T | I | N | A | T | E | |
| | K | | K | | | | M | | R | |

## 41

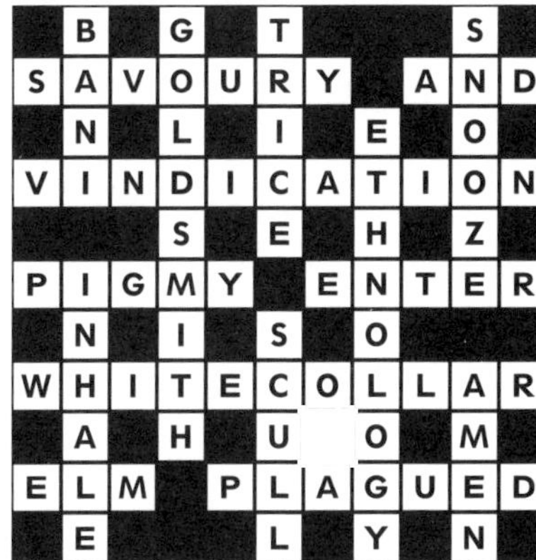

| | B | | G | | T | | | | S | |
|---|---|---|---|---|---|---|---|---|---|---|
| S | A | V | O | U | R | Y | | A | N | D |
| | N | | L | | I | | E | | O | |
| V | I | N | D | I | C | A | T | I | O | N |
| | | | S | | E | | H | | Z | |
| P | I | G | M | Y | | E | N | T | E | R |
| | N | | I | | S | | O | | | |
| W | H | I | T | E | C | O | L | L | A | R |
| | A | | H | | U | | O | | M | |
| E | L | M | | P | L | A | G | U | E | D |
| | E | | | | L | | Y | | N | |

1
28 runners. Divide 168 by 6 (legs on horses = 4, legs on jockeys = 2) = 28.

2
7

3
A, B and D

4

| 1 | 3 | 5 | 9 | 7 | 9 | 3 | 1 | 7 | 5 | 3 | 1 |
|---|---|---|---|---|---|---|---|---|---|---|---|
| 3 | 9 | 5 | 3 | 1 | 5 | 7 | 9 | 3 | 1 | 5 | 9 |
| 5 | 1 | 7 | 1 | 1 | 1 | 3 | 5 | 9 | 7 | 1 | 7 |
| 3 | 5 | 1 | 3 | 5 | 9 | 7 | 1 | 5 | 9 | 3 | 5 |
| 9 | 7 | 5 | 3 | **9** | 7 | 1 | 3 | 9 | 3 | 5 | 1 |
| 1 | 9 | 3 | 5 | **7** | 9 | 1 | 5 | 3 | 7 | 9 | 3 |
| 9 | 3 | 7 | 9 | **5** | 1 | 3 | 9 | 1 | 3 | 7 | 5 |
| 5 | 5 | 9 | 5 | **3** | 7 | 5 | 1 | 9 | 1 | 5 | 9 |
| 7 | 9 | 5 | 7 | **1** | 3 | 9 | 7 | 5 | 9 | 1 | 7 |
| 9 | 7 | 3 | 1 | 7 | 9 | 5 | 3 | 1 | 5 | 7 | 9 |
| 9 | 7 | 1 | 1 | 3 | 5 | 1 | 1 | 3 | 7 | 9 | 1 |
| 9 | 7 | 5 | 9 | 7 | 9 | 5 | 3 | 1 | 9 | 5 | 9 |

5
3547. All the other numbers have their digits in ascending order.

6
33 + 12 ÷ 3 x 10 – 7 = 143

7
19

8
28 ÷ 7 x 3 + 5 = 17

9
4. Each circle has a value of 2, each star a value of 3 and each triangle a value of 5, so four stars are needed to balance scale C.

2. Each star has a value of 1, each triangle a value of 3 and each circle a value of 6, so two circles are needed to balance scale C.

10
35 minutes

11

| | | 4 | 7 | 6 | 0 | 8 | | 6 | 1 | 1 | 2 | 5 | 2 | |
|---|---|---|---|---|---|---|---|---|---|---|---|---|---|---|
| 5 | 3 | 9 | | 4 | | 3 | | 2 | | 4 | | 1 | | |
| 9 | | 1 | 6 | 7 | 4 | 1 | | 8 | 0 | 9 | 8 | 6 | 0 | 4 |
| 0 | | 7 | | 4 | | 9 | | 4 | | 1 | | 4 | | 0 |
| 7 | 8 | 2 | 1 | | 3 | 7 | 3 | 7 | 3 | | 8 | 7 | 2 | 7 |
| 7 | | 8 | | 2 | | 4 | | 8 | | 2 | | 2 | | 5 |
| 5 | 7 | 5 | 3 | 7 | 6 | 5 | | 7 | 3 | 4 | 2 | 8 | 1 | 8 |
| | | | | 9 | | | | | | 3 | | | | |
| 9 | 2 | 1 | 5 | 9 | 4 | 4 | | 7 | 8 | 9 | 2 | 4 | 2 | 1 |
| 0 | | 8 | | 7 | | 3 | | 0 | | 3 | | 7 | | 9 |
| 2 | 9 | 0 | 4 | | 4 | 6 | 2 | 2 | 7 | | 5 | 9 | 4 | 1 |
| 4 | | 9 | | 9 | | 5 | | 4 | | 5 | | 2 | | 0 |
| 3 | 8 | 0 | 4 | 2 | 1 | 4 | | 2 | 0 | 8 | 2 | 9 | | 5 |
| | | 4 | | 1 | | 7 | | 6 | | 6 | | 4 | 9 | 3 |
| | 8 | 3 | 7 | 7 | 0 | 1 | | 7 | 5 | 3 | 5 | 4 | | |

12
In a 3x3 magic square, the central number is always one third of the magic number. Given that the central number was 3, the magic number (i.e. the number to which each row, column and diagonal must add up) must be 9. From here, it's easy to work out. Note the negative number in the right-hand column.

| 0 | 5 | 4 |
|---|---|---|
| 7 | 3 | -1 |
| 2 | 1 | 6 |

13
9 (each clock is set 1 hour 40 minutes earlier than the last one).

14
387. All the others can be paired off as they use the same three digits: 384/843, 481/148, 794/479, 296/926.

15

| 2 | + | 4 | – | 1 | x | 3 | = | 15 |
|---|---|---|---|---|---|---|---|---|
| + | | + | | + | | x | | |
| 1 | x | 3 | + | 2 | – | 4 | = | 1 |
| x | | – | | x | | + | | |
| 3 | – | 1 | x | 4 | + | 2 | = | 10 |
| – | | x | | – | | – | | |
| 4 | x | 2 | – | 3 | + | 1 | = | 6 |
| = | | = | | = | | = | | |
| 5 | | 12 | | 9 | | 13 | | |

16
10. BC=BD; By Pythagorus' theorem,
$26^2 = 24^2 + BC^2$
$676 = 576 + BC^2$
$100 = BC^2$,
$BC = \sqrt{100} = 10$

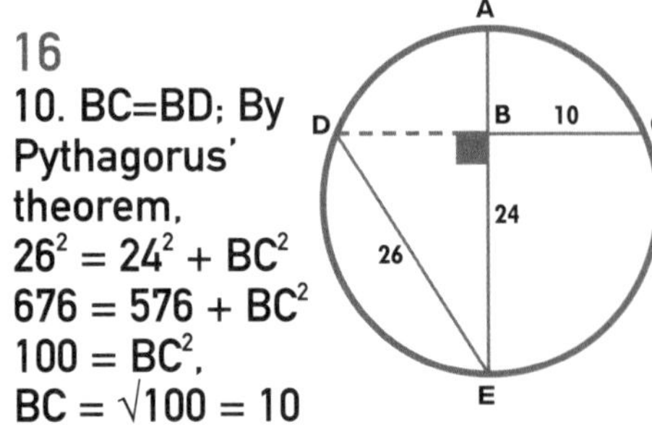


17
75%. $(\pi \times 10^2)$ minus $(\pi \times 5^2)$

18

19

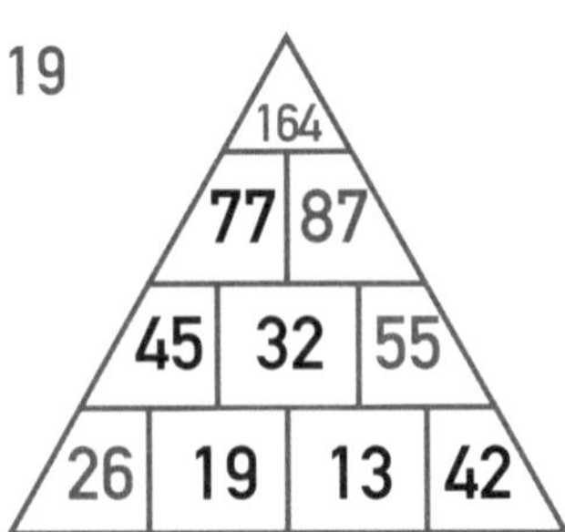


20
15. In each line, add the two figures at each side and divide by 2 to get the central figure. So (17 + 13) ÷ 2 = 15

21
Each consonant has a value of 6 and each vowel a value of 7, so England = 44.

22

| | | | | | |
|---|---|---|---|---|---|
| 7 | 2 | 9 | 4 | 3 | 6 |
| 2 | 8 | 1 | 3 | 5 | 4 |
| 9 | 1 | 7 | 5 | 8 | 2 |
| 4 | 3 | 5 | 9 | 2 | 7 |
| 3 | 5 | 8 | 2 | 1 | 3 |
| 6 | 4 | 2 | 7 | 3 | 8 |

23 The picture shows a television set.

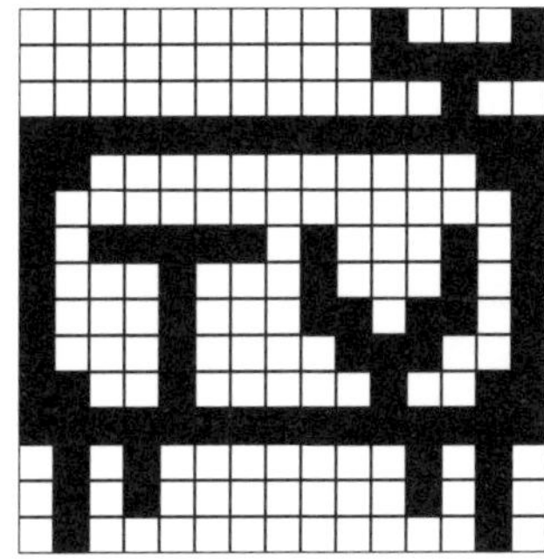

24
One-third. (Cylinder = $\pi r^2$ x 6r = $6\pi r^3$. Three spheres = $\frac{4}{3}\pi r^3$ x 3 = $4\pi r^3$. $\frac{4}{6} = \frac{1}{3}$.)

25
1080°. It can be worked out thus: divide the octagon into 8 triangles. In each the middle angle is 45°. The other two angles must then equal 135°. 135° x 8 = 1080°.

26
35 + 7 ÷ 14 + 4 = 7

27
84 months (or 7 years). This is because 84 is the lowest common multiple of 6 and 28 – i.e., the lowest number that both 6 and 28 divide into without remainder.

28
4. The numbers the hands point to on each face can be multiplied together to make 12 (12 x 1, 6 x 2, 4 x 3, 3 x 4).

29
75 – 12 ÷ 7 x 22 + 2 = 200

30

| | | | | | | | | |
|---|---|---|---|---|---|---|---|---|
| 7 | + | 1 | x | 3 | – | 4 | = | 20 |
| + | | + | | – | | x | | |
| 4 | x | 3 | – | 1 | + | 7 | = | 18 |
| x | | x | | x | | – | | |
| 1 | + | 7 | – | 4 | x | 3 | = | 12 |
| – | | – | | + | | + | | |
| 3 | x | 4 | – | 7 | + | 1 | = | 6 |
| = | | = | | = | | = | | |
| 8 | | 24 | | 15 | | 26 | | |

31
4. There are two alternating sequences: 10, 8, 6, 4 and 1, 3, 5 etc.

32

| | | | |
|---|---|---|---|
| **1** | **1089** | **8** | **88888** |
| **2** | **1998** | **9** | **995** |
| **3** | **3125** | **10** | **113** |
| **4** | **191** | **11** | **5808** |
| **5** | **1980** | **12** | **180** |
| **6** | **39483** | **13** | **1001** |
| **7** | **5929** | | |

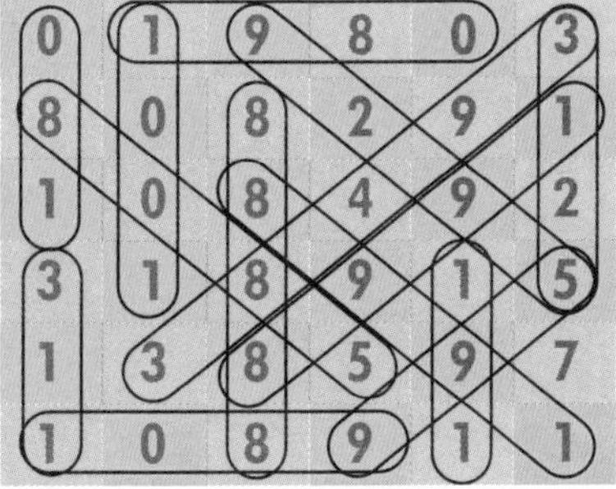

33
1 Degrees in three right angles 270
2 Years of marriage for a diamond anniversary 60
3 Isotope of uranium used in an atomic bomb 235
4 Minutes in a day 1440
5 Cost of the utility spaces in Monopoly 150
6 Number of the White House on Pennsylvania Avenue 1600
7 Age to which Methuselah lived 969
8 Number for a hurricane on the Beaufort Scale 12
9 Minutes of sound held on a standard CD 74
10 Chromosomes of a human being 46

34
The total number of spots on each domino increases in value by three each time, thus C is missing.

 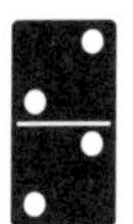 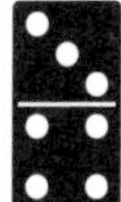 

35

36

| | | | | | |
|---|---|---|---|---|---|
| 1 | 2 | 3 | 2 | 3 | 1 |
| 2 | 1 | 1 | 3 | 2 | 3 |
| 3 | 1 | 1 | 3 | 2 | 2 |
| 2 | 3 | 3 | 2 | 1 | 1 |
| 3 | 2 | 2 | 1 | 1 | 3 |
| 1 | 3 | 2 | 1 | 3 | 2 |

37

| | | | | |
|---|---|---|---|---|
| 17 | 24 | 1 | 8 | 15 |
| 23 | 5 | 7 | 14 | 16 |
| 4 | 6 | 13 | 20 | 22 |
| 10 | 12 | 19 | 21 | 3 |
| 11 | 18 | 25 | 2 | 9 |

The top-right to bottom-left diagonal adds up to 90, while all the other lines add up to 65. To correct this, move the bottom two rows up to the top, and then move the left-hand column to the right. Note how this brings the middle number – 13 – into the central square.

38
ACROSS
The value of a club is one more than a heart (rows 3 and 4) and that of a spade is 4 more than a heart (2 and 3). Thus two diamonds + heart + heart + 1 = 39 (1), i.e., two diamonds + two hearts = 38, so diamond + heart = 19. Similarly (row 2) heart + 1 + diamond + two hearts + 8 = 44, i.e., three hearts + diamond = 35. Therefore two hearts = 35 – 19 = 16, so a heart is 8. Thus a diamond is 11. A spade = heart + 4 (above), so a spade is 12. A club = heart + 1 (above), so is 9.
Thus:
Heart = 8, club = 9, diamond = 11 and spade = 12.
DOWN
The value of a heart is 8 more than a spade (columns 2 and 3) and that of a diamond is 2 more than a spade (3 and 4). Thus (3) four spades + 10 = 46. So four spades = 36, so spade = 9. A heart = 17 (above). A diamond = 11 (above), so (1) a club = 10.
Thus:
Heart = 17, club = 10, diamond = 11 and spade = 9

39
19

40
2. Look at the numbers formed by the diagonals of the other two. 19 x 2 = 38, 12 x 2 = 24, 16 x 2 = 32

41

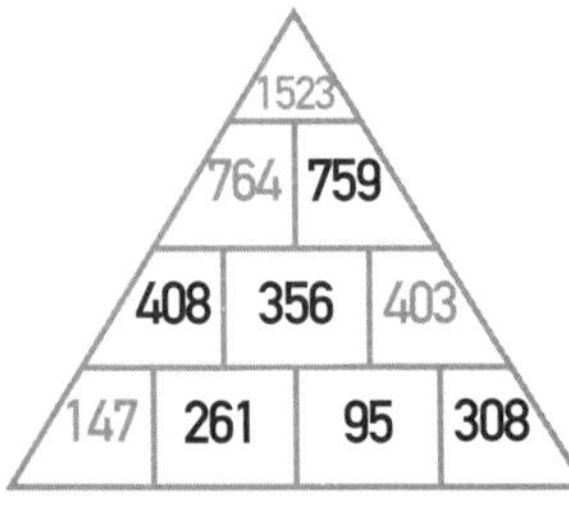


42
8. The number of the minute hand is twice that of the hour hand in each case.

43
76304. In all the others the number formed by the last three digits is the number formed by the first two digits multiplied by 3. In 76304, 76 x 4 = 304.

44

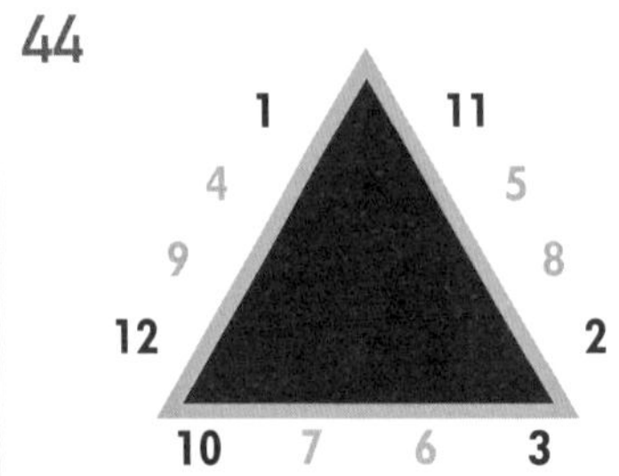


45

| | | | | | | | | | | | | | | |
|---|---|---|---|---|---|---|---|---|---|---|---|---|---|---|
| | | 8 | 4 | 2 | 0 | 7 | | 1 | 8 | 3 | 6 | 4 | 3 | |
| 6 | 9 | 8 | | 5 | | 8 | | 4 | | 7 | | 6 | | |
| 9 | | 2 | 1 | 8 | 5 | 8 | | 3 | 9 | 3 | 0 | 5 | 8 | 5 |
| 7 | | 2 | | 6 | | 7 | | 3 | | 5 | | 7 | | 9 |
| 8 | 6 | 0 | 3 | | 6 | 1 | 5 | 2 | 5 | | 4 | 5 | 8 | 4 |
| 3 | | 5 | | 8 | | 3 | | 3 | | 8 | | 4 | | 2 |
| 5 | 9 | 6 | 8 | 4 | 1 | 7 | | 1 | 7 | 9 | 0 | 2 | 4 | 1 |
| | | | | 7 | | | | | | 4 | | | | |
| 7 | 1 | 1 | 0 | 4 | 1 | 8 | | 1 | 7 | 5 | 8 | 1 | 0 | 5 |
| 2 | | 6 | | 7 | | 1 | | 5 | | 5 | | 5 | | 9 |
| 2 | 0 | 4 | 6 | | 8 | 4 | 4 | 7 | 1 | | 1 | 2 | 1 | 7 |
| 6 | | 8 | | 2 | | 1 | | 5 | | 3 | | 8 | | 0 |
| 3 | 0 | 5 | 9 | 2 | 3 | 6 | | 1 | 0 | 1 | 3 | 1 | | 9 |
| | | 6 | | 6 | | 0 | | 8 | | 6 | | 7 | 4 | 4 |
| | 9 | 4 | 8 | 8 | 6 | 1 | | 1 | 8 | 8 | 8 | 7 | | |

46
1 Points required to win a game of cribbage 121
2 Whole degrees C below zero of 'absolute zero' 273
3 Square yards in an acre 4840
4 Psalms in the Bible 150
5 Days of gestation for an average human baby 266
6 Beads in a rosary 165 (A)
7 The number in a great gross 1728 (B)
8 Spaces on a Go board 361
9 The year Theodore Roosevelt won the Nobel Peace Prize 1906
10 The year the prophet Muhammad died 632

Note A: 15 sets of ten Hail Marys, each separated by a Lord's Prayer.
Note B: A dozen gross = 12 x 144 = 1728.

47
10.75. Add 1, 1.5, 2, 2.5...

48
You win £53. You will always win the same number of units as the number of times that heads comes face-up in the sequence, providing the final toss is heads.

49

| | | | |
|---|---|---|---|
| 1 | 9999 | 8 | 1728 |
| 2 | 8000 | 9 | 3125 |
| 3 | 7744 | 10 | 1400 |
| 4 | 4884 | 11 | 9988 |
| 5 | 444 | 12 | 22000 |
| 6 | 9090 | 13 | 118120 |
| 7 | 202 | | |

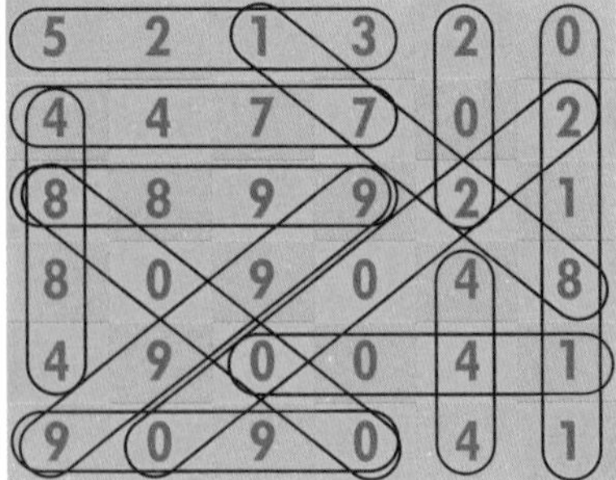


50
8 + 3 x 2 – 5 = 17
8 x 3 ÷ 2 + 5 = 17

51
You can solve this by trial and error, but the mathematical way goes like this: let the missing number be 'x'. Filling in the rest of the pyramid (see illustration) means that the top number must equal 2x + 21.
We know this is equal to 67, hence 2x = 67 – 21 = 46, so x = 23.

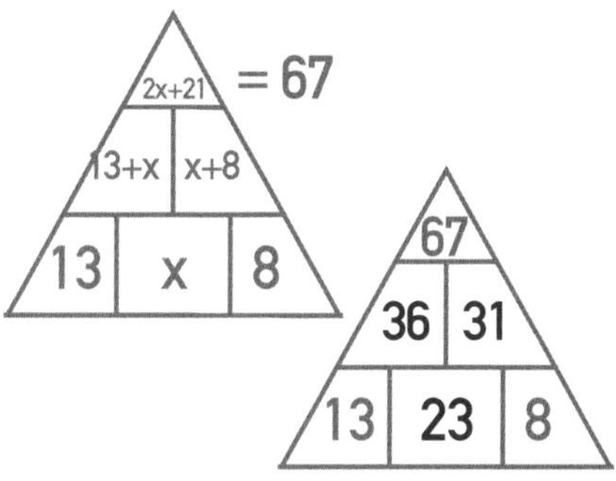


52 x = 1m

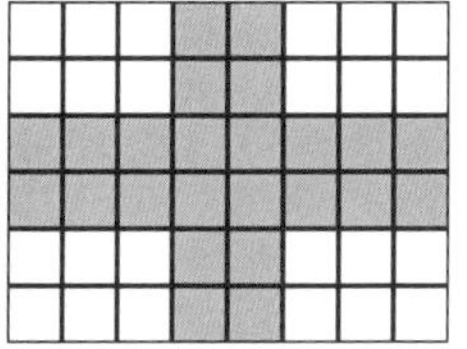

53
9. The total of each clock's hands follows the sequence 5, 10, 15, 20.

54
(10 x 7 x 5) + 9 = 359

55

| 8 | + | 3 | – | 7 | x | 5 | = | 20 |
|---|---|---|---|---|---|---|---|---|
| x | | + | | x | | x | | |
| 5 | x | 8 | + | 3 | – | 7 | = | 36 |
| + | | x | | + | | – | | |
| 7 | x | 5 | – | 8 | + | 3 | = | 30 |
| – | | – | | – | | + | | |
| 3 | + | 7 | x | 5 | – | 8 | = | 42 |
| = | | = | | = | | = | | |
| 44 | | 48 | | 24 | | 40 | | |

56

| 8 | 1 | 1 | 3 | 5 | 3 | 2 | 8 | 8 | 1 | 3 | 1 |
|---|---|---|---|---|---|---|---|---|---|---|---|
| 8 | 2 | 3 | 5 | 3 | 1 | 8 | 2 | 2 | 8 | 5 | 3 |
| 2 | 8 | 5 | 2 | 8 | 5 | 2 | 8 | 3 | **8** | 2 | 5 |
| 8 | 3 | 2 | 3 | 8 | 2 | 8 | 3 | **2** | 2 | 2 | 3 |
| 3 | 5 | 8 | 8 | 5 | 2 | 3 | **8** | 8 | 1 | 8 | 5 |
| 5 | 3 | 3 | 2 | 3 | 5 | **3** | 1 | 5 | 5 | 2 | 2 |
| 1 | 1 | 5 | 8 | 8 | **5** | 1 | 8 | 8 | 3 | 5 | 8 |
| 1 | 3 | 3 | 5 | **3** | 8 | 2 | 2 | 8 | 5 | 3 | 8 |
| 2 | 5 | 1 | **1** | 2 | 8 | 3 | 1 | 5 | 3 | 1 | 3 |
| 8 | 2 | 8 | 3 | 5 | 2 | 1 | 2 | 3 | 1 | 2 | 5 |
| 8 | 3 | 2 | 8 | 1 | 2 | 5 | 3 | 8 | 2 | 8 | 3 |
| 1 | 8 | 1 | 3 | 8 | 3 | 5 | 2 | 8 | 8 | 5 | 1 |

57
46. Take the last digit of each number and multiply the rest of the figure by it, and so on. So, 369 x 2 = 738, 73 x 8 = 584, 58 x 4 = 232, 23 x 2 = 46

58
Looking from top to bottom, 7 and 4. In each hexagon, starting in the top right section, pairs of numbers total the same. In the first hexagon they total 12, in the second 15, and in the third 18. So, 6 + 12, 14 + 4 and 11 + 7 all total 18.

59
1. The year (AD) when Roman emperor Claudius was poisoned 54
2. Warriors in Valhalla 800
3. Temperature at which paper catches fire, in degrees F 451*
4. Length of the Nile, in miles 4145
5. Nick Leeson's account number which caused Barings Bank to collapse 88888
6. Possible positions in a chess game, after Black's second move 71852
7. The year (AD) in which H.G. Wells's Time Machine arrives 802701
8. Length of Noah's Ark in cubits 300
9. Speed of light, in miles per second 186272
10. Elvis Presley's army serial number 53310761

* Hence the title *Fahrenheit 451*, a novel by Ray Bradbury

60
1. Seconds in November (2,592,000). There are 1,609,344 millimetres in a mile.
2. 22,500
3. 12
4. 177 (20 + 144 + 13)
5. –2
6. 4 years ago
7. 1, 2, 3
8. 2 (half a rabbit can't eat anything!)

61

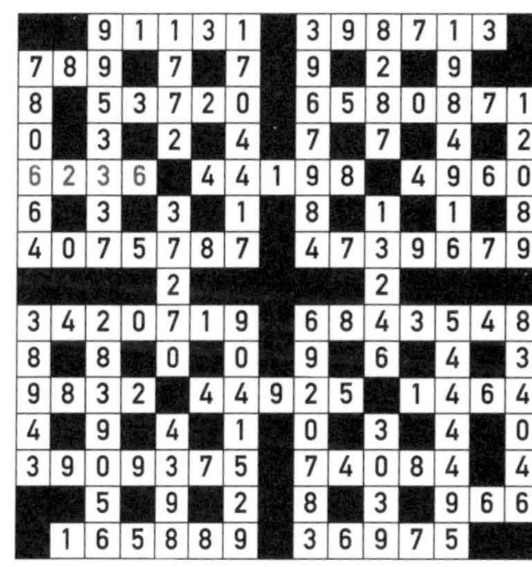

| | | 9 | 1 | 1 | 3 | 1 | | 3 | 9 | 8 | 7 | 1 | 3 | |
|---|---|---|---|---|---|---|---|---|---|---|---|---|---|---|
| 7 | 8 | 9 | | 7 | | 7 | | 9 | | 2 | | 9 | | |
| 8 | | 5 | 3 | 7 | 2 | 0 | | 6 | 5 | 8 | 0 | 8 | 7 | 1 |
| 0 | | 3 | | 2 | | 4 | | 7 | | 7 | | 4 | | 2 |
| 6 | 2 | 3 | 6 | | 4 | 4 | 1 | 9 | 8 | | 4 | 9 | 6 | 0 |
| 6 | | 3 | | 3 | | 1 | | 8 | | 1 | | 1 | | 8 |
| 4 | 0 | 7 | 5 | 7 | 8 | 7 | | 4 | 7 | 3 | 9 | 6 | 7 | 9 |
| | | | | 2 | | | | | | 2 | | | | |
| 3 | 4 | 2 | 0 | 7 | 1 | 9 | | 6 | 8 | 4 | 3 | 5 | 4 | 8 |
| 8 | | 8 | | 0 | | 0 | | 9 | | 6 | | 4 | | 3 |
| 9 | 8 | 3 | 2 | | 4 | 4 | 9 | 2 | 5 | | 1 | 4 | 6 | 4 |
| 4 | | 9 | | 4 | | 1 | | 0 | | 3 | | 4 | | 0 |
| 3 | 9 | 0 | 9 | 3 | 7 | 5 | | 7 | 4 | 0 | 8 | 4 | | 4 |
| | | 5 | | 9 | | 2 | | 8 | | 3 | | 9 | 6 | 6 |
| | 1 | 6 | 5 | 8 | 8 | 9 | | 3 | 6 | 9 | 7 | 5 | | |

62
In a 3x3 magic square, the central number is always one third of the magic number. Given that the magic number is 17, the central number must be 17 ÷ 3. From here, it's easy to fill out the rest.

| 10 | $^{2}/_{3}$ | $^{19}/_{3}$ |
|---|---|---|
| 2 | $^{17}/_{3}$ | $^{28}/_{3}$ |
| 5 | $^{32}/_{3}$ | $^{4}/_{3}$ |

63

64
1337. Multiply each number by 3 and subtract 1.

65
17

66
22½ months. In this time, A will have performed 3¾ orbits, while B will have done 1½ orbits.

67
177. The sequence is:
+1, –2, x3, ÷4, then repeat.

68
Each number's digits add up to 9, apart from 64 whose digits total 10. All, except 64, are also divisible by 6.

69
27 triangles (including one upside down). The total area of separate triangles would be 174 square metres.

70
67 x 18 ÷ 6 + 17 – 18 = 200

71
(8+3) x 7 + 4 x (8 + 3) = 891
or (8+4) x 7 – 3 x (8 + 3) = 891

72 Each row, column and main diagonal adds up to 111.

| 4 | **30** | 8 | 31 | **3** | 35 |
|---|---|---|---|---|---|
| 36 | **5** | 28 | **9** | 32 | **1** |
| **29** | 34 | **33** | 2 | **7** | 6 |
| **13** | 12 | **17** | 22 | **21** | **26** |
| 18 | **14** | 10 | **27** | 23 | **19** |
| **11** | **16** | **15** | 20 | **25** | 24 |

73
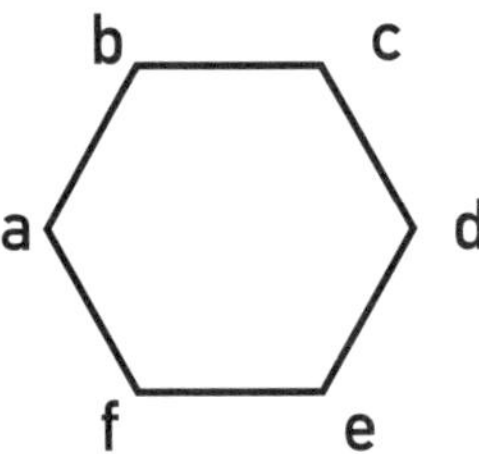


12. Take (a + b + c) and subtract (d + e + f) to get the number in the middle.

(6 + 17 + 10) = 33
– (15 + 9 + 2) = 26
7

(2 + 12 + 11) = 25
– (3 + 3 + 6) = 12
13

(7 + 8 + 9) = 24
– (2 + 9 + 1) = 12
12

74

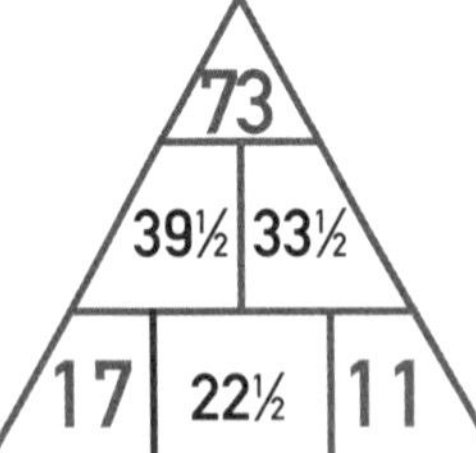


75
6. The hour hand expresses the number of letters in the number of the minute hand.

76
1 Patents filed by Thomas Edison 1093
2 Gestation of an African elephant, in days 660
3 Spots drawn by the animators for the Disney film of *101 Dalmatians* 6469952
4 Miles from Chicago to Hong Kong 8280
5 Sesame seeds on the average Big Mac bun 178
6 Number of different words used by Shakespeare 17677
7 Airports in the USA 13387
8 Diameter of the Pantheon in Rome, in feet 143
9 Population of Antarctica in summer 4115
10 Words in the King James Bible 773696

77
80°F

78
1⅞

79

| 4 | + | 9 | x | 5 | – | 3 | = | 62 |
|---|---|---|---|---|---|---|---|---|
| + | | – | | x | | + | | |
| 5 | – | 3 | + | 9 | x | 4 | = | 44 |
| – | | x | | + | | x | | |
| 3 | x | 5 | + | 4 | – | 9 | = | 10 |
| x | | + | | – | | – | | |
| 9 | – | 4 | + | 3 | x | 5 | = | 40 |
| = | | = | | = | | = | | |
| 54 | | 34 | | 46 | | 58 | | |

80
1 The Black Sea (the Red Sea is 453,000 km²)
2 4 + 4 + 4/4 = 9
3 252
4 11/60
5 159 (125 + 34 or 124 + 35)
6 39030915
7 28 (1 + 2 + 4 + 7 + 14 = 28)
8 £137 (£136.89)

81
115. Add the sum of the two digits of each number to that number in order to find the next number in the series. For example, 6 + 1 = 7, 61 + 7 = 68; 6 + 8 = 14, 68 + 14 = 82 etc.

82
From the diagram, we can see that 10 = 3 + 2X + Y, so 7 = 2X + Y. Also, 18 = 7 + X + 2Y, so 11 = X + 2Y. Adding those two equations together, we get 18 = 3X + 3Y, so 6 = X + Y. From the pyramid, the central block on row 2 is X + Y, so 6. Therefore Y + 7 = 12, so Y = 5, therefore X = 1. It is now easy to fill in the rest of the pyramid.

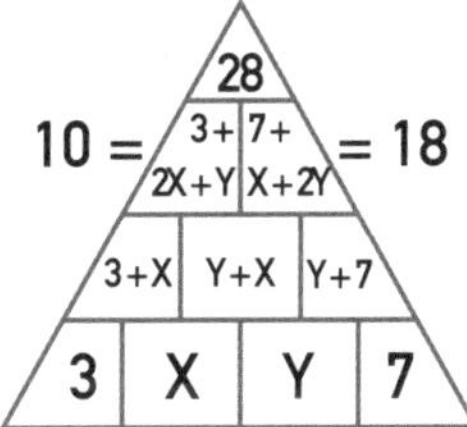


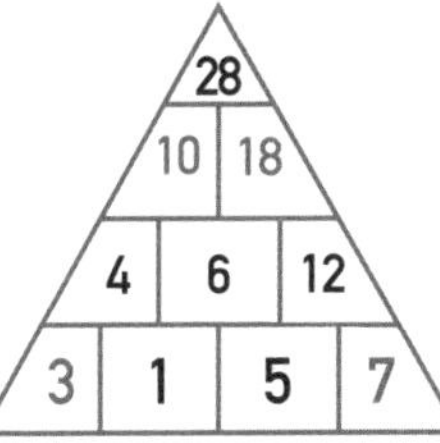


83

84
13

85

| | | | | | |
|---|---|---|---|---|---|
| 1 | 2 | 5 | 4 | 3 | 6 |
| 2 | 5 | 3 | 1 | 6 | 4 |
| 5 | 3 | 4 | 6 | 1 | 2 |
| 4 | 1 | 6 | 5 | 2 | 3 |
| 3 | 6 | 1 | 2 | 4 | 5 |
| 6 | 4 | 2 | 3 | 5 | 1 |

86
$14\frac{1}{4}$. There are two series:
($-\frac{3}{4}$) 16, $15\frac{1}{4}$, $14\frac{1}{4}$, $13\frac{3}{4}$
($-2\frac{1}{4}$) 21, $18\frac{3}{4}$, $16\frac{1}{2}$, $14\frac{1}{4}$

87
41. The others are square numbers: 52, 62, 72, 82, 92.

88 The picture shows a kangaroo.

89 The picture shows a woman with a pram.

1

1 *The Old Curiosity Shop*
2 Björk
3 Texas
4 Blue, green, indigo, orange, red, violet, yellow
5 Calista Flockhart
6 Buzz Aldrin
7 Claude Monet
8 Anti-lock braking system
9 American football
10 Captain Corelli's
11 Fashion design
12 1929
13 Derek Jacobi
14 Captain Lawrence Oates
15 Helen Fielding
16 Eurythmics
17 Trigger
18 Stephen Fry
19 Drachma
20 The flag of the European Union
21 Exodus
22 James Cameron
23 Digital versatile disc
24 The fox
25 Grosvenor Square
26 Gail Platt
27 Elvis Costello
28 *Macbeth*
29 112
30 Ken Loach

2

1 Rocco John Ritchie
2 Warwickshire
3 Bob Kiley
4 Pizza Hut
5 Jack Higgins
6 Sacha Baron Cohen
7 Dr John Reid MP
8 Sharon Stone
9 Coldplay
10 West Ham United
11 An Enigma code machine
12 Foot and mouth disease
13 Tom Cruise
14 Delia Smith
15 Bertrand Delanoë

3

| | | |
|---|---|---|
| 1 b | 5 c | 9 b |
| 2 d | 6 a | 10 c |
| 3 d | 7 b | 11 a |
| 4 b | 8 a | 12 c |

4

1 *Born to Do It*
2 Twix
3 Nick Hornby
4 Athens
5 Galapagos
6 Kidderminster Harriers
7 *The Sopranos*
8 Vojislav Kostunica
9 Ben Elton
10 He was selling them by the pound (not the kilogram)
11 Congo
12 Jonathan Pryce
13 Wycombe Wanderers
14 Ariel Sharon
15 Napster

5

| | | |
|---|---|---|
| 1 b | 5 c | 9 c |
| 2 a | 6 d | 10 c |
| 3 d | 7 a | 11 d |
| 4 c | 8 b | 12 a |

6

Correct versions of false statements:

- The first Boeing 747 flight was in February 1969
- On a suit of armour, the gorget protected the neck
- Pink Lady cocktails are made from egg white and grenadine
- Coryza is another term for the common cold
- St Matthew is the patron saint of tax collectors
- Pluto's only natural satellite is called Charon
- Methane is otherwise known as marsh gas
- Joe Loss's signature tune was 'In the Mood'

Unused false answers:

- Terpsichore was the Greek Muse of song and dance
- Calvados is an apple-flavoured brandy
- The national airline of Paraguay is LAP

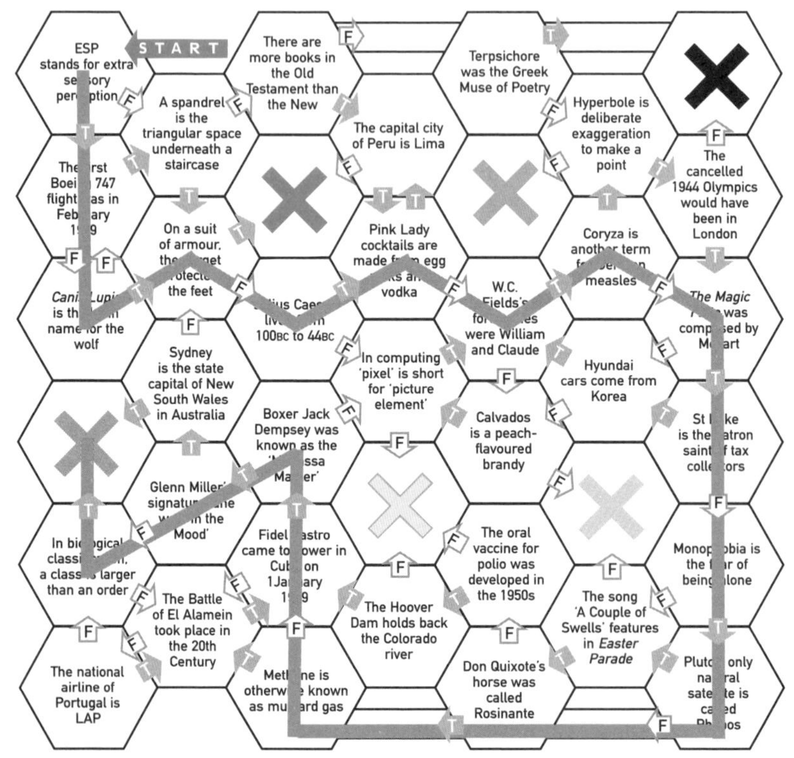

7

1 False (it's 8 pints or 5 litres)
2 True
3 False (though it's eight times as common in men)
4 False (it's the windpipe)
5 False (it's the shinbone)
6 True
7 False
8 True
9 True (it is odourless until bacteria act on it)
10 True

8

1 False (they are potatoes)
2 True
3 True
4 False
5 True
6 False (it is made with spinach)
7 True
8 False (it is the Gamay grape)
9 False (it was the Chinese gooseberry)
10 False (it is made in Italy)

9

1 True
2 False (he executed only two of them)
3 True
4 True
5 False (her name was Alexandrina Victoria)
6 True
7 False (six on her left hand, five on her right)
8 True

10

1 False (it's from Charlotte Brontë's *Jane Eyre*)
2 True
3 False (*Alice's Adventures in Wonderland* came out in 1865, and *Through the Looking Glass* was published in 1871)
4 True
5 False (Tennyson wrote 'never to have *loved* at all'; the parody was by Samuel Butler)
6 False (the first line of *Twelfth Night*)
7 True
8 True

11

The combination is 87.
Correct versions of the false statements:
E The White and Blue Niles meet at Khartoum
H Chives, garlic and onions all belong to the lily family
K It takes 23 seconds for the blood of a human being to circulate once
N Moscow stands on the Moskva river

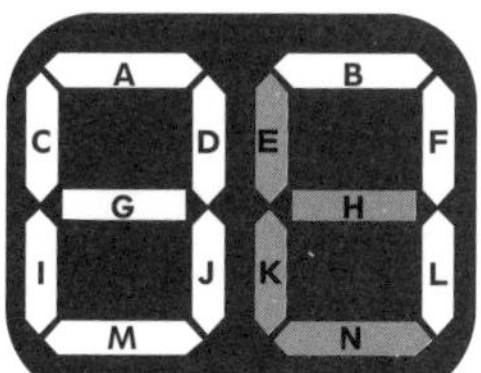


12

The combination is 45.
Correct versions of the false statements:
A The lowest region of the atmosphere is the troposphere
F *The X Files* TV series was created by Chris Carter
I The lowest vertebra in the human body is the coccyx
K On TV, Ed Asner played the role of Lou Grant
M Narita Airport is found in Tokyo

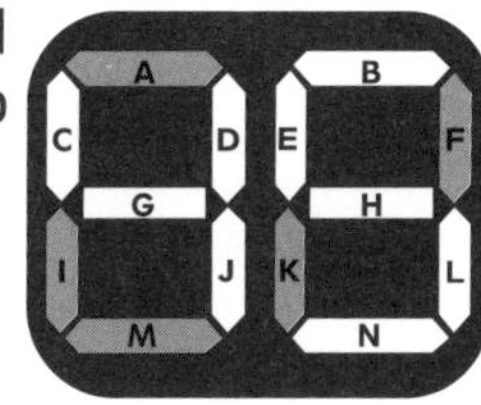


13

| | | |
|---|---|---|
| 1 c | 5 a | 9 d |
| 2 b | 6 b | 10 d |
| 3 d | 7 a | 11 b |
| 4 b | 8 c | 12 c |

14

| | | |
|---|---|---|
| 1 b | 5 a | 9 b |
| 2 c | 6 c | 10 d |
| 3 d | 7 d | 11 a |
| 4 b | 8 a | 12 c |

15

| | | |
|---|---|---|
| 1 a | 5 b | 9 b |
| 2 b | 6 a | 10 a |
| 3 c | 7 b | |
| 4 a | 8 d | |

16

| | | |
|---|---|---|
| 1 c | 5 b | 9 c |
| 2 b | 6 d | 10 b |
| 3 a | 7 b | 11 a |
| 4 a | 8 d | 12 a |

17

| | | |
|---|---|---|
| 1 b | 6 b | 11 b |
| 2 c | 7 c | 12 c |
| 3 d | 8 a | 13 d |
| 4 a | 9 d | 14 a |
| 5 c | 10 c | 15 a |

18

Said by Steve Martin at the 2001 Oscars ceremony.

| | | | | | | | | | | | | | |
|---|---|---|---|---|---|---|---|---|---|---|---|---|---|
| | H | O | S | T | I | N | G | | T | H | E | | O |
| S | C | A | R | S | | I | S | | L | I | K | E | |
| M | A | K | I | N | G | | L | O | V | E | | T | O |
| | A | | B | E | A | U | T | I | F | U | L | | W |
| O | M | A | N | | I | T' | S | | O | N | L | Y | |
| S | O | M | E | T | H | I | N | G | | I | | G | E |
| T | | T | O | | D | O | | W | H | E | N | | B |
| I | L | L | Y | | C | R | Y | S | T | A | L | | I |
| S | | O | U | T | | O | F | | T | O | W | N | |

A High treason
B Kicks
C Legislation
D Moves
E Snows
F Youthful
G Abomination
H Well-worn
I Toys
J Bloodiest
K Touching
L Legitimate
M Fatty

19
1 Loch Lomond
2 Carlisle
3 Severn, Thames, Clyde, Avon
4 Co. Donegal (Malin Head)
5 Cathedrals
6 Birmingham
7 Essex
8 Temple Meads
9 Republic of Ireland
10 Grampians
11 Wiltshire
12 The Menai Strait
13 Swindon
14 Derwentwater
15 Leeds and Liverpool Canal

20
1 Asia, Africa, North America, South America, Antarctica, Europe, Australasia
2 Indian Ocean
3 Florence
4 St Lucia (it's one of the Windward Islands)
5 Potomac
6 Austria (Österreich)
7 Tanzania
8 New York–Seattle (3862km/2400 miles), Sydney–Perth (3288km/2043 miles), London–Moscow (2496km/1551 miles)
9 Maine, New Hampshire, Vermont, Connecticut, Rhode Island, Massachusetts
10 Mount Everest
11 Australia
12 One
13 USA (Hawaii)
14 The Bahamas
15 Mongolia (Ulan Bator)

21
1 Butterfly
2 Sled dog racing
3 Ed Moses
4 Sabre, épée and foil
5 Rod Laver
6 Archery (he makes arrows)
7 Rally driving
8 Fencing and riding
9 French (Philippe Sella)
10 Clay, grass and hard
11 Speed skating
12 Saints, Bengals and Browns
13 Argentina
14 Badminton
15 Badminton

22
1 8
2 16
3 $4^1/_2$
4 3
5 3 inches
6 170
7 9
8 5
9 15
10 6
11 7
12 408 metres
13 8 seconds
14 16
15 6 feet 9 inches

23
1 Beautiful singing (meaning a full, rich tone)
2 Benjamin Britten
3 Grammy awards
4 Rossini's *William Tell*
5 The World Cup finals in Italy, 1990
6 Whipped
7 The Metropolitan, New York
8 Isadora Duncan
9 A national anthem
10 Mozart
11 Dame Nellie Melba
12 Placido Domingo
13 Napoleon Bonaparte
14 Violin
15 British

24
The combination is 39.
Correct versions of the false statements:

C The Beatles' first US record label was Capitol
I 'American Pie' is a song about the death of Buddy Holly
K The term 'heavy metal' comes from the William Burroughs novel *Naked Lunch*

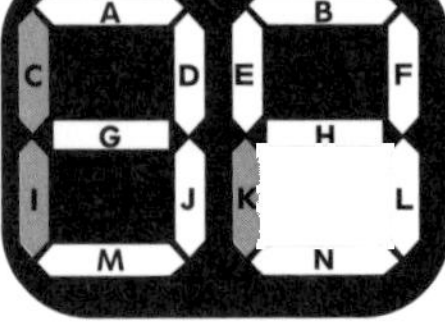


25
The combination is 63.
Correct versions of the false statements:

D Duke Ellington led a band at New York's Cotton Club during the 1920s
E Saxophonist Paul Desmond composed the jazz standard 'Take Five'
K Zoot Sims and Stan Getz played the tenor saxophone

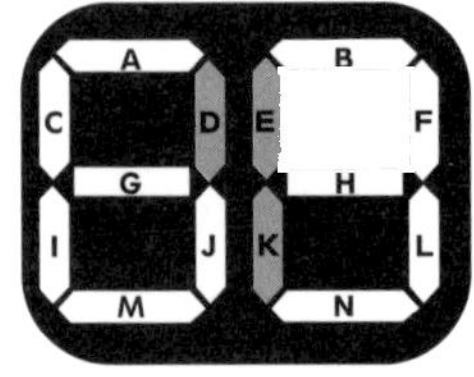


26
1 A Pianola
2 Antonio
3 Drumstick
4 Harpsichord
5 Steinway
6 Panpipes
7 Flageolet
8 Bronze or brass
9 Harp
10 An organ
11 Glockenspiel
12 Bugle

13 Big Ben
14 Jimi Hendrix
15 Tuba

27
1 Harp
2 Didgeridoo
3 New Orleans
4 Edith Piaf
5 Maracas
6 Mexico
7 Ravi Shankar
8 Sitar
9 Accordion
10 Three
11 Flamenco
12 The Folies-Bergère
13 Bagpipes
14 Trinidad
15 Conch

28
1 Rolf Harris (with 'Two Little Boys' in 1969)
2 The Gibb brothers (The Bee Gees)
3 'Dancing Queen'
4 Natalie
5 *The Bodyguard*
6 Sweden
7 Ringo Starr
8 1964
9 'Moon River'
10 Benny Goodman, clarinet
11 *Dark Side of the Moon* (Pink Floyd)
12 *For Your Eyes Only*
13 'Kiss'
14 Step on it
15 Mel G (Gulzar)

29 A connects with D
B connects with E
C connects with F

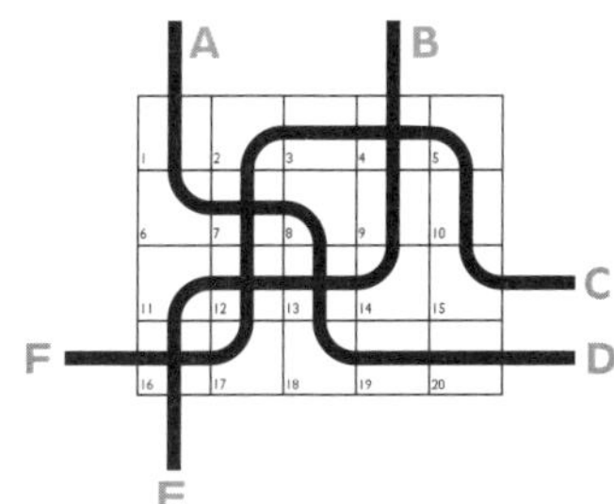


30
1 Carbon
2 She was the first sheep created by cloning technology
3 Ernest Rutherford
4 It's a bone in the forearm
5 Because the salt in seawater makes it heavier and better able to support objects
6 Dr Christiaan Barnard
7 *Destiny*
8 Because sound waves bounce off hard surfaces such as bare walls and floors but are absorbed by soft items, such as furnishing fabrics
9 Measuring the height of tall objects
10 Incandescence means glowing with heat. Phosphorescence means emission of light without burning or heat
11 Hydrogen and helium
12 John Boyd Dunlop
13 Argon
14 *Enterprise*, after the starship in the television series *Star Trek*
15 That the person is asleep

31
1 No two individuals have exactly the same pattern
2 70–75 per cent
3 Because their favourite food, shrimps, contain carotene that gives them their distinctive colour
4 A marsupial (not a bear)
5 Albino
6 A pod
7 The mudskipper – it can get oxygen from air as well as water and uses its fins as legs
8 Cinchona bark, from the 'fever tree' of South America, whose active ingredient is quinine
9 They act as a form of camouflage, reflecting light like a mirror and making it harder for underwater predators to spot the fish
10 Their tongues
11 The shark
12 A type of deer or elk found in North America
13 They must remain constantly in motion to avoid sinking to the bottom of the sea
14 Formic acid
15 The hummingbird

32
1 *Madame Bovary*
2 Colin Creevey
3 *Sense and Sensibility*
4 Daisy
5 *Danny the Champion of the World*
6 *Slow Waltz in Cedar Bend*
7 *Bonfire of the Vanities* by Tom Wolfe
8 Erich Maria Remarque
9 He was imprisoned in Auschwitz
10 Ruth Rendell
11 *The Magus* by John Fowles
12 *Robinson Crusoe*
13 V.S. Naipaul
14 Milan Kundera
15 He was excommunicated as an atheist

33
1 Hamlet
2 'The Jumblies'
3 Homer
4 Beatrice
5 Harold Pinter
6 The 'Nibelungenlied'
7 Dorothy Parker
8 Nijinsky

9 David Lean
10 'The Lady of Shalott'
11 Bertolt Brecht
12 'The Vedas'
13 The Nobel Prize for literature (1913)
14 Because he was involved with the Irish Republican Army (IRA)
15 They both trained as doctors

## 34

1 E.H. Shepard
2 A wall painting made on fresh plaster
3 Auguste
4 Impressionism
5 Sandro Botticelli
6 Pablo Picasso
7 Norman Rockwell
8 Henry VIII
9 M.C. Escher
10 The Medici family
11 Salvador Dalì
12 *David* (based on the biblical figure who killed the giant Goliath with a stone from a sling)
13 Claude Monet
14 Paul Gauguin
15 Giuseppe Arcimboldo

## 35

The combination is 74. Correct versions of the false statements:

B A bound volume of literary work can be termed a 'codex'
C In Australia, a 'jumbuck' is slang for a sheep
G The title of C.S. Forester's *The African Queen* refers to a boat
I In 'The Owl and the Pussy Cat', the wedding ring costs one shilling
K *La Stampa* is the name of an Italian newspaper
M A Japanese haiku poem contains 17 syllables
N Sherlock Holmes's brother is called Mycroft

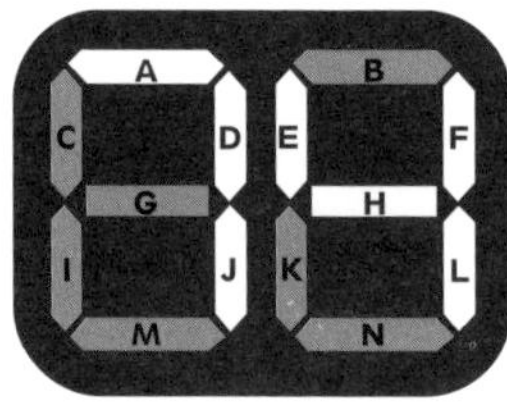


## 36

The combination is 20. Correct versions of the false statements:

C The Gutenberg Bible is the most valuable book
H A palimpsest is a manuscript written on re-used vellum
J According to the nursery rhyme, Thursday's child has far to go

## 37

1 Alexander the Great
2 Buddha
3 The Samurai
4 Boadicea (also called Boudicca)
5 The monster devoured them
6 Nothing – they ran naked
7 The Vikings
8 Canopic jars
9 Mark Antony and Cleopatra (defeated by Octavian, Caesar's heir)
10 Mongolia
11 Gilgamesh
12 A type of dagger carried by Roman foot-soldiers
13 The Minoans (in Crete)
14 The Phoenicians (in what is now Lebanon)
15 The Aztecs

## 38

1 King William I
2 The Bastille
3 The Taj Mahal
4 Henry Morton Stanley
5 Gold
6 Sir Stamford Raffles
7 The Battle of Gettysburg
8 The English
9 Napoleon Bonaparte
10 The United States of America
11 'Fat boy'
12 Battle of Wounded Knee
13 Set up a trade union
14 Che Guevara
15 Ian Smith in Rhodesia

## 39

1 1980
2 The 1970s
3 1981 (for *On Golden Pond*)
4 1980
5 The 1970s (1979)
6 The 1900s (1909)
7 1929
8 1990
9 1982
10 The 1980s
11 1974
12 1962
13 1942
14 The 1920s
15 The 1880s (1889)

## 40

1 *The Phantom Menace*
2 'The Pi'
3 Cruella De Vil
4 An orang-utan
5 *East of Eden*
6 Raymond
7 *The Color of Money*
8 Baseball
9 A steel-rimmed hat
10 *Good Will Hunting*
11 Sports agent
12 Patrick Swayze
13 A child's sled
14 Bill Clinton
15 'Friendship'

## 41

1 Dead men
2 Ray Liotta
3 *Never Say Never Again*
4 Ingrid Bergman

5 Marilyn Monroe (from Norma Jean Baker)
6 Cameron Diaz
7 Marcel Marceau
8 Robert Downey Jr
9 Bruce Willis
10 Simon Callow
11 *Shakespeare In Love*
12 Cary Grant (born Archibald Leach)
13 Batman
14 Archery
15 Tin Cup

## 42

1 *The Flintstones*
2 Laura Palmer
3 Columbo
4 Norm
5 *Happy Days*
6 The Biscuit
7 Simon Groom
8 Rimmer
9 *M*A*S*H*
10 Alaska
11 Brady
12 *The Dukes of Hazzard*
13 Animal
14 Festive Road
15 'I Could Be So Good for You'

## 43

1 Constance
2 Sam Wanamaker
3 Trevor Bayliss
4 Desdemona
5 She threw herself under the king's racehorse at the Epsom Derby
6 Six
7 Joseph Stalin
8 *Book at Bedtime*
9 Chatsworth
10 James Joyce
11 Estonia
12 Jane Russell
13 Robert Maxwell
14 The Granny Smith apple
15 P.D. James

## 44

1 The Doors
2 Alan Clark
3 Purple
4 John Nash
5 South Africa
6 Flying doctor
7 William Blake
8 *Carmen*
9 Houston, Texas
10 Force 8
11 Greg Dyke
12 Battle of the Nile
13 Ecuador
14 Sheep
15 Nike

## 45

1 Seaweed
2 'Come On'
3 It uses all the digits once, arranged in alphabetical order
4 Ronald Reagan
5 116 years
6 Ethiopia
7 Lord Byron
8 *Back to the Future*
9 6 inches
10 Irving Berlin
11 Bertrand Piccard, Brian Jones
12 Albert
13 Carmelites
14 William Wordsworth
15 Worstead (which gave us the name worsted)

## 46

You may have noticed that all the red herrings began with the word 'no'.

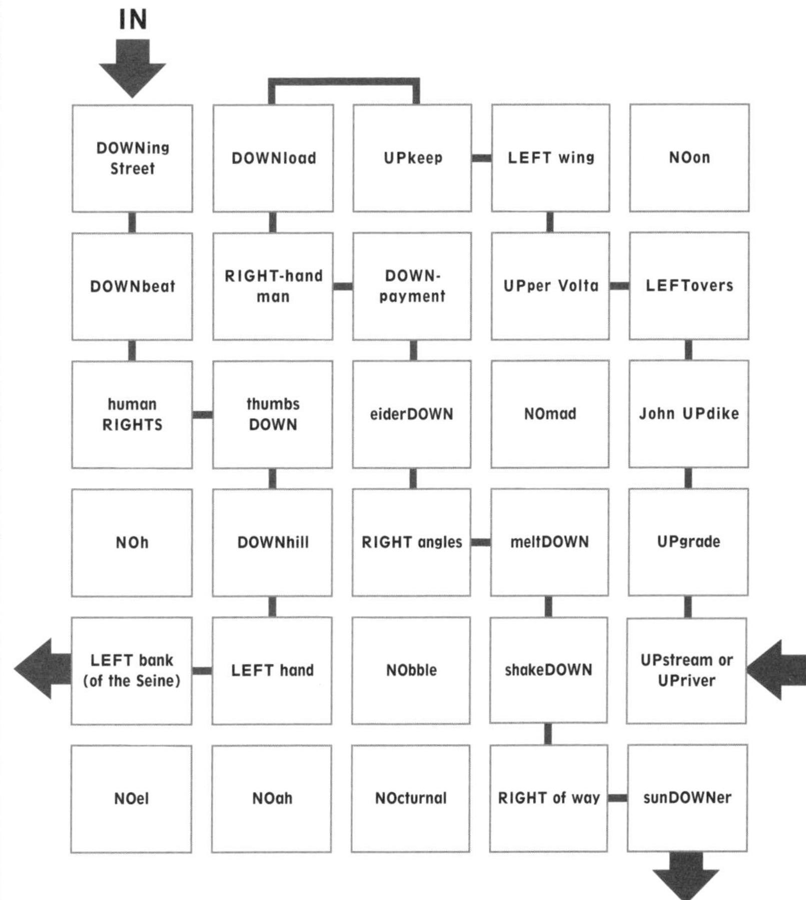

1

2

D

Each line has one blue, one grey and one black shape; one square, one pentagon and one triangle; one X, one Y and one Z. It is therefore possible to work out that D is the missing shape.

3

44% is yellow, 56% is white

4

B. There are three types of arrows being repeated in sequence. Every second arrow points upwards.

5

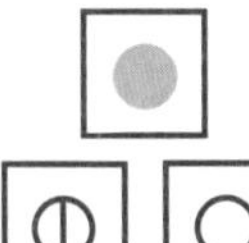

A. The square in the middle goes to the top of the pyramid. The remaining two squares remain at the bottom but swap over.

6

7

1 Yes
2 Yes
3 Yes
4 No, the last one is smaller
5 No, a merlin is a bird
6 No, green should be black
7 No, there is a J missing
8 Yes

8 The completed puzzle reveals a wine bottle and glasses.

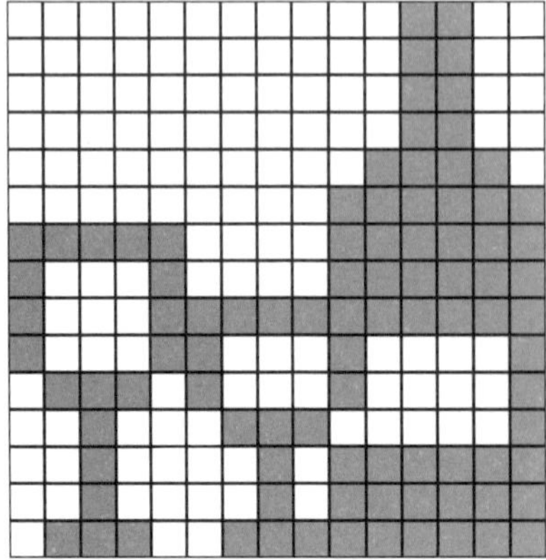

9

Here, '3R4' means 'push crate number 3 four spaces to the right'. The individual moves for the sokoban himself have not been listed, but the crate moves given at the top of the next column are possible.

The first few moves are very important. Push 4R1 (crate 4 right one space), then 2D1, then 3R1 and finally 1R1. From here you can push 5 out. You now have a gap between each pair of crates (1 and 2, 3 and 6, 4 and 7) and it's easy to push them out from there.

10

Here's one possible solution.

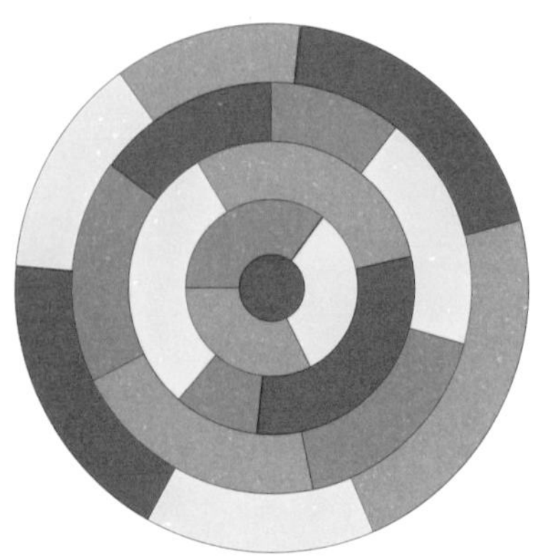

11

A The Capitol, Washington, DC
B St Basil's Cathedral, Moscow
C The Millennium Dome, London
D Dome of the Rock, Jerusalem

12

1. Five. 2. A lamp. 3. On the man in the painting behind the statue on the right.
4. Between a bird and an elephant on top of the dresser. 5. A clock, on the chair. 6. The glass-enclosed one on top of the dresser.
7. On the arm of the chair.
8. Three-quarters – three out of four. 9. Three. 10. To the extreme bottom right of the picture.

13
One solution is as follows:

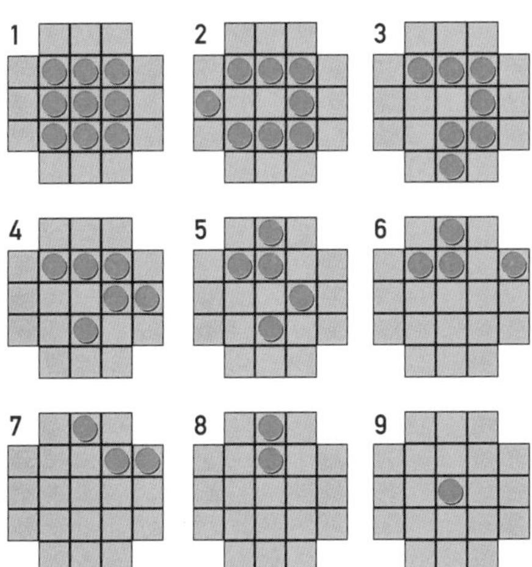


14
D. The total number of spots on each domino reduces in value by one each time, thus D is the missing one:

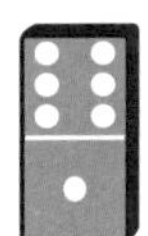
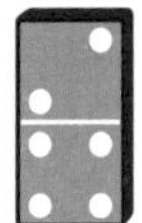
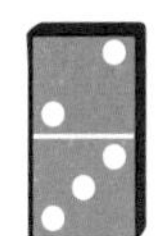

15
4 revolutions. To solve this type of puzzle you must find the lowest common multiple, i.e. the smallest number into which all the numbers of cog teeth can be divided. The answer is this number divided by the number of teeth on the largest cog.

To find the lowest common multiple, list all the prime factors of each number.

Thus:
27 = 3 x 3 x 3
18 = (3 x 3) x 2
9 = (3 x 3)
4 = (2) x 2

Eliminating prime factors that are duplicated (shown in the brackets above) leaves 3 x 3 x 3 x 2 x 2 = 108, which is the lowest number into which 27, 18, 9 and 4 can all be divided. Divide 108 by 27 for the answer, 4.

16

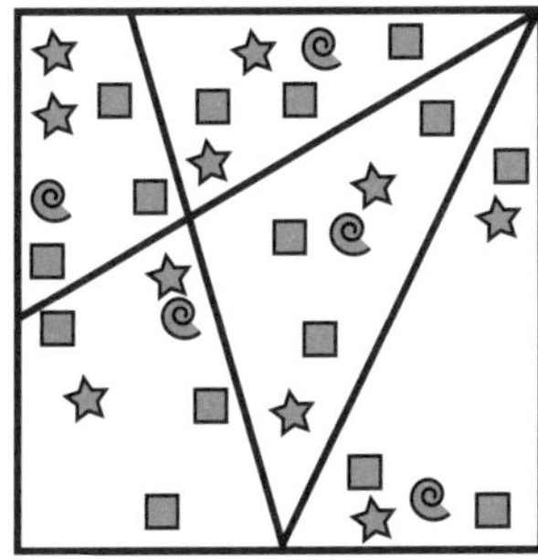

17
Cube D

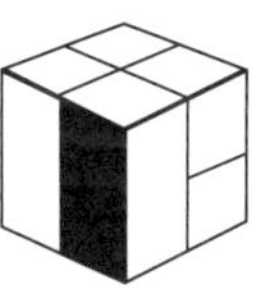

18
C and D are the same

19
1 Yes
2 Yes: Cairo, Copenhagen, Cardiff and Canberra
3 No, RSVP is French
4 No
5 Yes
6 No, it spells OSO
7 Yes: Germany, Britain, Spain and Italy
8 No. 40 is shorter

20
The arrangement now spells aitch in Morse code (taking the boxes as dots and the double boxes as dashes).

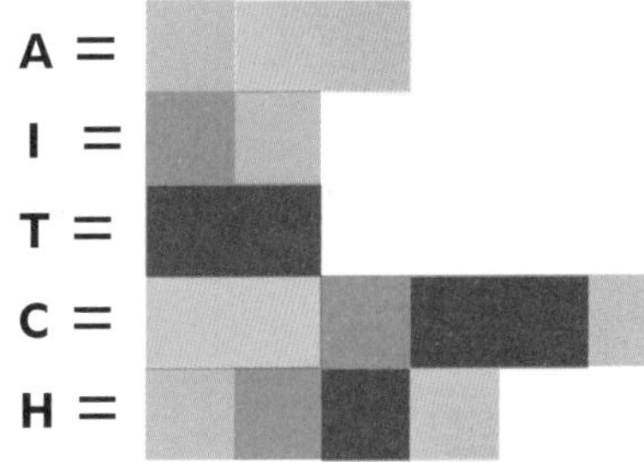


21
E is different

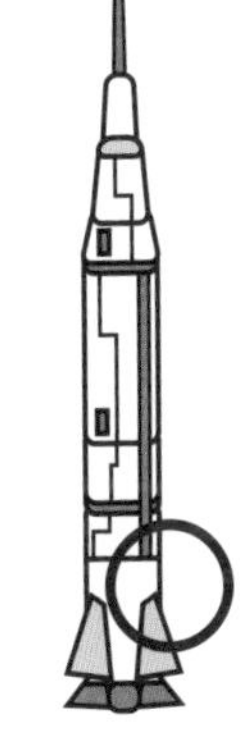

22
A and C, thus:

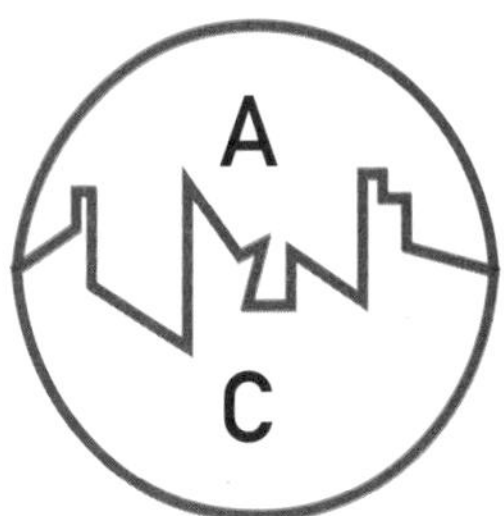


23 The completed puzzle shows a candle and holder.

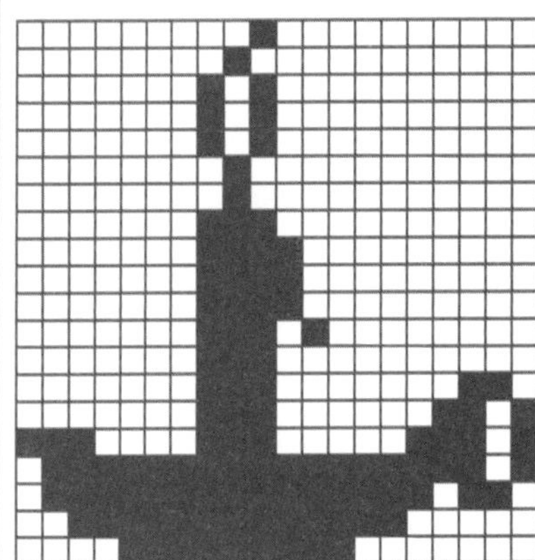

24
40. Each dice has a total of 21 spots. We can see 23 spots, so there are 63 – 23 = 40 hidden from view.

25
19 triangles

26
One-third is shaded

27

28
B. Each line has a blue, a black and a white outer circle; a blue, a black and a white middle circle; and a small black and a small white inner circle (with one shape having no inner circle). The missing shape must therefore have a blue outer circle, a blue middle circle (since no other middle circles are showing in the third row it follows that the first must be black and the second white) and no inner circle, hence B.

29
The forty-ninth Parallel. The forty-ninth pair of lines in the 49 squares are the only pair of lines that are parallel.

30
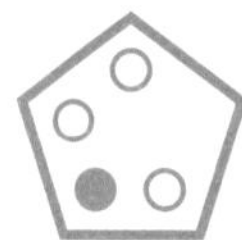
B. Only when the same coloured dot appears twice (not once or three times) in the same position in the previous three pentagons is it carried forward to the final pentagon.

31
Here, '3R4' would mean 'push crate number 3 four spaces to the right'. The individual moves for the sokoban himself have not been listed, but the crate moves given below are possible.

First, 1R1 followed by 4L1 and U3. Now we need to make room via 7R1, 6R1 and 5L1. Now 4D4 then R4 and out. Crates 3, 1 and 2 are pushed out in similar ways. 5L2 then U3 then D4 then L4 and out. Similarly for 6 and 7.

32
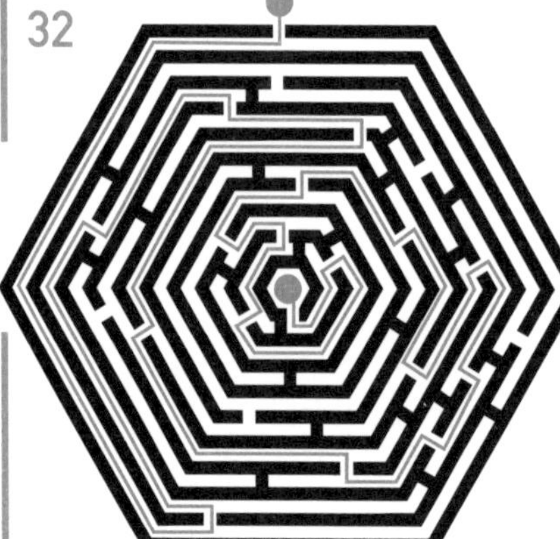

33
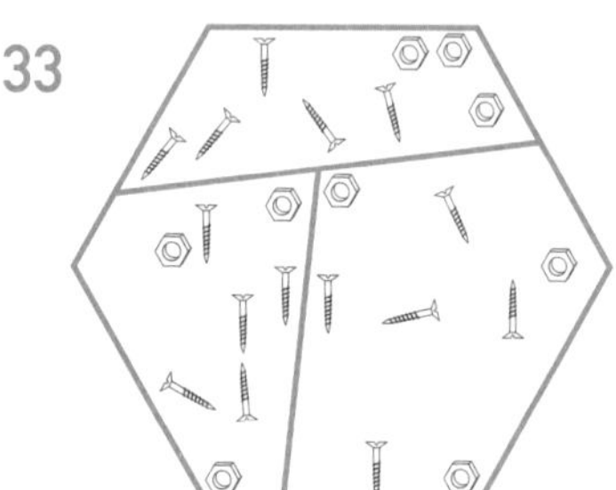

34
D is the odd one out.

35
1 Triangle
2 Pentagon
3 Three
4 Eight
5 Four
6 Nine
7 Circle
8 19

36

C. The dot moves one corner clockwise at each stage, while the circle moves two places anti-clockwise.

37
The missing domino is B – they all have even numbers of spots.

38
5 revolutions. Find the lowest common multiple of all the numbers (in this case 140), then divide that number by the number of teeth in the largest cog to get the number of revolutions, in this case 5. For a fuller method, see answer 15, page 329.

39
Here's one possible solution:

40
B and E

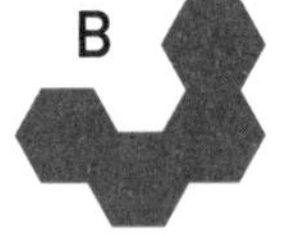

41
Each of the images contains the word 'tin' (fire ex*tin*guisher, knit*tin*g needle, valen*tin*e and s*tin*gray.) 'K*nittin*g' contains it twice, once backwards.

42
Cube A

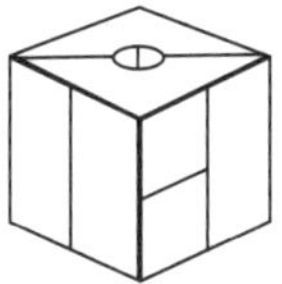

43
C is different because the visible spots on two adjacent sides add up to 7. On all standard dice, the spots on opposite sides add up to 7.

44
91. $(1^2 + 2^2 + 3^2 + 4^2 + 5^2 + 6^2)$

45

A. In each case the sequence contains a black and a blue circle, and a black and a blue square. These move about at random.

46
Here 'R' means right, 'L' means left, 'U' means up and 'D' means down. So '7U4' means push piece 7 up 4 places.

To start, push 7U4, 4L1, 2U1, 3D1, then 6 can be forced out by pushing from the left.

It's now easy to push 5 and 3 out. To get 7 out, push it down four spaces, go the long way around and push it from the left and out. A similar trick is used for 2 and 4. Use the trick again for crate 1, although that uses the left-hand intersection instead.

47
40% is blue, 60% is white

48
4 revolutions. Find the lowest common multiple of all the numbers (204), then divide that number by the largest number of teeth. This gives 4 revolutions. For a fuller method, see answer 15, page 329.

49

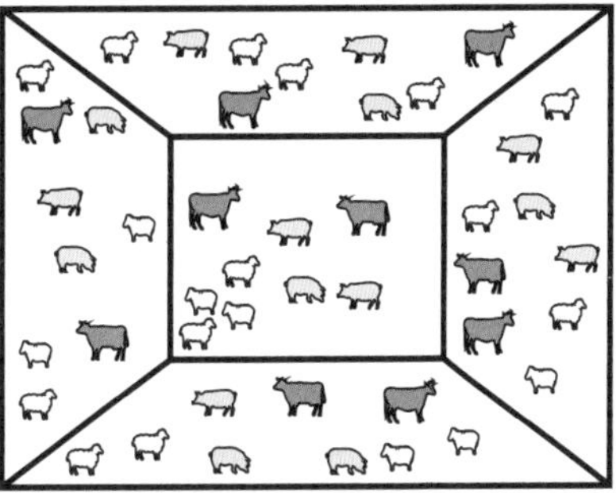

50 The picture reveals a skull and crossbones.

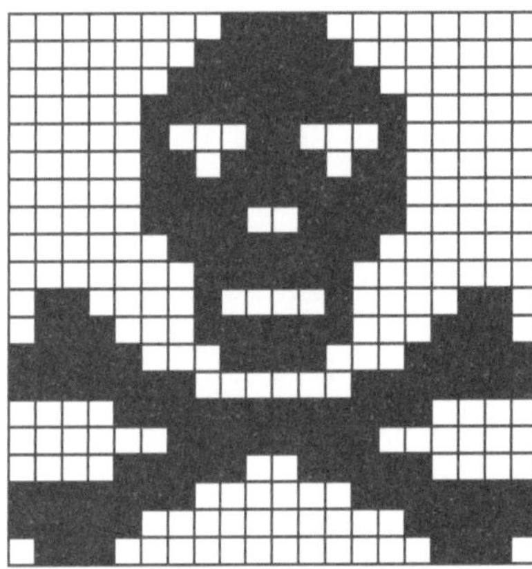

51
Take away any one of the three safety matches. Since the two remaining ones will be identical, they too will be a match.

52
Miss Flannel should buy C and E.

53

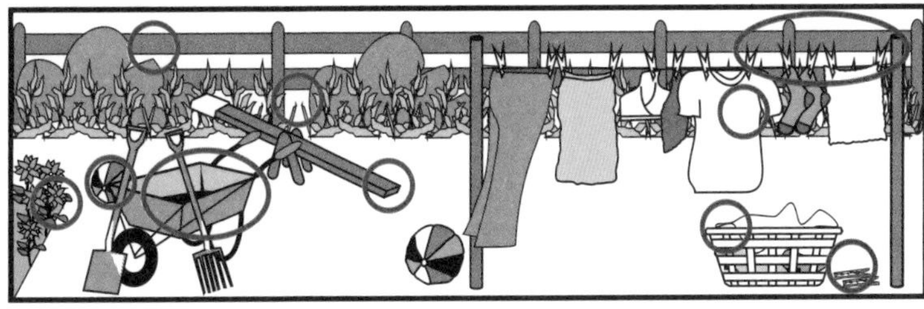

54
Take the first dice, the 3, as an example. Because opposite faces always add up to 7, you know that 4 is on the opposite face. Thus the four numbers on a quarter turn away from the 3 are 1, 2, 5 and 6. The same is similar for the other two dice. So the options are: (1, 2, 5 or 6) + (1, 3, 4 or 6) x (2, 3, 4 or 5) = 12

By considering each combination in turn, we find that there are four solutions, as follows:

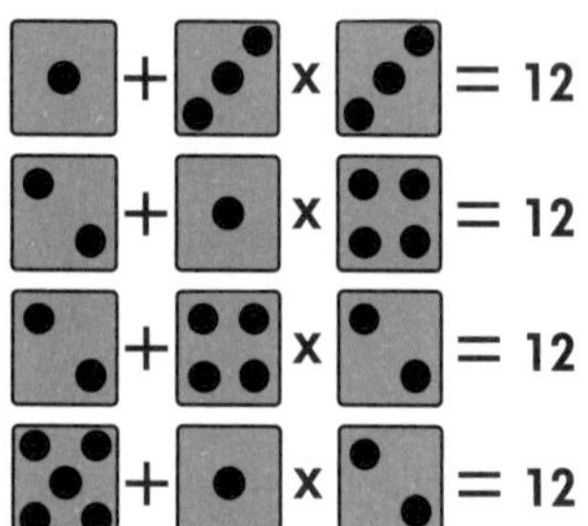


55
1 No, 13. 2 Yes. 3 No, Texas is on the coast of the Gulf of Mexico. 4 No, you have 21. 5 No. 6 No, the 305 is a French Peugeot. 7 Yes. 8 No, a basketball team has only five players.

56

D. The yellow circle moves 90° clockwise, the pale blue circle 135° clockwise.

57
The whole puzzle is the odd one out. The letters are an anagram of OUTSIDER, a synonym for misfit or odd one out.

58

D. Each line has no hankie, blue hankie, white hankie; no buttons, one button, two buttons; no collar, blue collar, white collar. From that we can work out that D is the missing shape.

59
C is odd, since A is a mirror image of D, and B is a mirror image of E.

60
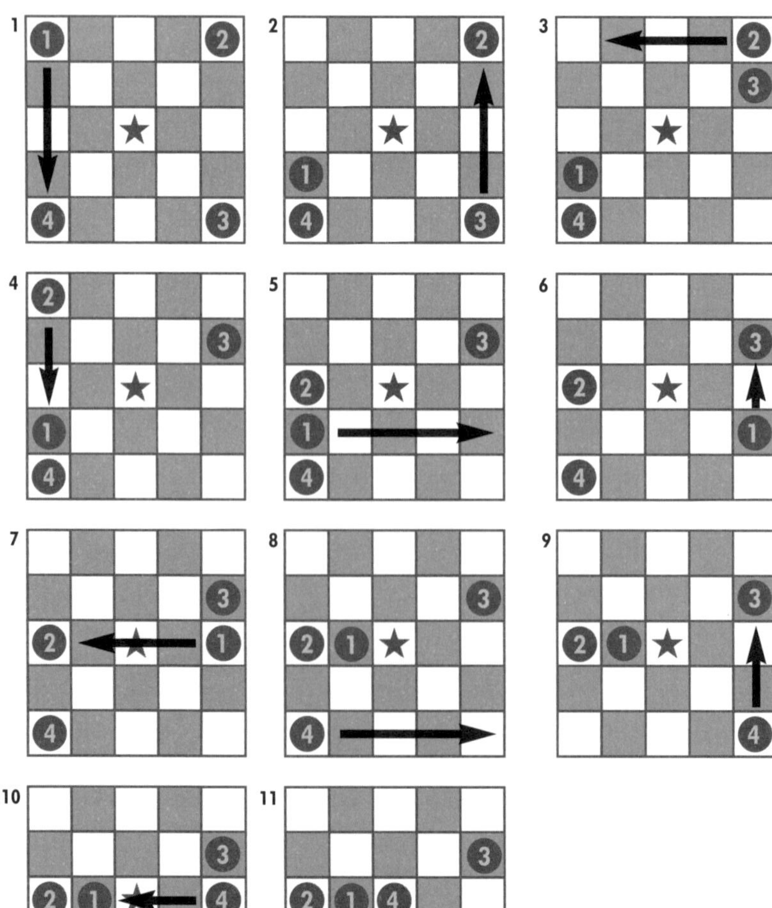


61
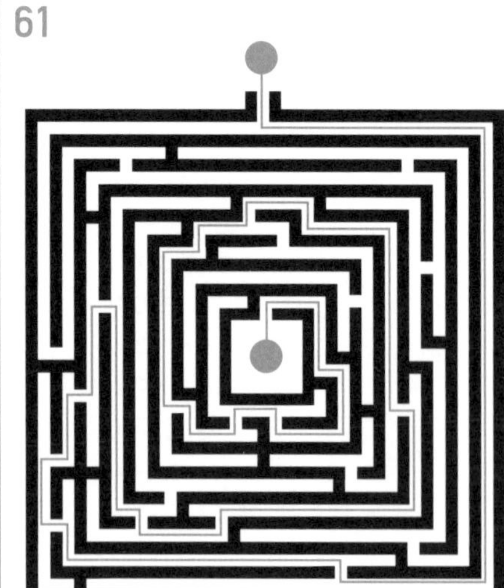

62

C. Each line has a light blue, a darker blue and a black square; a black face, a darker blue face and a white face in some order. In the bottom row the darker blue square must have a darker blue face on it as it isn't showing, leaving a black face on the black square as the only possible solution, which is C.

63

D and G, thus:

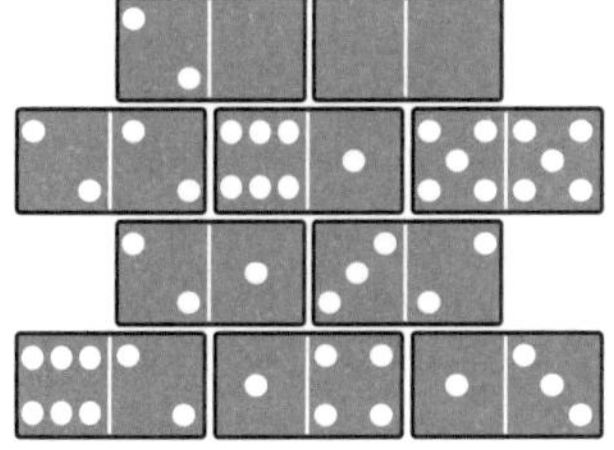


64

65

1 Rectangle
2 Two
3 Triangle
4 Semi-circle
5 Square
6 Triangle
7 Star
8 None

66

C. The trick is to close up the vertical gaps between the top group of shapes and the bottom shapes to get the words 'tilt' and 'lilt'.

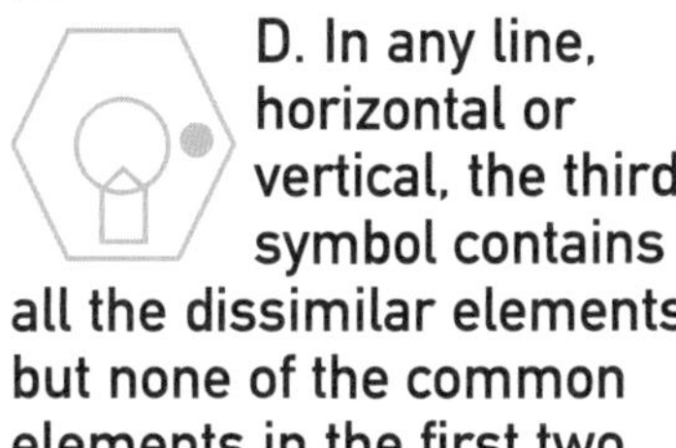

67

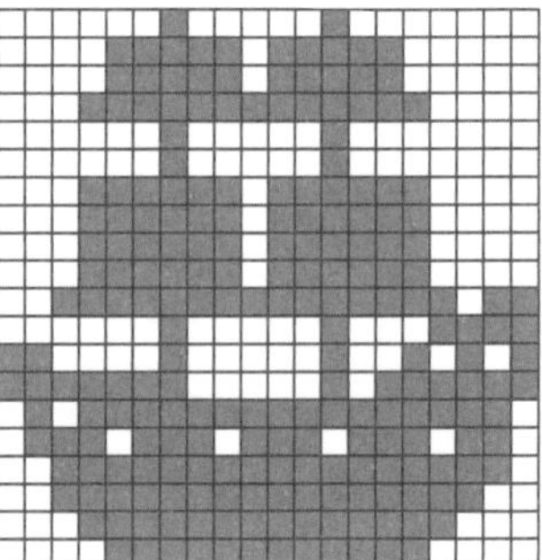

D. In any line, horizontal or vertical, the third symbol contains all the dissimilar elements, but none of the common elements in the first two.

68

Replace 1s and 10s with letters to get this phrase. Jones the tenor's tone was often softened by honey.

69

70 revolutions. Find the lowest common multiple of all the numbers (1330) together and divide by the largest number of teeth to get the answer, 70. See answer 15, page 329, for a fuller method.

70 A boat is revealed.

71

F is the odd one out, since each of the orange segments moves one space clockwise of the previously lettered arrangement, but the orange segments on F move one space anti-clockwise of the arrangement on A.

72

I will be at the chalet. The number indicates the position of the letter in the word 'white' or 'black'. So, for example, a '3' in a white circle is the letter 'i', a '1' in a white circle is the letter 'w' etc., giving the answer.

73

1 No, vanity isn't. 2 Yes. 3 No, the second one is Pisces, the fishes. The others are Taurus (bull), Aries (ram) and Gemini (twins), which do have four legs. 4 Yes. 5 No. The fourth symbol is percentage (the others are at, asterisk, ampersand (or and)). 6 No. 7 Yes: Austin, Albany, Atlanta, Augusta. 8 Yes: Gold, Silver, Copper and Iron.

74

One possible solution is:

75

'R' means move right etc., so '3R1' means move number 3 one place to the right, and '8D1' means move number 8 down one place.

Push 3R1, then 5 out. This allows 3D1 and out. Also, 8 D1 and out.

Now a crucial move: 10U1, which allows 11 out then 9 out. Now move 7R2, U3, D1 and out.

Another important move: 4R1 allows you to push 6D1 (from above) and out.

Now 10L1, go all the way around the top for 10D1 and out. Finally, push 1D4 and out, and do the similar thing for 2 and 4. Finished!

76
13

77
The value of the missing domino is 0-0. The total number of spots on every domino is the value of the total numbers of spots on the two dominoes immediately beneath it.

78
A and F are identical.

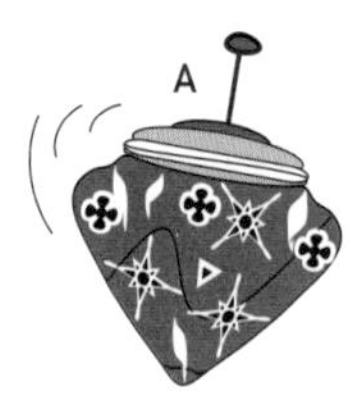

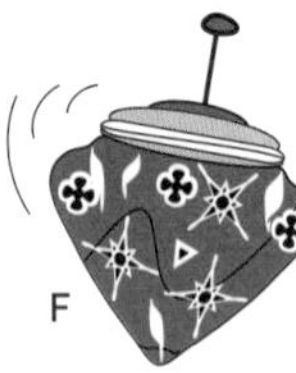


79
27

80
Cube D

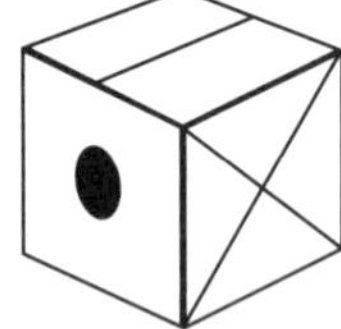

81

82

83
Rendezvous. Replace every number in the bottom half of the shape with the French for that number, e.g., trois for 3, deux for 2 etc. The number in the top half of the shape indicates the position of the letter in the word, so 2/3 indicates the second letter of trois (R) etc.

84
E.

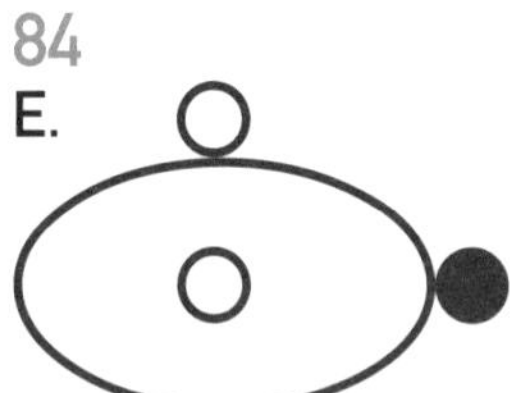

The shape changes either from flat to standing or vice versa; the spot in the middle changes colour, the spot on the top stays the same; the spot on the side stays the same but moves to the opposite side.

85

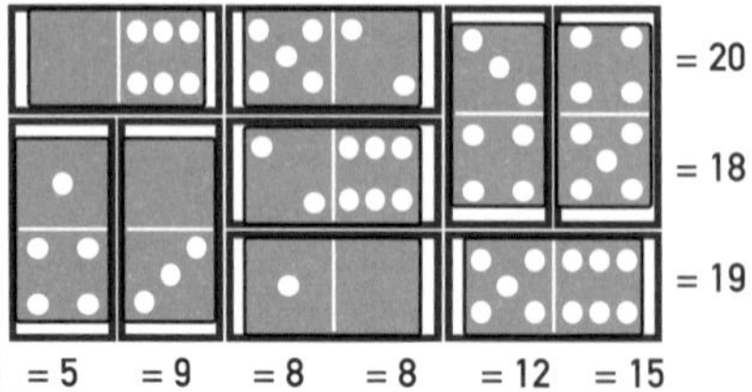


86
B and F.
Rotate B by 90 degrees anti-clockwise and F by 90 degrees clockwise.

87

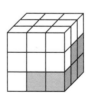

B. Each line contains a light blue, a dark blue and a grey box. Inside the box there's always a white Q, a light blue Q and a black Q; and inside these there's always an upright blue question mark, an upright white question mark or an upside-down white question mark. Thus we can work out that B is the missing shape.

88
E

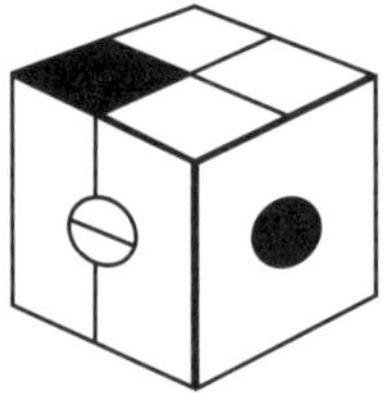

89
There are nine differences between the two pictures, as shown.

1
Feeble

2

| T | A | L | E |
|---|---|---|---|
| A | R | I | D |
| L | I | N | G |
| E | D | G | E |

3
Accidental

4
Ant (pageant and anthem).

5
Botany

6
Brainwave is the only word in which a letter (a) is repeated.

7
KERCA = creak

8
Whoever bet on Leveller won £5 (clue 4), so whoever bet on Champion won £9 (clue 1) and whoever bet on Deliberator won £10.
 Kathleen who backed Post Pipper won £14 and whoever bet on Showman won £6 (3). Deliberator ran in the 4pm race (1). No horse ran at 3.30 (grid), so Arthur's, which ran half an hour later than Roger's (2), didn't run at 4pm. Thus Arthur didn't bet on Deliberator (1), so Arthur didn't win £10 (above). Thus (2) Arthur won £9 and Roger won £5.
 Deliberator wasn't backed by Frank (5), so must have been backed by Debbie. Frank backed Showman. Since Debbie's horse ran at 4pm, the person whose horse ran at 4.30 isn't Arthur or Roger (2) or Frank (5), so must be Kathleen.
 The one whose horse ran at 2pm isn't Arthur (2) or Frank (5), so must be Roger.
 Arthur's ran at 2.30 (2), so Frank's must have run at 3pm.

Thus:
Arthur – Champion – 2.30pm – £9;
Debbie – Deliberator – 4pm – £10;
Frank – Showman – 3pm – £6;
Kathleen – Post Pipper – 4.30pm – £14;
Roger – Leveller – 2pm – £5.

9
Mosaic

10
A Hot
B Hire
C Seedy
D Dream
E Exams
F Crowd
G Thoughts
H Approach

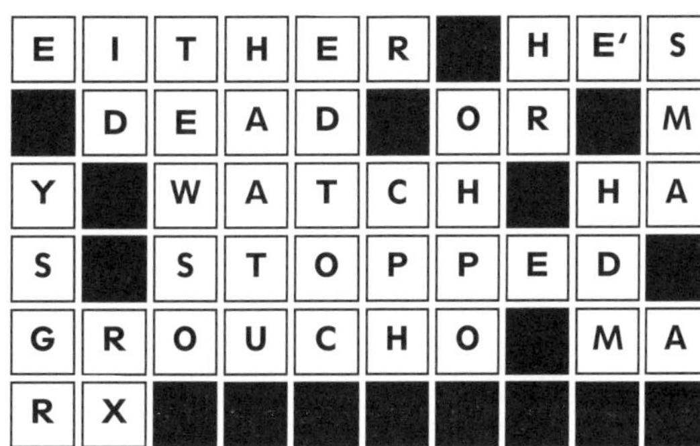

E I T H E R H E' S
D E A D O R M
Y W A T C H H A
S S T O P P E D
G R O U C H O M A
R X


11
Possible answers include:

AIR
ALERT
ALIEN
ARC
ARE
ART
CERTAIN
CERTAINLY
ERA
ICE
ITALY
LATIN
LAY
LIE
LINE
LIT
LITRE
NICE
NICELY
NICER
RAIL
RAIN
RAT
RAY
RECITAL
RELAY
RELY
RICE
TAIL
TALE
TAR
TIE
TILE
TIN
TIRE
TRAIL
TRAIN
TRAY
TRIAL

12

| | | | | | | |
|---|---|---|---|---|---|---|
| 1 | P | E | R | M | I | T |
| 2 | O | R | N | A | T | E |
| 3 | P | A | L | A | C | E |
| 4 | U | M | P | I | R | E |
| 5 | L | A | T | E | L | Y |
| 6 | A | N | T | L | E | R |
| 7 | T | H | R | I | L | L |
| 8 | I | M | P | E | D | E |
| 9 | O | P | P | O | S | E |
| 10 | N | E | A | R | B | Y |

13

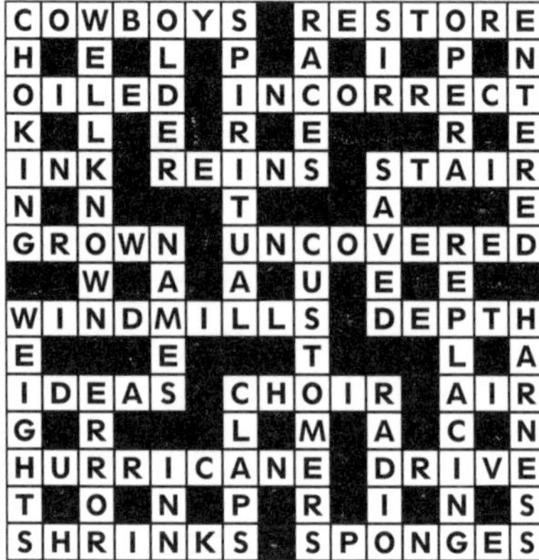


14

Large dish

15

Steady

16

| T | O | U | C | A | N | P | L | B | H | C | N | I | F |
|---|---|---|---|---|---|---|---|---|---|---|---|---|---|
| O | R | A | N | G | E | V | A | E | L | G | A | E | N |
| R | A | Q | W | S | M | T | R | K | F | J | W | C | T |
| R | Z | H | U | D | U | C | K | L | X | V | S | Y | U |
| A | G | E | L | O | Y | P | J | I | B | O | V | E | T |
| P | L | A | X | V | U | W | A | K | W | S | T | E | R |
| R | U | Q | T | E | R | N | M | L | Z | I | X | S | P |
| D | E | V | Y | L | G | Q | I | O | W | P | R | E | Y |
| L | H | J | F | N | K | O | U | R | N | D | A | J | B |
| W | N | C | H | E | L | U | O | I | O | X | V | N | C |
| A | S | J | W | H | A | B | N | S | R | D | E | F | M |
| C | L | A | R | J | I | O | Y | N | E | C | N | V | N |
| A | O | Y | H | N | R | Q | Z | L | H | K | L | O | B |
| M | Z | C | B | K | S | H | A | U | T | Z | V | B | C |

17

WARM

WARD

CARD

CORD

COLD

18

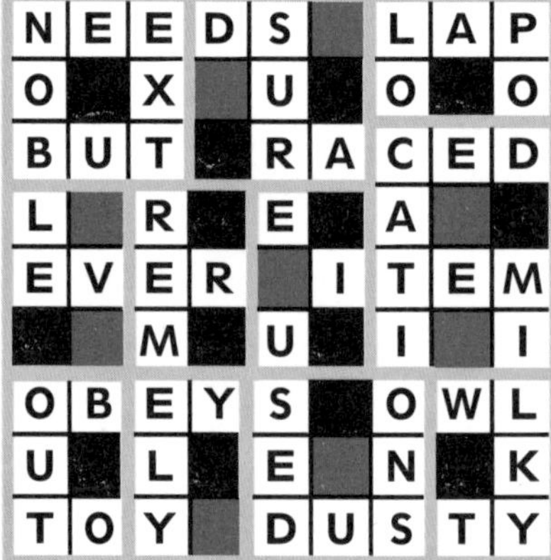


19

Double

20

14-letter word: cinematography.

21

Scientific equipment APPARATUS
Blown spheres BUBBLES
It preys on your mind CONSCIENCE
United we stand, ___ we fall DIVIDED
St _____, US hospital drama ELSEWHERE
The golden anniversary FIFTIETH
Swimmers wear them GOGGLES
A vital statistic HEIGHT
Type of police parade IDENTIFICATION
A feeling of envy JEALOUSY
Rap with the knuckles KNOCK
Without exaggeration LITERALLY
Embalmed body MUMMY
A golfer's favourite hole? NINETEENTH
The other side OPPOSITION
Marionette PUPPET
In a line, like its five vowels? QUEUEING
Store of water RESERVOIR
Don't run with them SCISSORS
You go to a doctor for it TREATMENT
That's odd UNUSUAL
Clear in the memory VIVID
Native American dwelling WIGWAM
Newton-John's favourite disco XANADU
The day before YESTERDAY
Jagged line ZIGZAG

22

Diane lives at (odd-numbered) either No 17 or No 21 (clue 2), so her husband is neither Andrew nor Fred (clue 1), each of whom either lives at No 10 or is Barbara's husband. Diane's husband isn't Samuel or Martin (2), so must be William. They didn't move in on Friday (2).

The man who moved in on Friday isn't Andrew (1), Samuel (2) or Fred (4), so must be Martin.

Since William/Diane live at either No 17 or No 21 (2), Lucy and her husband live at No 14 (3). Thus Lucy's husband isn't Andrew or Fred (1) or Martin (2), so must be Samuel. Samuel didn't move in on Thursday (2), so the couple at No 17 moved in on Thursday (5).

Martin doesn't live at No 10 (1). William/Diane didn't move in on Monday (2), so it must have been Tuesday (3) and those at No 10 moved in on Wednesday.

Samuel moved in on Monday (2). Fred didn't move in on Wednesday (4), so it must have been Thursday and Martin lives at No 32.

By elimination, Andrew moved in on Wednesday and William lives at No 21. Andrew lives at No 10, so (1) Fred is married to Barbara. Andrew's wife isn't Pauline (5), so must be Tina. Martin is married to Pauline.

Thus:
Andrew – Tina – No 10 – Wednesday;
Fred – Barbara – No 17 – Thursday;
Martin – Pauline – No 32 – Friday;
Samuel – Lucy – No 14 – Monday;
William – Diane – No 21 – Tuesday.

23

Room aboard a ship = Cabin
Clergyman = Vicar
Nimble = Agile
Bring up to date = Renew
Reflection = Image

| V | I | C | A | R |
|---|---|---|---|---|
| I | M | A | G | E |
| C | A | B | I | N |
| A | G | I | L | E |
| R | E | N | E | W |

24

| Q | I | K | W | A | E | B | N | Z | I | T | H | E | R |
|---|---|---|---|---|---|---|---|---|---|---|---|---|---|
| E | M | F | G | C | N | J | T | C | P | S | P | V | A |
| L | W | T | R | I | F | L | E | K | Y | U | Z | D | T |
| G | X | V | S | H | A | L | L | O | W | L | U | R | I |
| U | Y | P | J | W | L | K | U | N | U | F | C | B | U |
| B | A | N | J | O | E | W | A | T | C | H | X | H | G |
| Q | O | R | K | Y | N | V | E | U | E | N | P | R | A |
| D | E | O | W | P | R | A | H | S | T | E | A | D | Y |
| K | Q | H | V | L | N | F | I | I | U | B | W | J | L |
| E | Z | Y | U | T | R | U | M | P | E | T | H | G | L |
| W | A | J | I | K | L | U | N | I | A | Z | E | Q | A |
| S | T | A | R | S | R | U | L | P | N | T | P | A | R |
| A | V | L | A | D | O | C | L | E | F | I | C | B | G |
| E | N | T | E | R | T | A | I | N | T | E | M | P | O |

25

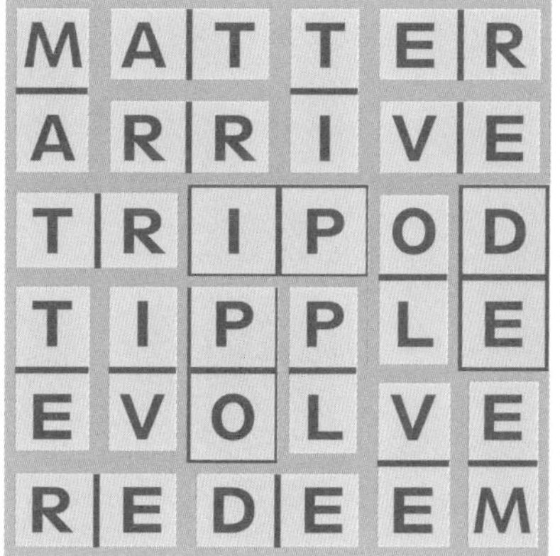


26

27
NETDR = trend

28
Ton (canton and tonsure).

29

| T | I | L | E |
|---|---|---|---|
| I | R | I | S |
| L | I | M | P |
| E | S | P | Y |

30
Linen. If you take alternate letters of the others, the sequence of Roman numerals is revealed – i, ii, iii, iv, vi. Linen spoils this sequence; the word 'eve' would have continued it.

31
Possible answers include:

ALERT
ARE
ART
EAR
EARN
ERA
INSERT
INTERVAL
INTERVALS
LEARN
LEARNS
LEARNT
LENS
LENT
LET
NEAR
NET
REAL
REIN
REINS
RENT
SALE
SAVE
SAVER
SEA
SEAL
SENT
SLAVE
TEA
TEAR
TEAS
TEN
TENS
TRAVEL
TRAVELS
VASE
VEIN
VEINS
VET

32
No one started collecting in March or June. The person who started a collection in August isn't Gina (clue 1), Daphne (clue 2), Hugh (3), Christian (4) or David (5), so must be Amelia.

Daphne began in either January or April (2), in the

month before a man. Miss Marks began collecting two months later than Mr Quiller (1), so it must have been in either April or July and Mr Quiller in either February or May.

Gina began in either January, February or April (1) and isn't Miss Marks. Thus Daphne is Miss Marks and (above) began collecting in April. Mr Quiller began in February and Gina in January (1).

David's surname is Grant (5). The person surnamed Willis didn't start collecting in January or August and isn't Christian (4), so (by elimination) Hugh's surname is Willis. Christian is thus Mr Quiller. Gina's surname isn't Frost (5), so must be MacDonald. Amelia's is Frost. David started collecting in May (5), so Hugh must have started in July.

Christian is collecting stamps from France (1), David from Spain (2) and Amelia from the USA (4). The collector of Japanese stamps isn't Hugh or Gina (3), so must be Daphne. Gina is collecting stamps from Australia (1) and Hugh stamps from Britain.

Thus:
Amelia – Frost – August – USA;
Christian – Quiller – February – France;
Daphne – Marks – April – Japan;
David – Grant – May – Spain;
Gina – MacDonald – January – Australia;
Hugh – Willis – July – Britain.

33
A Palestinian
B Wall
C Amen
D Beautify
E Hyper
F Lucky
G Voodoo
H Bayonet
I Undo
J Obedient
K Pooch

| A | | B | A | N | K | | I | S | | A |
|---|---|---|---|---|---|---|---|---|---|---|
| | P | L | A | C | E | | T | H | A | T |
| | W | I | L | L | | L | E | N | D | |
| Y | O | U | | M | O | N | E | Y | | I |
| F | | Y | O | U | | C | A | N | | P |
| R | O | V | E | | Y | O | U | | D | O |
| | N | O | T | | N | E | E | D | | I |
| T | | B | O | B | | H | O | P | E | |

34
Dc. The others, Na, Pb, Cd and Fe, are all chemical symbols.

35
Here today, gone tomorrow
Each letter moves two places back in the alphabet.

36
NEED
WEED
WEND
WANT
WANT

37

| | | | | | | |
|---|---|---|---|---|---|---|
| 1 | L | E | A | D | E | R |
| 2 | O | X | Y | G | E | N |
| 3 | C | A | R | R | O | T |
| 4 | O | B | T | A | I | N |
| 5 | M | A | Y | D | A | Y |
| 6 | O | C | C | U | L | T |
| 7 | T | H | R | I | V | E |
| 8 | I | N | H | A | L | E |
| 9 | V | E | R | B | A | L |
| 10 | E | N | L | I | S | T |

38
The word is trigonometrical.

39

| A | N | A | V | A | H | T | S | G | H | E | N | O | W |
|---|---|---|---|---|---|---|---|---|---|---|---|---|---|
| T | O | R | O | N | T | O | B | V | I | E | N | N | A |
| Q | B | T | S | F | D | C | G | N | M | P | J | M | R |
| O | S | U | T | Q | P | Z | R | T | O | O | I | L | S |
| Y | I | L | P | A | K | W | E | X | T | L | M | H | A |
| U | L | P | R | E | W | B | C | R | I | Z | S | L | W |
| R | O | I | A | N | I | A | N | S | O | T | K | O | U |
| K | S | T | Y | V | I | X | M | J | G | M | C | N | Y |
| D | A | S | L | R | A | L | L | W | U | S | E | D | C |
| U | E | S | O | F | I | A | D | R | O | A | J | O | S |
| B | L | L | V | W | Q | R | A | M | Y | T | U | N | E |
| L | B | U | S | R | L | U | B | A | K | W | I | J | L |
| I | T | E | W | D | S | B | L | A | O | S | W | U | K |
| N | A | I | R | O | B | I | A | N | T | P | L | I | Q |

40
Attempt

41
Gain (bargain and gainsay).

42

| | | | | | | | | | | | | | | |
|---|---|---|---|---|---|---|---|---|---|---|---|---|---|---|
| | R | A | G | G | E | D | | R | E | P | E | A | T | |
| S | | L | | A | | A | | E | | A | | C | | G |
| E | N | A | B | L | E | D | | E | M | P | E | R | O | R |
| N | | R | | L | | O | | D | | E | | O | | A |
| S | Y | M | B | O | L | | E | | T | R | I | B | E | S |
| E | | E | | P | U | N | C | H | E | S | | A | | S |
| S | I | D | E | | N | | O | | A | | S | T | A | Y |
| | | | | S | C | E | N | E | R | Y | | | | |
| D | U | S | T | | H | | O | | I | | H | O | O | P |
| I | | P | | G | E | R | M | A | N | Y | | U | | O |
| S | P | E | A | R | S | | Y | | G | E | N | T | L | E |
| M | | C | | A | | E | | Z | | A | | L | | T |
| A | B | I | L | I | T | Y | | E | A | R | L | I | E | R |
| Y | | A | | N | | E | | R | | L | | N | | Y |
| | C | L | A | S | P | S | | O | X | Y | G | E | N | |

43
Confectionery

44
Sluggish

45
Hand (backhand and handsome).

46
Isobar

47

IT
BIT
BITE
BITER
BITTER
BITTERN

48
Possible answers include:

AIM
CAMP
CAMPS
CAP
CAPS
CHAIN
CHAIN
CHAINS
CHAMPIONS
CHIMP
CHIMPS
CHIN
CHIP
CHIPS
COIN
COINS
HAM
HIM
HIPS
HIS
INCH
MAIN
MAP
MAPS
PAIN
PAINS
PIN
PINCH
PINS
SPAIN
SPIN

49
The word that doesn't appear in the grid is WAGON.

| | | | | | | | | | | | | | |
|---|---|---|---|---|---|---|---|---|---|---|---|---|---|
| Y | E | T | T | J | K | L | N | Y | M | F | H | G | W |
| A | H | S | T | C | G | V | X | R | Q | Z | B | A | C |
| C | L | G | K | A | F | H | M | R | E | D | I | L | G |
| H | O | R | N | Z | B | W | P | E | L | N | B | O | X |
| T | T | V | A | I | C | E | L | F | J | Z | H | D | T |
| D | W | R | S | E | D | A | N | K | R | C | W | N | L |
| Q | Y | H | A | A | N | P | X | C | I | P | G | O | H |
| A | X | V | L | I | B | A | Z | E | L | T | U | G | L |
| Q | M | N | E | C | N | P | J | H | R | G | F | E | Y |
| I | A | Z | E | R | H | T | N | A | V | A | V | S | W |
| G | F | O | H | E | T | S | M | V | B | S | H | L | E |
| F | Q | T | W | F | U | E | L | H | U | H | O | U | R |
| M | C | N | A | P | D | Y | J | B | L | I | X | A | T |
| C | A | R | R | O | T | O | M | S | K | P | O | E | J |

50
Nothing in the affairs of man is worthy of great anxiety.
Plato.

51

| | | | | | | | | |
|---|---|---|---|---|---|---|---|---|
| | | | H | | U | | O | |
| E | F | F | E | C | T | I | V | E |
| | R | | M | | T | | E | |
| B | I | G | | B | E | A | R | |
| | E | | R | | R | | H | |
| | N | E | E | D | | N | E | W |
| | D | | I | | U | | A | |
| A | L | O | N | G | S | I | D | E |
| | Y | | S | | E | | | |

52
Lerdca = Cradle

53
SOS HELP
Read the missing letters between each of the groups (e.g. 'S' between the 'R' and 'T' of SVQAR and TBCIN, etc.).

54

DINE
- - - - - - - - - - - -
FINE
- - - - - - - - - - - -
FIND
- - - - - - - - - - - -
FEND
- - - - - - - - - - - -
FEED

55
Gang (chaingang and gangway).

56
Mangetout. The answer is hidden in the shopkeeper's reply 'I don't have any, man. Get out!'

57
Merchant.

58
You'll need a bit of lateral thinking to discover the answer.
1543 – 1816 = –273, which is ABSOLUTE ZERO IN DEGREES CENTIGRADE.

59
Argued. The other words can be paired off in such a way that they end and start with the same four letters, albeit in a different order: calculator/oratorio, balloonist/stings, aromatic/taciturn, decapitate/attendant.

60

Mr Bishop bought either the flat in Cloudy View or the one in Lofty Reach (clue 1), so Miss Walters bought the flat in Tall Towers (clue 6).

The (most expensive) £98,000 flat isn't in Grande Vista (2), Happy Heights (3), Lofty Reach (4), Cloudy View (5) or Tall Towers (6), so must be Sky Scraper.

The (cheapest) £73,000 flat wasn't sold by Sellmore's or Hearth & Home (2), Sayle & Sons (5), Grinn & Bearitt (6) or Shark & Co (7), so must have been sold by Proffitts.

Mr Bishop bought the flat priced at £78,000 (1), which isn't in Lofty Reach (4), so (1) must be Cloudy View.

Proffitts sold to Ms Dimarco (5) and Sayle & Sons sold the £83,000 flat. The one priced at £93,000 isn't in Grande Vista (2), Happy Heights (3) or Tall Towers (6), so must be Lofty Reach. The £98,000 flat was bought by Mrs Cairn (4). The £88,000 flat was sold by either Hearth & Home or Shark & Co (4), so (6) the £93,000 flat must have been sold by Grinn & Bearitt. The £78,000 flat wasn't sold by Sellmore's (2) or Shark & Co (7), so must have been Hearth & Home; thus the £88,000 flat was sold by Shark & Co (4).

The flat in Sky Scraper was sold by Sellmore's. The £93,000 flat wasn't bought by Mr Brown (7), so must have been Mr Goring. The flat in Grande Vista was sold for £73,000 (2), so Sayle & Sons (3) sold the flat in Happy Heights and Miss Walters bought the £88,000 flat.

Thus:
Grinn & Bearitt – £93,000 – Lofty Reach – Mr Goring;
Hearth & Home – £78,000 – Cloudy View – Mr Bishop;
Proffitts – £73,000 – Grande Vista – Ms Dimarco;
Sayle & Sons – £83,000 – Happy Heights – Mr Brown;
Sellmore's – £98,000 – Sky Scraper – Mrs Cairn;
Shark & Co – £88,000 – Tall Towers – Miss Walters.

61

Trickery

62

| L | O | S | T |
|---|---|---|---|
| O | B | O | E |
| S | O | L | E |
| T | E | E | M |

63

| S | T | U | N | S | | E | N | J | O | Y | A | B | L | E |
|---|---|---|---|---|---|---|---|---|---|---|---|---|---|---|
| U | | P | | K | | A | | E | | O | | A | | R |
| B | A | R | R | I | E | R | | T | H | U | N | D | E | R |
| T | | I | | | | T | | | | R | | G | | O |
| R | I | G | I | D | | H | O | U | R | S | | E | R | R |
| A | | H | | U | | | | N | | | | R | | |
| C | U | T | | C | O | U | R | T | | T | A | S | T | Y |
| T | | | | K | | P | | I | | I | | | | E |
| S | T | A | Y | S | | S | T | E | E | R | | W | A | S |
| | | M | | | | E | | | | E | | H | | T |
| E | Y | E | | A | T | T | I | C | | D | R | O | V | E |
| X | | R | | S | | | | A | | | | E | | R |
| T | H | I | C | K | E | R | | R | E | M | O | V | E | D |
| R | | C | | E | | A | | E | | U | | E | | A |
| A | B | A | N | D | O | N | E | D | | M | E | R | C | Y |

64

TRIM
TRAM
TEAM
TEAT
NEAT

65

Semi-precious stone

66

| V | E | S | T |
|---|---|---|---|
| E | C | H | O |
| S | H | O | P |
| T | O | P | E |

67

| | | | | | | |
|---|---|---|---|---|---|---|
| 1 | C | H | A | N | C | E |
| 2 | A | T | T | I | R | E |
| 3 | L | E | S | S | O | N |
| 4 | C | A | N | Y | O | N |
| 5 | U | R | A | N | U | S |
| 6 | L | A | T | H | E | R |
| 7 | A | C | T | I | V | E |
| 8 | T | R | E | M | O | R |
| 9 | O | B | J | E | C | T |
| 10 | R | E | M | E | D | Y |

68

| C | A | M | E |
|---|---|---|---|
| A | R | E | A |
| M | E | W | S |
| E | A | S | Y |

69

| | | | | | | |
|---|---|---|---|---|---|---|
| 1 | G | O | B | L | E | T |
| 2 | Y | E | L | L | O | W |
| 3 | M | I | N | U | T | E |
| 4 | N | E | E | D | L | E |
| 5 | A | T | T | A | C | K |
| 6 | S | T | A | M | E | N |
| 7 | T | A | R | G | E | T |
| 8 | I | M | M | U | N | E |
| 9 | C | O | L | O | N | Y |
| 10 | S | U | B | M | I | T |

70

71

ELRUAL = laurel

72

HAKE
LAKE
LIKE
LINE
LING

73

A pack of cards (including two jokers)

74

| E | R | T | E | M | M | A | R | G | D | R | I | L | L |
|---|---|---|---|---|---|---|---|---|---|---|---|---|---|
| I | L | S | N | V | K | U | V | R | W | B | G | R | E |
| R | E | U | S | E | C | H | K | A | E | J | O | A | B |
| O | N | T | O | M | P | Q | Y | I | N | I | Z | H | I |
| L | O | R | W | J | I | P | I | N | T | W | N | I | C |
| A | C | C | O | U | N | T | W | O | S | P | R | E | E |
| C | A | R | A | T | B | D | N | V | H | U | J | K | D |
| Y | E | L | L | I | Q | X | P | R | N | M | F | T | L |
| G | A | O | S | B | K | M | O | V | E | D | B | W | F |
| F | V | U | Z | U | A | L | Y | X | W | P | R | U | A |
| A | B | L | S | C | R | E | E | N | K | R | V | I | T |
| M | A | O | R | X | W | E | L | L | N | Z | E | T | H |
| J | P | E | G | E | H | F | N | C | O | T | S | A | O |
| K | L | Z | Q | T | Y | P | E | S | T | H | E | R | M |

75

Possible answers include:

ADO
ADORN
AND
ANT
ANY
ARM

ARMY
ART
ARTY
DAN
DARN
DART

DORM
DORMY
DORY
DRY
LYRA
MOD
MORAN
MORDANT
MORN
MYNA
NARD

NARY
RAD
RAN
RAND
RANDOM
RANDOMLY
RANT
ROD
TROD
TRY
TYRO

76

Possible answers include:

APT
ART
ARTS
ATE
EAR
EAST
EAT
EATS
OAR
OAT
OATS
ORATE
ORATES
PAR
PARQUET
PARQUETS
PART
PARTS
PAST
PASTE

PAT
PATE
PATES
PATS
PRAT
PRATE
PRATES
PRATS
PRO
QUART
QUARTS
QUEST
RAP
RAPT
RASE
RAT
RATE
RATES
RATS
ROAST

SAP
SAT
SATE
SEA
SEAR
SEAT
SET
STAR
STRAP
TAO
TAP
TAR
TARO
TAU
TEA
TEAR
TEAS
TRAP
TSAR

77

Type of duck

78

LUDIB = build

79

Pen (fountain pen, penknife).

80

Atoned; the rest form a magic square in which the words are the same when read both across and down.

| E | S | T | A | T | E |
|---|---|---|---|---|---|
| S | H | A | V | E | N |
| T | A | L | E | N | T |
| A | V | E | R | S | E |
| T | E | N | S | E | R |
| E | N | T | E | R | S |

81

Pamper

82

The word that doesn't appear is SHOWER.

83

Cardinal

84

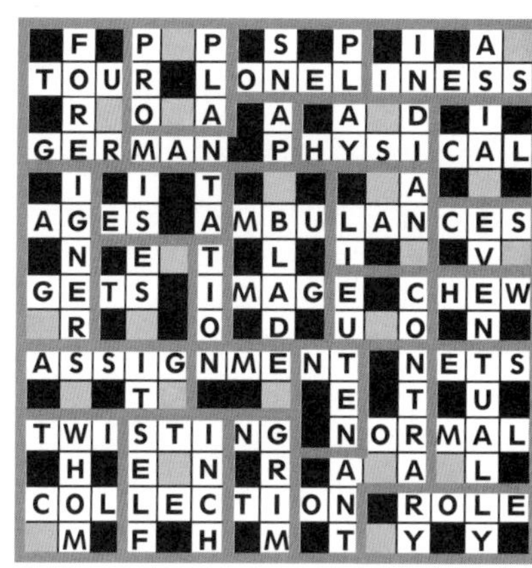

85

| 1 | N | O | R | M | A | L |
|---|---|---|---|---|---|---|
| 2 | A | B | L | A | Z | E |
| 3 | V | I | S | I | O | N |
| 4 | I | N | F | A | N | T |
| 5 | G | L | O | B | A | L |
| 6 | A | R | C | H | E | R |
| 7 | T | I | M | B | E | R |
| 8 | I | G | N | O | R | E |
| 9 | O | P | T | I | O | N |
| 10 | N | E | P | H | E | W |

86

| 1 | S | A | M | E |
|---|---|---|---|---|
| 2 | A | N | E | W |
| 3 | M | E | R | E |
| 4 | E | W | E | S |

87
The names are an anagram of *Alice in Wonderland.*

88
Wronged. All the others have the consecutive letters ONE embedded in them.

89

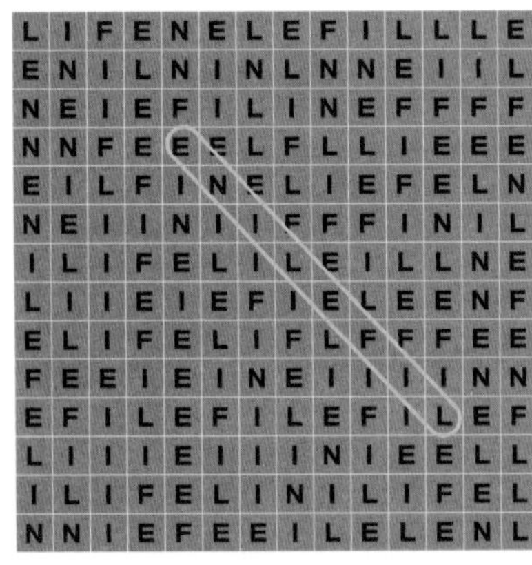

90
A Agitated
B Yet
C Manifest
D Phenomenon
E Now
F Pinpoint
G Irreversible
H Tool
I Rook
J Involvement
K Churches
L Standpoint

| T | I | M | E | | S | P | E | N | T | | O |
|---|---|---|---|---|---|---|---|---|---|---|---|
| N | | A | N | Y | | I | T | E | M | | O |
| F | | T | H | E | | A | G | E | N | D | A |
| | W | I | L | L | | B | E | | I | N | |
| I | N | V | E | R | S | E | | P | R | O | P |
| O | R | T | I | O | N | | T | O | | T | H |
| E | | S | U | M | | I | N | V | O | L | V |
| E | D | | C | | N | O | R | T | H | C | O |
| T | E | | P | A | R | K | I | N | S | O | N |

91
Remember throughout that each family's forenames and surname contains five different initials (intro).

Bella's son's forename has the same initial as Kevin's mother's forename (1). Kevin's mother isn't Sharon (2) and Bella's son isn't Liam (6). If Kevin's mother is Jean, then (3) Billy's mother is Katrina and (1) Bella's son is John. But then Lynne's son is Sean (7), which isn't possible (4). So Kevin's mother is Rachel, and Bella's son is Ricky (1). Lynne's son is Billy (7). Jean's son is Liam (3). By elimination, Sharon's son is John and Katrina's is Sean.

John's surname is Bates (6), so Jean is Mrs King (2). Larry's son is Sean (4) and Kenneth's wife is Sharon. Steve's wife is Lynne (10). By elimination, Bella's husband is Jerry, Rachel's is Brian and Jean's is Robert. Mrs Race isn't Katrina (9), so must be Lynne. Katrina's surname is Jones. Katrina's daughter isn't Brenda (8), so must be Rebecca. Sharon's daughter is Liza and Jean's is Brenda. Jerry's surname is Stoppard (5), so Brian's is Love. Jerry's daughter is Karla, Steve's is Joanne and Brian's is Samantha.

Thus (father – mother – daughter – son – surname):
Brian – Rachel – Samantha – Kevin – Love;
Jerry – Bella – Karla – Ricky – Stoppard;
Kenneth – Sharon – Liza – John – Bates;
Larry – Katrina – Rebecca – Sean – Jones;
Robert – Jean – Brenda – Liam – King;
Steve – Lynne – Joanne – Billy – Race.

1
A golf ball

2
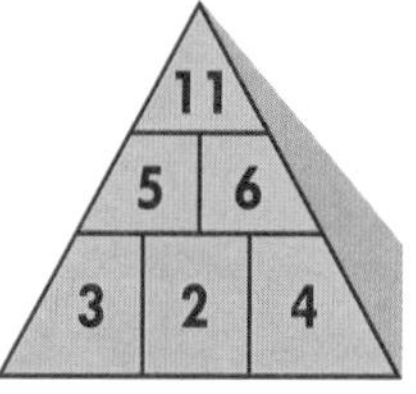


3
Investigator

4
Possible answers include:

| | | |
|---|---|---|
| ACNE | FACT | PICTS |
| ACTS | FACTS | PITS |
| ANEW | FANE | RUGS |
| BANE | FITS | RUST |
| BANK | GETS | RUSTIC |
| CANE | GUST | STEW |
| CITE | KEGS | SUET |
| ENACT | KNEW | SURGE |
| ENACTS | NEGUS | URGE |
| FACE | NETS | VICE |
| FACET | PICA | WEAN |
| FACETS | PICT | WETS |

5
HYPOTENUSE (the longest side of a right-angled triangle)

6
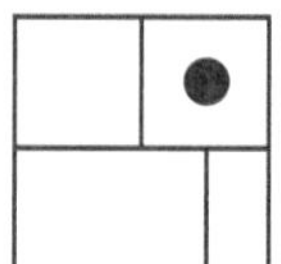
B. The box rotates 90° clockwise at each stage. The circle moves to a different section each time going clockwise, and alternates white/purple.

7
121 feet. Take CB (143 feet) and divide it by CE (13 feet) = 11 feet. AB is proportionate to DE (i.e., 11 x 11 = 121 feet).

8
Gorse

9
Night and day

10
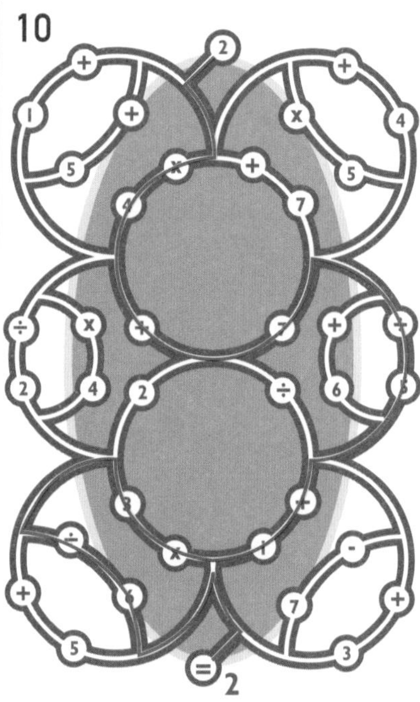

11
Pomfret, which is a fish. The remainder are birds.

12
Pragmatic

13
Planet A travels through $360 \div 5 = 72$ degrees each year. The figure for planet B is $360 \div 4 = 90$ degrees. Therefore, B is 18 degrees faster than A. They will be in a straight line again in 180 degrees' time (with A and B on opposite sides of the sun), which will occur in $180 \div 18 = 10$ years' time. (In this time, A will have done 2 orbits, B will have done 2½.)

14
The 13-year-old (oldest) girl isn't at Mill Street school (clue 1), St James's or Reed House (clue 2), The Grove (4) or St Claire's (6), so is at The Academy and (3) wears grey. Willow's uniform is red (4).

The pupil at The Academy isn't Karen or Judi (1), Shirley (2) or Marilyn (3), so must be Amy. The 10-year-old isn't Judi or Karen (1), Shirley (2) or Marilyn (6), so must be Willow.

The girl in navy is 8 years old (4) and the one at The Grove is 9. Karen is 9 (6), the St Claire's pupil 10, the one in green is 11 and Marilyn is 12. The Grove's uniform isn't brown (1), so must be lilac. Marilyn's is brown. The Mill Street pupil's uniform isn't green (3), nor is she Judi (1). Judi isn't at St James's (2), so must be at Reed House. The St James's uniform is brown (1). The Mill Street uniform is navy and (by elimination) worn by Shirley. Reed House's is green.

Girl C attends Mill Street (5). Girl B attends The Grove (4). Girl D attends The Academy (5) and girl F goes to St Claire's. Girl A attends St James's (1), so girl E is a pupil at Reed House.

Thus:
A – Marilyn – 12 – St James's – brown;
B – Karen – 9 – The Grove – lilac;
C – Shirley – 8 – Mill Street – navy;
D – Amy – 13 -The Academy – grey;
E – Judi – 11 – Reed House – green;
F – Willow – 10 – St Claire's – red.

15
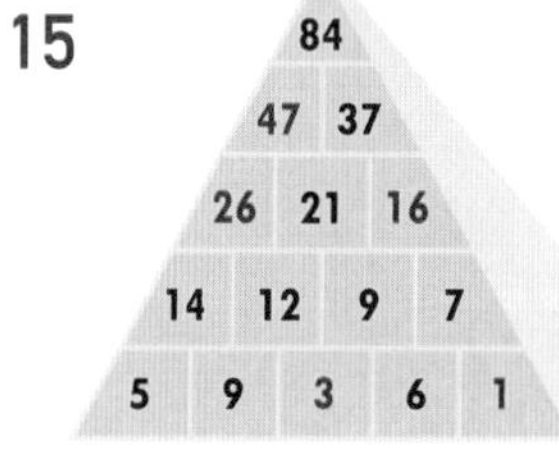


16
A rugby field

17
56 revolutions. To solve this type of puzzle you must find the lowest common multiple, i.e. the smallest number into which all the numbers of cog teeth can be divided. The answer is this number divided by the number of teeth on the largest cog.

To find the lowest common multiple, list all the prime factors of each number. Thus:
11 = 1 x 11
8 = 2 x 2 x 2
7 = (1) x 7
4 = (2 x 2)
Eliminating prime factors that are duplicated (shown in the brackets above) leaves 11 x 2 x 2 x 2 x 7 = 616, which is the lowest number into which 11, 8, 7 and 4 can all be divided. Divide 616 by 11 for the answer, 56.

18

| | | |
|---|---|---|
| AVOCET | GANDER | OSTRICH |
| BUDGERIGAR | GOOSE | PARROT |
| BUZZARD | GOSLING | PENGUIN |
| CANARY | GREBE | PIGEON |
| CHAFFINCH | GROUSE | RAVEN |
| CHICKEN | KESTREL | RAZORBILL |
| COCKATIEL | MACAW | ROBIN |
| CONDOR | MAGPIE | ROOSTER |
| CURLEW | MARTIN | STORK |
| EAGLE | MERLIN | TURKEY |
| FLAMINGO | OSPREY | |

| | | | | | | | | | | | | | | | |
|---|---|---|---|---|---|---|---|---|---|---|---|---|---|---|---|
| C | V | L | L | I | B | R | O | Z | A | R | M | T | K | T | R |
| A | V | O | C | E | T | F | L | A | M | I | N | G | O | S | I |
| Y | R | A | N | A | C | M | G | R | E | B | E | N | T | R | Y |
| P | U | G | W | Y | E | R | E | D | N | A | G | O | E | K | E |
| I | P | D | O | R | C | G | H | I | L | E | R | T | S | E | K |
| G | W | B | L | O | O | O | Y | C | B | K | S | C | N | K | R |
| E | I | I | U | S | S | B | C | K | I | O | J | P | O | N | U |
| O | N | N | L | D | E | E | K | K | O | R | H | O | M | S | T |
| N | A | I | I | I | G | H | S | R | A | C | T | K | E | R | C |
| T | N | U | P | D | T | E | Y | U | N | T | N | S | D | O | R |
| G | E | G | B | Z | O | E | R | I | O | I | I | R | O | D | A |
| T | A | N | K | F | R | Y | F | I | T | R | A | E | N | N | V |
| M | G | E | J | P | R | F | R | R | G | Z | G | I | L | O | E |
| A | L | P | S | W | A | C | A | M | Z | A | B | X | N | C | N |
| T | E | O | Q | H | P | M | B | U | N | O | R | A | M | Y | I |
| C | H | I | C | K | E | N | B | C | R | C | U | R | L | E | W |

19
PACESETTER

20
John GALLIANO
Jean-Paul GAULTIER
Bruce OLDFIELD
Franco MOSCHINO
Johji YAMAMOTO

21

22
4pm Tuesday. Work it out as follows: at 2am on Monday I fly from Nuuk (–3 GMT) east for six hours to Istanbul (+2 GMT). I land 5 + 6 = 11 hours later, i.e. 1pm on Monday. Half a day later it is 1am Tuesday. I fly three hours later to Helsinki (also +2 GMT = 4am in Finland), wait two hours (6am) then take an 11-hour ferry to Copenhagen (+1 GMT) = 4pm Tuesday.

23
E. The contents of each hexagon are determined by the contents of the two hexagons immediately below it. Only when the same coloured dot appears in the same corner in these two hexagons is it carried forward to the hexagon above; however, yellow dots turn to white and vice versa.

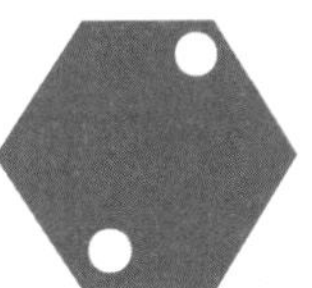

24 B.

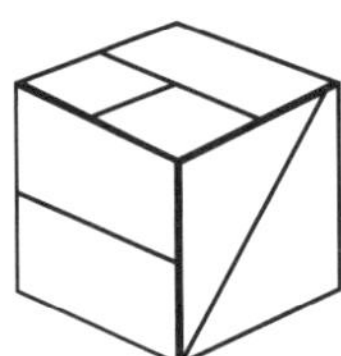

25
Bone in the ear

26
Planet C travels through 360 ÷ 8 = 45 degrees each year. The figure for planet D is 360 ÷ 5 = 72 degrees. Therefore, D is 27 degrees faster than C. Planet D will be on the line between planet C and the sun in 360 degrees' time (with C and D on the same side of the sun), which will occur in 360 ÷ 27 = 13 years and 4 months' time. (In this time, C will have completed $1\frac{2}{3}$ orbits and D will have done $2\frac{2}{3}$.)

27
Cordoba (coin). The remainder are boats.

28

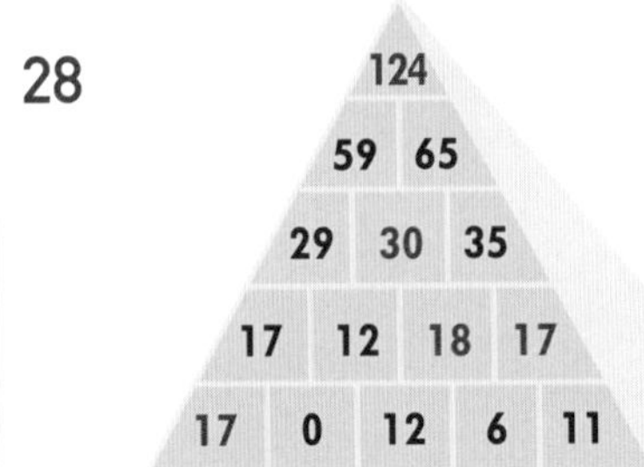


29
A splinter

30
Mellifluous

31
21 revolutions. Find the lowest common multiple of

all the numbers (168), then divide that number by the number of teeth in the largest cog to get the number of revolutions, in this case, 21. See answer 17, page 344 for a fuller method.

32
2. The direction is shown in the form of a parallelogram as illustrated below.

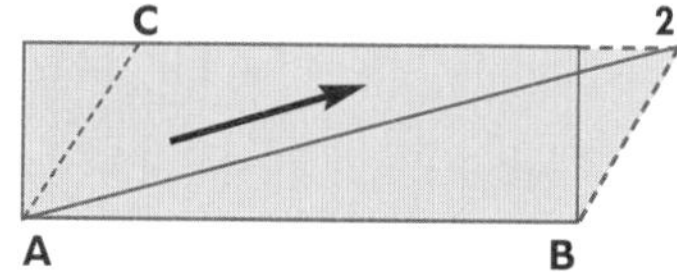


33
Substituting the correct letters for the flags in EMMA, by a process of elimination you can arrive at the answer: It is my turn now; and if I come back, it is yours.

34
Carpetbagger

35
Trampolinist

36
11.30am on Thursday. Work it out as follows: at 3pm on Sunday, Jambyn in Mongolia (+8 GMT) rings Fidel in Manila (+8 GMT) and talks for one hour (4pm). After 30 minutes (4.30pm), Fidel sends an email to New Zealand (+12 GMT so 8.30pm). Jenny reads it two hours later (10.30pm in NZ). Eleven hours later (9.30am on Monday), she spends one hour writing a letter (10.30am Monday). $3^1/_2$ days later (Thursday at 10.30pm) it reaches Helen in Spain (+1 GMT so –11 hours) = Thursday 11.30am.

37
AMONTILLADO
APERITIF
BENEDICTINE
BOLLINGER
BOURBON
BUTTERMILK
CALVADOS
CHAMPAGNE
CHARTREUSE
CHERRYADE
CIDER
CLARET
CORDIAL
DARJEELING
HIGHBALL
JULEP
KIRSCH
MADEIRA
MANHATTAN
MOCHA
MUSCADET
OOLONG
PILSNER
RETSINA
SCHNAPPS
SHANDY
SIDECAR
SLING
SOUCHONG
VERMOUTH

| B | H | G | N | I | L | S | H | I | G | H | B | A | L | L | S | U |
|---|---|---|---|---|---|---|---|---|---|---|---|---|---|---|---|---|
| A | E | E | R | G | N | O | H | C | U | O | S | O | U | C | P | D |
| E | T | N | D | M | A | N | H | A | T | T | A | N | X | I | P | B |
| E | B | E | E | A | I | A | P | E | R | I | T | I | F | D | A | U |
| B | A | O | D | D | Y | R | E | T | S | I | N | A | P | E | N | T |
| I | O | A | L | A | I | R | H | A | S | K | A | O | P | R | H | T |
| G | S | U | M | L | C | C | R | G | O | S | I | I | D | L | C | E |
| D | B | V | R | O | I | S | T | E | X | C | L | R | T | H | S | R |
| P | A | E | E | B | N | N | U | I | H | S | O | Q | S | U | P | M |
| E | L | R | A | N | O | T | G | M | N | C | R | R | E | C | W | I |
| L | Q | M | J | H | G | N | I | E | A | E | Z | R | D | S | H | L |
| U | V | O | A | E | C | A | R | L | R | R | T | Z | O | I | O | K |
| J | Q | U | R | H | E | O | P | H | L | R | I | O | B | D | A | F |
| S | K | T | P | P | T | L | M | M | A | A | L | E | W | E | E | L |
| O | S | H | A | N | D | Y | I | H | A | O | D | A | D | C | K | V |
| S | O | D | A | V | L | A | C | N | N | H | W | O | Y | A | H | L |
| T | E | R | A | L | C | C | C | G | G | N | C | D | D | R | M | Y |

38

39
42 revolutions. Find the lowest common multiple of all the numbers (546), then divide that number by the largest number of teeth to get the number of revolutions, in this case, 42. See answer 17, page 344, for a fuller method.

40
Enfeeble

41
P. Place it at the beginning to get PRE-EMPT.

42
Whoopi GOLDBERG
Melanie GRIFFITH
Michelle PFEIFFER
Emma THOMPSON
Honor BLACKMAN

43
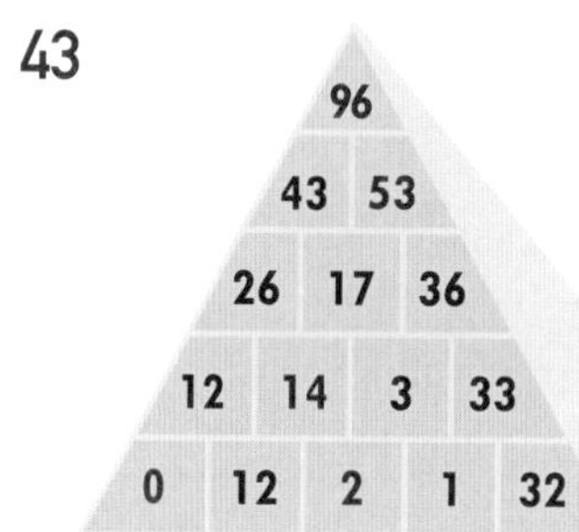


44
Hanover = 3pm
Havana = 9am

45

46

Italian lessons are taken on the same evening as either Hindi or Burmese (clue 1), so (clue 7) lessons in Kurdish are taken on the same evening as French by (9) Kay. The person studying on Saturday isn't learning Swahili (2), Hindi (4), Kurdish (7), Burmese (8) or Cantonese (9), so must be learning Hebrew.

The one who takes lessons on Monday isn't surnamed Killick (3), Fitzpatrick (4), Agnew (5), Burstow (6) or Morris (7), so must be Holmes. Italian lessons are on Tuesday (1). Kay's surname isn't Holmes (9).

The person studying Hebrew (Saturday, above) isn't learning Greek (3), German (4) or Dutch (5), so must be learning Spanish. The one learning Burmese doesn't do so on Tuesday (8), so (1) Hindi lessons are on Tuesday. The student surnamed Fitzpatrick (4) has lessons on Wednesday and the one surnamed Holmes is learning German.

Friday's lessons aren't in Swahili (2), Kurdish (7) or Cantonese (9), so must be Burmese. Terry studies on Saturday (8). The student learning Hindi (Tuesday, above) isn't surnamed Killick (3), Agnew (5) or Morris (7), so must be Burstow. Clifford's surname is Holmes (6). Kay studies on Thursday (9). Clifford is learning Swahili (2) and Sandy's lessons are on Tuesday.

The student surnamed Fitzpatrick is studying Cantonese and (6) is Rosa. Mike has Dutch lessons on Fridays and Rosa is learning Greek. Terry's surname is Agnew (5) and Mike's is Morris (7). Kay's surname is Killick.

Thus:
Clifford – Holmes – Monday – German – Swahili;
Kay – Killick – Thursday – French – Kurdish;
Mike – Morris – Friday – Dutch – Burmese;
Rosa – Fitzpatrick – Wednesday – Greek – Cantonese;
Sandy – Burstow – Tuesday – Italian – Hindi;
Terry – Agnew – Saturday – Spanish – Hebrew.

47

Blue flower

48

Quarantine (from the French 'quarantaine', meaning 'about 40').

49

B; every third triangle is inverted, every fourth triangle is blue and every fifth triangle has a circle in it.

50

Chervil, which is a plant. The remainder are animals.

51

The hands are coincident between the 1 and 2 of 12.

52

Electrifying

53

120°. You can work it out by dividing the shape into six equilateral triangles as shown and working out the angles in each.

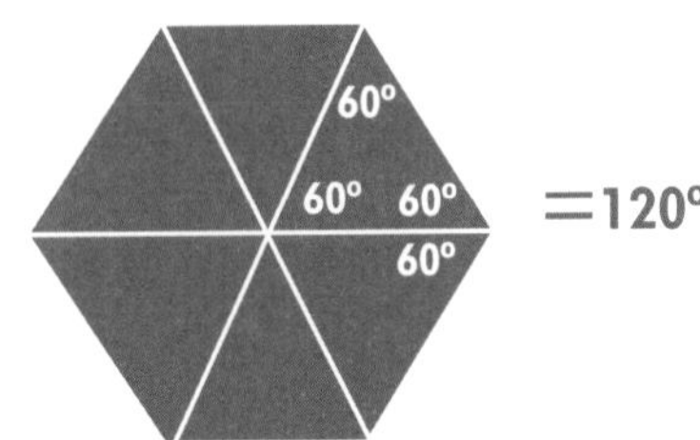


54

A leather glove

55

Lavish

56

Planet E travels through 360 ÷ 10 = 36 degrees each year. The figure for planet F is 360 ÷ 9 = 40 degrees. Therefore, F is 4 degrees faster than E. Planet F will be on the line between planet E and the sun in 300 degrees' time (with E and F on the same side of the sun), which will occur in 300 ÷ 4 = 75 years' time. (In this time, E will have done $7\frac{1}{2}$ orbits, F will have done $8\frac{1}{3}$.)

57

Possible answers include:

| | | |
|---|---|---|
| ACRES | CATION | CURES |
| AROSE | CATLING | EATING |
| CARES | CRAGS | FLOAT |
| CAROL | CRATING | FLOATING |
| CARTING | CREATING | FLOGS |
| CARTON | CREATION | FLORA |

FLORAE
FLORAS
FROGS
GATOR
GOITRE
GORES
HURTING
HURTLING
IGNORE
IGNORES
INGOT
IOTAS
LIGATURE
LINGO
LINGS
LINOS
LITRE
LITRES
LOACH
LONGS
LORES
LOSER
NITRO
OLIGARCH
RACES
RATING
RATINGS
RATIO
RATION
RATIOS
REACH
REASON
RECUT
RESOLD
ROACH
SARONG
SATIN
SATING
SEARCH
SOLING
SORTING
TARES
TAROS
TAXER
TAXES
TINGS
TOGAS
TONGA
TONGAS
TONGS
TORCH
TRACE
TRACES
TRUCE
TRUCES

58

Remember throughout that there are five different initial letters in each case (intro).

The woman who started a new job in January didn't move in March (clue 3) or September (clue 6). The woman who moved in September didn't start a new job in August (7), so the one who started a new job in January didn't move in August (6). If the woman who started a new job in January moved in October, then (4) the woman who moved in January started a new job in September, so (5) the one who moved in August started a new job in March. But then clue 8 doesn't work.

Thus the woman who started a new job in January moved in February. The one who started a new job in February moved in September (6). The one who moved in August started a new job in September (5). The one with a new job in August moved in October (4). By elimination, the one with a new job in March moved in January; and the woman who moved in March started a new job in October. The one who moved in October took a holiday in January (3). Mandy moved in August (8).

The woman who holidayed in September started a new job in October (7) and the one who holidayed in February moved in August (9). Jane started a new job and Alison went on holiday (8) in (by elimination) October.

Frances's move wasn't in January (6), so must have been October. Suzanne didn't start a new job in March (1), so must have started in January. Frances didn't get engaged in September (2), so must have in March. Olivia's holiday wasn't in August (2), so must have been March, thus she started a new job in February. Alison started a new job in March. Suzanne holidayed in August, so got engaged in October.

Thus, Mandy got engaged in January, Olivia in August, Jane in February and Alison in September.

Thus (holidayed – moved – engaged – new job):
Alison – October – January – September – March;
Frances – January – October – March – August;
Jane – September – March – February – October;
Mandy – February – August – January – September;
Olivia – March – September – August – February;
Suzanne – August – February – October – January.

59

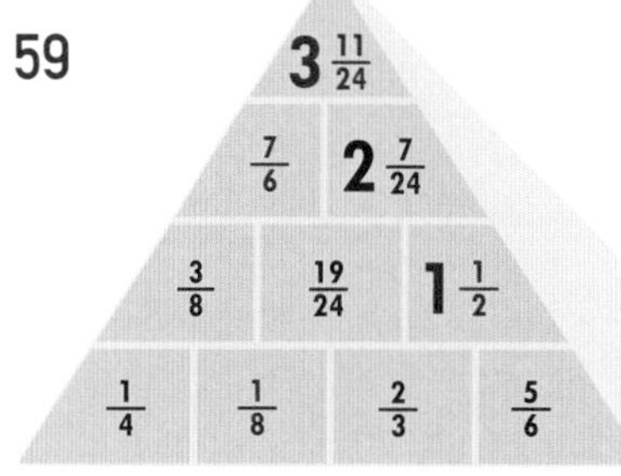


60

Read the words aloud, running one into another, to get the following: purchase a ticket on Friday for Cape Horn at the railway station.

61

B and E

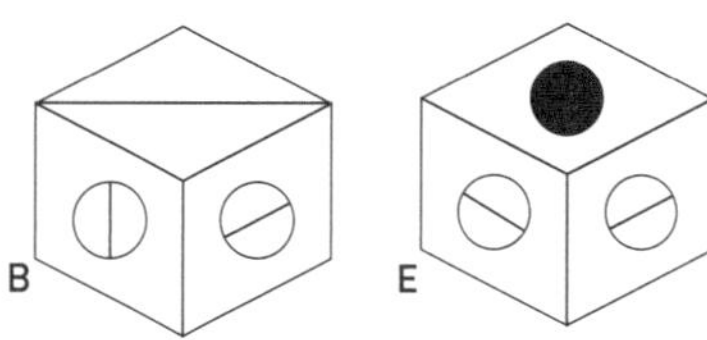


62

Ben CRENSHAW
Jack NICKLAUS
Jose Maria OLAZABAL
Jesper PARNEVIK
Lee WESTWOOD

63

Number 7 on a telephone keypad

64

540°. You can work it out by dividing the shape into three equilateral and two right-angle triangles as shown.

65

Skinned. All the other words contain an animal (ape, cat, cur, elk).

66
XENOPHOBIA (fear of aliens/foreigners)

67
Westminster. Sir Percy KBE is a knight, so, on a chessboard, he moves forward one space either vertically or horizontally, and then forward one space diagonally. Moving in this way from the 'W, you can trace out 'Westminster'.

68
Possible answers include:

| | |
|---|---|
| ABIDE | IDEAL |
| ABIDER | IDEALS |
| AIDER | IDEAS |
| AMBIDEXTROUS | LAYER |
| AMBIDEXTROUSLY | MAYOR |
| BAITED | REALM |
| BAITER | REALS |
| BAYED | ROYAL |
| BIDET | ROYALS |
| BITER | SAYER |
| CIDER | SLAYER |
| CITED | SLYER |
| DEALS | SORTED |
| DEXTROUS | SORTIE |
| DIALS | SORTIED |
| FAERY | TEALS |
| FIERY | TREYS |

69
A & B

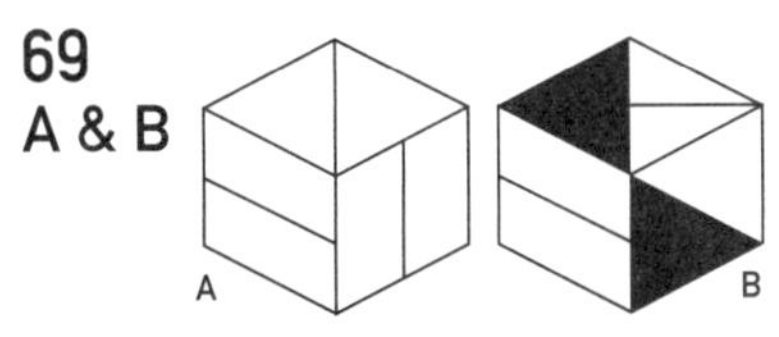


70
Clive sent a card to Zoë (clue 1) and Xenia sent one to Bob (clue 3). Wilma sent a card to the man who sent a card to Xenia (7), so (3) Zoë sent a card to the man who sent a card to Wilma. Ursula sent to the man who sent to Yolande (7). The man who sent a card to Xenia and received one from Wilma isn't Andrew (7), George (1), David (2), Edward (4) or Frank (5 and above), so must be Hank.

Bob sent to Ursula (6). Wilma sent to Hank (7). Andrew sent to Wilma (7) and received from Zoë (3). Ursula sent to George (3), who sent to Yolande (7), who sent to Clive (1).

No woman sent a card to the man from whom she'd received one (intro). Frank didn't send to Venetia (4). If Frank sent to Tanya, then (5) Tanya sent to either David or Edward, who sent a card to either Selina or Venetia, who sent to Frank. But then either David or Edward (whoever didn't receive a card from Tanya) sent a card to the woman who then sent one back to him. So Frank didn't send to Tanya (above), thus must have sent to Selina, who didn't send to David (2), so must have sent to Edward. Venetia sent to Frank (4).

Edward sent to Tanya (2), who sent to David. David sent to Venetia.

Thus:
Andrew – Wilma;
Selina – Edward;
Bob – Ursula; Tanya – David;
Clive – Zoë; Ursula – George;
David – Venetia; Venetia – Frank;
Edward – Tanya; Wilma – Hank;
Frank – Selina; Xenia – Bob;
George – Yolande; Yolande – Clive;
Hank – Xenia. Zoë – Andrew.

71
If we let X = the missing number and fill in the puzzle as normal (see illustration), then the top number is equal to $3X + 28$. Since we know this equals 112, then $3X = 112 - 28 = 84$, so $X = 28$.

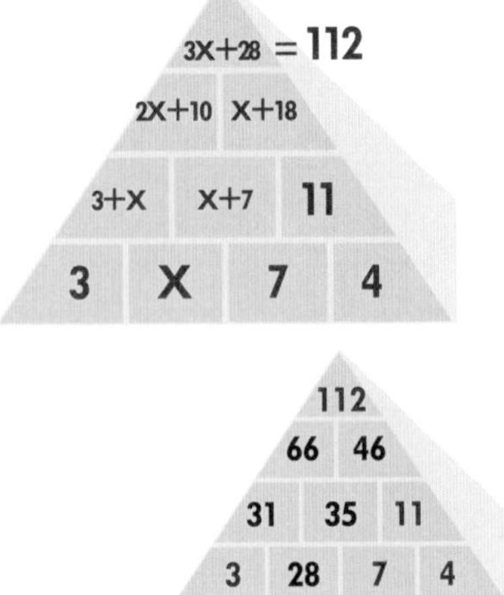


72

| | | | | | | | | | | | | | | | |
|---|---|---|---|---|---|---|---|---|---|---|---|---|---|---|---|
| S | L | E | E | E | Z | E | E | C | E | X | H | A | U | S | T |
| B | E | X | X | X | H | X | L | X | X | J | W | S | T | E | T |
| E | G | M | Y | T | P | T | E | L | P | M | A | X | E | S | C |
| X | R | N | E | E | I | E | N | B | E | E | O | J | D | N | A |
| C | J | X | I | R | Q | N | R | O | D | D | C | E | M | E | X |
| I | I | N | A | N | T | D | C | T | I | A | T | T | Z | P | E |
| T | T | T | M | A | I | X | E | T | T | S | R | C | K | X | N |
| E | N | T | N | L | H | A | E | R | I | V | O | T | C | E | O |
| D | E | I | E | E | N | Q | L | X | O | C | Q | L | X | Q | I |
| L | L | B | X | X | M | E | E | P | N | L | A | Y | P | E | T |
| Y | L | I | P | P | P | I | X | W | X | I | P | E | S | X | P |
| E | E | H | O | A | U | R | R | A | M | E | G | X | S | O | E |
| B | C | X | R | N | J | F | E | E | M | L | Q | C | E | T | C |
| O | X | E | T | D | G | N | D | S | P | I | G | U | C | I | X |
| W | E | D | O | L | P | X | E | A | S | X | N | S | X | C | E |
| A | L | E | X | T | E | N | S | I | V | E | E | E | E | X | Z |

73
Cosmopolitan

74
Stormy

75
1am on 1 March (the Bering Strait is bisected by the International Date Line, and 2000 was a Leap Year).

76
Because the orbits are not in the same plane, G and H will only be on the same line with the sun after each half of an orbit. Hence, the answer is 70 years because 70 is the lowest common multiple of 14 and 10 (i.e., half of 28 and 20). (In this time, G will have done 2½ orbits, H will have done 3½.)

77
Cheerful

78
FRATRICIDE (killing one's brother; in the Bible, Cain killed Abel).

79 C

80
I never think of the future. The first letter is 'I'. Count five letters in the alphabet to 'N', then nine letters back from 'N' to 'E' and so on.

81
Coincidentally it is COINCIDENTALLY. This puzzle is simply a description of this word (COIN+CIDE+N+TALLY).

82
Jacques COUSTEAU (invented scuba equipment)
Benjamin FRANKLIN (patented hundreds of inventions)
Charles GOODYEAR (invented vulcanized rubber)
King GILLETTE (invented the safety razor)
Clarence BIRDSEYE (invented frozen food)

83
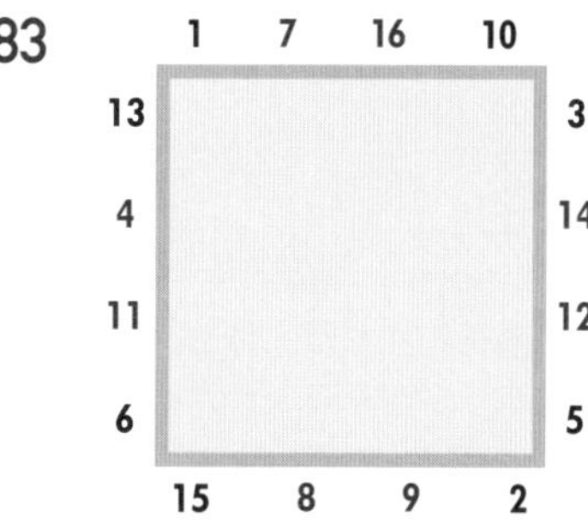


84
175. K will be at the collision point at 7, 35, 63, 91, 119, 147, 175... years from now. The first of these figures to be divisible by 25 is 175, so that's the answer.

85
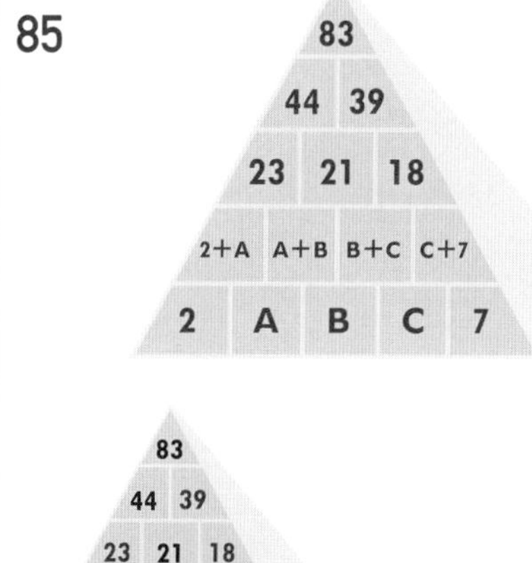

83
44 39
23 21 18
10 13 8 10
2 8 5 3 7

86
Andrew – 1pm – Chile
Brian – 7pm – Greece
Caroline – 10.30pm – Sri Lanka
Dave – 10pm – Pakistan
Elizabeth – 11am – El Salvador
Fiona – 1am – Brunei

87

| | | | | | | | | | | |
|---|---|---|---|---|---|---|---|---|---|---|
| ■ | E | V | I | D | E | N | T | ■ | ■ | ■ |
| T | ■ | I | ■ | I | ■ | E | ■ | B | ■ | I |
| I | N | C | O | N | G | R | U | O | U | S |
| E | ■ | E | ■ | E | ■ | V | ■ | T | ■ | I |
| D | U | G | ■ | S | W | E | E | T | E | N |
| Y | ■ | E | ■ | ■ | O | ■ | ■ | L | ■ | G |
| E | A | R | S | H | O | T | ■ | E | E | L |
| I | ■ | E | ■ | O | ■ | H | ■ | F | ■ | A |
| N | O | N | E | T | H | E | L | E | S | S |
| G | ■ | T | ■ | U | ■ | I | ■ | E | ■ | S |
| ■ | ■ | ■ | U | P | G | R | A | D | E | ■ |

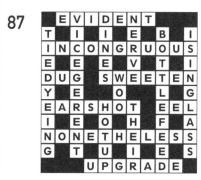

88
Lena had 40 pennies (clue 3). Ruby had 20 or 70 pennies (clue 1). Ms Vale isn't Ruby (8), so if Ruby had 70 and Mrs Macey 90 (1), this leaves none for Ms Vale (8). So Ruby had 20 and Mrs Macey 40 pennies (1).

Lena had 100 dollars more than Pamela (3), so (10) Pamela's surname is Franks. Lena's purse isn't pink (5), so (9) is green. Ann had 60 pennies (7). The woman with the black purse who isn't Ann (6) had 20 pennies and Hannah had 10. Pamela had 70 or 90, as did Daphne, so (8) Daphne is Ms Vale. Miss Lestrange isn't Ann (7), so (5) Miss Lestrange had 20 pennies and the 10 pennies were in the pink purse.

Miss Rosenberg's purse is white (4), so she's Ann, and Hannah is Ms Watson. Pamela's purse is brown (2) and Daphne's blue. Daphne had 90 pennies (2) and Pamela 70. Ann had 200 dollars more than Ruby (6) and 100 more than Daphne (8) who had fewer than Pamela (10). So Daphne hadn't 10,800 dollars.

So Ann had 10,500 dollars, Daphne 10,400 and Ruby 10,300. The woman with 10,700 wasn't Lena (3) or Hannah (9), so is Pamela. Lena had 10,800 (3) and Hannah 10,900 dollars.
Thus:
Ann – Rosenberg – 10,500 – 60 – white;
Daphne – Vale – 10,400 – 90 – blue;
Hannah – Watson – 10,900 – 10 – pink;
Lena – Macey – 10,800 – 40 – green;
Pamela – Franks – 10,700 – 70 – brown;
Ruby – Lestrange – 10,300 – 20 – black.

# acknowledgments


## Contributors

### hot topics

Jeffery Pike: 1, 2, 4, 8, 18, 27, 37, 39, 44, 54, 57, 59, 60, 64, 67, 70, 79, 81;
Ken Russell and Philip Carter: 3, 11, 58, 71;
David Bodycombe: 5, 17, 22-24, 36, 38, 49, 51, 56, 62, 63, 82;
Brainwarp: 6, 10, 12, 13, 16, 25, 26, 33, 35, 43, 48, 50, 55, 61, 65, 76, 80, 83;
Puzzlemakers: 7, 14, 34, 41, 46, 53, 66, 74, 75, 77, 78;
Probyn Puzzles: 15, 21, 32, 40, 42, 52, 68, 69;
Justin Scroggie: 19, 20, 45, 72, 73.

### simply crosswords

Probyn Puzzles: 1-6, 8, 10, 12-15, 18, 20-24, 27, 28, 32-34, 37, 38;
David Bodycombe: 7, 11, 16, 17, 19, 25, 26, 30, 31, 35, 36, 39-41;
Brainwarp: 9, 29.

### number know-how

Ken Russell and Philip Carter: 1-3, 5, 8, 10, 14, 16, 20, 25, 26, 31, 40, 43, 44, 47, 48, 50, 57, 58, 63, 65, 67, 68, 70, 73, 77, 78, 81, 83, 86, 87;
Puzzlemakers: 4, 9, 21-23, 34, 35, 38, 56, 88, 89;
Justin Scroggie: 6, 7, 13, 17, 24, 28, 29, 33, 42, 52-54, 60, 69, 71, 75, 80;
Probyn Puzzles: 11, 15, 30, 45, 55, 61, 79;
David Bodycombe: 12, 19, 27, 36, 37, 41, 46, 51, 59, 62, 66, 72, 74, 76, 82, 85;
Moran Campbell da Vinci: 18, 32, 39, 49.

### testing trivia

Jeffery Pike: 1-5, 7-10, 13-17, 19, 20, 43-45;
David Bodycombe: 6, 11, 12, 18, 24, 25, 29, 35, 36, 46;
Moran Campbell da Vinci: 21-23, 26-28, 39-42;
Sheena Meredith: 30-34, 37, 38.

### eye see

Puzzlemakers: 1, 7, 14, 16, 18, 21-24, 27, 33, 34, 37, 40, 43, 49, 50-54, 59, 63, 64, 70, 71, 77, 78, 82, 85, 86, 89;
Moran Campbell da Vinci: 2, 6, 12, 19, 28, 32, 45, 55, 58, 61, 62, 73, 87;
Justin Scroggie: 3, 8, 26, 47, 68, 83;
Ken Russell and Philip Carter: 4, 5, 9, 15, 17, 25, 30, 36, 38, 42, 44, 48, 56, 67, 69, 76, 79, 80, 84, 88;
David Bodycombe: 10, 13, 31, 39, 46, 60, 74, 75;
Lloyd King: 20, 29, 51, 57, 66, 81.

### take a letter

Jeffery Pike: 1, 14, 40, 43, 44, 61, 65, 73, 77, 81;
Ken Russell and Philip Carter: 2-7, 9, 15, 17, 19, 20, 23, 25, 27-30, 35, 36, 38, 41, 45-47, 50, 52-55, 57, 59, 62, 64, 66, 68, 71, 72, 78-80, 83, 86, 88;
Puzzlemakers: 8, 22, 32, 60, 91;
David Bodycombe: 10, 11, 13, 18, 21, 26, 31, 33, 42, 48, 51, 63, 70, 75, 76, 84, 90;
Probyn Puzzles: 12, 37, 67, 69, 85;
Brainwarp: 16, 24, 39, 49, 74, 82, 89;
Lloyd King: 34, 56, 58, 87.

### the ultimate challenge

Jeffery Pike: 1, 8, 9, 25, 29, 40, 47, 54, 63;
David Bodycombe: 2, 4, 5, 13, 15, 18-21, 26, 28, 37, 42, 43, 45, 48, 55, 59, 62, 66, 68, 71, 72, 76, 78, 82, 84, 85, 87;
Ken Russell and Philip Carter: 3, 6, 7, 11, 12, 17, 23, 24, 27, 30-32, 34, 35, 39, 49, 50, 52, 53, 57, 61, 64, 65, 69, 73, 74, 77, 79, 83;
Moran Campbell da Vinci: 10, 38;
Puzzlemakers: 14, 46, 58, 70, 88;
Lloyd King: 16, 36, 41, 51, 81;
Justin Scroggie: 22, 33, 44, 56, 60, 67, 75, 80, 86.

All other puzzles compiled by the team at Book Creation Services.

### PICTURE CREDITS

Cover: Pictorial Press, photographer H. Miller (Catherine Zeta Jones); Spectrum Colour (ostrich)

p13 Spectrum Colour/Anne Cumbers (dogs)

p24 Spectrum Colour (birds); Pictorial Press, photographer H. Miller (Catherine Zeta Jones)

p25 Rex Features, photographer Taborelli & Derambaksh, © Sipa Press (caviar); © Reader's Digest, photographer Martin Brigdale (sushi), photographer William Lingwood (burger), photographer Gus Filgate (spaghetti); Pictorial Press (Nicole Kidman)

p35 Rex Features (all images), photographer Julian Makey (Craig Phillips), photographer Ken McKay (Vanessa Feltz)

pp64 and 78 Sylvie Rabbe (camera and guitar illustrations)

p176 Spectrum Colour (Capitol, St Basil's and Dome of the Rock); Britain on View (Millennium Dome)

p193 © Reader's Digest, photographer Steven Mays (fire extinguisher); Bruce Coleman Collection, photographer Andrew Purcell (stingray)

Digital Vision: cover, pp8, 54, 124,168, 220, 261, 300

Hemera Technologies Inc.: pp1, 6, 10, 11, 18, 27, 38, 49, 56, 57, 58, 60, 63, 68, 70, 73, 74, 76, 81, 86, 87, 126, 127, 138, 143, 166, 170, 171, 193 x 2, 204, 223, 224, 228, 231, 232, 233, 239, 262, 263, 281, 285, 299

Letraset fonts: pp 33, 47, 52, 53, 82, 83, 84, 122, 123, 129, 134, 137, 145, 146, 148, 149, 154, 156, 158, 163, 165, 166, 167, 218, 219, 251, 258, 259, 298, 299

Photo Disc, Inc.: cover, pp130/1, 140/1, 163, 166, 222

Puzzles Annual 2002 was published by
The Reader's Digest Association Limited, London




We are committed to both the quality of our products and the service we provide to our customers. We value your comments, so please feel free to contact us on 08705 113366 or by email at: cust_service@readersdigest.co.uk
If you have any comments or suggestions about the content of our books, email us at gbeditorial@readersdigest.co.uk




Reader's Digest production credits:
BOOK PRODUCTION MANAGER Fiona McIntosh
PRE-PRESS MANAGER Howard Reynolds
PRE-PRESS TECHNICAL ANALYST Martin Hendrick

ORIGINATION Colour Systems Ltd
PRINTING AND BINDING MOHN Media, Germany

ISBN 0 276 42607 X
BOOK CODE 440-002-01
CONCEPT CODE UK 1406/IC/A